Math+

2nd Edition

Lesson Guide

Book Staff and Contributors

Tony Freedman *Content Specialist*
Michelle Kitt *Director, Instructional Design for Science, Mathematics, Learning Models, and Platforms*
Jill Tunick *Senior Text Editor*
Debra Foulks *Text Editor*
Suzanne Montazer *Creative Director, Print and ePublishing*
Jacquie Rosenborough *Print Visual Designer*
Julie Jankowski *Cover Designer*
Steve Mawyer *Media Editor*
Judith Keller, David Stienecker *Writers*
Amy Eward *Senior Manager, Writers*
Susan Raley *Senior Manager, Editors*
Luz Long *Senior Project Manager*
Nols Myers *Director K–8, Program Management*

Lynda Cloud *Executive Vice President, Product Development*
David Pelizzari *Vice President, K^{12} Content*
Kim Barcas *Vice President, Creative*
Christopher Frescholtz *Senior Director, Program Management*

Lisa Dimaio Iekel *Director, Print Production and Manufacturing*

Illustrations Credits

All illustrations © K12 Inc. unless otherwise noted
Cover: Volunteers painting a mural at Cody High School in Detroit, Michigan. © Jim West/Alamy

About K12 Inc.

K12 Inc., a technology-based education company, is the nation's leading provider of proprietary curriculum and online education programs to students in grades K–12. K^{12} provides its curriculum and academic services to online schools, traditional classrooms, blended school programs, and directly to families. K12 Inc. also operates the K^{12} International Academy, an accredited, diploma-granting online private school serving students worldwide. K^{12}'s mission is to provide any child the curriculum and tools to maximize success in life, regardless of geographic, financial, or demographic circumstances. K12 Inc. is accredited by CITA. More information can be found at www.K12.com.

ISBN: 978-1-60153-441-5 (online book)
ISBN: 978-1-60153-453-8 (printed book)
Printed by Quad Graphics, Versailles, KY, USA, April 2015

Contents

Fractions: Multiplication and Division

Problems Involving Fractions

Decimals: Addition and Subtraction

Decimals: Multiplication and Division

Semester Review and Checkpoint

Algebra

Coordinate Planes

Perimeter, Area, and Volume

Math Reasoning: Methods and Strategies

Math Reasoning: Solutions

Data Analysis and Representation

Semester Review and Checkpoint

Glossary

Program Overview

Lesson Overview

The table at the beginning of each lesson tells you what activities are in the lesson and whether students are on the computer (**ONLINE**) or at a table or desk (**OFFLINE**). The expected time for each activity is given.

Lesson Objectives and Prerequisite Skills

Each lesson teaches the Lesson Objectives. The lesson assumes that students know the Prerequisite Skills from their previous math experience. The Get Ready activity is designed to remind students of the Prerequisite Skills and to prepare them for the lesson.

Content Background

The Content Background tells you what students will learn in the lesson, and it explains any complex math concepts, putting the lesson into perspective with wider math knowledge.

Advance Preparation

Some lessons require preparation that extends beyond gathering materials. In these cases, the lesson includes an Advance Preparation section.

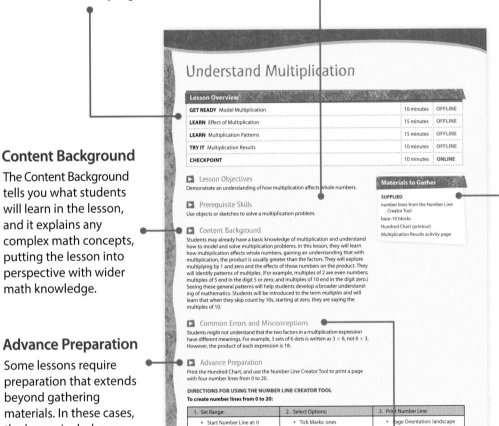

Understand Multiplication

Lesson Overview

GET READY Model Multiplication	10 minutes	OFFLINE
LEARN Effect of Multiplication	15 minutes	OFFLINE
LEARN Multiplication Patterns	15 minutes	OFFLINE
TRY IT Multiplication Results	10 minutes	OFFLINE
CHECKPOINT	10 minutes	ONLINE

Lesson Objectives
Demonstrate an understanding of how multiplication affects whole numbers.

Prerequisite Skills
Use objects or sketches to solve a multiplication problem.

Content Background
Students may already have a basic knowledge of multiplication and understand how to model and solve multiplication problems. In this lesson, they will learn how multiplication affects whole numbers, gaining an understanding that with multiplication, the product is usually greater than the factors. They will explore multiplying by 1 and zero and the effects of those numbers on the product. They will identify patterns of multiples. (For example, multiples of 2 are even numbers; multiples of 5 end in the digit 5 or zero; and multiples of 10 end in the digit zero.) Seeing these general patterns will help students develop a broader understanding of mathematics. Students will be introduced to the term *multiples* and will learn that when they skip count by 10s, starting at zero, they are saying the multiples of 10.

Common Errors and Misconceptions
Students might not understand that the two factors in a multiplication expression have different meanings. For example, 3 sets of 6 dots is written as 3×6, not 6×3. However, the product of each expression is 18.

Advance Preparation
Print the Hundred Chart, and use the Number Line Creator Tool to print a page with four number lines from 0 to 20.

DIRECTIONS FOR USING THE NUMBER LINE CREATOR TOOL
To create number lines from 0 to 20:

1. Set Range:	2. Select Options:	3. Print Number Line:
• Start Number Line at: 0	• Tick Marks: ones	• Page Orientation: landscape
• End Number Line at: 20	• Labels: ones	• Number Lines per Sheet: 4

124 WHOLE NUMBER MULTIPLICATION SENSE

Materials to Gather

SUPPLIED
number lines from the Number Line Creator Tool
base-10 blocks
Hundred Chart (printout)
Multiplication Results activity page

Materials

This box tells you what materials students will need in the lesson. More information about the materials is included on the next page of this overview.

Common Errors and Misconceptions

Research shows that students might misunderstand certain concepts, which then leads to misunderstanding of more advanced concepts. When certain research applies to a lesson, the lesson has a Common Errors and Misconceptions section.

Materials

K[12] supplies this Lesson Guide and the Activity Book, the student book. K[12] also supplies a protractor, which students will use to measure angles.

Printouts, Plastic Sheet Cover, and Dry-Erase Markers

A lesson may ask you to print a document showing a number line, a grid, or another math tool. These documents will be reused throughout the course. We recommend that you obtain a plastic sheet cover and dry-erase markers so students can place the sheet over the printout and write answers on the sheet. They can then erase the answers and reuse the printout multiple times.

   Important: Some printouts, including graded Checkpoints, require students to measure shapes or angles. By default, many printers scale documents to fit to a printable area. Be sure to turn off page scaling so that documents print at 100% of their intended size.

Number and Symbol Cards

Index cards labeled with numbers or symbols are frequently called for in the lessons. We recommend that you create a set of index cards numbered 0–100 and a few sets numbered 0–9. You can also write on index cards the symbols that will be used most frequently: − (minus), + (plus), × (multiplication), ÷ (division), = (equals), > (greater than), < (less than), ((opening parenthesis),) (closing parenthesis). You can then use these cards throughout the course.

Math Notebook, Paper, and Pencil

Obtain a binder or spiral notebook to serve as the Math Notebook in which students will work problems, make sketches, and write answers to the problems in the Activity Book. Students should always have the Math Notebook, paper, and a pencil handy. These materials are not listed in each lesson.

Also Needed

Other common items are called for in lessons, designated in the materials list as "Also Needed." Gather or purchase these materials, such as a ruler, scissors, and index cards.

Working Through a Lesson

When you go online with students to do a math lesson, you will see a list of the activities that are included in the lesson.

   The Lesson Guide also gives an overview of lesson activities. Instructions for online activities are online. Students may complete these activities independently, or you may sit at the computer with them, reading text to them as necessary. The Lesson Guide may include a teaching tip or other information. In some cases, such as when an open-ended Learning Tool is used, there will be instructions to follow in the Lesson Guide. The online screen will guide you to follow these instructions.

   Instructions for offline activities are in the Lesson Guide. These activities may use supplied or common materials, and some include pages from the Activity Book.

Types of Activities

Skills Update Some lessons contain a short problem set covering previously learned math skills taught in previous units or a game to build fluency, or speed, with math facts. Skills Updates appear online only. Students should complete them independently.

Get Ready Review of previous math knowledge that will be needed for this lesson. The Get Ready activities can be online or offline.

Learn Presentation of math concepts, or guided practice. The Learn activities can be online or offline.

Try It Practice problems on the concepts taught in the lesson. Students should complete these problems independently. The Try It activities can be online or in the Activity Book.

Checkpoint Assessments of whether students have learned the objectives taught in the lesson or lessons. Not every lesson has a Checkpoint. In some Checkpoints, students show or explain their answers, and you record their performance.

In addition to the regular Checkpoints, **Unit Reviews** and **Unit Checkpoints** are lessons at the end of each unit. Each semester ends with a **Semester Review** and **Semester Checkpoint**.

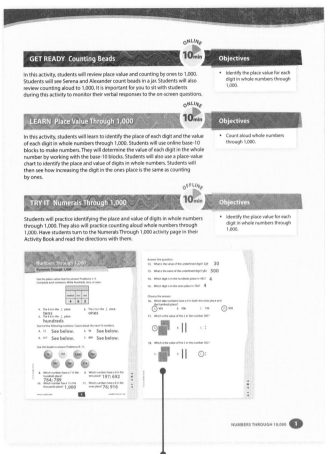

Answer Keys

The Lesson Guide includes the answers, shown in magenta, to the Activity Book pages. The answer keys for offline Checkpoints and Use What You Know activities are provided online. Online Checkpoints are scored by the computer, so no answer key is provided.

Extended Problems An opportunity at the end of each unit to solve problems by integrating the mathematical concepts and skills students have learned from previous units and within the current unit. These lessons contain real-world problems and other problems requiring more complex reasoning. Students submit their completed work.

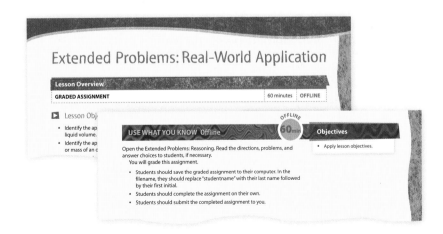

Online Activities

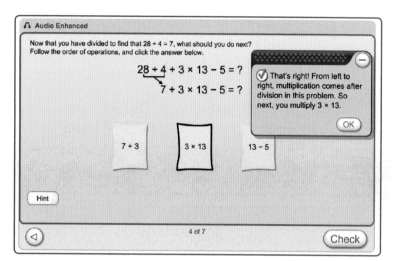

Online activities show whether students answered correctly.

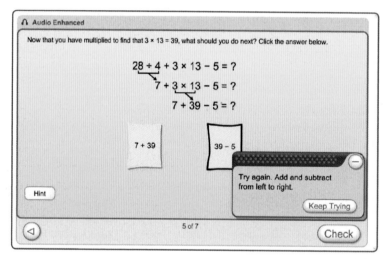

If students answer incorrectly, they see feedback. They should select Keep Trying to try again. If they answer incorrectly a second time, they can select Show Me to see the correct answer.

Learning Tools are online activities that you set up to give students math exercises that apply to what they are learning in a specific lesson.

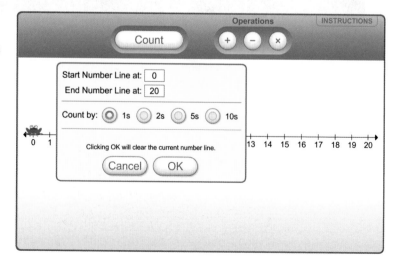

Whole Numbers and Powers

▶ Unit Objectives

- Round whole numbers in a story problem.

- Estimate or calculate a sum or a difference in a whole-number problem.

- Estimate or calculate a sum or a difference in a whole-number story problem.

- Determine whether multiplication or division is the appropriate operation to use to solve a story problem.

- Determine which operations are appropriate to use to solve a multistep story problem.

- Explain and apply standard step-by-step approaches for multiplication.

- Fluently multiply multidigit whole numbers using the standard algorithm.

- Solve with proficiency for quotients of up to a four-digit dividend by a two-digit divisor using strategies.

- Represent and compute a power by using repeated multiplication.

- Solve a problem that involves powers.

- Solve multistep problems using multiple operations.

- Recognize that in a multidigit number, a digit in one place represents 10 times as much as it represents in the place to its right and $\frac{1}{10}$ of what it represents in the place to its left.

▶ Big Ideas

Estimation can be a useful tool in problem solving.

▶ Unit Introduction

Students will explore whole numbers and powers in this unit. The unit begins with rounding whole numbers in story problems. Students will round whole numbers in the context of a problem but will not solve problems. The next sequence of lessons explores whole-number computation problems as well as story problems. Students will estimate and calculate in addition, subtraction, multiplication, and division number sentences. Then students will use strategies such as area models and arrays to multiply and divide multidigit numbers. They will also perform these operations using the standard algorithms. Students will then solve simple and complex story problems. Solutions may involve multiple steps, multiple operations, and alternative solutions. In the next part of this unit, students are introduced to powers with whole numbers, such as 5^3, as well as how to represent a power using repeated multiplication. For example, 5^3 can be shown as $5 \times 5 \times 5$ or $5 \cdot 5 \cdot 5$. Students will solve problems involving powers with whole numbers. They will complete the unit by solving extended problems that focus on reasoning. Students will use multiplication and division, place value, and powers of 10 to solve the extended problems.

▶ Keywords

addend	commutative	equation	product
algorithm	property	factor	quotient
area	cubed	friendly numbers	rate
area model	difference	inverse operations	remainder
array	dividend	multiplication fact	round (v.)
bases	divisor	family	squared
clustering	exponent	partial products	sum
	expression	power	whole numbers

Round Whole Numbers in Story Problems

Lesson Overview

GET READY Rounding Numbers	10 minutes	ONLINE
LEARN Strategies for Rounding	15 minutes	ONLINE
LEARN Rounding Distances	15 minutes	ONLINE
TRY IT Round Numbers in Story Problems	10 minutes	OFFLINE
CHECKPOINT	10 minutes	ONLINE

▶ Lesson Objectives

Round whole numbers in a story problem.

▶ Prerequisite Skills

- Round a whole number.
- Identify and explain when rounding is useful.

▶ Content Background

In this lesson, students will round whole numbers in a story problem. They will learn several methods of rounding, including front-end estimation, friendly numbers, and rounding to a specific place value. Students will learn to base their choice of an appropriate rounding strategy on the context of each problem. They will continue to use rounding strategies when they solve story problems in future lessons.

Rounding numbers makes it easier to estimate. Students have learned several rounding strategies. One rounding strategy is using friendly numbers. In that strategy, students round to the nearest 5, 10, 25, or 100. For example, they can round 28 to the friendly number 25. The number 25 is close to 28 and easy to work with.

In another strategy, front-end estimation, students round a number to its greatest place value. For example, with front-end estimation, 125 rounds to 100.

Finally, students may choose to round to a place value. Suppose students want to round 72,819 to the nearest thousand. They would choose between the boundary numbers 72,000 and 73,000. Because 72,819 is closer to 73,000, the answer is 73,000.

Students will learn to write numerals with commas between each period, or group of three digits. In this course, numbers with four or more digits include commas. For example, eleven thousand, two hundred twenty will be shown as 11,220.

You should encourage students to use commas when they enter numeric answers to questions online. The computer, however, will still score a question as correct if students omit the commas.

Materials to Gather

SUPPLIED

Round Numbers in Story Problems activity page

GET READY Rounding Numbers

ONLINE 10 min

Students will use number lines to round whole numbers. The number lines will give students a way to round numbers to a place value. They will round to the nearest thousand, hundred thousand, and million.

Objectives

- Round a whole number.

LEARN Strategies for Rounding

ONLINE 15 min

Students will review place value and learn three methods of rounding numbers:

- Round to a friendly number. Friendly numbers are usually multiples of 5, 10, 25, or 100.
- Use front-end estimation.
- Round to a certain place value.

Students should see that rounding makes working with numbers easier. Most importantly, students should understand that there is more than one way to round numbers.

Objectives

- Round whole numbers in a story problem.

Tips

Have students practice counting by 5s, 10s, 25s, and 100s to review the multiples of those numbers before they use friendly numbers to round a number.

LEARN Rounding Distances

ONLINE 15 min

Students will use a variety of ways to round whole numbers in story problems. Each problem presents the distance between two cities.

Students will round a number by using three different strategies. They will see how different rounding strategies produce different rounded numbers. For example, the number 1,969 rounds to 1,975 if the friendly-number strategy is used to round to a multiple of 25; to 2,000 if the front-end estimation strategy is used; and to 1,970 if the strategy is to round to the nearest 10.

Objectives

- Round whole numbers in a story problem.

TRY IT Round Numbers in Story Problems

Students will practice using different strategies for rounding numbers as they work with story problems. Have students turn to the Round Numbers in Story Problems activity page in their Activity Book and read the directions with them.

Students should copy the problems from the Activity Book into their Math Notebook as necessary and solve them there.

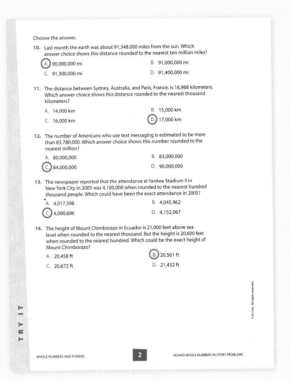

Round Whole Numbers in Story Problems
Round Numbers in Story Problems

Reagan wants to buy a new van. The chart shows how much a new van costs at different car dealers. Use the two strategies in the table to round each price.

	Car dealer	Friendly numbers	Nearest thousand
1.	Car Dealer A $39,528	$39,525	$40,000
2.	Car Dealer B $36,102	$36,100	$36,000
3.	Car Dealer C $38,999	$39,000	$39,000

Friendly-number answers will vary.

4. Reagan wants to be sure he has enough money to buy the van from Car Dealer A. Which rounded number should Reagan use to estimate the amount of money he needs? Explain.
See below.

Round the numbers as directed.

5. In 1987, professional football player Walter Payton set a new record for career rushing yards. His record was 16,726 rushing yards. Round Payton's record to the nearest hundred yards. **16,700 yd**

6. The Empire State Building in New York City cost $24,718,000 to build in 1931. Round the total cost to the nearest million dollars.
$25,000,000

7. In 2005 there were 3,844,829 people living in Los Angeles. Round the population to the nearest ten thousand.
3,840,000

8. The total cost of building the Washington Monument was $1,187,710. Round the total cost to the nearest ten thousand dollars.
$1,190,000

9. The total number of people attending professional football games for the 2007 regular season was 17,341,012. Round the total attendance to the nearest hundred thousand.
17,300,000

WHOLE NUMBERS AND POWERS | 1 | ROUND WHOLE NUMBERS IN STORY PROBLEMS

Choose the answer.

10. Last month the earth was about 91,348,000 miles from the sun. Which answer choice shows this distance rounded to the nearest ten million miles?
(A) 90,000,000 mi   B. 91,000,000 mi
C. 91,300,000 mi   D. 91,400,000 mi

11. The distance between Sydney, Australia, and Paris, France, is 16,968 kilometers. Which answer choice shows this distance rounded to the nearest thousand kilometers?
A. 14,000 km   B. 15,000 km
C. 16,000 km   (D) 17,000 km

12. The number of Americans who use text messaging is estimated to be more than 83,780,000. Which answer choice shows this number rounded to the nearest million?
A. 80,000,000   B. 83,000,000
(C) 84,000,000   D. 90,000,000

13. The newspaper reported that the attendance at Yankee Stadium II in New York City in 2005 was 4,100,000 when rounded to the nearest hundred thousand people. Which could have been the exact attendance in 2005?
A. 4,017,598   B. 4,045,962
(C) 4,090,696   D. 4,152,067

14. The height of Mount Chimborazo in Ecuador is 21,000 feet above sea level when rounded to the nearest thousand. But the height is 20,600 feet when rounded to the nearest hundred. Which could be the exact height of Mount Chimborazo?
A. 20,458 ft   (B) 20,561 ft
C. 20,672 ft   D. 21,432 ft

WHOLE NUMBERS AND POWERS | 2 | ROUND WHOLE NUMBERS IN STORY PROBLEMS

Additional Answer

4. Reagan should use the number rounded to the nearest thousand. That number is greater than the exact price. The other rounded number is less than the exact price, so he wouldn't have enough money to buy the van.

CHECKPOINT

Students will complete an online Checkpoint. If necessary, read the directions, problems, and answer choices to students and help them with keyboard or mouse operations.

Estimate and Find Sums and Differences

Lesson Overview

GET READY Estimate & Work with a Number Line	10 minutes	OFFLINE
LEARN Different Ways to Estimate	25 minutes	ONLINE
LEARN Finding Estimates and Exact Answers	15 minutes	ONLINE
TRY IT Estimate and Solve	10 minutes	OFFLINE

▶ Lesson Objectives

Estimate or calculate a sum or a difference in a whole-number problem.

▶ Prerequisite Skills

- Estimate sums and differences on a number line.
- Explain and apply standard step-by-step approaches for addition.
- Explain and apply standard step-by-step approaches for subtraction.

▶ Content Background

Students will learn different ways to estimate addition and subtraction problems. They will also calculate to find the exact answer to an addition or subtraction problem.

▶ Common Errors and Misconceptions

- Students might become so concerned about getting the correct answer when estimating that they first find the exact answer, and then round it. For example, when asked to estimate $348 + 176$, students might find the sum (524), and then round it to the nearest hundred (500).
- Students might have difficulty accepting that there is more than one correct approach and answer to an estimation problem.

▶ Advance Preparation

The Number Line Creator Tool will print number lines that students will use in the Get Ready. The link to the Number Line Creator Tool is in the online Advance Preparation. Print one page of number lines at a time. You may choose up to five number lines per page. You'll print three pages.

DIRECTIONS FOR USING THE NUMBER LINE CREATOR TOOL

To create number lines from 0–60:

1. Set Range:	**2.** Select Options:	**3.** Print Number Line:
• Start Number Line at: 0 • End Number Line at: 60	• Tick Marks: tens, ones • Labels: tens	• Page Orientation: landscape • Number Lines per Sheet: 4

Materials to Gather

SUPPLIED

Estimate and Solve activity page

number lines from Number Line Creator Tool

To create number lines from 0–220:
Repeat Steps 1–3, but in Step 1, set the beginning of the number line as 0 and the end of the number line as 220. In Step 2, for tick marks, click hundreds and tens. For labels, click hundreds.

To create number lines from 0–360.
Repeat Steps 1–3, but in Step 1, set the beginning of the number line as 0 and the end of the number line as 360. In Step 2, for tick marks, click hundreds and tens. For labels, click hundreds.

GET READY Estimate & Work with a Number Line

OFFLINE **10** min

Objectives

- Estimate sums and differences on a number line.
- Explain and apply standard step-by-step approaches for addition.
- Explain and apply standard step-by-step approaches for subtraction.

Students will use a number line to estimate sums in addition problems and then calculate the exact answers. They will then use a number line to estimate differences in subtraction problems and then calculate exact answers. Students will round to friendly numbers before estimating the sum or difference. If you haven't printed the number lines, go to Advance Preparation and use the Number Line Creator Tool.

Gather the number lines 0–60, 0–220, and 0–360 that you printed. Students may label additional tick marks on the printouts to help them.

ESTIMATE SUMS

1. The first problem students will work with is $42 + 14 = ?$
   Have students use a 0–60 number line to round the addends as follows:
   - Mark 0 to start.
   - Decide how to round 42 and 14 by using friendly numbers that are multiples of 5. Jump to 40, which is the closest multiple of 5.
   - Decide how to round 14 by using a friendly number that is a multiple of 5. Fifteen is the closest friendly number that is a multiple of 5. Start at 40 and jump 15 spaces. Land on 55.

Tips

The decision of which multiple (5, 10, 25, 50, or 100) to use when working with friendly numbers is the student's choice. In this activity, reasonable multiples have been suggested.

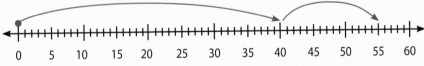

2. Now students will calculate the exact answer on another 0–60 number line. Guide them to use the number line as follows:
   - Mark 0 to start.
   - Jump and mark 42.
   - Jump and mark 14 more spaces. Land on 56.

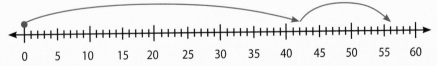

3. The estimated sum is 55. The exact sum is 56. Students should see that their estimated sum was reasonable because the exact sum is so close to the estimated sum.

4. Repeat Steps 1 and 2 with the 0–220 number line and this problem:
   $51 + 138 = ?$ Round the numbers to friendly numbers that are multiples of 25.
   - The estimated sum is 200. (The closest multiples of 25 are 50 and 150.)
   - The exact sum is 189. Ask students if their estimate is reasonable.

ESTIMATE DIFFERENCES

5. Tell students that they can also estimate to find the answer to a subtraction problem, the difference. The first problem they will work with is $347 - 23 = ?$ Round the numbers to friendly numbers that are multiples of 25.

   - Mark 0 to start at the beginning of a 0–360 number line.

   - Decide how to round 347. It can be rounded to 350. Jump and mark 350.

   - Decide how to round 23. It can be rounded to the friendly number of 25. Jump back 25 from 350, landing on 325. The estimated difference of $347 - 23$, using rounded numbers, is 325.

6. Now students will calculate the exact answer on another 0–360 number line.

   - Mark 0 to start.

   - Jump and mark 347.

   - Jump back 23. Land on 324.

   - The exact difference is 324 and the estimated difference was 325. Ask students if their estimated difference was reasonable.

7. Tell students that, when they use the friendly numbers strategy to round numbers, they should look for a number on the number line that is close to the number given. The estimate will then be close to the exact answer. If they learn to make estimates that are close to exact answers, they will be able to rely on their estimating as they continue in math.

ONLINE
25 min

LEARN Different Ways to Estimate

Objectives

- Estimate or calculate a sum or a difference in a whole-number problem.

Students will work with different strategies for rounding numbers. They will see clustering and the use of friendly numbers for rounding. This activity also reviews rounding a whole number to a specific place. Students will use a number line to round whole numbers.

Tips — If students are having trouble deciding if their answers are reasonable, talk about what range of numbers is considered reasonably close to the answer.

ONLINE
15 min

LEARN Finding Estimates and Exact Answers

Objectives

- Estimate or calculate a sum or a difference in a whole-number problem.

Students will round numbers that are in the hundreds, thousands, and ten thousands. They will round numbers to a specified place value and then estimate answers to addition and subtraction problems. Then they will find the exact answer to decide if their estimate is reasonable.

TRY IT Estimate and Solve

Objectives

- Estimate or calculate a sum or a difference in a whole-number problem.

Students will practice various ways to estimate sums and differences. They will also find the exact answer and determine if their estimate is reasonable compared to the exact answer. Have students turn to the Estimate and Solve activity page in their Activity book and read the directions with them.

Students should copy the problems from the Activity Book into their Math Notebook as necessary and solve them there.

Estimate and Find Sums and Differences
Estimate and Solve

Use clustering to estimate the sum. Choose the answer.

1. $377 + 386 + 372 + 389 = ?$
   A. 400
   B. 1,000
   C. 1,600

2. $43 + 32 + 44 + 35 = ?$
   A. 160
   B. 120
   C. 200

Round to friendly numbers that are multiples of 100 to estimate. Choose the answer.

3. $9,629 + 8,573 = ?$
   A. 17,000
   B. 18,200
   C. 19,200

4. $76,999 - 68,205 = ?$
   A. 6,000
   B. 7,200
   C. 8,800

Estimate by rounding the numbers to the nearest ten thousand. Choose the answer.

5. $56,880 + 43,375 = ?$
   A. 90,000
   B. 100,000
   C. 110,000

6. $325,686 - 124,478 = ?$
   A. 200,000
   B. 210,000
   C. 250,000

Complete the table. Estimate each sum or difference by using one of the strategies above. Then find the exact answer. Decide if the estimate is reasonable.

	Problem	Estimate	Exact answer
7.	$2,134 + 7,322 = ?$	?	?
8.	$34,672 - 13,440 = ?$	?	?

See below.

Estimate by first rounding the numbers to the nearest hundred thousand. Then find the exact answer. Are your estimate and exact answer close?

9. $8,925,181 + 2,820,084$
   Estimated: 11,700,000
   Calculated: 11,745,265
   WHOLE NUMBERS AND POWERS

10. $8,189,378 - 5,428,310$
    Estimated: 2,800,000
    Calculated: 2,761,068
    ESTIMATE AND FIND SUMS AND DIFFERENCES

3

Additional Answers

For Problems 7 and 8, estimates will vary. Sample estimates are given.

	Problem	Estimate	Exact answer
7.	$2,134 + 7,322 = ?$	Friendly numbers that are multiples of 25: $2,125 + 7,325 = 9,450$ Round to the nearest hundred: $2,100 + 7,300 = 9,400$	9,456
8.	$34,672 - 13,440 = ?$	Friendly numbers that are multiples of 25: $34,675 - 13,450 = 21,225$ Round to the nearest thousand: $35,000 - 13,000 = 22,000$	21,232

For Problems 7–10, if the estimate and the exact answer can be rounded to a place value and still be close, the estimate is reasonable. In Problem 10, for example, 11,745,265 rounded to the nearest hundred thousand is 11,700,00, which is the same number as the estimate. The estimate is reasonable.

Estimate Sums and Differences (A)

Lesson Overview

GET READY Estimate in Different Ways	20 minutes	ONLINE
LEARN Estimate Addition Story Problems	15 minutes	ONLINE
LEARN Estimate and Calculate Addition	15 minutes	ONLINE
TRY IT Estimate Story Problems	10 minutes	OFFLINE

▶ Lesson Objectives

Estimate or calculate a sum or a difference in a whole-number story problem.

▶ Prerequisite Skills

- Use estimation to predict a solution to a story problem and to verify the reasonableness of the calculated result.
- Estimate or calculate a sum or a difference in a whole-number problem.

▶ Content Background

Students will learn to estimate and calculate addition story problems. They should understand that comparing estimates to exact answers will help them decide if their estimate was reasonable.

▶ Common Errors and Misconceptions

- Students might become so concerned about getting the correct answer when estimating that they first find the exact answer and then round it. For example, when asked to estimate $348 + 176$, students might find the sum (524) and then round it to the nearest hundred (500).
- Students might have difficulty accepting that there is more than one correct approach and answer to an estimation problem.

Materials to Gather

SUPPLIED

Estimate Story Problems activity page

GET READY Estimate in Different Ways

ONLINE
20min

Students will review how to estimate sums by rounding the addends to a certain place value, using friendly numbers, and clustering. They will work problems that include data about U.S. national parks. The data will involve numbers up to the ten thousands place.

Objectives

- Use estimation to predict a solution to a story problem and to verify the reasonableness of the calculated result.
- Estimate or calculate a sum or a difference in a whole-number problem.

LEARN Estimate Addition Story Problems

ONLINE 15 min

Objectives

- Estimate or calculate a sum or a difference in a whole-number story problem.

Students will use a variety of rounding strategies to round the addends in addition story problems that deal with national parks. Students will not solve the estimation problems in this activity. They will begin to learn how to determine which strategy would be best to use. The data will involve numbers up to the ten millions place.

LEARN Estimate and Calculate Addition

ONLINE 15 min

Objectives

- Estimate or calculate a sum or a difference in a whole-number story problem.

Students will estimate answers and find exact answers to addition story problems about national parks. They will check to see if their estimate was reasonable. They will determine which rounding strategy is best to use in the context of the story problem.

TRY IT Estimate Story Problems

OFFLINE 10 min

Objectives

- Estimate or calculate a sum or a difference in a whole-number story problem.

Students will practice estimating and calculating addition story problems. They will use a rounding strategy to estimate sums and then compare their estimates to exact answers to find out if the estimate is reasonable. Have students turn to the Estimate Story Problems activity page in their Activity Book and read the directions with them.

Students should copy the problems from the Activity Book into their Math Notebook as necessary and solve them there.

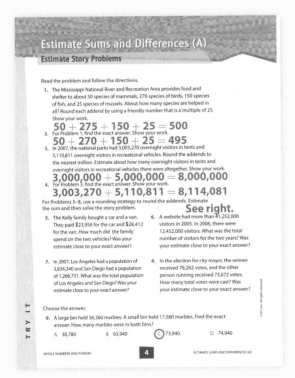

Additional Answers

5. **Example:** Rounding to the nearest thousand or using front-end estimation: $52,000 ($24,000 + $28,000). The Kellys spent $52,368. The estimate should be close to the exact answer.

6. **Example:** Rounding to the nearest million or using front-end estimation: 50,000,000 (40,000,000 + 10,000,000). The website had 53,704,000 visitors. The estimate should be close to the exact answer.

7. **Example:** Rounding to the nearest hundred thousand: 5,100,000 (3,800,000 + 1,300,000). The two cities had a total population of 5,101,071. The estimate should be close to the exact answer.

8. **Example:** Rounding to the nearest thousand: 150,000 (76,000 + 74,000). There were 149,934 voters. The estimate should be close to the exact answer.

Estimate Sums and Differences (B)

Lesson Overview

GET READY Estimate Differences in Story Problems	10 minutes	ONLINE
LEARN Subtraction Estimates	15 minutes	ONLINE
LEARN Subtraction Estimates and Exact Answers	15 minutes	ONLINE
TRY IT Practice Estimating with Subtraction	10 minutes	OFFLINE
CHECKPOINT	10 minutes	ONLINE

▶ Lesson Objectives

Estimate or calculate a sum or a difference in a whole-number story problem.

▶ Prerequisite Skills

- Use estimation to predict a solution to a story problem and to verify the reasonableness of the calculated result.
- Estimate or calculate a sum or a difference in a whole-number problem.

▶ Content Background

Students will learn to estimate and calculate subtraction story problems. They should understand that comparing estimates to exact answers will help them decide if their estimate was reasonable.

▶ Common Errors and Misconceptions

- Students might become so concerned about getting the correct answer when estimating that they first find the exact answer, and then round it. For example, when asked to estimate $348 + 176$, students might find the sum (524) and then round it to the nearest hundred (500).
- Students might have difficulty accepting that there is more than one correct approach and answer to an estimation problem.

Materials to Gather

SUPPLIED

Practice Estimating with Subtraction activity page

GET READY Estimate Differences in Story Problems

ONLINE
10 min

Students will review how to use different estimation strategies for subtraction: rounding to a place value and using friendly numbers. They will estimate differences in subtraction problems. They will also calculate the differences. Students will then compare their estimates to the differences and will decide if their estimate was reasonable.

Objectives

- Use estimation to predict a solution to a story problem and to verify the reasonableness of the calculated result.
- Estimate or calculate a sum or a difference in a whole-number problem.

LEARN Subtraction Estimates

ONLINE 15min

Students will use a variety of strategies to round numbers. Then they will estimate differences in subtraction story problems about space travel and the solar system.

Objectives

- Estimate or calculate a sum or a difference in a whole-number story problem.

LEARN Subtraction Estimates and Exact Answers

ONLINE 15min

Students will estimate the differences in subtraction story problems about the planets and moon by using rounded numbers. Students will then calculate exact answers to determine if their estimate is reasonable.

Students may need paper and pencil to find the exact differences of the subtraction story problems. Allow them to solve the problems on paper and then type their answers online.

Objectives

- Estimate or calculate a sum or a difference in a whole-number story problem.

TRY IT Practice Estimating with Subtraction

OFFLINE 10min

Students will practice estimating and calculating subtraction story problems. They will choose the rounding strategies to round the numbers. They will estimate differences and solve for exact answers. They will compare their estimates to exact answers to see if the estimate was reasonable. Have students turn to the Practice Estimating with Subtraction activity page in their Activity Book.

Students should copy the problems from the Activity Book into their Math Notebook as necessary and solve them there.

Objectives

- Estimate or calculate a sum or a difference in a whole-number story problem.

Estimate Sums and Differences (B)
Practice Estimating with Subtraction

Solve. Show your work.

1. British astronomer William Herschel discovered the planet Uranus in 1781. In the year 2015, how long will it have been, rounded to the nearest hundred years, since Uranus was discovered?
   2,000 − 1,800 = 200   200 years
2. For Problem 1, find the exact difference.
   2,015 − 1,781 = 234   234 years
3. Satellite orbits vary in their distance from the earth. Orbits can be anywhere from 252,800 to 35,200,000 yards. What is the greatest distance between satellite orbits? Round to the nearest ten thousand yards to estimate.
   See right.
4. For Problem 3, find the exact difference.
   See right.

Use a rounding strategy to round the numbers. Estimate the difference. Then find the exact answer. Explain whether your estimate was reasonable.

5. Last year the local newspaper printed 931,244 newspapers. This year it printed only 310,201 newspapers. How many fewer newspapers did it print this year?
   See right.
6. Sofia's mom traveled 78,109 miles for work two years ago. Last year she traveled 21,311 miles. How many more miles did she travel two years ago than last year?
   See right.

Choose the answer.

7. During last year's baseball season, 52,462 people attended the local team's home games. This year, only 33,200 people attended the home games. If you round each number to the nearest ten thousand, what is the estimated difference between the attendance in the two years?
   A. 9,000   B. 19,000   C. 20,000   D. 21,000

8. When the Smiths bought their house, they paid $480,400. Several years later, the price rose to $590,500. How much more is the house worth now than when they bought it? Find the exact answer.
   A. $111,000   B. $110,100   C. $101,100   D. $100,110

WHOLE NUMBERS AND POWERS   5   ESTIMATE SUMS AND DIFFERENCES (B)

TRY IT

Additional Answers

3. 35,200,000 − 250,000 = 34,950,000   34,950,000 yards
4. 35,200,000 − 252,800 = 34,947,200   34,947,200 yards
5. **Example:** Rounding to the nearest ten thousand to estimate the difference: 620,000 newspapers (930,000 − 310,000)

   Exact difference: 621,043 newspapers
   621,043 rounded to the greater ten thousand is 620,000. That is the same number as the estimate. The estimate is reasonable.
6. **Example:** Rounding to the nearest thousand to estimate the difference: 57,000 miles (78,000 − 21,000)

   Exact difference: 56,798 miles
   56,798 rounded to the nearest thousand is 57,000. That is the same number as the estimate. The estimate is reasonable.

CHECKPOINT

Objectives

Students will complete an online Checkpoint. If necessary, read the directions, problems, and answer choices to students and help them with keyboard or mouse operations.

- Estimate or calculate a sum or a difference in a whole-number problem.

- Estimate or calculate a sum or a difference in a whole-number story problem.

Multiply Whole Numbers

Lesson Overview

GET READY Multiplication Strategies	10 minutes	ONLINE
LEARN Multiply with Partial Products	15 minutes	ONLINE
LEARN Multiply with the Algorithm	15 minutes	ONLINE
TRY IT Practice: Multiply Whole Numbers	10 minutes	ONLINE
CHECKPOINT	10 minutes	ONLINE

▶ Lesson Objectives

- Explain and apply standard step-by-step approaches for multiplication.
- Fluently multiply multidigit whole numbers using the standard algorithm.

▶ Content Background

Students will investigate multiple strategies for multiplying whole numbers, including using partial products and the standard algorithm.

▶ Common Errors and Misconceptions

Students might have difficulty accepting that there is more than one correct approach when solving a multiplication problem.

Materials to Gather

There are no materials to gather for this lesson.

GET READY Multiplication Strategies

ONLINE
10min

Objectives

- Explain and apply standard step-by-step approaches for multiplication.

Students will review strategies for multiplying by one-digit numbers.

LEARN Multiply with Partial Products

ONLINE
15min

Objectives

- Explain and apply standard step-by-step approaches for multiplication.

Students will solve multiplication problems by understanding the array and area models and partial products.

LEARN Multiply with the Algorithm

ONLINE 15min

Students will learn the standard algorithm for multiplying multidigit numbers.

Objectives

- Fluently multiply multidigit whole numbers using the standard algorithm.

TRY IT Practice: Multiply Whole Numbers

ONLINE 10min

Students will solve multiplication computation problems with multidigit whole numbers.

Objectives

- Fluently multiply multidigit whole numbers using the standard algorithm.

CHECKPOINT

ONLINE 10min

Students will complete an online Checkpoint. If necessary, read the directions, problems, and answer choices to students and help them with keyboard or mouse operations.

Objectives

- Fluently multiply multidigit whole numbers using the standard algorithm.

Divide Whole Numbers

Lesson Overview

GET READY Division Overview	10 minutes	ONLINE
LEARN Division Strategies	10 minutes	ONLINE
LEARN The Division Algorithm	15 minutes	ONLINE
TRY IT Practice: Divide Whole Numbers	15 minutes	ONLINE
CHECKPOINT	10 minutes	ONLINE

▶ ## Lesson Objectives

Solve with proficiency for quotients of up to a four-digit dividend by a two-digit divisor using strategies.

▶ ## Prerequisite Skills

Explain and apply standard step-by-step approaches for division of a multidigit number by a 1- or 2-digit divisor.

▶ ## Content Background

Students will investigate multiple strategies for dividing whole numbers, including the standard algorithm.

▶ ## Common Errors and Misconceptions

Students might have difficulty accepting that there is more than one correct approach when solving a division problem.

Materials to Gather

There are no materials to gather for this lesson.

GET READY Division Overview

ONLINE 10min

Students will review strategies for division of whole numbers.

Objectives

- Explain and apply standard step-by-step approaches for division of a multidigit number by a 1- or 2-digit divisor.

LEARN Division Strategies

Objectives

Students will use multiple strategies and the inverse relationship between multiplication and division to solve division problems with a one-digit divisor.

- Solve with proficiency for quotients of up to a four-digit dividend by a two-digit divisor using strategies.

LEARN The Division Algorithm

Objectives

Students will use the division algorithm to solve story problems and computation problems with one- and two-digit divisors.

- Solve with proficiency for quotients of up to a four-digit dividend by a two-digit divisor using strategies.

TRY IT Practice: Divide Whole Numbers

Objectives

Students will practice solving division computation and story problems.

- Solve with proficiency for quotients of up to a four-digit dividend by a two-digit divisor using strategies.

CHECKPOINT

Objectives

Students will complete an online Checkpoint. If necessary, read the directions, problems, and answer choices to students and help them with keyboard or mouse operations.

- Solve with proficiency for quotients of up to a four-digit dividend by a two-digit divisor using strategies.

Solve Story Problems

Lesson Overview

GET READY Multiplication and Division	10 minutes	ONLINE
LEARN Multiply or Divide?	15 minutes	ONLINE
LEARN Multiply or Divide to Solve	20 minutes	ONLINE
TRY IT Practice: Solve Story Problems	15 minutes	ONLINE

▶ Lesson Objectives

- Determine whether multiplication or division is the appropriate operation to use to solve a story problem.
- Fluently multiply multidigit whole numbers using the standard algorithm.
- Solve with proficiency for quotients of up to a four-digit dividend by a two-digit divisor using strategies.

▶ Content Background

In this lesson, students will determine which operation to use to solve a story problem. They will also use their knowledge of multiplication and division to solve story problems.

Materials to Gather

There are no materials to gather for this lesson.

GET READY Multiplication and Division

ONLINE
10min

Students will practice their multiplication and division computational skills.

Objectives

- Fluently multiply multidigit whole numbers using the standard algorithm.
- Solve with proficiency for quotients of up to a four-digit dividend by a two-digit divisor using strategies.

LEARN Multiply or Divide?

Students will analyze some simple problems and focus on the operation needed to solve the problem. They will also solve story problems involving multiplication and division.

Objectives

- Determine whether multiplication or division is the appropriate operation to use to solve a story problem.
- Fluently multiply multidigit whole numbers using the standard algorithm.
- Solve with proficiency for quotients of up to a four-digit dividend by a two-digit divisor using strategies.

LEARN Multiply or Divide to Solve

Students will solve story problems involving multiplication and division.

Objectives

- Determine whether multiplication or division is the appropriate operation to use to solve a story problem.
- Fluently multiply multidigit whole numbers using the standard algorithm.
- Solve with proficiency for quotients of up to a four-digit dividend by a two-digit divisor using strategies.

TRY IT Practice: Solve Story Problems

Students will complete an online Try It. If necessary, read the directions, problems, and answer choices to students and help them with keyboard or mouse operations.

Objectives

- Determine whether multiplication or division is the appropriate operation to use to solve a story problem.
- Fluently multiply multidigit whole numbers using the standard algorithm.
- Solve with proficiency for quotients of up to a four-digit dividend by a two-digit divisor using strategies.

Multistep Story Problems

▶ Lesson Objectives

- Determine which operations are appropriate to use to solve a multistep story problem.
- Solve multistep problems using multiple operations.
- Fluently multiply multidigit whole numbers using the standard algorithm.
- Solve with proficiency for quotients of up to a four-digit dividend by a two-digit divisor using strategies.

▶ Prerequisite Skills

- Analyze a problem-solving situation by identifying the question, recognizing relevant information, and developing a solution strategy.
- Determine whether multiplication or division is the appropriate operation to use to solve a story problem.

▶ Content Background

Students will apply their knowledge of multiplication and division to solve multistep story problems.

Although the context and numbers in story problems vary, good problem solvers realize that they can use certain strategies over and over to solve different problems. That skill relies on students being able to identify similarities between problems. More complex problems can include problems with greater numbers and multistep problems that have more parts.

As students work on simple and complex problems, they should follow the 4-step problem-solving plan. The following 4-step problem-solving method was developed by George Pólya and it is an effective way to solve a variety of problems: (1) understand the problem; (2) devise a plan; (3) carry out the plan; and (4) look back. When solving multistep problems, the second step is particularly important. Students need to spend time analyzing the problem and planning how they will address the various parts of the problem, which will then be used to determine the final solution.

Materials to Gather

There are no materials to gather for this lesson.

GET READY Relevant Information

ONLINE
5min

Students will practice identifying relevant information in story problems.

Objectives

- Analyze a problem-solving situation by identifying the question, recognizing relevant information, and developing a solution strategy.

LEARN Which Operations?

ONLINE
15min

Students will determine which operations are appropriate to solve multistep problems. They will see how breaking the problem into parts gives them the information they need to determine the final solution.

Objectives

- Determine which operations are appropriate to use to solve a multistep problem.
- Solve multistep problems using multiple operations.
- Fluently multiply multidigit whole numbers using the standard algorithm.
- Solve with proficiency for quotients of up to a four-digit dividend by a two-digit divisor using strategies.

LEARN Solve Story Problems

ONLINE
15min

Students will apply strategies to solve multistep problems involving all four operations, but with a focus on multiplication and division. They will be given questions to ask themselves to help them become successful problem solvers.

Objectives

- Determine which operations are appropriate to use to solve a multistep problem.
- Solve multistep problems using multiple operations.
- Fluently multiply multidigit whole numbers using the standard algorithm.
- Solve with proficiency for quotients of up to a four-digit dividend by a two-digit divisor using strategies.

TRY IT Practice: Multistep Story Problems

ONLINE
10min

Objectives

Students will complete an online Try It. If necessary, read the directions, problems, and answer choices to students and help them with keyboard or mouse operations.

- Determine which operations are appropriate to use to solve a multistep story problem.
- Solve multistep problems using multiple operations.
- Fluently multiply multidigit whole numbers using the standard algorithm.
- Solve with proficiency for quotients of up to a four-digit dividend by a two-digit divisor using strategies.

CHECKPOINT

ONLINE
15min

Objectives

Students will complete an online Checkpoint. If necessary, read the directions, problems, and answer choices to students and help them with keyboard or mouse operations.

- Determine whether multiplication or division is the appropriate operation to use to solve a story problem.
- Determine which operations are appropriate to use to solve a multistep story problem.
- Solve multistep problems using multiple operations.
- Fluently multiply multidigit whole numbers using the standard algorithm.
- Solve with proficiency for quotients of up to a four-digit dividend by a two-digit divisor using strategies.

Place-Value Patterns

LEARN Patterns in Place Values | 30 minutes | **OFFLINE**

▶ Lesson Objectives

Recognize that in a multidigit number, a digit in one place represents 10 times as much as it represents in the place to its right and $\frac{1}{10}$ of what it represents in the place to its left.

Materials to Gather

SUPPLIED

Patterns in Place Values activity page

LEARN Patterns in Place Values

Students will compare the place values of digits in a number. View or print the Patterns in Place Values activity page. Students should copy the problems into their Math Notebook and solve them there.

1. Have students read Problem 1 of the Worked Examples.

2. Have students read Step 1 of the solution, point to each digit, and say the place value associated with that digit.

3. Read Step 2 of the solution with students. Some students may need to see or verify that 10 hundreds is equivalent to 1 thousand. You can show this fact with standard multiplication.

4. Have students read the answer aloud, pointing to the appropriate digits in the number.

5. Have students reread the answer, this time pointing to the appropriate columns in the place-value chart.

6. Read Problem 2 of the Worked Examples with students. Point out that they are to compare place values from right to left this time. They may struggle with the fact that 1 thousand is $\frac{1}{10}$ of 10 thousand. Use the values students wrote on the place-value chart to help them with this idea.

7. Have students read the answer to Problem 2.

   Ask: What pattern do you see when comparing the place values of two digits that are next to each other? The place value of the digit to the right is $\frac{1}{10}$ as great as the place value of the digit to its left.

8. Have students work Problems 1–5. Provide assistance as necessary. Students may wish to use the place-value chart as they work.

Objectives

- Recognize that in a multidigit number, a digit in one place represents 10 times as much as it represents in the place to its right and $\frac{1}{10}$ of what it represents in the place to its left.

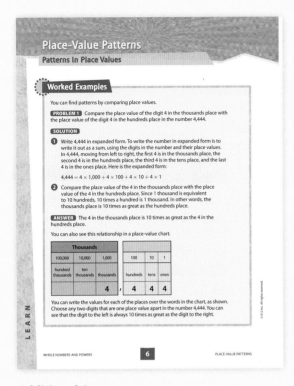

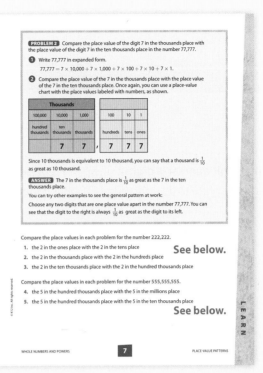

Additional Answers

1. The 2 in the ones place is $\frac{1}{10}$ as great as the 2 in the tens place.

2. The 2 in the thousands place is 10 times as great as the 2 in the hundreds place.

3. The 2 in the ten thousands place is $\frac{1}{10}$ as great as the 2 in the hundred thousands place.

4. The 5 in the hundred thousands place is $\frac{1}{10}$ as great as the 5 in the millions place.

5. The 5 in the hundred thousands place is 10 times as great as the 5 in the ten thousands place.

Bases and Exponents (A)

Lesson Overview

LEARN Expressions with Exponents	10 minutes	ONLINE
LEARN Show Exponent Expressions	20 minutes	ONLINE
LEARN Explain and Compute Exponents	15 minutes	ONLINE
TRY IT Evaluate Expressions	15 minutes	OFFLINE

▶ **Lesson Objectives**

Represent and compute a power by using repeated multiplication.

▶ **Prerequisite Skills**

Explain and apply standard step-by-step approaches for multiplication.

▶ **Content Background**

In this lesson, students will learn about expressions like 7^3 and identify which numeral is the base and which numeral is the exponent. Then they will learn how to use repeated multiplication to write and calculate expressions. Students will focus on exponents of 1, 2, and 3, or numbers to the first, second, and third powers. A number with an exponent of 2 is squared. A number with an exponent of 3 is cubed.

This lesson shows models as a way to represent square and cubic numbers. The lesson also helps students memorize the squaring of numbers through 10.

An expression is made up of numbers, symbols, or both and represents a mathematical relationship. In the expression 7^3, 7 is the base and 3 is the exponent. There is a mathematical relationship between the base and the exponent. The base is the number that is multiplied, and the exponent tells how many times the base is a factor. Therefore, the expression 7^3 is the same as $7 \times 7 \times 7$ or $7 \cdot 7 \cdot 7$.

Materials to Gather

SUPPLIED

Evaluate Expressions activity page

ALSO NEEDED

index cards (optional)

LEARN Expressions with Exponents

ONLINE 10 min

Students will learn why expressions with a base and an exponent make it easier to write greater numbers. They will also learn about the relationship between repeated multiplication and expressions with a base and an exponent.

Objectives

- Represent and compute a power by using repeated multiplication.

LEARN Show Exponent Expressions

Students will learn about expressions that have various exponents. They will learn that bases with exponents can also be shown by using multiple equal factors. They will also learn to find the value, or standard form, of an expression with an exponent. For instance, the value, or standard form, of 3^2 is 9. Students will learn ways to describe expressions with exponents—for example, "3 to the third power" or "3 cubed."

LEARN Explain and Compute Exponents

Students will describe and compare expressions that have bases and exponents. They will use the Grid Learning Tool to model expressions with an exponent of 2. They also will play a game to help them memorize the standard form for 1 squared through 10 squared.

Have students write the following in their Math Notebook. They will provide the answers when they use the Grid Learning Tool.

$1^2 = \underline{?}$ $2^2 = \underline{?}$ $3^2 = \underline{?}$ $4^2 = \underline{?}$

$5^2 = \underline{?}$ $6^2 = \underline{?}$ $7^2 = \underline{?}$ $8^2 = \underline{?}$

$9^2 = \underline{?}$ $10^2 = \underline{?}$

DIRECTIONS FOR USING THE GRID LEARNING TOOL

1. Have students choose a color and then click one square. Tell them that the shaded square represents 1^2 because it is 1 square long and 1 square wide.

2. Have students write 1 as the answer in the equation $1^2 = \underline{?}$ that they wrote in their Math Notebook. Tell them that 1 is the standard form for the expression 1^2.

3. Have students choose another color and then click 4 squares in a 2 by 2 area model.

   Ask: How many squares long is the area you shaded? 2

   Ask: How many squares wide is the area you shaded? 2

   Tell students that the shaded area represents 2^2 because it is 2 squares long and 2 squares wide.

4. **Ask:** What is 2^2? 4

   Have students write 4 as the answer in the equation $2^2 = \underline{?}$ in their Math Notebook. Tell them that 4 is the standard form for the expression 2^2.

5. Have students clear the squares they have shaded.

6. Students should shade areas for the following expressions, clearing the squares as they need space. Have them write the standard form for each expression in their Math Notebook, completing the equations that they wrote at the beginning of the activity.

   $3^2 = 9$ $4^2 = 16$ $5^2 = 25$ $6^2 = 36$

   $7^2 = 49$ $8^2 = 64$ $9^2 = 81$ $10^2 = 100$

   Students will then play an online game to help them memorize 1 squared through 10 squared in standard form.

Objectives

- Represent and compute a power by using repeated multiplication.

Objectives

- Represent and compute a power by using repeated multiplication.

Tips

To help students memorize the standard form of the expressions for 1 squared through 10 squared, have them create index cards with the exponent expression on one side and the standard form on the other side. Students can quiz themselves by looking at the exponent expression side and trying to name the standard form. Then they can turn the card over to see if they are correct.

TRY IT Evaluate Expressions

Students will show the relationship between a base with an exponent and repeated multiplication. They will evaluate expressions with exponents of 2 and 3. Have students turn to the Evaluate Expressions activity page in their Activity Book and read the directions with them.

Students should copy the problems from the Activity Book into their Math Notebook as necessary and solve them there.

- Represent and compute a power by using repeated multiplication.

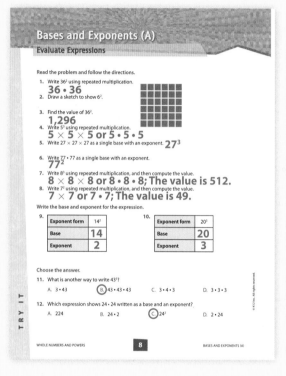

Bases and Exponents (A)

Evaluate Expressions

Read the problem and follow the directions.

1. Write 36^2 using repeated multiplication.
   36 • 36
2. Draw a sketch to show 6^2.
3. Find the value of 36^2.
   1,296
4. Write 5^3 using repeated multiplication.
   $5 \times 5 \times 5$ or $5 \cdot 5 \cdot 5$
5. Write $27 \times 27 \times 27$ as a single base with an exponent. **27^3**
6. Write $77 \cdot 77$ as a single base with an exponent.
   77^2
7. Write 8^3 using repeated multiplication, and then compute the value.
   $8 \times 8 \times 8$ or $8 \cdot 8 \cdot 8$; The value is 512.
8. Write 7^2 using repeated multiplication, and then compute the value.
   7×7 or $7 \cdot 7$; The value is 49.

Write the base and exponent for the expression.

9.
Exponent form	14^2
Base	**14**
Exponent	**2**

10.
Exponent form	20^3
Base	**20**
Exponent	**3**

Choose the answer.

11. What is another way to write 43^3?
   A. $3 \cdot 43$ (B.) $43 \cdot 43 \cdot 43$ C. $3 \cdot 4 \cdot 3$ D. $3 \cdot 3 \cdot 3$

12. Which expression shows $24 \cdot 24$ written as a base and an exponent?
   A. 224   B. $24 \cdot 2$ (C) 24^2 D. $2 \cdot 24$

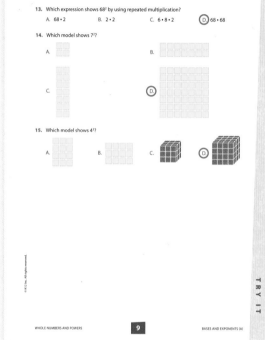

13. Which expression shows 68^2 by using repeated multiplication?
   A. $68 \cdot 2$ B. $2 \cdot 2$ C. $6 \cdot 8 \cdot 2$ (D) $68 \cdot 68$

14. Which model shows 7^2?
   A.   B.
   C.   (D)

15. Which model shows 4^3?
   A.   B.   C.   (D)

Bases and Exponents (B)

LEARN Exponents: 1, 2, and 3	10 minutes	ONLINE
LEARN Exponents of 4 and 5	15 minutes	ONLINE
LEARN Compare Exponents of 4 and 5	15 minutes	OFFLINE
TRY IT Work with Exponents of 4 and 5	10 minutes	OFFLINE
CHECKPOINT	10 minutes	ONLINE

▶ Lesson Objectives

Represent and compute a power by using repeated multiplication.

▶ Prerequisite Skills

Explain and apply standard step-by-step approaches for multiplication.

▶ Content Background

Students will review modeling, explaining, and calculating expressions with exponents of 1, 2, and 3. Then they will extend their learning to model, explain, and calculate expressions with exponents of 4 and 5.

An expression is made up of numbers, symbols, or both, and represents a mathematical relationship. In the expression 7^3, 7 is the base and 3 is the exponent. There is a mathematical relationship between the base and the exponent. The base is the number that is multiplied, and the exponent tells how many times the base is a factor. Therefore, the expression 7^3 means that 7 is the same as $7 \times 7 \times 7$ or $7 \cdot 7 \cdot 7$.

Materials to Gather

SUPPLIED

Work with Exponents of 4 and 5 activity page

LEARN Exponents: 1, 2, and 3

ONLINE 10 min

Students will work with expressions with exponents of 1, 2, or 3. They will use their knowledge of expressions with bases and exponents to play a hidden pictures game. They will match expressions with models, written forms (for example, thirty-six), and standard forms (for example, 36).

Objectives

- Represent and compute a power by using repeated multiplication.

LEARN Exponents of 4 and 5

ONLINE 15 min

Students will learn how to evaluate expressions with exponents of 4 and 5. They are reminded that the exponent tells how many times the base appears as a factor in the multiplication expression.

Objectives

- Represent and compute a power by using repeated multiplication.

Tips Students may need paper and pencil. Allow them to work the problems on paper and then type their answers online.

LEARN Compare Exponents of 4 and 5

Objectives

- Represent and compute a power by using repeated multiplication.

Students will model, explain, compare, and compute expressions with exponents of 4 and 5.

1. Students will review and compare exponents to the fourth and fifth powers. Have students write their answers to the questions in their Math Notebook.

2. Remind students that the base is the number to be multiplied. The exponent tells how many times the base will be a factor. Remind students that numbers with an exponent of 2 are said to be squared and numbers with an exponent of 3 are said to be cubed.

3. Remind students that they have seen models for expressions with exponents of 1, 2, and 3, but that they can't use geometric figures to show a model for expressions with exponents of 4 or greater. Tell them that they will use other ways, such as standard form or written form, to show expressions with exponents of 4 or greater.

4. Write 2^4 and have students identify the base and the exponent. The base is 2 and the exponent is 4.

   Then have students write the multiple factors for 2^4. $2 \cdot 2 \cdot 2 \cdot 2$

   Have students determine the standard form for 2^4. 16

5. Repeat Step 4 with the expression 2^2. base is 2; exponent is 2; multiple factors is $2 \cdot 2$; standard form is 4

6. Have students write "$2^2 \underline{?} 2^4$" in their Math Notebook. Using Steps 4 and 5 as reference, help students compare the expressions by using the symbols $<$ (less than), $>$ (greater than), or $=$ (equals). Discuss how the expressions 2^2 and 2^4 are alike and different. They are alike because they have the same base; they are different because they have different exponents; students should also compare the multiple factors and standard form for each expression.

   Students should conclude that the correct comparison is $2^2 < 2^4$.

7. Have students write $2^4 \underline{?} 4^2$ in their Math Notebook.

   Ask: How are the two expressions different? They have different bases and exponents.

   Say: Compute the two expressions and compare them. Write the number sentence that compares them. $2^4 = 4^2$

8. Repeat Step 7 with students. Use the expressions 2^5 and 5^2. The correct comparison is $2^5 > 5^2$.

9. Have students work on their own to find the correct comparisons for these expressions:

   - 3^4 and 4^3 $3^4 > 4^3$
   - 3^5 and 5^3 $3^5 > 5^3$

10. **Ask:** After you have compared sets of expressions, is there a difference between the base and the exponent when you evaluate an expression? Why? There is a difference between the base and the exponent. The exponent tells you how many times the base is a factor in an expression.

TRY IT Work with Exponents of 4 and 5

Objectives

- Represent and compute a power by using repeated multiplication.

Students will practice identifying bases and exponents, using repeated multiplication to evaluate exponent expressions. They will also compare expressions that have exponents. Have students turn to the Work with Exponents of 4 and 5 activity page in their Activity Book.

Students should copy the problems from the Activity Book into their Math Notebook as necessary and solve them there.

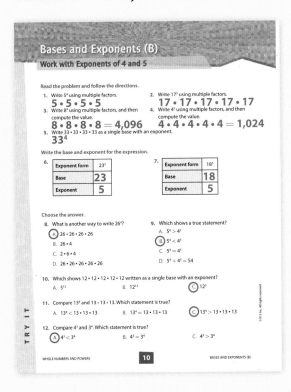

Bases and Exponents (B)
Work with Exponents of 4 and 5

Read the problem and follow the directions.

1. Write 5^4 using multiple factors.
$5 \cdot 5 \cdot 5 \cdot 5$

2. Write 17^5 using multiple factors.
$17 \cdot 17 \cdot 17 \cdot 17 \cdot 17$

3. Write 8^4 using multiple factors, and then compute the value.
$8 \cdot 8 \cdot 8 \cdot 8 = 4{,}096$

4. Write 4^5 using multiple factors, and then compute the value.
$4 \cdot 4 \cdot 4 \cdot 4 \cdot 4 = 1{,}024$

5. Write $33 \cdot 33 \cdot 33 \cdot 33$ as a single base with an exponent.
33^4

Write the base and exponent for the expression.

6.
Exponent form	23^5
Base	23
Exponent	5

7.
Exponent form	18^5
Base	18
Exponent	5

Choose the answer.

8. What is another way to write 26^4?
- (A) $26 \cdot 26 \cdot 26 \cdot 26$
- B. $26 \cdot 4$
- C. $2 \cdot 6 \cdot 4$
- D. $26 \cdot 26 \cdot 26 \cdot 26 \cdot 26$

9. Which shows a true statement?
- A. $5^4 > 4^5$
- (B) $5^4 < 4^5$
- C. $5^4 = 4^5$
- D. $5^4 + 4^5 = 54$

10. Which shows $12 \cdot 12 \cdot 12 \cdot 12 \cdot 12$ written as a single base with an exponent?
- A. 5^{12}
- B. 12^{12}
- (C) 12^5

11. Compare 13^4 and $13 \cdot 13 \cdot 13$. Which statement is true?
- A. $13^4 < 13 \cdot 13 \cdot 13$
- B. $13^4 = 13 \cdot 13 \cdot 13$
- (C) $13^4 > 13 \cdot 13 \cdot 13$

12. Compare 4^3 and 3^4. Which statement is true?
- (A) $4^3 < 3^4$
- B. $4^3 = 3^4$
- C. $4^3 > 3^4$

WHOLE NUMBERS AND POWERS

10

BASES AND EXPONENTS (B)

TRY IT

CHECKPOINT

Objectives

- Represent and compute a power by using repeated multiplication.

Students will complete an online Checkpoint. If necessary, read the directions, problems, and answer choices to students and help them with keyboard or mouse operations.

Core Focus
Multiplication and Division

Lesson Overview

LEARN Multiplication and Division Computation	15 minutes	ONLINE
LEARN Multiplication and Division Stories	15 minutes	ONLINE
TRY IT Practice: Multiply and Divide	20 minutes	OFFLINE
CHECKPOINT	10 minutes	ONLINE

▶ Lesson Objectives

- Fluently multiply multidigit whole numbers using the standard algorithm.
- Solve with proficiency for quotients of up to a four-digit dividend by a two-digit divisor using strategies.
- Solve multistep problems using multiple operations.
- Determine which operations are appropriate to use to solve a multistep story problem.

▶ Content Background

Students have learned to multiply and divide whole numbers with strategies including the standard algorithm. They have also solved one-step and multistep story problems. Students need to understand the steps for problem solving and know the key questions to ask themselves when thinking through and solving a problem.

Materials to Gather

SUPPLIED

Practice: Multiply and Divide activity page

LEARN Multiplication and Division Computation
ONLINE 15min

Students will review the parts and characteristics of multiplication and division problems, and they will solve computation problems.

Objectives

- Fluently multiply multidigit whole numbers using the standard algorithm.
- Solve with proficiency for quotients of up to a four-digit dividend by a two-digit divisor using strategies.

LEARN Multiplication and Division Stories
ONLINE 15min

Students will review the problem-solving plan and practice using this plan by solving some multistep problems. They will also review how to determine whether to multiply or divide when solving problems involving one or both of these operations.

Objectives

- Fluently multiply multidigit whole numbers using the standard algorithm.
- Determine which operations are appropriate to use to solve a multistep story problem.
- Solve multistep story problems using multiple operations.

Objectives

Students will practice both computation and story problems involving multiplication and division. Some of the multistep story problems may also involve addition or subtraction. View or print the Practice: Multiply and Divide activity page. Students should copy the problems into their Math Notebook and solve them there.

- Fluently multiply multidigit whole numbers using the standard algorithm.
- Solve with proficiency for quotients of up to a four-digit dividend by a two-digit divisor using strategies.
- Solve multistep problems using multiple operations.

Core Focus
Multiplication and Division
Practice: Multiply and Divide

Solve.

1. The Children's Theater can seat 1,575 people in 63 equal rows. The Bartell Theater can seat 2,048 people in 64 equal rows. How many more or fewer people are seated in each row at the Bartell Theater than at the Children's Theater, if all the seats are filled at both theaters?
   (a) Draw a diagram to represent the problem.
   (b) Solve the problem. Explain how you found your answer.
   See right.

2. Jake and Lacy work at a golf driving range. At the end of the day, Jake collected 408 golf balls and Lacy collected 374 golf balls. They need to put them into baskets with 34 golf balls in each basket. How many baskets will Jake and Lacy fill altogether?
   (a) Use equations to represent the problem. Solve the problem and explain your thinking.
   (b) Use equations to represent another way to solve the problem. Solve the problem this different way and explain your thinking.
   See below.

3. Maddy has a dog walking business. She charges $6.75 per hour to walk 1 dog and $10.50 per hour to walk 2 dogs. Maddy can walk up to 4 dogs at a time. How much will Maddy make if she walks Chloe's 2 dogs and Deon's 1 dog for a total of 2 hours?
   (a) What operations can be used to solve the problem? How do you know?
   (b) Explain and solve the problem in two different ways.
   See below.

4. Izzie multiplied 436 × 203. She said the partial products she used to solve the problem are 1,308 and 87,200. Do you agree? Explain your answer.
   See below.

WHOLE NUMBERS AND POWERS   **11**   CORE FOCUS MULTIPLICATION AND DIVISION

TRY IT

Additional Answers

1. (a) Sample drawing:

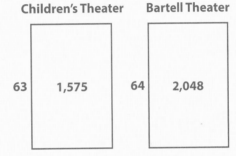

Children's Theater   **Bartell Theater**

| 63 | 1,575 |

| 64 | 2,048 |

(b) There are 7 more people in each row at the Bartell Theater than at the Children's Theater. I divided 1575 ÷ 63 = 25 to find the number of people in each row at the Children's Theater. I divided 2,048 ÷ 64 = 32 to find the number of people in each row at the Bartell Theater. Then I subtracted 25 from 32 to get 7.

2. (a) **Possible answer:** I divided 408 ÷ 34 = 12 and divided 374 ÷ 34 = 11 to find the number of baskets each person filled. Then I added 12 + 11 = 23 to get the total number of baskets.

   Possible answer: I added 408 + 374 = 782 to get the total number of golf balls they collected. Then I divided 784 ÷ 34 = 23 to get the total number of baskets.

   (b) See Part (a)

3. (a) multiplication and addition; I multiply because I have cost-per-hour rates and Maddy is walking the dogs for 2 hours. I need to add to find how much Maddy makes for walking Chloe's 2 dogs and Deon's 1 dog.

   (b) I can add $6.75 and $10.50 = $17.25. Then I can multiply $17.25 × 2 = $34.50. Another solution is that I can multiply $6.75 × 2 = $13.50 and multiply $10.50 × 2 = $21. Then I add $13.50 + $21.00 = $34.50.

4. Yes. **Possible explanation:** Izzie multiplied 436 by 3 ones and got 1,308. There were no tens to multiply by 436 because there is a 0 in the second factor, 208. She multiplied 436 by 200 and got 87,200.

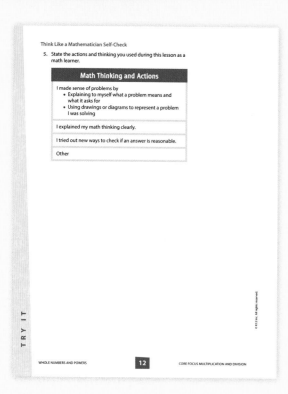

CHECKPOINT

ONLINE 10 min

Objectives

Students will complete an online Checkpoint. If necessary, read the directions, problems, and answer choices to students and help them with keyboard or mouse operations.

- Fluently multiply multidigit whole numbers using the standard algorithm.
- Solve with proficiency for quotients of up to a four-digit dividend by a two-digit divisor using strategies.
- Solve multistep problems using multiple operations.

Unit Review

▶ Unit Objectives

- Round whole numbers in a story problem.
- Estimate or calculate a sum or a difference in a whole-number problem.
- Estimate or calculate a sum or a difference in a whole-number story problem.
- Determine whether multiplication or division is the appropriate operation to use to solve a story problem.
- Determine which operations are appropriate to use to solve a multistep story problem.
- Explain and apply standard step-by-step approaches for multiplication.
- Fluently multiply multidigit whole numbers using the standard algorithm.
- Solve with proficiency for quotients of up to a four-digit dividend by a two-digit divisor using strategies.
- Represent and compute a power by using repeated multiplication.
- Solve a problem that involves powers.
- Solve multistep problems using multiple operations.
- Recognize that in a multidigit number, a digit in one place represents 10 times as much as it represents in the place to its right and $\frac{1}{10}$ of what it represents in the place to its left.

Materials to Gather

There are no materials to gather for this lesson.

▶ Advance Preparation

In this lesson, students will have an opportunity to review previous activities in the Whole Numbers and Powers unit. Look at the suggested activities in Unit Review: Prepare for the Checkpoint online and gather any needed materials.

ONLINE 10 min

UNIT REVIEW Look Back

Students will review key concepts from the unit to prepare for the Unit Checkpoint.

Objectives

- Review unit objectives.

UNIT REVIEW Checkpoint Practice

ONLINE 50 min

Students will complete an online Checkpoint Practice to prepare for the Unit Checkpoint. If necessary, read the directions, problems, and answer choices to students. Have students answer the problems on their own. Review any missed problems with students.

Objectives

- Review unit objectives.

UNIT REVIEW Prepare for the Checkpoint

What you do next depends on how students performed in the previous activity, Unit Review: Checkpoint Practice. If students had difficulty with any of the problems, complete the appropriate review activity listed in the table online.

Unit Checkpoint

UNIT CHECKPOINT Online   60 minutes   **ONLINE**

▶ ## Unit Objectives

- Round whole numbers in a story problem.
- Estimate or calculate a sum or a difference in a whole-number problem.
- Estimate or calculate a sum or a difference in a whole-number story problem.
- Determine whether multiplication or division is the appropriate operation to use to solve a story problem.
- Determine which operations are appropriate to use to solve a multistep story problem.
- Explain and apply standard step-by-step approaches for multiplication.
- Fluently multiply multidigit whole numbers using the standard algorithm.
- Solve with proficiency for quotients of up to a four-digit dividend by a two-digit divisor using strategies.
- Represent and compute a power by using repeated multiplication.
- Solve a problem that involves powers.
- Solve multistep problems using multiple operations.
- Recognize that in a multidigit number, a digit in one place represents 10 times as much as it represents in the place to its right and $\frac{1}{10}$ of what it represents in the place to its left.

Materials to Gather

There are no materials to gather for this lesson.

ONLINE

60min

UNIT CHECKPOINT Online

Students will complete the online Unit Checkpoint. If necessary, read the directions, problems, and answer choices to students and help them with keyboard or mouse operations.

Objectives

- Assess unit objectives.

Extended Problems: Reasoning

USE WHAT YOU KNOW Offline

60 minutes   OFFLINE

▶ Lesson Objectives

This lesson assesses the following objectives:

- Recognize that in a multidigit number, a digit in one place represents 10 times as much as it represents in the place to its right and $\frac{1}{10}$ of what it represents in the place to its left.
- Fluently multiply multidigit whole numbers using the standard algorithm.
- Solve with proficiency for quotients of up to a four-digit dividend by a two-digit divisor using strategies.
- Solve a problem that involves powers.

Materials to Gather

SUPPLIED

Extended Problems: Reasoning
    (printout)

Extended Problems: Reasoning
    Answer Key (printout)

USE WHAT YOU KNOW Offline

OFFLINE

60 min

Objectives

- Apply lesson objectives.

The Extended Problems: Reasoning and its answer key are located online in the Resources section of *Math+ Yellow Lesson Guide*. Give students the Extended Problems: Reasoning. Read the directions, problems, and answer choices to students, if necessary.

You will grade this assignment.
- Students should complete the assignment on their own.
- Students should submit the completed assignment to you.

Geometry

▶ Unit Objectives

- Identify, measure, and draw angles with appropriate math tools.
- Identify and draw perpendicular or parallel lines with appropriate math tools.
- Define and sketch different types of triangles and identify their attributes.
- Identify that the sum of the interior angles of any triangle is 180° and solve related problems.
- Identify that the sum of the interior angles of any quadrilateral is 360° and solve related problems.

- Know how to define and sketch different quadrilaterals.
- Classify two-dimensional figures in a hierarchy based on their properties.
- Understand that attributes that apply to a category of two-dimensional figures also apply to all subcategories of that category.
- Construct rectangles or triangles with appropriate math tools.

▶ Big Ideas

- A right angle forms a square corner that measures 90°; an acute angle is less than a right angle and an obtuse angle is greater than a right angle.
- Geometric figures can be described and classified by the shapes of their faces and by how many faces, sides, edges, or vertices they have.

▶ Unit Introduction

Students will investigate two-dimensional figures in this geometry unit. They will define and categorize two-dimensional figures by characteristics such as the lengths of their sides and their angle measurements; for quadrilaterals, they will determine whether the opposite sides are parallel. Students will learn that quadrilaterals and triangles have characteristics that place them in certain categories and that often those categories overlap. They will use rulers, protractors, and compasses to draw angles, lines, quadrilaterals, and triangles. Students will explore the measures of the interior angles of triangles and quadrilaterals to understand the relationship between the sum of the angle measures and the number of angles in each shape.

▶ Keywords

acute angle
acute triangle
angle
compass
congruent
degree
equiangular triangle
equilateral triangle
interior angle
intersecting lines

isosceles triangle
obtuse angle
obtuse triangle
parallel lines
parallelogram
perpendicular lines
protractor
quadrilateral
ray
rectangle

rhombus (plural: rhombuses)
right angle
right triangle
ruler
scalene triangle
square
straight angle
sum of angle measures
trapezoid
triangle
vertex (plural: vertices)

Angles (A)

Lesson Overview

GET READY Sort Angles	5 minutes	ONLINE
LEARN Angles and Shapes	15 minutes	ONLINE
LEARN Tools for Measuring Angles	25 minutes	ONLINE
TRY IT Measure Angles	15 minutes	OFFLINE

▶ ## Lesson Objectives

Identify, measure, and draw angles with appropriate math tools.

▶ ## Prerequisite Skills

- State and recognize the definitions of a right angle, an acute angle, an obtuse angle, and a straight angle.
- Demonstrate understanding of relative angle measures.

▶ ## Content Background

Students will measure angles with a protractor. On many protractors, there are two sets of numbers along the curved edge of the tool. These numbers are the scales for reading the measure of an angle in degrees. Each scale goes from 0 to 180. One scale goes from 0 on the left to 180 on the right. The other scale is arranged in the opposite direction to the first scale.

Having two scales on a protractor makes it easier to find the measure of an angle, no matter how the angle is oriented. Students should use one scale to measure an angle. They should check where the 0 and 180 degree marks are on the scale they are using, so they can accurately measure the angle.

▶ ## Common Errors and Misconceptions

Students might focus on the length of the line segments that form an angle's sides, the tilt of the top line segment, the area enclosed by the sides, or the proximity of the two sides rather than look at the actual size of the angle. For example, students might indicate that in the two triangles shown here, angle *A* is smaller than angle *X*.

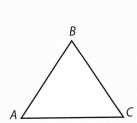
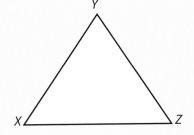

Materials to Gather

SUPPLIED

protractor

Measure Angles activity page

ALSO NEEDED

ruler (optional)

GET READY Sort Angles

Objectives

Students will identify acute, right, obtuse, and straight angles. They will match the names of angles to correct angles.

- State and recognize the definitions of a right angle, an acute angle, an obtuse angle, and a straight angle.
- Demonstrate understanding of relative angle measures.

LEARN Angles and Shapes

Objectives

Students will learn about the parts of an angle. Then they will use the Pattern Blocks Learning Tool to put shapes together to create other shapes. They will explore the angles in the shapes.

- Identify, measure, and draw angles with appropriate math tools.

DIRECTIONS FOR USING THE PATTERN BLOCKS LEARNING TOOL

1. Click Free Play. Then read the instructions, and click Start.

   Ask: What unit of measure do you use to describe an angle? a degree or degrees

2. Have students drag one triangle to the canvas.

   Ask: What type of angle is formed where two sides of this triangle meet in an angle less than 90°? acute

3. Have students drag five more triangles to the canvas near the first triangle. Show them how to rotate the triangles using the Rotate arrows.

4. Have students rotate the triangles and drag them next to each other to make a hexagon. Focus attention on the angles formed by the sides of the hexagon.

   Ask: What type of angle is formed where two sides of a hexagon meet? an obtuse angle measuring more than 90°

5. Have students drag three triangles to the canvas and make a trapezoid with them by using the Rotate arrows.

   Ask: Look at all the angles formed where two sides of the trapezoid meet. Are all the angles the same type? no

   Ask: What types of angles are formed by the sides of the trapezoid? obtuse and acute angles

6. Have students drag one square to the canvas.

   Ask: What is the measure of the angle formed where two sides of the square meet? 90°

   Ask: What is the name of a 90° angle? a right angle

   Ask: How many angles does a square have? 4

7. Have students drag two more squares to the canvas and join them with the first square to make a rectangle.

   Ask: What is the measure of the angle formed where two sides of a rectangle meet? 90°

   Ask: How many angles does a rectangle have? 4

8. Have students create other shapes from pattern blocks and describe the shapes' angles.

LEARN Tools for Measuring Angles

Objectives

- Identify, measure, and draw angles with appropriate math tools.

Students will learn the parts of a protractor. Then they will learn step-by-step procedures for measuring angles with a protractor. They will measure given angles with an online protractor. Then they will create their own angles with the Advanced Protractor Learning Tool and will measure the angles.

DIRECTIONS FOR USING THE ADVANCED PROTRACTOR LEARNING TOOL

1. Click Draw an Angle.

2. Have students drag point *A* to make the following types of angles. Have them read aloud the measure of each angle they make.

   - acute
   - right
   - obtuse

3. Have students make a 0° angle.

   Ask: What is a 0° angle? an angle that measures no degrees and that lies on a ray

4. Have students make a straight angle.

   Ask: What is the measure of a straight angle? 180°

   Ask: What is the difference between a straight angle and a 0° angle? A straight angle lies on a line, and a 0° angle lies on a ray.

5. Click Menu. Then click Measure an Angle.

6. Have students drag point *A* to create an angle of any measure.

7. Have students drag the protractor over the angle, placing the origin on the vertex of the angle.

8. Have students read the angle's measure on the protractor and enter the measure in the box.

9. Have them click Check. The learning tool will either show the answer as correct or say how many degrees too small or too large the answer is.

10. Have students create acute, right, obtuse, and straight angles; measure them; and check answers.

TRY IT Measure Angles

Objectives

- Identify, measure, and draw angles with appropriate math tools.

Students will practice using a protractor to measure angles. They will classify the angle as acute, right, straight, or obtuse. Make sure they find the angle measure in degrees. Gather a protractor. Have students turn to the Measure Angles activity page in their Activity Book and read the directions with them.

Students should copy the problems from the Activity Book into their Math Notebook as necessary and solve them there.

Tips When students use a protractor to measure an angle, they may need to extend the sides of the angle to reach the outer scale of the protractor. Have students practice using a sharp pencil and a straightedge (or ruler) to extend the sides of several angles before beginning the activity.

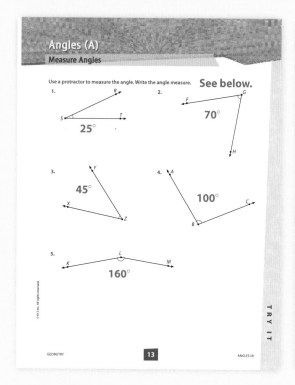

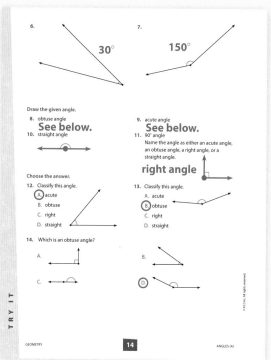

Additional Answers

1–7. Accept angle measurements that are within 2° of the given answer. For example, for Problem 1, which has an answer of 25°, students may answer 23°, 24°, 26°, or 27° and still be counted as correct.

8. Answers will vary. Other correct drawings are acceptable.

9. Answers will vary. Other correct drawings are acceptable.

Angles (B)

Lesson Overview

GET READY Use Unit Angles	10 minutes	**ONLINE**
LEARN How to Draw Angles	10 minutes	**ONLINE**
LEARN Draw Angles with a Protractor	15 minutes	**OFFLINE**
TRY IT Draw and Measure Angles	15 minutes	**OFFLINE**
CHECKPOINT	10 minutes	**OFFLINE**

Lesson Objectives

Identify, measure, and draw angles with appropriate math tools.

Prerequisite Skills

Demonstrate understanding of relative angle measures.

Content Background

Student will continue to measure angles with a protractor. On many protractors, there are two sets of numbers along the curved edge of the tool. These numbers are the scales for reading the measure of an angle in degrees. Each scale goes from 0 to 180. One scale goes from 0 on the left to 180 on the right. The other scale is arranged in the opposite direction to the first scale.

Having two scales on a protractor makes it easier to find the measure of an angle, no matter how the angle is oriented. Students should use one scale to measure an angle. They should check where the 0 and 180 degree marks are on the scale they are using, so they can accurately measure the angle.

Common Errors and Misconceptions

- Students might think that the size of an image of an angle relates to the angle's measurement. It is best to use terminology such as "the angle with the greater (or greatest) measure" instead of "the greater (or greatest) angle."
- Students might think they have to line up one ray of an angle with 0° on a protractor. Instead, they can line up one ray with a friendly number, and then subtract the readings where the two rays cross the protractor scale.

Materials to Gather

SUPPLIED

protractor

Draw and Measure Angles activity page

Checkpoint (printout)

ALSO NEEDED

ruler

GET READY Use Unit Angles

Objectives

- Demonstrate understanding of relative angle measures.

Students will learn how to compare angles to determine which angle has a greater measure than another angle and which has a lesser measure than another angle.

LEARN How to Draw Angles

Objectives

- Identify, measure, and draw angles with appropriate math tools.

Students will learn to draw angles. They will learn how to draw an angle by using a ruler. They will also learn how to draw an angle by using a ruler and a protractor.

Point out that when students draw an angle with a ruler and do not use a protractor, they do not know the exact degree measure of the angle. But students can estimate the measure of the angle and classify the angle as acute, obtuse, right, or straight.

LEARN Draw Angles with a Protractor

OFFLINE
15 min

Objectives

- Identify, measure, and draw angles with appropriate math tools.

Tips

When students are using the protractor to *draw* angles, remind them to make sure the center of the protractor stays on the endpoint of the ray. When they use the protractor to *measure* angles, remind them to make sure the center of the protractor stays on the vertex of the angle.

Students will use tools to draw angles. Gather the ruler and the protractor.

1. Have students use only a ruler to sketch a 60° angle.

   Ask: How does a 60° angle compare in measure to a right angle? A right angle measures 90°, so a 60° angle has a lesser measure than a right angle.

   The sketch of the 60° angle should look like it has a lesser measure than a 90° angle.

2. Give students the protractor and guide them as they draw a 60° angle with the protractor and the ruler. Use the following directions:

   - Make a point on your paper. Label the point B. This will be the endpoint of the rays that form the angle. This endpoint is the vertex of the angle you will draw.

   - Use a ruler to draw a ray from the endpoint. Mark a point on the ray. Label the point A.

   - Place the center, or origin, of the protractor on the endpoint of the ray.

   - Line up the ray with any friendly degree measure on the protractor. A friendly degree measure is a number that is easy to compute mentally.

   - Locate the degree measure on the protractor that is 60° greater than the friendly degree measure you used. Mark a point at that location.

   - Draw a ray from the endpoint through the point. Label the point C. Make an arc inside the angle to mark the angle you drew. Label the arc 60°. The name of the angle is ∠ABC.

   You can also position the protractor to line up with the base line of 0° on the protractor. Use the following directions:

   - Make a point on your paper. Label the point B. This will be the endpoint of the rays that form the angle. This endpoint is the vertex of the angle you will draw.

- Use a ruler to draw a ray from the endpoint. Mark a point on the ray. Label the point *A*.
- Place the center of the protractor on the endpoint of the ray.
- Line up the protractor's base line with the ray so that the ray points to 0°.
- Locate 60° on the inside scale of the protractor. Mark a point at that location.
- Draw a ray from the endpoint through the point. Label the point *C*. Make an arc inside the angle to mark the angle you drew. Label the arc 60°. The name of the angle is ∠*ABC*.

3. Have students compare the angle they sketched with the angle they drew using a protractor. Point out that the angles should be about the same measure but will probably not be exactly the same measure.

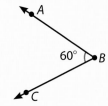

4. Repeat Steps 1–3 for a 75° angle, a 95° angle, a 150° angle, and a 180° angle. Students may choose different labels for the points on their sketches.

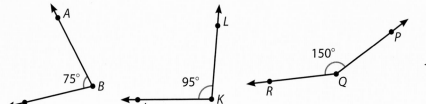

5. Repeat Steps 1–3, having students decide what angle measures they want to draw. Tell students that they should mark the vertex with a point and show an arc on the angle. They do not need to mark points on the rays or label the vertex. Use a protractor to check that the angles are correctly drawn.

OFFLINE

15 min

TRY IT Draw and Measure Angles

Students will practice measuring and drawing angles. Gather a protractor and a ruler. When students measure angles on the activity page with the protractor, accept answers that are 2° greater than or less than the answer given as correct. Have students turn to the Draw and Measure Angles activity page in their Activity Book and read the directions with them.

Students should copy the problems from the Activity Book into their Math Notebook as necessary and solve them there.

Objectives

- Identify, measure, and draw angles with appropriate math tools.

Tips

If needed, have students review the steps they learned for drawing and measuring angles before they begin the activity page.

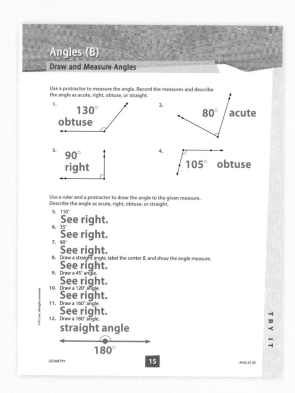

5. obtuse angle

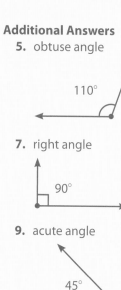

110°

6. acute angle

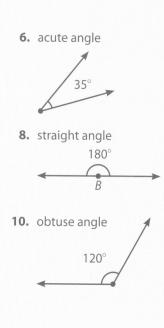

35°

7. right angle

90°

8. straight angle

180°

B

9. acute angle

45°

10. obtuse angle

120°

11. obtuse angle

160°

T R Y I T

CHECKPOINT

OFFLINE

10 min

Objectives

The Checkpoint and its answer key are located in the Resources section for this unit in the Online Book Menu of *Math+ Yellow Lesson Guide*. Open the Checkpoint. Give students a protractor. Use the answer key to score the Checkpoint, and then enter the results online.

- Identify, measure, and draw angles with appropriate math tools.

Perpendicular and Parallel Lines

Lesson Overview

GET READY Identify Lines	10 minutes	ONLINE
LEARN Use a Compass to Construct Lines	10 minutes	ONLINE
LEARN Construct Lines with a Compass	20 minutes	OFFLINE
TRY IT Practice Types of Lines	10 minutes	OFFLINE
CHECKPOINT	10 minutes	ONLINE

▶ Lesson Objectives
Identify and draw perpendicular or parallel lines with appropriate math tools.

▶ Prerequisite Skills
- Identify lines that are parallel or intersecting.
- Identify lines that are perpendicular.

▶ Content Background
Students will learn how mathematicians draw lines and angles and use math tools to draw and measure lines and angles.

Lines may be parallel, intersecting, or perpendicular. This drawing shows parallel, intersecting, and perpendicular lines.

1. Line *EF* is parallel to line *GH*.
2. Line *GH* intersects line *AB*.
3. Lines *EF* and *GH* are perpendicular to line *CD*.

▶ Safety
Make sure students handle the compass carefully and be sure to store it in a safe place.

Materials to Gather

SUPPLIED

protractor

Practice Types of Lines activity page

ALSO NEEDED

compass

ruler

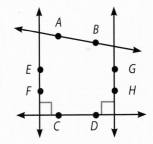

GET READY Identify Lines

ONLINE **10min**

Students will review the meanings of the geometric terms *intersecting, parallel,* and *perpendicular*. Then they will identify intersecting, parallel, and perpendicular lines on a map.

Objectives

- Identify lines that are parallel or intersecting.
- Identify lines that are perpendicular.

Tips If students are having difficulty identifying intersecting, parallel, or perpendicular lines, have them look for the three types of lines in everyday places. Make a list of places each type of line is found. A set of railroad tracks is an example of parallel lines.

LEARN Use a Compass to Construct Lines

Students will learn how to use a compass and a ruler to construct perpendicular and parallel lines.

- Identify and draw perpendicular or parallel lines with appropriate math tools.

LEARN Construct Lines with a Compass

Objectives

Students will practice identifying and constructing parallel and perpendicular lines. Gather a compass, protractor, ruler, and sheet of paper.

- Identify and draw perpendicular or parallel lines with appropriate math tools.

DRAWING AND CONSTRUCTING PERPENDICULAR LINES

1. Remind students that perpendicular lines intersect at one point. Perpendicular lines always make a right angle at the point where they intersect.

2. Have students sketch a line on a sheet of paper.

3. Have them sketch another line that looks perpendicular to the first line.

4. Remind students that to accurately construct perpendicular lines, they must use tools such as a compass and ruler.

5. Now have students draw a line segment about 3 inches long and label the endpoints *A* and *B*.

6. Have students set the point of the compass at point *A* and open the compass a width that is not all the way to point *B*, but beyond the middle of the segment. Ask students to draw an arc that extends from above the middle of the segment to below the middle of the segment.

7. Have students leave the compass the same width and set the point of the compass at point *B*. Have them draw a second arc that crosses their first arc both above and below the segment. Students should label the point where the arcs cross above the segment as point *C* and the point where the arcs cross below the segment as point *D*.

8. Be sure students use a ruler to draw line *CD*, which will be perpendicular to line segment *AB*. Students should label the point where line *CD* and line segment *AB* intersect as point *E*.

9. Have students use the protractor to measure angles *CEA* and *CEB* to check that each angle measures exactly 90°. Angles *DEA* and *DEB* will also measure exactly 90°.

DRAWING AND CONSTRUCTING PARALLEL LINES

10. Remind students that parallel lines are always in the same plane, or two-dimensional space. Parallel lines are always the same distance apart. They never intersect, or cross each other.

11. Have students sketch a line on a sheet of paper.

12. Have students sketch another line that looks parallel to the first line.

13. Remind students that to accurately construct parallel lines, they must use tools such as a compass and ruler.

Tips

If students are having trouble constructing parallel lines, practice constructing perpendicular lines several times before moving to parallel lines.

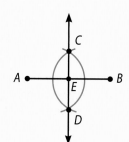

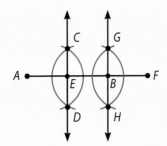

14. Using the line *CD* and line segment *AB* they have drawn, have students set the compass width the same as the length of segment *EB*. Then have them extend the line segment to the right beyond point *B* to a point they will label as point *F*. By using the compass, they should make the length of segment *BF* the same as the length of segment *EB*.

15. Have students repeat the construction of a perpendicular line to create a second perpendicular line to line segment *AF*, following Steps 7–9.

16. Have students set the point of the compass at point *E* and open the compass a width that is not all the way to point *F*, but beyond point *B*. Ask students to draw an arc that extends from above point *B* to below point *B*.

17. Have students leave the compass the same width and set the point of the compass at point *F*. Have them draw a second arc that crosses their first arc both above and below point *B*. Label the point where the arcs cross above the segment as point *G* and the point where the arcs cross below the segment as point *H*.

18. Be sure students use a ruler to draw line *GH*, which will be perpendicular to line segment *AF*.

19. **Ask:** Which lines are parallel? Lines *CD* and *GH* are parallel.

20. Point out that when two lines are each perpendicular to another line or segment, as *CD* and *GH* are to segment *AF*, they are parallel to each other.

CONSTRUCTING PARALLEL AND PERPENDICULAR LINES TO MAKE A MAP

21. Have students create a simple map by making parallel and perpendicular lines. Students can label lines with names.

22. Remind students to use a ruler and compass as they construct the parallel and perpendicular lines.

23. Ask students to identify parallel and perpendicular lines on their map.

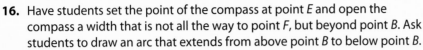

TRY IT Practice Types of Lines

OFFLINE 10 min

Objectives

Following the steps they have learned for constructing lines, students will construct and draw intersecting, perpendicular, and parallel lines. They will give examples of where these types of lines can be found every day. Gather a ruler, compass, and protractor. Have students turn to the Practice Types of Lines activity page in their Activity Book and read the directions with them.

Students should copy the problems from the Activity Book into their Math Notebook as necessary and solve them there.

- Identify and draw perpendicular or parallel lines with appropriate math tools.

Tips

To help students remember the differences between a perpendicular and a parallel line, write the word *parallel* for them. Point out the two l's in the middle of the word. These l's are parallel. Tell them to think of the parallel letter l's when they look for parallel lines.

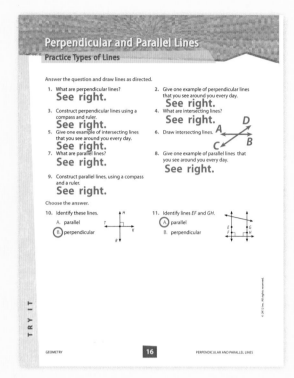

Additional Answers

1. Perpendicular lines intersect at one point. Perpendicular lines always make a right angle at the point where they intersect.

2. Answers will vary. Other correct examples are acceptable. **Sample answer:** the place where edges of a dresser meet, the place where rungs on a ladder meet the sides of the ladder

3. Students should follow the steps they have learned for constructing lines with a compass and a ruler.

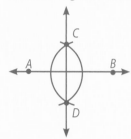

4. Intersecting lines cross each other. They can intersect, or cross each other, at one point or at all points.

5. Answers will vary. Other correct examples are acceptable. **Sample answer:** roads that cross each other, the cuts that make slices of pizza

7. Parallel lines are always in the same plane, or two-dimensional space. Parallel lines are always the same distance apart. They never intersect, or cross each other.

8. Answers will vary. Other correct examples are acceptable. **Sample answer:** railroad tracks, the rungs that make up a ladder

9. Students should follow the steps they have learned for constructing lines with a compass and a ruler.

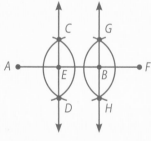

CHECKPOINT

ONLINE **10** min

Students will complete an online Checkpoint. If necessary, read the directions, problems, and answer choices to students and help them with keyboard or mouse operations.

Objectives

- Identify and draw perpendicular or parallel lines with appropriate math tools.

Identify and Classify Triangles

Lesson Overview

GET READY Two Types of Triangles	5 minutes	ONLINE
LEARN Different Types of Triangles	15 minutes	ONLINE
LEARN Triangle Classification	20 minutes	OFFLINE
TRY IT Classify Triangles	10 minutes	OFFLINE
CHECKPOINT	10 minutes	ONLINE

▶ Lesson Objectives

- Define and sketch different types of triangles and identify their attributes.
- Understand that attributes that apply to a category of two-dimensional figures also apply to all subcategories of that category.

▶ Prerequisite Skills

Identify attributes of isosceles, equilateral, and right triangles.

▶ Content Background

In this lesson, students will learn to identify and draw different types of triangles. They will classify triangles using angles and side lengths.

When students first learned to classify angles as *acute*, *obtuse*, or *right*, they physically compared angles to a corner of an index card. Therefore, they have previously referred to the *size* of an angle. But as students learn more about angles, avoid using the word *size* when referring to an angle. Instead, use the term *measure*.

A triangle is a polygon with 3 sides and 3 angles. Students can classify a triangle based on its angles, the relationship among the lengths of its sides, or, in some cases, a combination of both.

Since every triangle has at least 2 acute angles, students use the measure of the third angle to classify a triangle. If the third angle is a right angle (an angle whose measure equals 90°), the triangle is a right triangle; if the third angle is an acute angle (an angle whose measure is less than 90°), the triangle is an acute triangle; if the third angle is an obtuse angle (an angle whose measure is between 90° and 180°), the triangle is an obtuse triangle. Therefore, an acute triangle has 3 acute angles; a right triangle has 1 right angle and 2 acute angles; an obtuse triangle has 1 obtuse angle and 2 acute angles. A drawing of a plane geometric figure often shows marks that provide information. A small square in a corner shows that the angle is a right angle.

Students can also classify a triangle by the relationship among the lengths of its sides. A triangle with no sides that are the same length is a *scalene* triangle. A triangle with at least 2 sides that are the same length is an *isosceles* triangle. A triangle with 3 sides that are the same length is an *equilateral* triangle. At this level, students should identify a triangle with all sides the same length as an equilateral triangle. As students progress to a higher level of mathematics, they will learn that an equilateral triangle is actually a special type of isosceles triangle because it has *at least* 2 sides that are the same length. A drawing of a plane geometric figure often shows tick marks on the sides of a figure. Identical tick marks show sides that are equal in length.

Materials to Gather

SUPPLIED

Triangle Classification Chart (printout)

Classify Triangles activity page

ALSO NEEDED

pipe cleaners – 21

index cards – 7

scissors, pointed-end safety

book

ruler, dual-scale

equilateral triangle

isosceles triangle

scalene triangle

Students can often classify a triangle by its angles and the lengths of its sides.

acute isosceles triangle

obtuse isosceles triangle

right isosceles triangle

acute scalene triangle

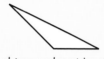
obtuse scalene triangle

right scalene triangle

▶ Advance Preparation

Print the Triangle Classification Chart.

Label 6 index cards with the following angle sizes and side lengths: acute, right, obtuse, equilateral, obtuse, scalene. Leave one index card blank.

▶ Safety

Use caution when working with, bending, and cutting pipe cleaners. If the interior wire of the pipe cleaner is exposed, it can be sharp.

Make sure students handle the scissors carefully and be sure to store them in a safe place.

GET READY Two Types of Triangles

ONLINE 5 min

Students will practice identifying triangles as isosceles or equilateral triangles. They will recognize that some isosceles triangles have a right angle.

Objectives

- Identify attributes of isosceles, equilateral, and right triangles.

LEARN Different Types of Triangles

ONLINE 15 min

Students will learn how to classify a triangle by its angle measure and then by the relationship among the length of its sides.

Objectives

- Define and sketch different types of triangles and identify their attributes.

LEARN Triangle Classification

Students will model different types of triangles classified by a given measure of their angles and a given relationship among the lengths of their sides. Students will learn that certain triangles cannot exist with certain characteristics.

Gather the pipe cleaners, scissors, index cards, ruler, book, and Triangle Classification Chart.

1. Have students study the Triangle Classification Chart with you. First read with students the bulleted information above the chart. Then describe to students that along the rows you can classify triangles by angle, and along the columns you can classify triangles by the relationship among side lengths.

2. **Say:** Since every triangle has at least 2 acute angles, we use the measure of the third angle to classify a triangle. If the third angle is a right angle, the triangle is a right triangle. If the third angle is an acute angle, the triangle is an acute triangle. If the third angle is an obtuse angle, the triangle is an obtuse triangle.

3. Guide students to each triangle in the chart, beginning with the top row and moving from left to right. Students should name the triangles as they go, by first saying the angle name and then the side-length name. equilateral triangle (or acute equilateral triangle); acute isosceles triangle; acute scalene triangle; right isosceles triangle; right scalene triangle; obtuse isosceles triangle; obtuse scalene triangle

4. Direct students' attention to the place where Right and Equilateral intersect as well as to the place where Obtuse and Equilateral intersect.

   Say: All equilateral triangles have 3 angles with the same measure. All 3 angles are acute angles whose measures are each less than 90°. So you cannot have an equilateral triangle with a right angle, which has a measure equal to 90°. And you cannot have an equilateral triangle with an obtuse angle, which has a measure greater than 90°.

5. Give students the pipe cleaners. Set aside the Triangle Classification Chart.

6. Separate the index cards into two groups—angle-size cards and side-length cards—and place them face down in two piles.

7. Have students draw one card from the angle-size group and link the pipe cleaners together to make the triangle on the card. Guide students to use the corner of a book to form a right angle.

8. Have students explain why their model triangle is an acute, obtuse, or right triangle. Repeat for the other two cards. An acute triangle has 3 acute angles. A right triangle has 1 right angle. An obtuse triangle has 1 obtuse angle.

9. Have students draw one card from the side-length group and model the triangle using the pipe cleaners. Have students use scissors to cut the pipe cleaners as needed. Guide students to use a ruler to check the side lengths of their models.

10. Have students explain why the triangle is equilateral, isosceles, or scalene. Repeat for the other two cards. An equilateral triangle has 3 equal side lengths. An isosceles triangle has 2 equal side lengths. A scalene triangle has no equal side lengths.

11. **Say:** A triangle may have two classifications; its angle size and its relationship among side lengths.

Objectives

- Define and sketch different types of triangles and identify their attributes.
- Understand that attributes that apply to a category of two-dimensional figures also apply to all subcategories of that category.

Tips

The label *acute equilateral triangle* is technically correct, but since all equilateral triangles are acute, this type of triangle is often just called an *equilateral triangle,* dropping the *acute.*

12. Return the index cards to their piles. Have students draw two cards, one from each group, and model the triangle using pipe cleaners.

13. Use the Triangle Classification Chart, ruler, and an index card to check that the triangle has the correct angle size and side length. If the triangle is impossible to draw with the given characteristics, have students explain why.

14. Replace the cards and continue to draw two new cards until all angle-size and side-length combinations have been attempted.

TRY IT Classify Triangles

OFFLINE

10 min

Students will practice naming and drawing triangles on the basis of the triangles' attributes. Gather the ruler and index card. Have students turn to the Classify Triangles activity page in their Activity Book and read the directions with them.

Students should copy the problems from the Activity Book into their Math Notebook as necessary and solve them there.

Objectives

- Define and sketch different types of triangles and identify their attributes.

- Understand that attributes that apply to a category of two-dimensional figures also apply to all subcategories of that category.

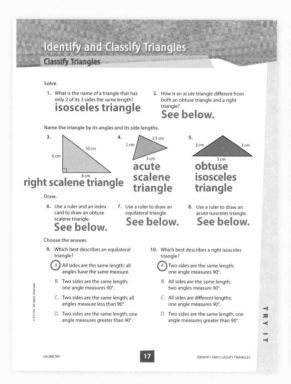

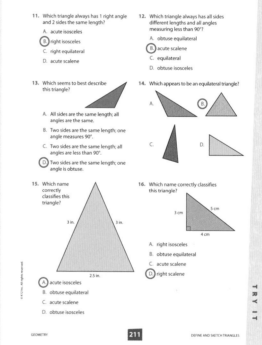

Additional Answers

2. An acute triangle has 3 acute angles. An obtuse triangle has 2 acute angles and 1 obtuse angle. A right triangle has 2 acute angles and 1 right angle.

6. Check students' drawings. One angle should be open wider than a square corner of an index card. None of the triangle's sides should have the same measure.

7. Check students' drawings. All of the triangle's sides should be the same length. All of the triangle's angles should be the same size.

8. Check students' drawings. None of the angles should be the same or open wider than the corner of an index card. At least two of the lengths of the triangle's sides should be equal.

Students will complete an online Checkpoint. If necessary, read the directions, problems, and answer choices to students and help them with keyboard or mouse operations.

- Define and sketch different types of triangles and identify their attributes.
- Understand that attributes that apply to a category of two-dimensional figures also apply to all subcategories of that category.

Identify and Classify Quadrilaterals (A)

Lesson Overview

GET READY Four-Sided Shapes	5 minutes	ONLINE
LEARN Find and Name Quadrilaterals	15 minutes	ONLINE
LEARN Build Quadrilateral Models	20 minutes	OFFLINE
LEARN Compare and Describe Quadrilaterals	10 minutes	OFFLINE
TRY IT Identify Quadrilaterals	10 minutes	OFFLINE

▶ Lesson Objectives

- Know how to define and sketch different quadrilaterals.
- Understand that attributes that apply to a category of two-dimensional figures also apply to all subcategories of that category.
- Classify two-dimensional figures in a hierarchy based on their properties.

▶ Prerequisite Skills

- Identify attributes of parallelograms, rectangles, and squares.
- State and recognize the definitions of a right angle, an acute angle, an obtuse angle, and a straight angle.

▶ Content Background

Students will learn how to define and sketch different quadrilaterals.

A *plane figure* is a figure that lies on a flat or two-dimensional surface. A *polygon* is a plane closed figure with straight sides that do not cross each other. A *quadrilateral* is a 4-sided polygon. Many quadrilaterals have special names based on characteristics, such as the lengths of their sides, their angle measurements, and whether opposite sides are parallel. A drawing of a plane geometric figure often shows tick marks on the sides of a figure. Identical tick marks show sides that are equal in length, or congruent. If 2 or more sides have the same number of tick marks, those sides are congruent. A small square in a corner shows that the angle is a right angle.

Here is a list of common quadrilaterals and their definitions.

- parallelogram – a quadrilateral with opposite sides parallel, and also equal in length
- rectangle – a quadrilateral with 4 right angles, opposite sides parallel, and also equal in length
- rhombus – a quadrilateral with opposite sides parallel and all 4 sides equal in length
- square – a quadrilateral with 4 right angles, opposite sides parallel, and all 4 sides equal in length
- trapezoid – a quadrilateral with only 1 pair of opposite sides parallel

If a 4-sided polygon does not fit into a specific category, it is simply called a quadrilateral. This lesson will also show that some quadrilaterals fall into overlapping categories.

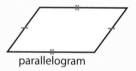

parallelogram

rectangle

rhombus

square

Quadrilateral Hierarchy

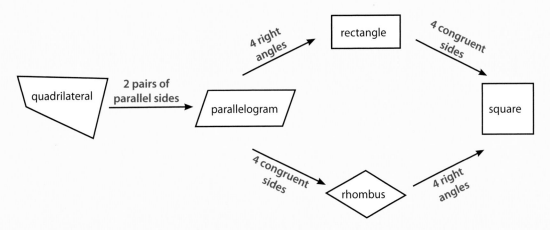

The following relationships exist among quadrilaterals:

- A square is also a special type of rectangle, a special type of rhombus, and a special type of parallelogram.

- A rectangle is also a special type of parallelogram.

- A rhombus is also a special type of a parallelogram.

▶ Advance Preparation

For the Learn: Classify Quadrilaterals activity, use the models from the Build Quadrilateral Models activity, or print the Name the Quadrilateral printout and cut it into cards for each quadrilateral.

ONLINE
5 min

GET READY Four-Sided Shapes

Students will identify and describe attributes of four-sided plane geometric shapes.

Objectives

- Identify attributes of parallelograms, rectangles, and squares.

- State and recognize the definitions of a right angle, an acute angle, an obtuse angle, and a straight angle.

ONLINE
15 min

LEARN Find and Name Quadrilaterals

Students will learn the definitions of different quadrilaterals. They will recognize quadrilaterals in the environment and, given clues, identify mystery shapes.

Objectives

- Know how to define and sketch different quadrilaterals.

LEARN Build Quadrilateral Models

Students will build models of specific quadrilaterals using clues you have given them. Gather the pipe cleaners, scissors, tape, book, and ruler.

1. Give students the materials. Tell them that they will build quadrilaterals based on clues that you read to them. Instruct students to build each quadrilateral, tape it to a sheet of paper, and write its geometric name and definition below the model.

2. Demonstrate how to bend a pipe cleaner around the square corner of a book to create a right angle. Show students that they can twist the ends of two or more pipe cleaners together if needed to complete a shape. Help them cut off ends that are too long and tape pipe cleaners together.

3. Read the following problems one at a time. Ask students which type of shape they will create and why. Help them with the mechanics of building the model if necessary.

   - I am a quadrilateral with opposite sides parallel. I have 4 sides of equal length. I have no right angles. rhombus

   - I am a quadrilateral with both pairs of opposite sides parallel, 4 sides of equal length, and 4 right angles. square

   - I am a quadrilateral. I have only one pair of parallel sides. trapezoid

   - I am a quadrilateral with 4 right angles. The lengths of my sides are not all equal. rectangle

   - I am a quadrilateral whose opposite sides are parallel and equal in length. I have no right angles. My 4 sides are not all the same length. parallelogram

   Students should choose from the following definitions.

   - parallelogram – a quadrilateral with opposite sides parallel and also equal in length

   - rectangle – a quadrilateral with 4 right angles, opposite sides parallel and also equal in length

   - rhombus – a quadrilateral with opposite sides parallel and all 4 sides equal in length

   - square – a quadrilateral with 4 right angles, opposite sides parallel, and all 4 sides equal in length

   - trapezoid – a quadrilateral with only 1 pair of opposite sides parallel

LEARN Compare and Describe Quadrilaterals

Objectives

- Understand that attributes that apply to a category of two-dimensional figures also apply to all subcategories of that category.

- Classify two-dimensional figures in a hierarchy based on their properties.

Students will classify quadrilaterals into categories and subcategories based on their attributes.

Gather the completed quadrilateral models from the Build Quadrilateral Models activity. If you do not have the models, gather the Name the Quadrilateral printout.

1. Refer to the diagram as you classify each quadrilateral. Follow the directions to build the hierarchy in stages.

Quadrilateral Hierarchy

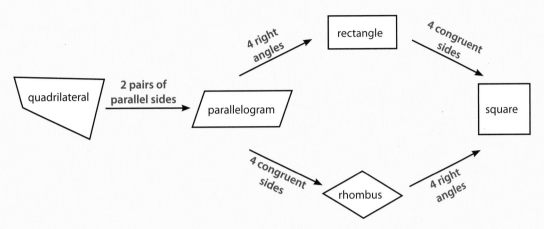

2. Point to the parallelogram.

   Say: Some quadrilaterals fall into overlapping categories. All parallelograms have 2 pairs of parallel sides. What other quadrilaterals have 2 pairs of parallel sides? rectangle, rhombus, and square

   Ask: Are a rectangle, rhombus, and square a type of parallelogram? Yes

3. Set the rectangle, rhombus, and square to the right of the parallelogram.

   Say: A rectangle has 2 pairs of parallel sides and 4 right angles. What other quadrilaterals have 2 pairs of parallel sides and 4 right angles? square

   Ask: Is a square a type of rectangle? Yes Is a rhombus always a type of rectangle? No

4. Place the square directly to the right of the rectangle.

   Say: A rhombus has 2 pairs of parallel sides and 4 equal sides. What other quadrilaterals have 2 pairs of parallel sides and 4 equal sides? square Is a square a type of rhombus? Yes

5. Move the square to the right of the rhombus and the rectangle to resemble the diagram.

6. Point to each quadrilateral in the model as you say the following:

   Say: Some quadrilaterals fall into overlapping categories. A rectangle is a type of parallelogram with 4 right angles. A rhombus is a type of parallelogram with 4 equal sides. And a square is a type of parallelogram, rectangle, and rhombus with 2 pairs of parallel lines, 4 right angles, and 4 equal sides.

   Ask: The order only goes in one direction. Why can't we say a parallelogram is a type of rectangle? It does not always have 4 right angles like a rectangle. Why can't we say a rectangle is a type of square? It does not have 4 congruent sides like a square.

TRY IT Identify Quadrilaterals

Objectives

Students will identify, compare, and describe quadrilaterals. Have students turn to the Identify Quadrilaterals activity page in their Activity Book and read the directions with them.

Students should copy the problems from the Activity Book into their Math Notebook as necessary and solve them there.

- Know how to define and sketch different quadrilaterals.

- Understand that attributes that apply to a category of two-dimensional figures also apply to to all subcategories of that category.

- Classify two-dimensional figures in a hierarchy based on their properties.

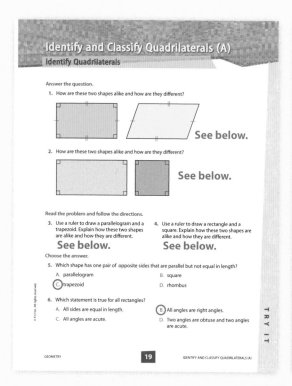

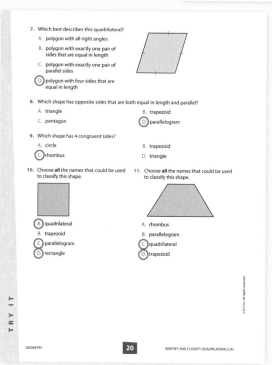

Additional Answers

1. Both are quadrilaterals and both are parallelograms with opposite sides equal in length and parallel. They are different because the shape on the left (a rectangle) has 4 right angles and the shape on the right (a parallelogram) does not.

2. Both are quadrilaterals, both are parallelograms, and both are rectangles with opposite sides equal in length and parallel. They both have 4 right angles. They are different because the square has 4 sides equal in length, but the rectangle does not.

3. **Example:** Check students' drawings. How they are alike: The parallelogram and the trapezoid both have 4 angles, 4 sides, and at least one pair of opposite sides that are parallel. How they are different: The trapezoid has 1 pair of parallel sides; the parallelogram has 2 pairs of parallel sides.

4. **Example:** Check students' drawings. How they are alike: The rectangle and square both have 4 angles, 4 sides, and both have 2 pairs of parallel equal sides. How they are different: A square has 4 equal sides but a rectangle may not have 4 equal sides.

Identify and Classify Quadrilaterals (B)

Lesson Overview

GET READY Name the Quadrilateral	5 minutes	**OFFLINE**
LEARN Look for Quadrilaterals	25 minutes	**ONLINE**
LEARN Recognize Quadrilateral Categories	15 minutes	**ONLINE**
TRY IT Define and Classify Quadrilaterals	15 minutes	**ONLINE**

▶ Lesson Objectives

- Know how to define and sketch different quadrilaterals.
- Understand that attributes that apply to a category of two-dimensional figures also apply to all subcategories of that category.
- Classify two-dimensional figures in a hierarchy based on their properties.

▶ Prerequisite Skills

- Identify attributes of parallelograms, rectangles, and squares.
- State and recognize the definitions of a right angle, an acute angle, an obtuse angle, and a straight angle.

▶ Content Background

Students will continue to learn how to define and sketch different quadrilaterals.

A *plane figure* is a figure that lies on a flat or two-dimensional surface. A *polygon* is a plane closed figure with straight sides that do not cross each other. A *quadrilateral* is a 4-sided polygon. Many quadrilaterals have special names based on characteristics, such as the lengths of their sides, their angle measurements, and whether opposite sides are parallel. A drawing of a plane geometric figure often shows tick marks on the sides of a figure. Identical tick marks show sides that are equal in length, or congruent. If 2 or more sides have the same number of tick marks, those sides are congruent. A small square in a corner shows that the angle is a right angle.

Following is a list of common quadrilaterals and their definitions.

- parallelogram – a quadrilateral with opposite sides parallel and also equal in length
- rectangle – a quadrilateral with 4 right angles, opposite sides parallel, and also equal in length
- rhombus – a quadrilateral with opposite sides parallel and all 4 sides equal in length
- square – a quadrilateral with 4 right angles, opposite sides parallel, and all 4 sides equal in length
- trapezoid – a quadrilateral with only 1 pair of opposite sides parallel

If a 4-sided polygon does not fit into a specific category, it is simply called a quadrilateral. This lesson will also show that some quadrilaterals fall into overlapping categories.

Materials to Gather

SUPPLIED

Classifications of Quadrilaterals (printout)

Name the Quadrilateral (printout)

ALSO NEEDED

scissors, adult

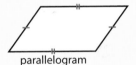
parallelogram

rectangle

rhombus

square

Quadrilateral Hierarchy

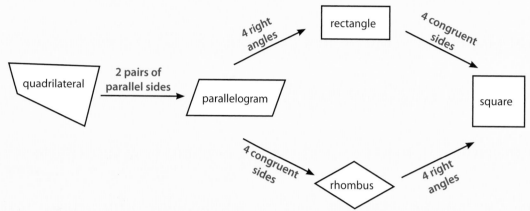

The following relationships exist among quadrilaterals:

- A square is also a special type of rectangle, a special type of rhombus, and a special type of parallelogram.
- A rectangle is also a special type of parallelogram.
- A rhombus is also a special type of a parallelogram.

▶ Advance Preparation

For the Get Ready: Name the Quadrilateral activity, print Name the Quadrilateral and cut it apart as shown.

Print two copies of Classifications of Quadrilaterals (one for the Learn: Look for Quadrilaterals activity and one for the Learn: Recognize Quadrilateral Categories activity).

OFFLINE
5min

GET READY Name the Quadrilateral

Objectives

Students will name, describe, and compare models of quadrilaterals.
Gather the Name the Quadrilateral printout.

1. Show students each quadrilateral and ask its name. Each quadrilateral is labeled, but have students themselves write the name of each quadrilateral as well.

2. Point out that there are two models of trapezoids to show that a trapezoid may have 2 right angles or it may have no right angles.

3. Choose two shapes and have students explain how they are alike and how they are different. Use the trapezoid model without the right angle for most comparisons. Use this checklist to keep track of students' comparisons.

☐ square and rectangle	☐ rectangle and rhombus
☐ square and parallelogram	☐ rectangle and trapezoid
☐ square and rhombus	☐ parallelogram and rhombus
☐ square and trapezoid	☐ parallelogram and trapezoid
☐ rectangle and parallelogram	☐ rhombus and trapezoid

- Identify attributes of parallelograms, rectangles, and squares.
- State and recognize the definitions of a right angle, an acute angle, an obtuse angle, and a straight angle.

LEARN Look for Quadrilaterals

ONLINE 25 min

Objectives

- Know how to define and sketch different quadrilaterals.

Students will identify, recognize, and name quadrilaterals in everyday situations.
Gather the Classifications of Quadrilaterals printout and tell students that they may use this printout as necessary to answer the questions. Go over the Classifications of Quadrilaterals printout before beginning the online activity. Explain that this chart summarizes the features, or characteristics, of each quadrilateral.

LEARN Recognize Quadrilateral Categories

ONLINE 15 min

Objectives

- Understand that attributes that apply to a category of two-dimensional figures also apply to all subcategories of that category.
- Classify two-dimensional figures in a hierarchy based on their properties.

Students will decide whether statements about certain quadrilaterals are true.
Gather the Classifications of Quadrilaterals printout and tell students that they may use this printout as necessary to answer the questions.

TRY IT Define and Classify Quadrilaterals

ONLINE 15 min

Objectives

- Know how to define and sketch different quadrilaterals.

Students will complete an online Try It. If necessary, read the directions, problems, and answer choices to students and help them with keyboard or mouse operations.

Identify and Classify Quadrilaterals (C)

Lesson Overview

GET READY Match Quadrilaterals	5 minutes	**ONLINE**
LEARN Special Quadrilaterals	10 minutes	**ONLINE**
LEARN Analyze Quadrilaterals	10 minutes	**OFFLINE**
TRY IT Identify and Classify Quadrilaterals	15 minutes	**OFFLINE**
CHECKPOINT	10 minutes	**ONLINE**

▶ Lesson Objectives

- Know how to define and sketch different quadrilaterals.
- Understand that attributes that apply to a category of two-dimensional figures also apply to all subcategories of that category.
- Classify two-dimensional figures in a hierarchy based on their properties.

Materials to Gather

SUPPLIED

Identify and Classify Quadrilaterals activity page

▶ Content Background

Students will continue to learn how to define and sketch different quadrilaterals.

A *plane figure* is a figure that lies on a flat or two-dimensional surface. A *polygon* is a closed plane figure with straight sides that do not cross each other. A *quadrilateral* is a 4-sided polygon. Many quadrilaterals have special names based on characteristics such as the lengths of their sides, their angle measurements, and whether opposite sides are parallel. A drawing of a plane geometric figure often shows tick marks on the sides of a figure. Identical tick marks show sides that are equal in length, or congruent. If 2 or more sides have the same number of tick marks, those sides are congruent. A small square in a corner shows that the angle is a right angle.

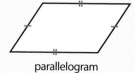

parallelogram   rectangle   rhombus   square

Here is a list of common quadrilaterals and their definitions.

- parallelogram – a quadrilateral with opposite sides parallel and also equal in length
- rectangle – a quadrilateral with 4 right angles, opposite sides parallel, and also equal in length
- rhombus – a quadrilateral with opposite sides parallel and all 4 sides equal in length
- square – a quadrilateral with 4 right angles, opposite sides parallel, and all 4 sides equal in length
- trapezoid – a quadrilateral with only 1 pair of opposite sides parallel

If a 4-sided polygon does not fit into a specific category, it is simply called a quadrilateral. This lesson will also show that some quadrilaterals fall into overlapping categories.

Quadrilateral Hierarchy

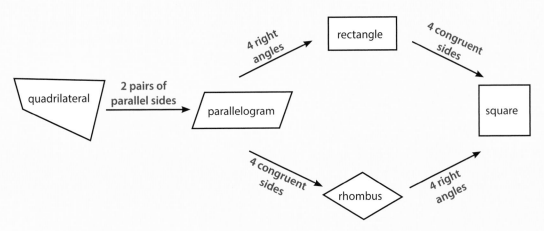

The following relationships exist among quadrilaterals:

- A square is also a special type of rectangle, a special type of rhombus, and a special type of parallelogram.
- A rectangle is also a special type of parallelogram.
- A rhombus is also a special type of a parallelogram.

GET READY Match Quadrilaterals

ONLINE **5 min**

Students will test their knowledge of quadrilaterals by matching a square, a rectangle, a rhombus, and a parallelogram with their definitions.

Objectives

- Know how to define and sketch quadrilaterals.

LEARN Special Quadrilaterals

ONLINE **10 min**

Students will learn the special properties of five types of quadrilaterals. These quadrilaterals are the parallelogram, the rectangle, the rhombus, the square, and the trapezoid.

Objectives

- Understand that attributes that apply to a category of two-dimensional figures also apply to all subcategories of that category.
- Classify two-dimensional figures in a hierarchy based on their properties.

LEARN Analyze Quadrilaterals

Students will determine whether statements about quadrilaterals are true or false. They will also complete partly worked, interactive examples of these types of problems.

Objectives

- Understand that attributes that apply to a category of two-dimensional figures also apply to all subcategories of that category.
- Classify two-dimensional figures in a hierarchy based on their properties.

TRY IT Identify and Classify Quadrilaterals

Students will practice identifying and classifying quadrilaterals. View or print the Identify and Classify Quadrilaterals activity page. Students should copy the problems into their Math Notebook and solve them there.

Objectives

- Know how to define and sketch different quadrilaterals.
- Understand that attributes that apply to a category of two-dimensional figures also apply to all subcategories of that category.
- Classify two-dimensional figures in a hierarchy based on their properties.

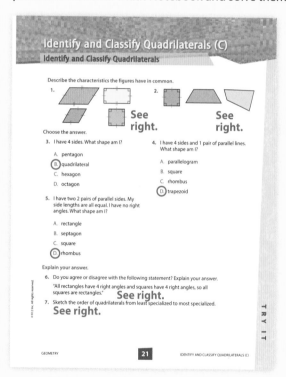

Additional Answers

1. The figures all have 4 sides and they all have 2 pairs of parallel sides. That means that they are all parallelograms.

2. The figures all have 4 sides. That means that they are all quadrilaterals.

6. **Possible answer:** I agree. Since a square has all the characteristics of rectangle, it is a type of rectangle.

7. **Possible answer:**

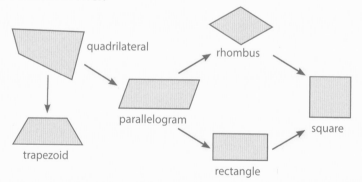

Objectives

Students will complete an online Checkpoint. If necessary, read the directions, problems, and answer choices to students and help them with keyboard or mouse operations.

- Know how to define and sketch different quadrilaterals.

- Understand that attributes that apply to a category of two-dimensional figures also apply to all subcategories of that category.

- Classify two-dimensional figures in a hierarchy based on their properties.

Construct Triangles and Quadrilaterals

Lesson Overview

GET READY Sketch Triangles and Quadrilaterals	10 minutes	OFFLINE
GET READY Identify Triangles	5 minutes	ONLINE
LEARN Construct Triangles and Quadrilaterals	10 minutes	ONLINE
LEARN Construct Each Shape	20 minutes	OFFLINE
TRY IT Practice Triangles and Quadrilaterals	10 minutes	OFFLINE
CHECKPOINT	5 minutes	OFFLINE

▶ **Lesson Objectives**

Construct rectangles or triangles with appropriate math tools.

▶ **Prerequisite Skills**

- Define and sketch different types of triangles and identify their attributes.
- Know how to define and sketch different quadrilaterals.

▶ **Content Background**

Students will use tools such as a compass (a drawing tool with two legs that are hinged to each other at one end) and ruler to construct quadrilaterals and triangles.

▶ **Safety**

Make sure students handle the compass carefully and be sure to store it in a safe place.

Materials to Gather

SUPPLIED

Construct Each Shape activity page

protractor

Practice Triangles and Quadrilaterals activity page

Checkpoint (printout)

ALSO NEEDED

compass

ruler

GET READY Sketch Triangles and Quadrilaterals

OFFLINE 10 min

Students will sketch as well as describe the attributes of different types of triangles and quadrilaterals.

There are no materials to gather for this activity.

SKETCHING TRIANGLES

1. **Ask:** How many sides and angles does a triangle have? 3 sides and 3 angles
2. Have students sketch an equilateral triangle and describe its attributes. Use the Types of Triangles chart to check the sketch and the description.
3. If students do not accurately sketch or describe an equilateral triangle, use the chart to review the attributes with them.

Objectives

- Define and sketch different types of triangles and identify their attributes.
- Know how to define and sketch different quadrilaterals.

4. Repeat Steps 2 and 3 for these triangles:

- isosceles triangle
- scalene triangle
- acute triangle
- equiangular triangle
- obtuse triangle
- right triangle

Types of Triangles		
Name	**Description**	**Example**
equilateral triangle	All sides are the same length.	
isosceles triangle	Two sides are the same length.	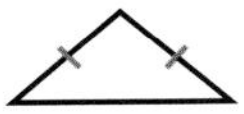
scalene triangle	All the sides are a different length.	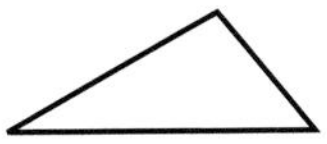
acute triangle	All angles measure less than 90°.	
equiangular triangle	All angles measure exactly 60°.	
obtuse triangle	One angle measures greater than 90°.	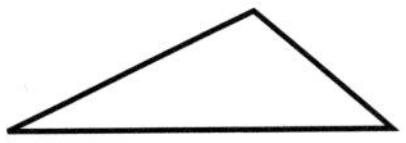
right triangle	One angle measures exactly 90°.	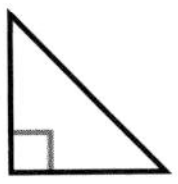

SKETCHING QUADRILATERALS

5. Ask: How many sides and angles does a quadrilateral have? 4 sides and 4 angles

6. Have students sketch an isosceles trapezoid and describe its attributes. Use the Types of Quadrilaterals chart to check the sketch and the description.

7. If students do not accurately sketch or describe an isosceles trapezoid, use the chart to review the attributes with them.

8. Repeat Steps 6 and 7 for these quadrilaterals:

- scalene trapezoid
- parallelogram
- rectangle
- rhombus
- square

Types of Quadrilaterals		
Name	**Description**	**Example**
isosceles trapezoid	Two sides are parallel and two sides are the same length.	
scalene trapezoid	Two sides are parallel; all four sides are different lengths.	
parallelogram	Opposite sides are parallel and equal in length.	
rectangle	Opposite sides are parallel and equal in length. All angles are 90°.	
rhombus	All four sides are equal in length.	
square	All four sides are equal in length and all angles are 90°	

GET READY Identify Triangles

Objectives

Students will match triangles to their descriptions. This matching activity includes acute, obtuse, equilateral, equiangular, right, scalene, and isosceles triangles.

- Define and sketch different types of triangles and identify their attributes.
- Know how to define and sketch different quadrilaterals.

Tips If students are having difficulty remembering the different types of triangles or quadrilaterals, have them draw and label each type on a separate sheet of paper. Staple the drawings together to create a reference book.

LEARN Construct Triangles and Quadrilaterals

Objectives

Students will watch a tutorial on how to use a compass and ruler to construct an equilateral triangle and square.

- Construct rectangles or triangles with appropriate math tools.

LEARN Construct Each Shape

OFFLINE
20min

Objectives

- Construct rectangles or triangles with appropriate math tools.

Tips

If students are having trouble remembering the steps for constructing triangles or rectangles, model most of the steps for them and have them finish. Then repeat, modeling fewer steps. Repeat until students can construct the shape(s) on their own.

Following the steps they have learned for constructing an equilateral triangle and square, students will construct and draw an equilateral triangle, square, right triangle, and rectangle. Gather a ruler, compass, and protractor. Have students turn to the Construct Each Shape activity page in their Activity Book and read the directions with them.

Students should copy the problems from the Activity Book into their Math Notebook as necessary and solve them there.

1. Review with students the Worked Examples, which show how to construct and draw perpendicular lines.

2. Have students follow the steps in Problem 1 to construct an equilateral triangle. If students struggle with a step, model the step for them.

3. Have students follow the steps in Problem 2 to construct a square. Again, if students have difficulty with a step, model that step for them.

4. Have students read the steps in Problem 3 to construct a right triangle. Answer any questions they may have before they begin constructing, and then have students construct a right triangle. Model any steps students have difficulty with.

5. Have students read the steps in Problem 4 to construct a rectangle. Answer students' questions, and then have them construct a rectangle. Model steps as needed.

You may share with students the steps shown in the answers, to help them construct the shapes.

Additional Answers

1.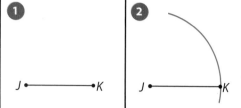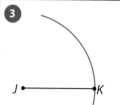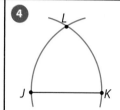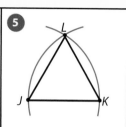

2.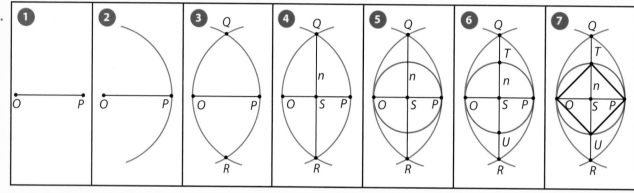

3.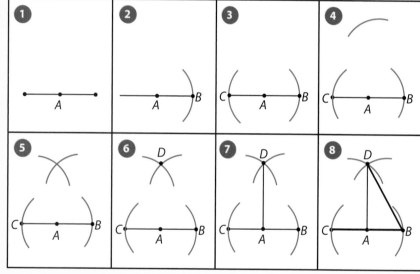

Additional Answers

4.

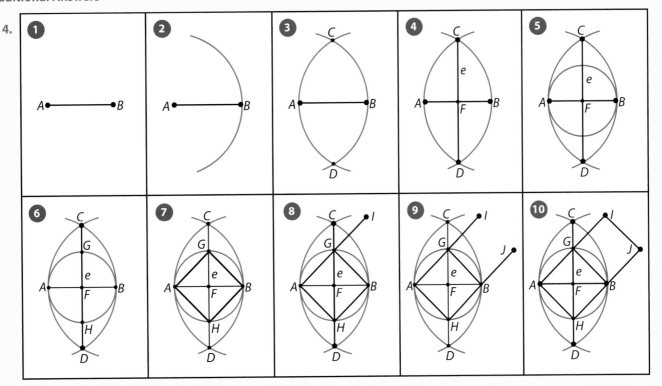

Objectives

- Construct rectangles or triangles with appropriate math tools.

Students will practice using a compass and ruler to construct triangles and quadrilaterals. Gather a compass and ruler. Have students turn to the Practice Triangles and Quadrilaterals activity page in their Activity Book and read the directions with them.

Students should copy the problems from the Activity Book into their Math Notebook as necessary and solve them there.

Tips

Extend the lesson by challenging students to construct different types of quadrilaterals and triangles.

Construct Triangles and Quadrilaterals
Practice Triangles and Quadrilaterals

Draw the shape.
1. square
2. rectangle
3. equilateral triangle
4. right triangle

Use a compass and ruler to construct the shape.
5. right triangle **See below.**
6. rectangle **See next page.**

TRY IT

Additional Answers

5.

1	2	3	4
5	6	7	8

6.

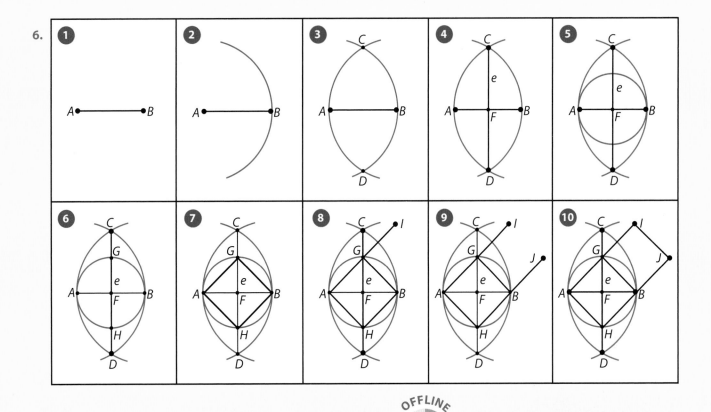

OFFLINE

5 min

CHECKPOINT

Objectives

The Checkpoint and its answer key are located in the Resources section for this Unit in the Online Book Menu of *Math+ Yellow Lesson Guide*. Open the Checkpoint. Give students a compass and a ruler. Record students' responses on the Learning Coach Recording Sheet. Use the answer key to score the Checkpoint, and then enter the results online.

- Construct rectangles or triangles with appropriate math tools.

Angles and Triangles (A)

Lesson Overview

GET READY Classify Triangles	15 minutes	OFFLINE
LEARN Sum of Angles in Triangles	15 minutes	ONLINE
LEARN Measure Angles in Triangles	30 minutes	OFFLINE

▶ Lesson Objectives

Identify that the sum of the interior angles of any triangle is 180° and solve related problems.

▶ Prerequisite Skills

- Define and sketch different types of triangles and identify their attributes.
- Identify attributes of isosceles, equilateral, and right triangles.

▶ Content Background

Triangles are two-dimensional shapes that have 3 sides made from line segments. Triangles can be classified by their characteristics. Equilateral triangles have 3 equal sides. Isosceles triangles have 2 equal sides. Scalene triangles have no equal sides.

One of the angles in a right triangle measures 90°. Acute triangles have 3 acute angles. Obtuse triangles have 1 obtuse angle and 2 acute angles. In equiangular triangles, all 3 angles have the same measure.

Students will learn that the sum of the angle measures of any triangle is 180°. They will also learn to find missing angle measures in triangles.

▶ Advance Preparation

Print 180° in a Triangle.

▶ Safety

Make sure students handle the scissors carefully and be sure to store them in a safe place.

Materials to Gather

SUPPLIED

protractor

180° in a Triangle (printout)

Measure Angles in Triangles activity page

ALSO NEEDED

scissors, pointed-end safety

GET READY Classify Triangles

Students will draw different types and sizes of triangles as preparation for learning that a triangle of any type has the same number of degrees. Tell them that they will sketch without measuring the triangles' sides. This activity is about recalling triangle attributes rather than exact measurements.

- Define and sketch different types of triangles and identify their attributes.
- Identify attributes of isosceles, equilateral, and right triangles.

1. **Ask:** What type of triangle has all 3 sides the same length? equilateral triangle

2. Have students sketch and mark with tick marks the sides of an equilateral triangle. Then have them sketch a second equilateral triangle that is larger or smaller than the first one. Throughout this activity, the second triangle can be oriented in a different way from the first triangle.

   Ask: What are the characteristics, or attributes of the two equilateral triangles? The triangles have sides that are equal in length. Each side has a tick mark.

3. **Ask:** What type of triangle has 2 sides the same length? isosceles triangle

4. Have students sketch and mark an isosceles triangle. Then have them sketch a second isosceles triangle that is larger or smaller than the first one.

   Ask: What are the attributes of the two isosceles triangles? The triangles have 2 sides that are of equal length and have a tick mark on them. The other side isn't of equal length and doesn't have a tick mark.

5. **Ask:** What type of triangle has no sides the same length? scalene triangle

6. Have students sketch a scalene triangle. Then have them sketch a second scalene triangle that is larger or smaller than the first one.

   Ask: What are the attributes of the scalene triangles? The 3 sides are each of a different length. No tick marks are on the triangles because none of the sides are of equal length.

7. **Ask:** What type of triangle has one 90° angle? right triangle

Tips

Scalene triangles may be a challenge for students to sketch. When you evaluate students' sketches of scalene triangles, have students describe the sketches to you. Their descriptions should indicate that no sides of a scalene triangle are the same length.

8. Have students sketch and put tick marks on a right triangle with 2 sides of the same length and mark the 90° angle to look like a small square. Then have them sketch and mark a second right triangle with 2 sides the same length that is larger or smaller than the first one.

Ask: What are the attributes of the right triangles? Two of the sides are the same length and are marked with tick marks. The right angle is marked.

LEARN Sum of Angles in Triangles

ONLINE
15min

Students will watch a tutorial that shows them how to find the sum of a triangle's angle measures. They will see how cutting angles from a triangle and placing the angles together form a straight angle. They can then conclude that because the measure of a straight angle is 180°, the sum of angle measures of a triangle is 180°.

Objectives

• Identify that the sum of the interior angles of any triangle is 180° and solve related problems.

LEARN Measure Angles in Triangles

OFFLINE
30min

Students will cut off angles and line them up on a straight angle to verify that angle measures of a triangle add up to 180°. To further demonstrate the idea, they will measure angles of triangles to test the idea that the angle measures of any triangle add to 180°. Using a protractor, students should find that angle measures add to 180°.

Gather scissors, a protractor, and the 180° in a Triangle printout. Later in the activity, students will use the Measure Angles in Triangles activity page in their Activity Book. Read the directions with them. Students should copy the problems from the Activity Book into their Math Notebook as necessary and solve them there.

1. Give students scissors and the 180° in a Triangle printout. Tell them that they will cut the 3 angles from each triangle and place the angles around a straight angle to show that the sum of the angle measures of a triangle is 180°.

2. Have students cut out one triangle. Guide them to carefully cut off each angle of the triangle.

3. Have students place angles together so they form a point on the straight angle at the top of the page.

Objectives

• Identify that the sum of the interior angles of any triangle is 180° and solve related problems.

Tips

If students' measurements of the 3 angles in the triangle do not add up to 180°, review how to use a protractor to measure angles.

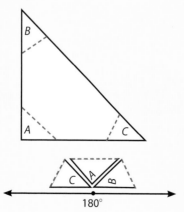

4. **Ask:** Do the 3 angle measures add to 180°? How do you know this is true?
   A straight angle measures 180°. When the 3 angles are cut from a triangle and placed together, the angles form a straight angle.

5. Repeat Steps 2–4 with the remaining four triangles from the printout. Have students describe the attributes of each triangle before using the angles to verify that the sum of the measures is 180°.

6. Have students number 1–5 in their Math Notebook. Tell students to use the protractor to measure the angles on the five triangles on the Measure Angles in Triangles activity page. Record the following for each triangle:

   • the 3 angle measures
   • the sum of the angle measures
   • the classification of each triangle: acute, right, obtuse, or equiangular

   Tell them an acute triangle has 3 acute angles. A right triangle has 1 angle that measures exactly 90°. An obtuse triangle has 1 obtuse angle. An equiangular triangle has 3 angles of equal measure.

   In their Math Notebook, have students verify that the sum of the angle measures for each triangle on the activity page is 180°.

7. Point to the straight angle at the bottom of the page. Have students measure the straight angle and confirm that it measures 180°.

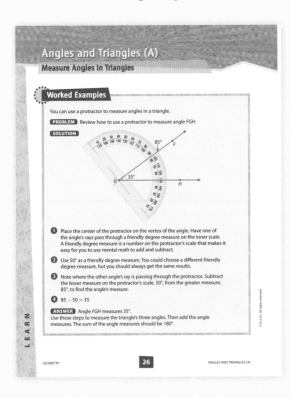

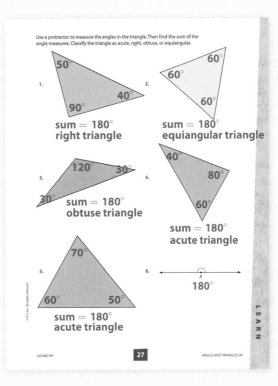

Angles and Triangles (B)

Lesson Overview

GET READY Types of Triangles	10 minutes	ONLINE
LEARN Triangles and 180°	15 minutes	ONLINE
LEARN Missing Angle Measures	15 minutes	ONLINE
TRY IT Find Missing Angle Measures	15 minutes	OFFLINE
CHECKPOINT	5 minutes	ONLINE

▶ Lesson Objectives

Identify that the sum of the interior angles of any triangle is 180° and solve related problems.

▶ Prerequisite Skills

- Define and sketch different types of triangles and identify their attributes.
- Identify attributes of isosceles, equilateral, and right triangles.

▶ Content Background

Triangles are two-dimensional shapes that have 3 sides made from line segments. Triangles can be classified by their characteristics. Equilateral triangles have 3 equal sides. Isosceles triangles have 2 equal sides. Scalene triangles have no equal sides.

One of the angles in a right triangle measures 90°. Acute triangles have 3 acute angles. Obtuse triangles have 1 obtuse angle and 2 acute angles. In equiangular triangles, all 3 angles have the same measure.

Students will continue to learn that the sum of the angle measures of any triangle is 180°. They will also learn to find missing angle measures in triangles.

Materials to Gather

SUPPLIED

protractor

Find Missing Angle Measures activity page

ALSO NEEDED

ruler

GET READY Types of Triangles

ONLINE
10 min

Objectives

- Define and sketch different types of triangles and identify their attributes.
- Identify attributes of isosceles, equilateral, and right triangles.

Students will create triangles using the Geoboard Learning Tool and describe each shape's attributes, or characteristics. See Triangles at the end of this activity for guidance about each triangle that students will create on the Geoboard.

DIRECTIONS FOR USING THE GEOBOARD LEARNING TOOL

1. Click Lesson Mode. If necessary, click Menu and Help to review the instructions for the learning tool.
2. Students will model different triangles on the Geoboard. Have students clear the Geoboard after they check their models.

   Note: Students can clear the Geoboard by clicking the scissors button.

3. Say: Make a triangle that has a right angle in the top left corner.

Ask: What is the name of this type of triangle? right triangle

Ask: What types of angles are the other angles in the triangle? acute angles

Have students click the angle button to see the triangle's angle measures. Have them check that 1 angle is a right angle (measures 90°) and the other 2 angles are acute (each measures less than 90°).

4. Say: Click the isometric button at the bottom left of the Geoboard. Make a triangle with all sides the same length.

Ask: What is the name of this type of triangle? equilateral triangle

Ask: What do the 3 angles have in common? They are all acute angles that measure 60°.

Have students click the angle button to see the triangle's angle measures. Have them check that each angle is an acute angle that measures 60°.

5. Say: Make a triangle that has an obtuse angle.

Ask: What is the name of this type of triangle? obtuse triangle

Ask: What do you notice about the lengths of the sides of the triangle? Two sides are the same length, or no sides are the same length.

Have students click the angle button to see the triangle's angle measures. Have them check that 1 angle is an obtuse angle (measures greater than 90° and less than 180°) and the other 2 angles are acute (each measures less than 90°).

6. Say: Make a triangle that has 2 sides the same length.

Ask: What is the name of this type of triangle? isosceles triangle

Ask: What do you know about the angles in an isosceles triangle? Two angles have the same measure and are at either end of the triangle side that doesn't have the same length as the other 2 sides.

Have students click the angle button to see the triangle's angle measures. Have them check that two angles have the same measure.

> **Tips**
>
> Point out to students that the vertices of the triangles they draw should be on the dots of the Geoboard, but the sides of the triangles will not always cross over the dots.
>
> Explain that on the Geoboard, the distance between two dots going up and down (vertically), or going sideways (horizontally), is one unit. This unit is not called an inch or a centimeter, because the distance may be different on different computers.

Triangles

 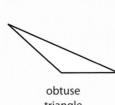

| right triangle | equilateral triangle | obtuse triangle | isosceles triangle |

LEARN Triangles and 180°

ONLINE 15min

Students will review how to find the sum of the angle measures of a triangle by seeing the relationship between the angle measures of a triangle and a straight angle. Then they will find the sum of the angle measures of right, isosceles, and equilateral triangles and reinforce the concept that the sum of the angle measures of any triangle is 180°. Students will also change the angle measures of a triangle to make acute, right, obtuse, and equiangular triangles.

Objectives

- Identify that the sum of the interior angles of any triangle is 180° and solve related problems.

LEARN Missing Angle Measures

ONLINE 15min

Students will find missing angle measures in triangles. They can use different strategies to solve the problems. Students may want to write an equation to find the missing angle measure, or they may choose to use mental math.

Objectives

- Identify that the sum of the interior angles of any triangle is 180° and solve related problems.

Tips
Some of the problems do not show a picture of a triangle. Students may find it helpful to sketch the triangle described in the problem and label the angles to help them find the missing angle measure in those problems.

TRY IT Find Missing Angle Measures

OFFLINE 15min

Students will practice finding the missing angle measures in different types of triangles. They will apply that skill to everyday situations. Gather a protractor. Have students turn to the Find Missing Angle Measures activity page in their Activity Book and read the directions with them.

Students should copy the problems from the Activity Book into their Math Notebook as necessary and solve them there.

Objectives

- Identify that the sum of the interior angles of any triangle is 180° and solve related problems.

Tips

Suggest to students that they check their work by adding all three angle measures in each triangle. The sum should be 180°.

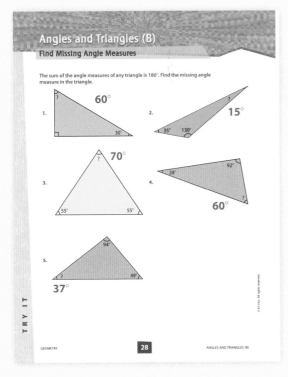

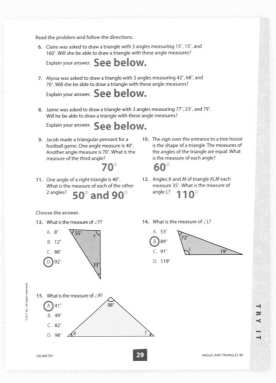

Additional Answers

6. No, the sum of the measures of the angles of a triangle is always 180° and the sum of the measures of these angles is 190°.

7. Yes, the sum of the measures of the angles of a triangle is always 180° and the sum of the measures of these angles is 180°.

8. No, the sum of the measures of the angles of a triangle is always 180° and the sum of the measures of these angles is 179°.

CHECKPOINT

ONLINE 5 min

Students will complete an online Checkpoint. If necessary, read the directions, problems, and answer choices to students and help them with keyboard or mouse operations.

Objectives

- Identify that the sum of the interior angles of any triangle is 180° and solve related problems.

Angles in a Quadrilateral (A)

Lesson Overview

GET READY Sketch Quadrilaterals	10 minutes	ONLINE
LEARN Total Angles to 360°	15 minutes	ONLINE
LEARN 360° in a Quadrilateral	15 minutes	OFFLINE
LEARN Measure Angles	20 minutes	OFFLINE

▶ **Lesson Objectives**

Identify that the sum of the interior angles of any quadrilateral is 360° and solve related problems.

▶ **Prerequisite Skills**

- Know how to define and sketch different quadrilaterals.
- Identify attributes of parallelograms, rectangles, and squares.

▶ **Content Background**

Quadrilaterals are two-dimensional shapes that have 4 sides made from line segments. Students will work with different types of quadrilaterals: trapezoids, parallelograms, rectangles, rhombuses, and squares.

▶ **Common Errors and Misconceptions**

Students might focus on the length of the line segments that form an angle's sides, the tilt of the top line segment, the area enclosed by the sides, or the proximity of the 2 sides rather than look at the actual size of the angle. For example, students might indicate that in the two triangles shown here, angle *A* is smaller than angle *X*.

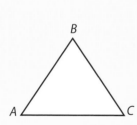 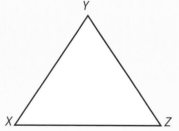

▶ **Advance Preparation**

Print 360° in a Quadrilateral.

▶ **Safety**

Make sure students handle the scissors carefully and be sure to store them in a safe place.

Objectives

- Know how to define and sketch different quadrilaterals.
- Identify attributes of parallelograms, rectangles, and squares.

Students will model different quadrilaterals using the Geoboard Learning Tool and describe each shape's attributes.

DIRECTIONS FOR USING THE GEOBOARD LEARNING TOOL

Note: Students can check their models by clicking Show Info. After they check their models, they can clear the Geoboard by clicking the scissors button and not selecting any scissors options.

1. Click Lesson Mode. If necessary, click Menu and Help to review the instructions for the learning tool.

2. **Say:** Make a quadrilateral with one pair of opposite sides parallel and the other pair of opposite sides not parallel. (Refer to the Quadrilaterals chart.)

   Ask: What is the name of this type of quadrilateral? trapezoid

   Have students draw another trapezoid and orient it differently from their first one.

   Have students check their model by clicking Show Info and then clear the Geoboard.

3. **Say:** Make a quadrilateral that has each pair of opposite sides parallel and opposite sides equal in length. (Refer to the Quadrilaterals chart.)

   Ask: What is the name of this type of quadrilateral? parallelogram

   Have students click the yellow ruler button to check that opposite sides are equal in length. Then have them draw another parallelogram and orient it differently from their first one.

   Have students check their model and then clear the Geoboard.

4. **Say:** Make a quadrilateral with each of its 4 angles measuring 90° and opposite sides that are equal in length. (Refer to the Quadrilaterals chart.)

   Ask: What is the name of this type of quadrilateral? rectangle

   Have students click the yellow ruler button to check that opposite sides are equal in length and click the angle button to check that each angle measures 90°. Then have them draw another rectangle and orient it differently from their first one.

   Have students check their model and then clear the Geoboard.

5. **Say:** Make a quadrilateral with all 4 sides equal in length. (Refer to the Quadrilaterals chart.)

   Ask: What is the name of this type of quadrilateral? rhombus

   Note: Students can make a square with the grid Geoboard (chosen with the grid-isometric toggle button), but to make any rhombus other than a square, they must use the isometric Geoboard.

   Have students click the yellow ruler button to check that all 4 sides are equal in length. Then have them draw another rhombus and orient it differently from their first one.

   Have students check their model and then clear the Geoboard.

Tips

Extend the activity by asking students to use paper and pencil to draw different examples of each type of quadrilateral. This will help them understand that quadrilaterals of the same kind can be different sizes and shapes.

6. Say: Make a quadrilateral that has all 4 sides equal in length and has four 90° angles. (Refer to the Quadrilaterals chart.)

Ask: What is the name of this type of quadrilateral? square

Have students click the yellow ruler button to check that opposite sides are equal in length and click the angle button to check that each angle measures 90°. Then have them draw another square and orient it differently from their first one.

Quadrilaterals		
Name	**Description**	**Example**
trapezoid	Two sides are parallel and two sides are not.	
parallelogram	Opposite sides are parallel and equal in length.	
rectangle	All interior angles are 90° and opposite sides are equal in length.	
rhombus	All four sides are equal in length.	
square	All four sides are equal in length and all interior angles are 90°.	

ONLINE 15 min

LEARN Total Angles to 360°

Students will learn that the measures of the interior angles of a quadrilateral total 360°. Then they will learn that a quadrilateral can be split into two triangles.

Students know that the sum of the measures of the angles of a triangle equals 180°. They will see that 6 torn angles from the two triangles formed by the split quadrilateral spiral around a straight angle. They will see that the sum of the angle measures equals 360°. They will also see that the sum of the angle measures of two triangles is $180 + 180 = 360$. That means that the sum of the angle measures of a quadrilateral is 360°. Finally, students will apply these concepts by using Free Play on the Pattern Blocks Learning Tool.

Students will use the Pattern Blocks Learning Tool to apply the concept that in a quadrilateral, the sum of the interior angles is 360°.

DIRECTIONS FOR USING THE PATTERN BLOCKS LEARNING TOOL

1. Start the Pattern Blocks Learning Tool.
2. Click the Free Play option. Click Start.
3. Have students put two squares next to each other.

4. Guide students to put two more squares below the first two squares so that their sides are touching.

5. Tell students that all four squares meet at a point.

6. Explain to students that the center point includes all 4 of a square's interior angles—the upper-right, lower-right, upper-left, and lower-left angles.

7. Tell students that the place where the four squares meet to form a large square has an angle measure of 360°.

8. Tell students that together, these 4 angles make a square. The sum of the angle measures of the 4 angles equals 360°.

9. Repeat Steps 3–8 for both types of rhombuses included in the tool. Students will need to use rotate tools while placing shapes.

LEARN 360° in a Quadrilateral

OFFLINE
15 min

Objectives

- Identify that the sum of the interior angles of any quadrilateral is 360° and solve related problems.

Students will cut off the angles of quadrilaterals to demonstrate that the 4 angles can spiral around a straight angle to verify that the measures of the angles add up to 360°.

Gather scissors, a protractor, ruler, and the 360° in a Quadrilateral printout.

1. Point to the straight angle at top of the page. Have students use the protractor to measure the straight angle and confirm that it measures 180°.

2. Remind students that both sides of a straight angle measure 360°. Have them measure both sides of the straight angle to verify this fact.

3. Tell students that they will first use the ruler to draw a line to divide a trapezoid into two triangles. They will then cut the 6 angles from the two triangles formed from the trapezoid and place the angles around a straight angle to show that the sum of the angle measures of a quadrilateral is 360°.

4. Give students scissors, the ruler, and the 360° in a Quadrilateral printout. Have them use the ruler to draw the line to divide the trapezoid into two triangles. Cut the two triangles from the trapezoid. Guide them to carefully cut off each angle of each triangle.

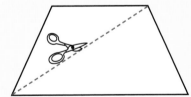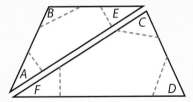

5. Have students place the 6 angles together so they form a spiral around the straight angle at the top of the page.

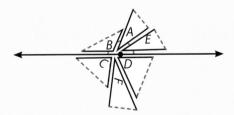

6. Ask: Do the 6 angle measures add up to 360°? How do you know this is true? *A straight angle measures 180°. The measure of the angles of both sides of a straight angle is 360°. When the 6 angles are cut from the two triangles and placed together, the angles form a spiral around the straight angle. The sum of the angle measures is 360°.*

7. Repeat Steps 3–6 with a parallelogram and a rectangle from the printout. Have students name each quadrilateral before dividing each shape into two triangles and using the angles to verify that the sum of the measures is 360°.

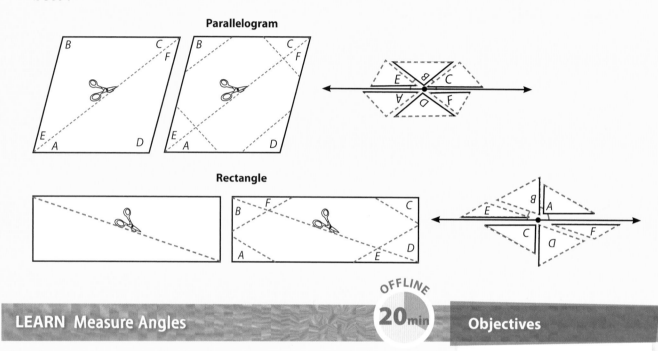

Parallelogram

Rectangle

LEARN Measure Angles

Objectives

- Identify that the sum of the interior angles of any quadrilateral is 360° and solve related problems.

Students will measure angles of quadrilaterals to test the idea that angle measures of any quadrilateral add to 360°. Using a protractor, they should find that angle measures do add up to 360°. Students will compare the sum of a quadrilateral's angle measures to the measure of both sides of a straight angle.

Gather a protractor. Have students turn to the Measure Angles activity page in their Activity Book and read the directions with them.

1. Point to the straight angle at bottom of the page. Have students measure the straight angle and confirm that it measures 180°.

2. Remind students that both sides of a straight angle measure 360°. Have them measure both sides of the straight angle to verify this fact.

3. Tell students that they will measure the four angles in quadrilaterals to find the sum of the angle measures. They will then compare the sum of the angle measures to the measure of both sides of a straight angle.

4. Have students number 1–5 in their Math Notebook. Tell students to use the protractor to measure the angles on the five quadrilaterals on the activity page. Record the following for each quadrilateral:

- the 4 angle measures
- the sum of the angle measures
- the classification of each quadrilateral (trapezoid, parallelogram, rectangle, rhombus, or square)

5. In their Math Notebook, have students verify that the sum of the angle measures for each quadrilateral is 360°.

6. **Ask:** What is the relationship between the sum of the angle measures of a quadrilateral and the measure of two sides of a straight angle? The sum of the angle measures of a quadrilateral are 360°. This is equal to the measure of both sides of a straight angle.

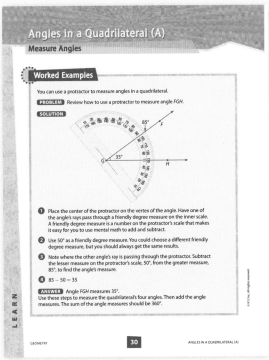

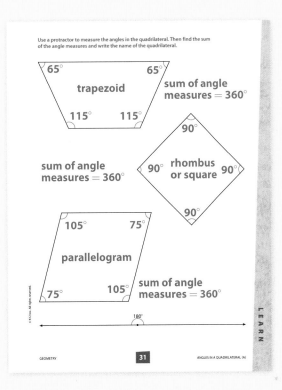

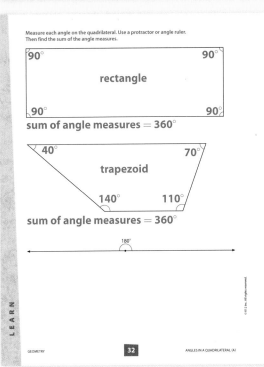

Angles in a Quadrilateral (B)

GET READY Classify Quadrilaterals	10 minutes	ONLINE
LEARN Quadrilateral Angles Total 360°	15 minutes	ONLINE
LEARN Solve Problems with Angles	20 minutes	ONLINE
TRY IT Practice Quadrilateral Angles	10 minutes	OFFLINE
CHECKPOINT	5 minutes	ONLINE

▶ Lesson Objectives

Identify that the sum of the interior angles of any quadrilateral is 360° and solve related problems.

▶ Prerequisite Skills

- Know how to define and sketch different quadrilaterals.
- Identify attributes of parallelograms, rectangles, and squares.

▶ Content Background

Quadrilaterals are two-dimensional shapes that have 4 sides made from line segments. Students will continue to work with different types of quadrilaterals: trapezoids, parallelograms, rectangles, rhombuses, and squares.

There are different types of quadrilaterals, based on the measure of the angles that are formed by the sides of the shape, the relationships between the lengths of the sides of the shape, and the number of pairs of parallel sides of the shape. Students will learn to find missing angle measures of quadrilaterals.

▶ Common Errors and Misconceptions

Students might focus on the length of the line segments that form an angle's sides, the tilt of the top line segment, the area enclosed by the sides, or the proximity of the 2 sides rather than look at the actual size of the angle. For example, students might indicate that in the two triangles shown here, angle A is smaller than angle X.

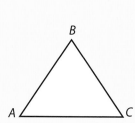
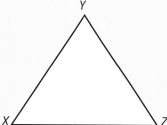

▶ Advance Preparation

Print Features of Quadrilaterals.

Materials to Gather

SUPPLIED

Practice Quadrilateral Angles activity page

Features of Quadrilaterals (printout)

GET READY Classify Quadrilaterals

ONLINE 10 min

Objectives

- Know how to define and sketch quadrilaterals
- Identify attributes of parallelograms, rectangles, and squares.

Students will determine which shapes can be classified as a specific type of quadrilateral. They will also match the names of quadrilaterals to shapes. Gather the Features of Quadrilaterals printout for students to use with the online activity.

LEARN Quadrilateral Angles Total 360°

ONLINE 15 min

Objectives

- Identify that the sum of the interior angles of any quadrilateral is 360° and solve related problems.

Students will review that a quadrilateral can be split into two triangles and that the sum of the angle measures of the two triangles is 360°. Students will then investigate this concept by measuring and typing angle measures into a number sentence to show that the sum of the angle measures of a quadrilateral equals 360°.

LEARN Solve Problems with Angles

ONLINE 20 min

Objectives

- Identify that the sum of the interior angles of any quadrilateral is 360° and solve related problems.

Students will solve problems to find the interior angles of quadrilaterals. They will also find missing angle measures in quadrilaterals.

Tips Students may find it helpful to sketch the quadrilateral described in the problem and label the angles to help them find the missing angle measure for problems that do not show a picture of the quadrilateral.

TRY IT Practice Quadrilateral Angles

OFFLINE 10 min

Objectives

- Identify that the sum of the interior angles of any quadrilateral is 360° and solve related problems.

Students will practice solving problems related to angle measures in quadrilaterals. Have students turn to the Practice Quadrilateral Angles activity page in their Activity Book and read the directions with them. Remind students that sometimes a 90° angle is indicated with a right angle corner, like the one shown here.

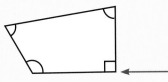

Students should copy the problems from the Activity Book into their Math Notebook as necessary and solve them there.

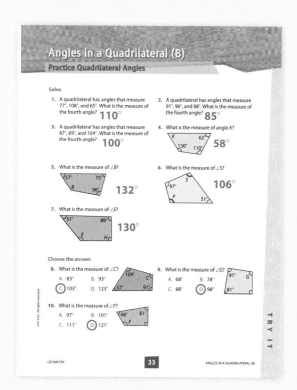

Angles in a Quadrilateral (B)

Practice Quadrilateral Angles

Solve.

1. A quadrilateral has angles that measure 77°, 108°, and 65°. What is the measure of the fourth angle? **110°**

2. A quadrilateral has angles that measure 91°, 96°, and 88°. What is the measure of the fourth angle? **85°**

3. A quadrilateral has angles that measure 87°, 69°, and 104°. What is the measure of the fourth angle? **100°**

4. What is the measure of angle *K*? **58°**

5. What is the measure of ∠*B*? **132°**

6. What is the measure of ∠*S*? **106°**

7. What is the measure of ∠*E*? **130°**

Choose the answer.

8. What is the measure of ∠*C*?
   A. 83° B. 93°
   C. 103° D. 123°

9. What is the measure of ∠*G*?
   A. 68° B. 78°
   C. 88° D. 98°

10. What is the measure of ∠*F*?
   A. 97° B. 101°
   C. 111° D. 121°

GEOMETRY   33   ANGLES IN A QUADRILATERAL (B)

TRY IT

CHECKPOINT

ONLINE
5 min

Objectives

Students will complete an online Checkpoint. If necessary, read the directions, problems, and answer choices to students and help them with keyboard or mouse operations.

- Identify that the sum of the interior angles of any quadrilateral is 360° and solve related problems.

Core Focus
Triangles and Quadrilaterals

Lesson Overview

LEARN Draw Triangles and Quadrilaterals	25 minutes	ONLINE
LEARN Classify Triangles and Quadrilaterals	15 minutes	ONLINE
TRY IT Triangles and Quadrilaterals	10 minutes	OFFLINE
CHECKPOINT	10 minutes	ONLINE

▶ Lesson Objectives

- Define and sketch different types of triangles and identify their attributes.
- Know how to define and sketch different quadrilaterals.
- Classify two-dimensional figures in a hierarchy based on their properties.
- Understand that attributes that apply to a category of two-dimensional figures also apply to all subcategories of that category.

▶ Content Background

Students will create triangles and quadrilaterals, given specific attributes for each figure. Creating these polygons from descriptions helps students focus on the necessary attributes for each type of figure, such as angle measures, parallel lines, and side lengths. Students will also learn how different triangles and quadrilaterals can be classified. They will learn that some triangles and some quadrilaterals are subcategories of others; for example, an equilateral triangle is a special type of isosceles triangle and a rectangle is a special type of parallelogram.

Materials to Gather

SUPPLIED

Triangles and Quadrilaterals activity page

LEARN Draw Triangles and Quadrilaterals

ONLINE
25min

Students will use the Geoboard Learning Tool to create triangles and quadrilaterals with specific attributes.

DIRECTIONS FOR USING THE GEOBOARD LEARNING TOOL

1. Click Lesson Mode. If necessary, click Menu and Help to review the instructions for the learning tool.

2. For each of the descriptions given in Step 3, have students:
   - Visualize the figure in their minds before building the figure.
   - Create each figure according to the given attributes. (When instructions indicate isometric mode, click the isometric button under the angle button.)
   - Click Show Info to check that their shape meets the specifications given. Student may also click the ruler button and angle button to verify lengths of sides and measures of angles. When two shapes are on the board, click the shape to reveal its information.

Objectives

- Define and sketch different types of triangles and identify their attributes.
- Know how to define and sketch different quadrilaterals.
- Understand that attributes that apply to a category of two-dimensional figures also apply to all subcategories of that category.

- Click Hide Info, and if used, the ruler button, the angle button, and the isometric button.
- Clear the Geoboard with the scissors button.

3. Descriptions of triangles and quadrilaterals to build:
   - a triangle with 1 obtuse angle and 2 acute angles
   - two right triangles: one isosceles, one scalene
   - an equilateral triangle (use isometric mode)
   - two different scalene triangles: one acute, one obtuse
   - two sizes of isosceles triangles that are not equilateral (use isometric mode)
   - a quadrilateral that has no sides parallel or equal in length
   - a quadrilateral with at least 1 angle greater than a right angle
   - a parallelogram that is not a rectangle or square
   - a rectangle that is not a square
   - a rhombus that is not a square (use isometric mode)
   - two different trapezoids, one that is isosceles

ONLINE 15 min

LEARN Classify Triangles and Quadrilaterals

Students will review the classification of triangles and quadrilaterals. They will focus on the definitions and attributes of the various figures.

Objectives

- Understand that attributes that apply to a category of two-dimensional figures also apply to all subcategories of that category.
- Classify two-dimensional figures in a hierarchy based on their properties.

OFFLINE 10 min

TRY IT Triangles and Quadrilaterals

Students will practice drawing and classifying triangles and quadrilaterals. View or print the Triangles and Quadrilaterals activity page. Students should copy the problems into their Math Notebook and solve them there.

Objectives

- Define and sketch different types of triangles and identify their attributes.
- Know how to define and sketch different quadrilaterals.
- Understand that attributes that apply to a category of two-dimensional figures also apply to all subcategories of that category.
- Classify two-dimensional figures in a hierarchy based on their properties.

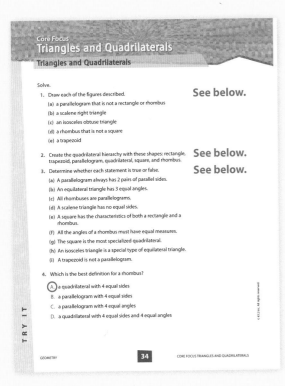

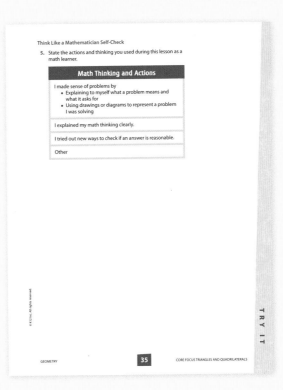

Additional Answers

1. Sample drawings:

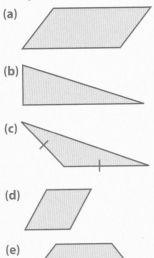

(a)

(b)

(c)

(d)

(e)

2. Sample diagram:

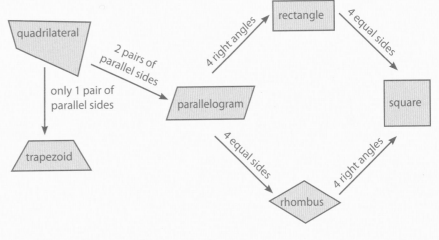

3.
(a) true

(b) true

(c) true

(d) true

(e) true

(f) false

(g) true

(h) false

(i) true

Students will complete an online Checkpoint. If necessary, read the directions, problems, and answer choices to students and help them with keyboard or mouse operations.

- Know how to define and sketch different quadrilaterals.
- Define and sketch different types of triangles and identify their attributes.
- Understand that attributes that apply to a category of two-dimensional figures also apply to all subcategories of that category.
- Classify two-dimensional figures in a hierarchy based on their properties.

Unit Review

▶ ## Unit Objectives

This lesson reviews the following objectives:

- Identify, measure, and draw angles with appropriate math tools.
- Identify and draw perpendicular or parallel lines with appropriate math tools.
- Define and sketch different types of triangles and identify their attributes.
- Identify that the sum of the interior angles of any triangle is 180° and solve related problems.
- Identify that the sum of the interior angles of any quadrilateral is 360° and solve related problems.
- Know how to define and sketch different quadrilaterals.
- Classify two-dimensional figures in a hierarchy based on their properties.
- Understand that attributes that apply to a category of two-dimensional figures also apply to all subcategories of that category.
- Construct rectangles or triangles with appropriate math tools.

Materials to Gather

SUPPLIED
Checkpoint Practice activity page
protractor

▶ ## Advance Preparation

In this lesson, students will have an opportunity to review previous activities in the Geometry unit. Look at the suggested activities in Unit Review: Prepare for the Checkpoint online and gather any needed materials.

ONLINE
10 min

UNIT REVIEW Look Back

Students will review key concepts from the unit to prepare for the Unit Checkpoint.

Objectives

- Review unit objectives.

OFFLINE
50 min

UNIT REVIEW Checkpoint Practice

Students will complete a Checkpoint Practice activity page to prepare for the Unit Checkpoint. Gather the protractor. If necessary, read the directions, problems, and answer choices to students. Have students answer the problems on their own. Carefully review any missed problems with students.

Objectives

- Review unit objectives.

Checkpoint Practice

Solve.

1. Which is an obtuse angle?

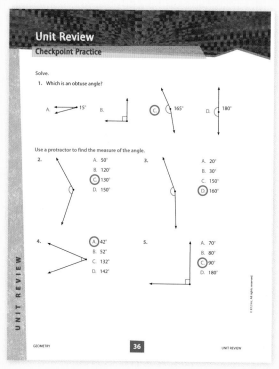

A. 15° B. C. 165° D. 180°

Use a protractor to find the measure of the angle.

2.
A. 50°
B. 120°
C. 130°
D. 150°

3.
A. 20°
B. 30°
C. 150°
D. 160°

4.
A. 42°
B. 52°
C. 132°
D. 142°

5.
A. 70°
B. 80°
C. 90°
D. 180°

Choose the answer.

6. Look at the blue lines in each picture. Which pair is an example of parallel lines?

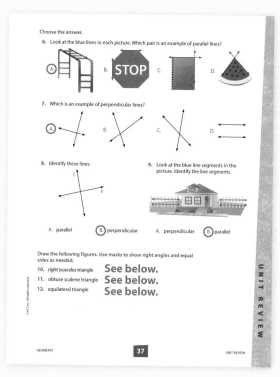

A. B. STOP C. D.

7. Which is an example of perpendicular lines?

A. B. C. D.

8. Identify these lines.

A. parallel B. perpendicular

9. Look at the blue line segments in the picture. Identify the line segments.

A. perpendicular B. parallel

Draw the following figures. Use marks to show right angles and equal sides as needed.

10. right isosceles triangle — See below.
11. obtuse scalene triangle — See below.
12. equilateral triangle — See below.

13. trapezoid — See right.
14. rectangle — See right.
15. rhombus — See right.
16. quadrilateral — See right.

Which category of two-dimensional shapes applies to all three of these shapes?

17.

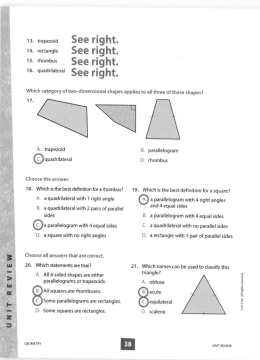

A. trapezoid
B. parallelogram
C. quadrilateral
D. rhombus

Choose the answer.

18. Which is the best definition for a rhombus?
A. a quadrilateral with 1 right angle
B. a quadrilateral with 2 pairs of parallel sides
C. a parallelogram with 4 equal sides
D. a square with no right angles

19. Which is the best definition for a square?
A. a parallelogram with 4 right angles and 4 equal sides
B. a parallelogram with 4 equal sides
C. a quadrilateral with no parallel sides
D. a rectangle with 1 pair of parallel sides

Choose all answers that are correct.

20. Which statements are true?
A. All 4-sided shapes are either parallelograms or trapezoids.
B. All squares are rhombuses.
C. Some parallelograms are rectangles.
D. Some squares are rectangles.

21. Which names can be used to classify this triangle?
A. obtuse
B. acute
C. equilateral
D. scalene

Additional Answers

10. Possible answer:

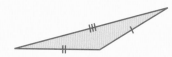

11. Possible answer:

12. Possible answer:

13. Possible answer:

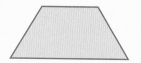

14. Possible answer:

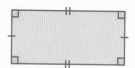

15. Possible answer:

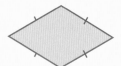

16. Possible answer:

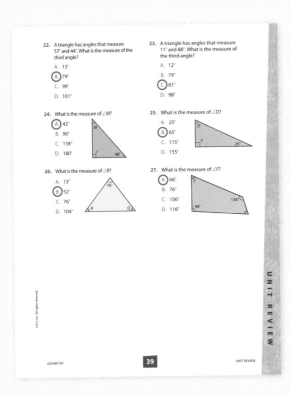

22. A triangle has angles that measure 57° and 44°. What is the measure of the third angle?
   A. 13°
   B. 79°
   C. 99°
   D. 101°

23. A triangle has angles that measure 11° and 88°. What is the measure of the third angle?
   A. 12°
   B. 79°
   C. 81°
   D. 98°

24. What is the measure of ∠M?
   A. 42°
   B. 90°
   C. 138°
   D. 180°

25. What is the measure of ∠D?
   A. 25°
   B. 65°
   C. 115°
   D. 155°

26. What is the measure of ∠R?
   A. 13°
   B. 52°
   C. 76°
   D. 104°

27. What is the measure of ∠F?
   A. 66°
   B. 76°
   C. 106°
   D. 116°

UNIT REVIEW

⇄ UNIT REVIEW Prepare for the Checkpoint

What you do next depends on how students performed in the previous activity, Unit Review: Checkpoint Practice. If students had difficulty with any of the problems, complete the appropriate review activity listed in the table online.

Unit Checkpoint

UNIT CHECKPOINT Online   60 minutes   **ONLINE**

▶ Unit Objectives

This lesson assesses the following objectives:

- Identify, measure, and draw angles with appropriate math tools.
- Identify and draw perpendicular or parallel lines with appropriate math tools.
- Define and sketch different types of triangles and identify their attributes.
- Identify that the sum of the interior angles of any triangle is 180° and solve related problems.
- Identify that the sum of the interior angles of any quadrilateral is 360° and solve related problems.
- Know how to define and sketch different quadrilaterals.
- Classify two-dimensional figures in a hierarchy based on their properties.
- Understand that attributes that apply to a category of two-dimensional figures also apply to all subcategories of that category.
- Construct rectangles or triangles with appropriate math tools.

Materials to Gather

There are no materials to gather for this lesson.

UNIT CHECKPOINT Online   ONLINE 60min

Students will complete an online Checkpoint. If necessary, read the directions, problems, and answer choices to students and help them with keyboard or mouse operations.

Objectives

- Assess unit objectives.

Extended Problems: Real-World Application

USE WHAT YOU KNOW Offline · 60 minutes · OFFLINE

▶ Lesson Objectives

This lesson assesses the following objectives:

- Know how to define and sketch different quadrilaterals.
- Define and sketch different types of triangles and identify their attributes.
- Understand that attributes that apply to a category of two-dimensional figures also apply to all subcategories of that category.
- Classify two-dimensional figures in a hierarchy based on their properties.
- Partition shapes into parts with equal areas and express the area of each part as a unit fraction of the whole.
- Solve multistep problems using multiple operations.
- Apply mathematical knowledge and skills to evaluate and analyze real-world situations.

Materials to Gather

SUPPLIED

Extended Problems: Real-World Application (printout)

USE WHAT YOU KNOW Offline

OFFLINE 60 min

Objectives

- Apply mathematical knowledge and skills to evaluate and analyze real-world situations.

The Extended Problems: Real-World Application and its answer key are located online in the Resources section for this unit in the Online Book Menu of *Math+ Yellow Lesson Guide.* Give students the Extended Problems: Real-World Application. Read the directions, problems, and answer choices to students, if necessary.

You will grade this assignment.

- Students should complete the assignment on their own.
- Students should submit the completed assignment to you.

Fractions: Multiplication and Division

▶ Unit Objectives

- Use models and equations to multiply a whole number or a fraction by a fraction.

- Interpret multiplication as scaling.

- Compare the size of a product to the size of one factor on the basis of the size of the other factor, without multiplying.

- Explain why multiplying a given number by a fraction greater than 1 results in a product greater than the given number.

- Explain why multiplying a given number by a positive fraction less than

1 results in a product smaller than the given number.

- Explain and give examples of different interpretations of fractions.

- Divide whole numbers by unit fractions and unit fractions by whole numbers.

- Represent division of a unit fraction by a whole number such as $\frac{1}{3} \div 7$ using objects and pictorial models, including area models.

- Solve real-world problems involving multiplication of fractions and mixed numbers.

▶ Big Ideas

Fractions can be added, subtracted, multiplied, and divided.

▶ Unit Introduction

In this unit, students will learn about multiplication and division of fractions. They will investigate different drawings and other models of multiplication and division of fractions. Then students will learn step-by-step approaches, also called algorithms, to multiply and divide with fractions. Students will also compare a product with one of its factors by thinking of multiplication as enlarging or shrinking.

Activities in this unit include multiplication of fractions by fractions, multiplication of fractions by a whole number, and multiplication of fractions by mixed numbers. Students will learn that they can divide out common factors before they multiply fractions to make computation easier.

Students will also divide whole numbers by fractions, fractions by whole numbers, fractions by fractions, mixed numbers by fractions, fractions by mixed numbers, and mixed numbers by mixed numbers.

They will complete the unit by solving extended problems that focus on reasoning. Students will multiply and divide to solve the extended problems.

▶ Keywords

algorithm
area model
common factor
divide out a common factor
dividend
division
divisor
enlargement

factor
fraction
greatest common factor
   (GCF)
improper fraction
inverse operations
least common multiple
   (LCM)
mixed number

multiplication
pictoral model
product
proper fractions
quotient
reciprocal
scaling effect
shrinking
simplest form of a fraction
unit fraction

Fraction Multiplication (A)

Lesson Overview

GET READY Simplifying Fractions	15 minutes	ONLINE
LEARN Multiplying a Fraction and a Whole Number	25 minutes	ONLINE
TRY IT Multiplying Fractions	10 minutes	OFFLINE
CHECKPOINT	10 minutes	OFFLINE

▶ Lesson Objectives

Use models and equations to multiply a whole number or a fraction by a fraction.

▶ Prerequisite Skills

Recognize and determine equivalent fractions.

▶ Content Background

In this lesson, students will use models to "see" how fraction multiplication works. Although the traditional algorithm of multiplying numerators and denominators certainly works to find the product of fractions, the rule gives students answers that they often do not understand. They struggle to know if their answers make sense. By modeling several problems, students begin acquiring an intuitive sense about the correctness of their answers. Encourage students to understand the models before moving directly into the algorithm.

Students will first multiply simple fractions by whole-number values. The models should reveal patterns in the types of answers students get for the different situations.

Students will also simplify fractions. Often you will hear the term *reducing* used for simplification. *Reducing* is a misleading term that gives students the mistaken impression that a fraction is getting smaller. Since the value of the fraction that is simplified has not reduced at all and is equal in value to the original fraction, the term *simplify* is used instead of *reduce*.

▶ Advance Preparation

Print the Fraction Strips for Multiplication. Have students cut out each of the fraction strips. Students will use the fraction strips for both the Try It and the Checkpoint.

▶ Safety

Make sure students handle the scissors carefully and be sure to store them in a safe place.

Materials to Gather

SUPPLIED

Multiplying Fractions activity page

Fraction Strips for Multiplication (printout)

Checkpoint (printout)

Checkpoint Answer Key (printout)

ALSO NEEDED

scissors, pointed-end safety

GET READY Simplifying Fractions

Students will review how to use the greatest common factor (GCF) to simplify fractions.

LEARN Multiplying a Fraction and a Whole Number

Students will use arrays, number lines, and fraction strips to multiply a fraction and a whole number. Students should think about how to explain the processes for these problems.

TRY IT Multiplying Fractions

Students will practice using models, such as arrays, number lines, and fraction strips, to multiply a fraction and a whole number. Gather the fraction strip cutouts from the Fraction Strips for Multiplication printout. View or print the Multiplying Fractions activity page. Printing is recommended so that students can use the number lines and arrays provided. Encourage students to fully explain their thinking.

Objectives

- Recognize and determine equivalent fractions.

Objectives

- Use models and equations to multiply a whole number or a fraction by a fraction.

Objectives

- Use models and equations to multiply a whole number or a fraction by a fraction.

Tips

Be sure students precisely align the fraction strips

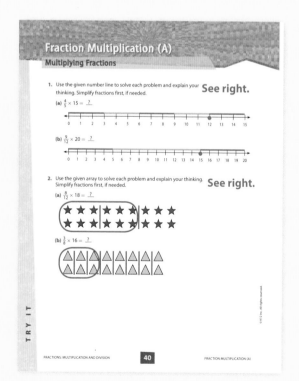

Additional Answers

1. **(a)** $\frac{4}{5} \times 15 = 12$; **Possible explanation:** I divided the 15 into 5 equal sections, since the denominator of the fraction is 5. Then I saw that 4 of the 5 sections, or $\frac{4}{5}$ of 15, ended at 12. So $\frac{4}{5} \times 15 = 12$.

   (b) $\frac{9}{12} \times 20 = 15$; **Possible explanation:** I used a GCF of 3 to simplify $\frac{9}{12}$ to $\frac{3}{4}$. Then I divided 20 into 4 equal sections, since the denominator of the simplified fraction is 4. Then I saw that 3 of the 4 sections, or $\frac{3}{4}$ of 20, ended at 15. So $\frac{3}{4} \times 20 = 15$, and therefore $\frac{9}{12} \times 20 = 15$.

2. **(a)** $\frac{8}{12} \times 18 = 12$; **Possible explanation:** I used a GCF of 4 to simplify $\frac{8}{12}$ to $\frac{2}{3}$. Then I divided the 18 stars into 3 equal groups of 6, since the denominator of the simplified fraction is 3. Then I saw that 2 of the 3 sections, or $\frac{2}{3}$ of 18, have a total of 12 stars. So $\frac{2}{3} \times 18 = 12$, and therefore $\frac{8}{12} \times 18 = 12$.

   (b) $\frac{3}{8} \times 16 = 6$; **Possible explanation:** I divided the 16 triangles into 8 equal groups of 2, since the denominator of the fraction is 8. Then I saw that 3 of the 8 sections, or $\frac{3}{8}$ of 16, have a total of 6 triangles. So $\frac{3}{8} \times 16 = 6$.

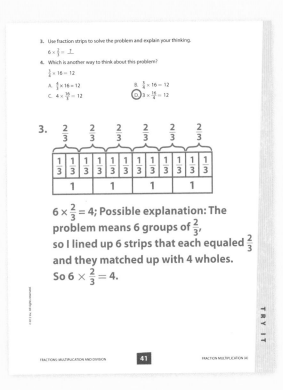

3. Use fraction strips to solve the problem and explain your thinking.

$6 \times \frac{2}{3} =$ ___

4. Which is another way to think about this problem?

$\frac{3}{4} \times 16 = 12$

A. $\frac{4}{3} \times 16 = 12$ B. $\frac{3}{4} \times 16 = 12$

C. $4 \times \frac{16}{3} = 12$ (D) $3 \times \frac{16}{4} = 12$

3.

$6 \times \frac{2}{3} = 4$; Possible explanation: The problem means 6 groups of $\frac{2}{3}$, so I lined up 6 strips that each equaled $\frac{2}{3}$ and they matched up with 4 wholes. So $6 \times \frac{2}{3} = 4$.

T R Y   I T

OFFLINE
10 min

CHECKPOINT

Objectives

- Use models and equations to multiply a whole number or a fraction by a fraction.

The Checkpoint and its answer key are located in the Resources section for this unit in the Online Book Menu of *Math+ Yellow Lesson Guide*. Give students the Checkpoint. Have students complete the Checkpoint on their own. Use the answer key to score the Checkpoint, and then enter the results online.

Fraction Multiplication (B)

LEARN Multiply with a Unit Fraction	15 minutes	OFFLINE
LEARN Multiply with Paper Models	15 minutes	OFFLINE
LEARN Multiply Fractions Less Than or Equal to 1	10 minutes	ONLINE
TRY IT Multiply Fractions	10 minutes	OFFLINE
CHECKPOINT	10 minutes	OFFLINE

▶ Lesson Objectives

Use models and equations to multiply a whole number or a fraction by a fraction.

▶ Content Background

In this lesson, students will use the area model and paper models to "see" how fraction multiplication works when multiplying two fractions that are each less than 1. Although the traditional algorithm of multiplying numerators and denominators certainly works to find the product of fractions, the rule gives students answers that they often do not understand. They struggle to know if their answers make sense. By modeling several problems, students begin to get an intuitive sense about the correctness of their answers.

When students draw a rectangle on grid paper for the area model, the directions will give them the dimensions for the rectangle, such as 2 by 3, or a way to determine the dimensions. The first dimension is the number of rows and the second is the number of columns. For example, a 2-by-3 rectangle would have 2 rows and 3 columns.

You will often hear the term *reducing* used for simplification. *Reducing* is a misleading term that gives students a mistaken impression that the fraction is getting smaller. Since the value of the fraction that is simplified has not reduced at all but is equal in value to the original fraction, the term *simplify* is used instead of *reduce*.

▶ Common Errors and Misconceptions

Students might believe that multiplication always gives products that are greater than or equal to the factors. This is true for whole numbers; for example, $9 \times 8 = 72$, $50 \times 3 = 150$, and $1 \times 1 = 1$. However, students might not realize that the product of a whole number and fraction less than 1 is less than the whole-number factor; for example, $\frac{2}{3} \times 12 = 8$ and $63 \times \frac{5}{7} = 45$.

▶ Advance Preparation

Print the Centimeter Grid Paper.

▶ Safety

Make sure students handle the scissors carefully and be sure to store them in a safe place.

Materials to Gather

SUPPLIED

Multiply Fractions activity page
Centimeter Grid Paper (printout)
Checkpoint (printout)
Checkpoint Answer Key (printout)

ALSO NEEDED

scissors, pointed-end safety

LEARN Multiply with a Unit Fraction

Objectives

- Use models and equations to multiply a whole number or a fraction by a fraction.

Students will use a model to multiply a fraction by a unit fraction. Unit fractions are fractions with a numerator of 1.

Gather the Centimeter Grid Paper.

1. **Say:** Suppose you wanted to find $\frac{1}{2}$ of a $\frac{1}{2}$, or $\frac{1}{2} \times \frac{1}{2}$. You could draw a circle on a piece of paper, divide it into 2 equal parts, or halves, and then shade in half of that half.

   Ask: How much of the circle would be shaded? $\frac{1}{4}$

2. **Say:** Working with halves is pretty familiar. Let's look at some models with unit fractions that may not be as obvious. We will use an area model with rectangles to find $\frac{3}{4}$ of $\frac{1}{5}$. You are finding a fraction of the unit fraction, $\frac{1}{5}$. This problem is the same as finding $\frac{3}{4} \times \frac{1}{5}$.

3. Have students outline a 4-by-5 rectangle on grid paper to model the problem, since the denominators of the factors are 4 and 5. The rectangle has 4 rows and 5 columns.

4. **Say:** Since we're finding $\frac{3}{4}$ of $\frac{1}{5}$, we model $\frac{1}{5}$ first. Divide your rectangle into 5 equal columns to represent the denominator of the factor $\frac{1}{5}$. Put an × in each equal square of 1 column, which represents $\frac{1}{5}$ of the rectangle. Write $\frac{1}{5}$ under your marked column.

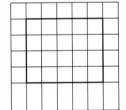 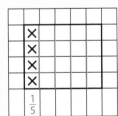 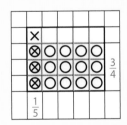

5. **Say:** Add horizontal lines to divide the rectangle into 4 equal parts to represent the denominator of the factor $\frac{3}{4}$. Horizontally, the rectangle is now divided into fourths.

6. **Say:** Now, to show $\frac{3}{4}$ of $\frac{1}{5}$, put circles in 3 of the 4 rows you just drew and write $\frac{3}{4}$ next to those rows. (When a square already has an × you can just circle the ×, like this: ⊗.)

7. Discuss the model with students.

   Ask: In how many squares do you have both an × and a circle? 3

   Into how many squares, or equal parts, is the whole rectangle divided? 20, since it's a 4-by-5 rectangle

   Say: Just like you can multiply 4 by 5 to find that there are 20 squares in the rectangle, you can multiply $\frac{3}{4}$ of the rectangle by $\frac{1}{5}$ of it to see that the product of the fractional parts is 3 of the 20 squares, or $\frac{3}{20}$ of the rectangle. $\frac{3}{4} \times \frac{1}{5} = \frac{3}{20}$

Tips

Point out that three of the four boxes that have an X in them are circled.

$\frac{3}{4}$ of $\frac{1}{5} = \frac{3}{20}$

8. Repeat Steps 3–6 to find $\frac{2}{3}$ of $\frac{1}{4}$ or $\frac{2}{3} \times \frac{1}{4}$. Begin with a 3-row by 4-column rectangle.

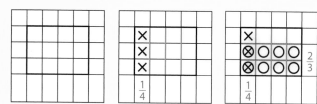

9. Discuss the model with students.

Say: This time you found a fraction of the unit fraction, $\frac{1}{4}$.

Ask: In how many squares do you have both an × and a circle? 2
Into how many squares, or equal parts, is the whole rectangle divided?
12, since it's a 3-by-4 rectangle

Ask: So what is the product of $\frac{2}{3} \times \frac{1}{4}$ before you simplify? $\frac{2}{12}$

Ask: And what is the simplified form of $\frac{2}{12}$? $\frac{1}{6}$

10. Summarize the activity with the following questions about the multiplication problems and the models:

Ask: Does the following rule work for each of the problems you worked before you simplified the product? "Multiply the numerators of the factors to get the numerator in the product, and multiply the denominators of the factors to get the denominator in the product." Yes

Ask: Is the product of each multiplication problem in the activity less than or greater than the first factor in the problem? less than

Say: So, when you multiply a fraction by 1, you get that same first-factor fraction. But, when you multiply a fraction by a unit fraction, the product is always less than the first-factor fraction.

LEARN Multiply with Paper Models

OFFLINE 15 min

Objectives

- Use models and equations to multiply a whole number or a fraction by a fraction.

Students will use a paper model to represent how to multiply a fraction by a fraction. Gather paper and scissors for the activity. The paper is for folding and cutting. Students will write the problem in their Math Notebook.

1. **Say:** Write $\frac{3}{4} \times \frac{2}{3} = ?$

2. **Say:** You can use the multiplication symbol, ×, or the multiplication dot, •, to write the number sentence to solve the problem. Write the problem again using the multiplication dot.

3. Check to see that students wrote $\frac{3}{4} \cdot \frac{2}{3} = ?$

4. **Say:** Let's use paper to model the problem $\frac{3}{4} \cdot \frac{2}{3} = ?$

Tips

Encourage students to come up with their own methods for using models to multiply fractions. Models can include folding and cutting paper or drawing diagrams.

5. Have students fold a sheet of paper into 3 equal parts, or thirds, and then cut out each third. Dividing the paper into thirds uses a model to show the factor $\frac{2}{3}$.

   Say: The paper is cut into 3 equal-sized pieces. We will use 2 of those pieces to represent the factor $\frac{2}{3}$ in the problem, because the pieces show 2 out of 3 equal-sized parts.

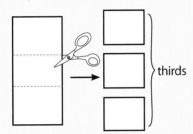

6. Have students fold each of the cut-out thirds into fourths, and then cut out each fourth. Dividing each third into fourths uses a model to show the factor $\frac{3}{4}$.

   Say: Each third is cut into 4 equal-sized pieces.

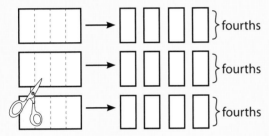

7. **Ask:** If the sheet of paper represents one whole, how many equal parts is the whole divided into? 12

8. Take 3 of the cut-out fourths $\left(\text{representing } \frac{3}{4}\right)$ from 2 sets of the cut-out thirds $\left(\text{representing } \frac{2}{3}\right)$.

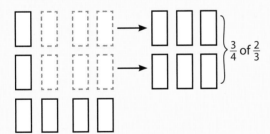

9. **Say:** We took $\frac{3}{4}$ from 2 sets of 3, or $\frac{2}{3}$. Each of the pieces represents $\frac{1}{12}$ of the whole. There are 6 pieces.

   Ask: How many twelfths are equal to $\frac{3}{4}$ of $\frac{2}{3}$? $\frac{6}{12}$ What is $\frac{3}{4} \cdot \frac{2}{3} = ?$ $\frac{6}{12}$

10. Tell students to write the answer in the equation.

LEARN Multiply Fractions Less Than or Equal to 1

Students will investigate models to multiply fractions that are each less than or equal to 1. They should study the approaches to modeling so that they can model fraction problems on their own.

Objectives

- Use models and equations to multiply a whole number or a fraction by a fraction.

TRY IT Multiply Fractions

Students will practice using models to multiply fractions that are each less than or equal to 1. Have students view or print the Multiply Fractions activity page in their Activity Book and read the directions with them.

Printing the page is recommended so that students can use the given diagrams.

Objectives

- Use models and equations to multiply a whole number or a fraction by a fraction.

Tips

Remind students to simplify fractions first, if possible, before modeling the problem.

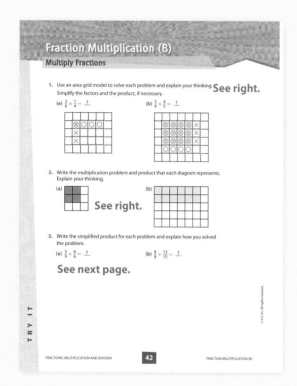

Additional Answers

1. **(a)** $\frac{2}{6} \times \frac{1}{4} = \frac{1}{12}$; **Possible explanation:** I used a GCF of 2 to simplify $\frac{2}{6}$ to $\frac{1}{3}$. Then I marked 1 row with Os to show $\frac{1}{3}$ and one column with Xs to show $\frac{1}{4}$. I saw that 1 of the 12 squares had both markings. So $\frac{1}{3} \times \frac{1}{4} = \frac{1}{12}$, and therefore, $\frac{2}{6} \times \frac{1}{4} = \frac{1}{12}$.

   (b) $\frac{3}{4} \times \frac{4}{5} = \frac{12}{20} = \frac{3}{5}$; **Possible explanation:** I marked 3 rows with Os to show $\frac{3}{4}$ and 4 columns with Xs to show $\frac{4}{5}$. I saw that 12 of the 20 squares had both markings, so $\frac{3}{4} \times \frac{4}{5} = \frac{12}{20}$. I noticed that $\frac{12}{20}$ could be simplified, so I used a GCF of 4 to simplify $\frac{12}{20}$ to $\frac{3}{5}$. So $\frac{3}{4} \times \frac{4}{5} = \frac{12}{20} = \frac{3}{5}$.

2. **(a)** $\frac{2}{3} \times \frac{2}{3} = \frac{4}{9}$; **Possible explanation:** If 2 of the 3 rows were marked one way and 2 of the 3 columns were marked another way, the shaded squares would be the ones marked both ways. The diagram shows that $\frac{2}{3}$ of $\frac{2}{3}$ is shaded. There are 4 out of a total of 9 squares shaded, so the diagram represents the problem $\frac{2}{3} \times \frac{2}{3} = \frac{4}{9}$.

   (b) $\frac{2}{5} \times \frac{6}{7} = \frac{12}{35}$; **Possible explanation:** If 2 of the 5 rows were marked one way and 6 of the 7 columns were marked another way, the shaded squares would be the ones marked both ways. The diagram shows that $\frac{2}{5}$ of $\frac{6}{7}$ is shaded. There are 12 out of a total of 35 squares shaded, so the diagram represents the problem $\frac{2}{5} \times \frac{6}{7} \frac{12}{35}$.

Additional Answers

3. (a) $\frac{5}{9} \times \frac{6}{6} = \frac{5}{9}$; **Possible explanation:** Since $\frac{6}{6} = 1$ and any number times 1 equals itself, then $\frac{5}{9} \times 1 = \frac{5}{9}$, and therefore $\frac{5}{9} \times \frac{6}{6} = \frac{5}{9}$.

(b) $\frac{8}{8} \times \frac{13}{15} = \frac{13}{15}$; **Possible explanation:** Since $\frac{8}{8} = 1$ and any number times 1 equals itself, then $1 \times \frac{13}{15} = \frac{13}{15}$, and therefore $\frac{8}{8} \times \frac{13}{15} = \frac{13}{15}$.

OFFLINE

10 min

CHECKPOINT

Objectives

The Checkpoint and its answer key are located in the Resources section for this Unit in the Online Book Menu of *Math+ Yellow Lesson Guide*. Open the Checkpoint. Give students the Checkpoint. Have students complete the Checkpoint on their own. Use the answer key to score the Checkpoint, and then enter the results online.

- Use models and equations to multiply a whole number or a fraction by a fraction.

Fraction Multiplication (C)

Lesson Overview

GET READY Improper Fractions and Mixed Numbers	5 minutes	ONLINE
LEARN Multiply with Improper Fractions	15 minutes	OFFLINE
LEARN Multiply with Fraction Circles	10 minutes	OFFLINE
LEARN Multiply Mixed Numbers with Area Models	10 minutes	ONLINE
TRY IT Fraction Multiplication	10 minutes	OFFLINE
CHECKPOINT	10 minutes	OFFLINE

▶ Lesson Objectives

Use models and equations to multiply a whole number or a fraction by a fraction.

▶ Prerequisite Skills

Recognize and determine equivalent fractions.

▶ Content Background

In this lesson, students will use models to "see" how fraction multiplication with fractions greater than 1 works. Adults often find the models cumbersome and irrelevant, especially those involving mixed numbers. However, many adults struggled with fractions and still do because they learned the algorithm without truly understanding the concept. Encourage students to understand the models before moving directly into the algorithm.

When students draw a rectangle on grid paper for the area model, the directions will give them the dimensions for the rectangle, such as 2 by 3, or a way to determine the dimensions. The first dimension is the number of rows and the second is the number of columns. For example, a 2 by 3 rectangle would have 2 rows and 3 columns.

Students will first review conversion between improper fractions and mixed numbers. They will then model multiplication problems involving such fractions. The models should reveal patterns in the types of answers students get for the different situations.

Students will also simplify fractions. Often you will hear the term *reducing* used for simplification. *Reducing* is a misleading term that gives students a mistaken impression that the fraction is getting smaller. Since the value of the fraction that is simplified has not reduced at all, but is equal in value to the original fraction, the term *simplify* is used instead of *reduce*.

Materials to Gather

SUPPLIED

Fraction Circles (printout)

Centimeter Grid Paper (printout)

Fraction Multiplication activity page

Checkpoint (printout)

Checkpoint Answer Key (printout)

▶ Common Errors and Misconceptions

Students might believe that multiplication always gives products that are greater than or equal to the factors. This is true for whole numbers; for example, $9 \times 8 = 72$, $50 \times 3 = 150$, and $1 \times 1 = 1$. However, students might not realize that the product of a whole number and fraction less than 1 is less than the whole-number factor; for example, $\frac{2}{3} \times 12 = 8$ and $63 \times \frac{5}{7} = 45$.

▶ Advance Preparation

Print one copy each of the Fraction Circles and Centimeter Grid Paper.

GET READY Improper Fractions and Mixed Numbers

Students will review converting mixed numbers to improper fractions and improper fractions to mixed numbers.

Objectives

- Recognize and determine equivalent fractions.

LEARN Multiply with Improper Fractions

Students will use a model to multiply a fraction by an improper fraction with a value greater than 1. (An improper fraction has a numerator equal to or greater than the denominator.)

Gather the Centimeter Grid Paper.

Objectives

- Use models and equations to multiply a whole number or a fraction by a fraction.

1. **Say:** You will use a model to find $\frac{1}{4}$ of $\frac{7}{6}$ or $\frac{1}{4} \times \frac{7}{6}$. We call the fraction $\frac{7}{6}$ an improper fraction because the value of the numerator is greater than the value of the denominator.

2. **Ask:** What are the denominators of the fractions you are multiplying? 4 and 6
   Say: One of our fractions, $\frac{7}{6}$, is an improper fraction greater than 1. That means that we will need more than one rectangle to show $\frac{7}{6}$.

3. **Say:** The fraction $\frac{1}{4}$ has a denominator of 4, so you will have 4 rows on your rectangles. The fraction $\frac{7}{6}$ has a denominator of 6, so you will have 6 columns on your rectangles. Draw two 4-by-6 rectangles side by side, and divide each rectangle into sixths using vertical lines. Each rectangle shows $\frac{6}{6}$.

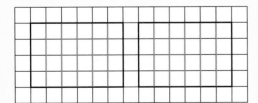

4. **Say:** Put an × in each square of 7 columns. You are showing $\frac{7}{6}$. Write $\frac{7}{6}$ under your marked columns.

5. **Say:** Add horizontal lines to divide the rectangles into 4 equal parts to represent the denominator of the factor $\frac{1}{4}$. To show $\frac{1}{4}$ of $\frac{7}{6}$, put circles in 1 of the 4 rows you just drew across both rectangles and write $\frac{1}{4}$ next to those rows. (When a square already has an × you can just circle the × like this: ⊗.)

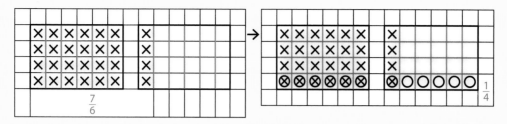

6. Discuss the model with students.

   Say: This time you found a fraction of an improper fraction, $\frac{7}{6}$.

   Ask: In how many squares do you have both an × and a circle? 7
   Into how many squares, or equal parts, is each whole rectangle divided? 24

   Ask: So what is the product of $\frac{1}{4} \times \frac{7}{6}$? $\frac{7}{24}$

7. Repeat Steps 2–5 to find $\frac{2}{5}$ of $\frac{7}{4}$ or $\frac{2}{5} \times \frac{7}{4}$. Begin with two 5-row by 4-column rectangles, each divided vertically into fourths.

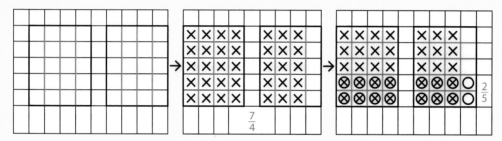

8. Discuss the model with students.

   Say: This time you found a fraction of the improper fraction, $\frac{7}{4}$.

   Ask: In how many squares do you have both an × and a circle? 14
   Into how many squares, or equal parts, is each whole rectangle divided? 20

   Ask: So what is the product of $\frac{2}{5} \times \frac{7}{4}$ before you simplify? $\frac{14}{20}$

   Ask: And what is the simplified form of $\frac{14}{20}$? $\frac{7}{10}$

9. Summarize the activity with the following questions about the multiplication problems and the models:

   Ask: Is the second factor in each multiplication problem in the activity less than or greater than 1? greater than

   Ask: Is the product of each multiplication problem in the activity less than or greater than the first-factor fraction? greater than

   Say: So,

   • When you multiply a simple fraction by 1, you get that same first-factor fraction.

   • When you multiply a simple fraction by a unit fraction (which is less than 1), the product is always less than the first-factor fraction.

   • And, when you multiply a fraction by an improper fraction, which is greater than 1, the product is always greater than the first-factor fraction.

LEARN Multiply with Fraction Circles

Objectives

- Use models and equations to multiply a whole number or a fraction by a fraction.

Students will use circles to model how to multiply a fraction and a mixed number. Gather the Fraction Circles printout.

1. Read the following problem to students:
   - Jesse likes to jump across the rectangular sections of cement in the sidewalk. He can jump across $1\frac{1}{2}$ sections in each jump. How many sections can Jesse jump across if he jumps 4 times in a row?

2. **Say:** The expression $1\frac{1}{2} \times 4 = ?$ represents the problem. We can use fraction circles to multiply $1\frac{1}{2} \times 4$. We can apply the commutative property to solve this problem. Using the property, change the problem to $4 \times 1\frac{1}{2} = ?$

3. Have students shade 4 groups of $1\frac{1}{2}$ circles.

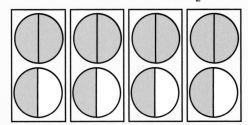

4. **Ask:** Count the number of shaded half-circles in the 4 groups of $1\frac{1}{2}$ shaded circles. How many shaded half-circles are there? 12

   Ask: Look at all the circles. How many half-circles are in each circle? 2

   Say: So $1\frac{1}{2} \times 4 = \frac{12}{2}$, which can be simplified to 6.

5. **Say:** Let's look at another problem where a mixed number and a fraction are multiplied.
   - Rhonda used $2\frac{3}{4}$ containers of strawberries to make fruit salad. Each container held $\frac{1}{3}$ quart of strawberries. How many quarts of strawberries did Rhonda use to make fruit salad?

   Ask: What number sentence represents the problem? $2\frac{3}{4} \times \frac{1}{3} = ?$

6. **Say:** We can use fraction circles to multiply $2\frac{3}{4} \times \frac{1}{3}$ and work in steps to find the product. First let's find 2 times $\frac{1}{3}$. Then we will find $\frac{3}{4}$ of $\frac{1}{3}$. We can add the two partial products to find the final product.

7. Have students shade $\frac{1}{3}$ of each of the first 2 circles in the second row on the Fraction Circles printout. They will work on the first part of the problem to find $2 \times \frac{1}{3}$.

$\frac{1}{3}$ $\qquad$ $\frac{1}{3}$

8. **Ask:** How many thirds did you shade in all? 2

    Say: The product of 2 times $\frac{1}{3}$ is $\frac{2}{3}$. This solves one step of the problem.

    Let's go to the next step to find the product by multiplying $\frac{3}{4} \times \frac{1}{3}$.

9. Tell students to shade $\frac{1}{3}$ of the third circle in the second row of the Fraction

    Circles printout and divide each third into fourths. This model represents $\frac{3}{4} \times \frac{1}{3}$.

10. Have students mark 3 of the 4 shaded sections with an X.

    Say: Three-fourths of $\frac{1}{3}$ is marked with an X. How many equal parts is the circle divided into? 12

    Ask: How many twelfths are now marked with an X? 3 twelfths

    Ask: The product of $\frac{3}{4} \times \frac{1}{3} = \frac{3}{12}$. In a previous step, you found the product of $2 \times \frac{1}{3}$. What was that? $\frac{2}{3}$

11. **Say:** We can add $\frac{2}{3} + \frac{3}{12}$ to find the product of $2\frac{3}{4} \times \frac{1}{3}$.

    Ask: $\frac{2}{3}$ is equivalent to $\frac{8}{12}$. Substitute $\frac{8}{12}$ for $\frac{2}{3}$, and the number sentence becomes $\frac{8}{12} + \frac{3}{12} = \frac{11}{12}$. So what is the product of $2\frac{3}{4} \times \frac{1}{3}$? $\frac{11}{12}$

ONLINE 10min

LEARN Multiply Mixed Numbers with Area Models

Students will use a rectangular area model to multiply mixed numbers.

Objectives

- Use models and equations to multiply a whole number or a fraction by a fraction.

OFFLINE 10min

TRY IT Fraction Multiplication

Students will practice multiplying fractions and mixed numbers. Have students print or view the Fraction Multiplication activity page in their Activity Book and read the directions with them.

Printing the activity page is recommended so that students can use the given diagrams.

Objectives

- Use models and equations to multiply a whole number or a fraction by a fraction.

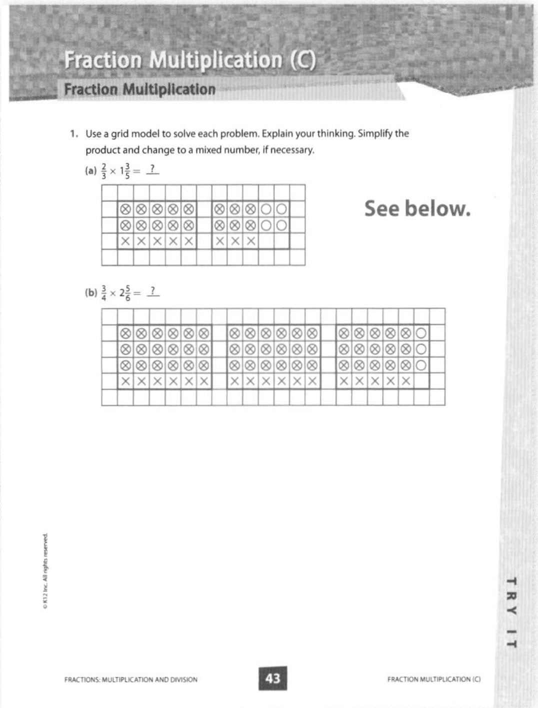

Fraction Multiplication (C)

Fraction Multiplication

1. Use a grid model to solve each problem. Explain your thinking. Simplify the product and change to a mixed number, if necessary.

(a) $\frac{2}{3} \times 1\frac{3}{5} = \underline{\ ?\ }$

See below.

(b) $\frac{3}{4} \times 2\frac{5}{6} = \underline{\ ?\ }$

© K12 Inc. All rights reserved.

TRY IT

FRACTIONS: MULTIPLICATION AND DIVISION 43 FRACTION MULTIPLICATION (C)

Additional Answers

1. **(a)** $\frac{2}{3} \times 1\frac{3}{5} = \frac{16}{15} = 1\frac{1}{15}$; **Possible explanation:** I marked 2 rows in each whole with Os to show $\frac{2}{3}$, and then I marked 1 whole and 3 additional columns with Xs to show $1\frac{3}{5}$. I saw that 16 squares had both markings. Since 1 whole has 15 squares, that's $\frac{16}{15}$, which I changed to a mixed number. So $\frac{2}{3} \times 1\frac{3}{5} = \frac{16}{15} = 1\frac{1}{15}$.

   (b) $\frac{3}{4} \times 2\frac{5}{6} = \frac{51}{24} = \frac{17}{8} = 2\frac{1}{8}$; **Possible explanation:** I marked 3 rows in each whole with Os to show $\frac{3}{4}$, and then I marked 2 wholes and 5 additional columns with Xs to show $2\frac{5}{6}$. I saw that 51 squares had both markings. Since 1 whole has 24 squares, that's $\frac{51}{24}$, which I simplified and wrote as a mixed number. So $\frac{3}{4} \times 2\frac{5}{6} = \frac{51}{24} = \frac{17}{8} = 2\frac{1}{8}$.

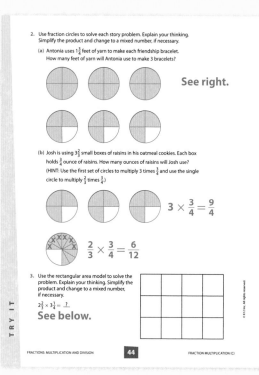

2. (a) $1\frac{3}{4} \times 3 = \frac{21}{4} = 5\frac{1}{4}$; Antonia will use $5\frac{1}{4}$ feet of yarn to make 3 bracelets. **Possible explanation:** I shaded $1\frac{3}{4}$ of the circles 3 times. I counted $\frac{21}{4}$ shaded. I changed $\frac{21}{4}$ to a mixed number, $5\frac{1}{4}$. Instead, I could have noticed that 3 wholes were shaded and mentally moved 2 of the shaded sections in the bottom right circle to make 2 more wholes in the circles to the left. Then I would have 5 whole circles and $\frac{1}{4}$ of another. So $1\frac{3}{4} \times 3 = \frac{21}{4} = 5\frac{1}{4}$.

(b) $3\frac{2}{3} \times \frac{3}{4} = \frac{9}{4} + \frac{6}{12} = \frac{9}{4} + \frac{2}{4} = \frac{11}{4} = 2\frac{3}{4}$; Josh will use $2\frac{3}{4}$ ounces of raisins in his cookies. **Possible explanation:** The distributive property says that $3\frac{2}{3} \times \frac{3}{4} = \left(3 + \frac{2}{3}\right) \times \frac{3}{4} = \left(3 \times \frac{3}{4}\right) + \left(\frac{2}{3} \times \frac{3}{4}\right)$. I broke the problem into two parts: $3 \times \frac{3}{4}$, which I could see is $\frac{9}{4}$, and $\frac{2}{3} \times \frac{3}{4}$, which I could see is $\frac{6}{12}$, or $\frac{2}{4}$. The sum of $\frac{9}{4}$ and $\frac{2}{4}$ is $\frac{11}{4}$, which equals $2\frac{3}{4}$. So $3\frac{2}{3} \times \frac{3}{4} = 2\frac{3}{4}$.

3.

1	1	1	$\frac{1}{4}$		
1	1	1	$\frac{1}{4}$		
$\frac{1}{3}$	$\frac{1}{3}$	$\frac{1}{3}$	$\frac{1}{12}$		
$\frac{1}{3}$	$\frac{1}{3}$	$\frac{1}{3}$	$\frac{1}{12}$		

$2\frac{2}{3} \times 3\frac{1}{4} = 6 + \frac{6}{3} + \frac{2}{4} + \frac{2}{12} = 6 + 2 + \frac{6}{12} + \frac{2}{12} = 8\frac{8}{12} = 8\frac{2}{3}$; **Possible explanation:** I divided the bottom row into thirds and the right column into fourths. I shaded a rectangle that measures $2\frac{2}{3} \times 3\frac{1}{4}$ and labeled all the partial products. I then found the simplified sum of the partial products to be $8\frac{2}{3}$. So $2\frac{2}{3} \times 3\frac{1}{4} = 8\frac{2}{3}$.

CHECKPOINT

OFFLINE 10 min

Objectives

The Checkpoint and its answer key are located in the Resources section for this Unit in the Online Book Menu of *Math+ Yellow Lesson Guide*. Open the Checkpoint. Give students the Checkpoint. Have students complete the Checkpoint on their own. Use the answer key to score the Checkpoint, and then enter the results online.

- Use models and equations to multiply a whole number or a fraction by a fraction.

Fraction Multiplication (D)

Lesson Overview

LEARN Connect to an Algorithm	10 minutes	**ONLINE**
LEARN Use the Algorithm	15 minutes	**OFFLINE**
LEARN Steps to Solutions	10 minutes	**ONLINE**
TRY IT More Fraction Multiplication	10 minutes	**OFFLINE**
CHECKPOINT	15 minutes	**ONLINE**

▶ Lesson Objectives

Use models and equations to multiply a whole number or a fraction by a fraction.

▶ Content Background

In this lesson, students will extend their knowledge of models of fraction multiplication to applying the standard algorithm.

When using the algorithm, students will learn to divide out common factors in the original problem. With mixed fractions, students will write the mixed number factors as improper fractions and then divide out common factors before multiplying. By dividing out common factors, students are simplifying the original problem and making the fractions simpler to multiply. Also, if they have in fact divided out all the common factors possible in the original problem, their answer will already be in lowest terms. If they miss some of the dividing out in the original problem, they will need to further simplify their answer. In some products, even though the answer is in lowest terms, students will need to convert an improper fraction to a mixed number to fully simplify their answer.

Although students will most often see fractions written with a horizontal fraction bar in math, such as $\frac{2}{3}$ or $5\frac{5}{6}$, they will occasionally see a diagonal fraction bar, such as 2/3 or 5 5/6. Students will very likely see the diagonal fraction bar in everyday experiences, but be sure they understand that using the horizontal fraction bar in their work will make problems involving fractions easier to interpret and solve.

Materials to Gather

SUPPLIED

More Fraction Multiplication activity page

ONLINE 10 min

LEARN Connect to an Algorithm

Students will see how the models they have learned connect to the standard algorithm for multiplying fractions.

Objectives

- Use models and equations to multiply a whole number or a fraction by a fraction.

LEARN Use the Algorithm

Students will use an algorithm to multiply two fractions that are each less than 1 and then two fractions that are each greater than 1. Students should write the problems and show their work in their Math Notebook.

- Use models and equations to multiply a whole number or a fraction by a fraction.

1. Have students write $\frac{1}{10} \times \frac{3}{7} = ?$

Say: To multiply fractions, we multiply the numerators and then we multiply the denominators. We then check to see if the answer needs to be simplified. Multiply the numerators.

Ask: What is 1×3? 3

Say: Multiply the denominators.

Ask: What is 10×7? 70

Ask: What is the product of $\frac{1}{10} \times \frac{3}{7}$? $\frac{3}{70}$

Ask: Can $\frac{3}{70}$ be simplified? Why? No. There is no common factor other than 1 that divides 3 and 70 evenly.

Have students write the product of the equation.

2. Have students write $\frac{8}{9} \times \frac{3}{4} = ?$ Guide students through this problem as you did in Step 1. When students write the product $\frac{24}{36}$, remind them that their answer must always be simplified. Students should divide a common factor of 12 from the numerator and denominator. $\frac{8}{9} \times \frac{3}{4}$ equals $\frac{2}{3}$.

Say: Before multiplying numerators and denominators, you can simplify any combination of one numerator and one denominator in the original problem by using a common factor. A common factor is a number that will divide both a numerator and a denominator evenly.

Say: Start with numerator 8 and denominator 4. A common factor of 8 and 4 is 4.

Ask: What is $8 \div 4$? 2

Say: Cross out 8 and write 2 next to it.

Ask: What is $4 \div 4$? 1

Say: Cross out 4 and write 1 next to it.

$$\frac{\overset{2}{\cancel{8}}}{9} \times \frac{3}{\underset{1}{\cancel{4}}}$$

Say: A common factor of 9 and 3 is 3.

Ask: What is $9 \div 3$? 3

Say: Cross out 9 and write 3 next to it.

Ask: What is $3 \div 3$? 1

Say: Cross out 3 and write 1 next to it.

$$\frac{\overset{2}{\cancel{8}}}{\underset{3}{\cancel{9}}} \times \frac{\overset{1}{\cancel{3}}}{\underset{1}{\cancel{4}}}$$

Say: After dividing out common factors, $\frac{8}{9} \times \frac{3}{4}$ can be rewritten as $\frac{2}{3} \times \frac{1}{1}$. Now multiply the numerators and then multiply the denominators.

Ask: What is 2×1? 2 What is 3×1? 3

Ask: What is the product of $\frac{2}{3} \times \frac{1}{1}$? $\frac{2}{3}$ So what is the product of $\frac{8}{9} \times \frac{3}{4}$? $\frac{2}{3}$

Have students write the product of the equation. Point out that the product is already simplified, and is the same as the product they calculated using the first method.

Say: Simplifying in the original problem makes multiplying easier, especially with more difficult factors.

3. Have students write $\frac{1}{10} \times \frac{5}{6} = ?$ Guide students through this problem as you did in Step 2. Students should answer that there are no common factors of 1 and 6 greater than 1. They should say that 5 is a common factor of 10 and 5. When students divide out the common factor of 5, the simplified problem is $\frac{1}{2} \times \frac{1}{6}$.

$$\frac{1}{\cancel{10}} \times \frac{\overset{1}{\cancel{5}}}{6}$$
$$2$$

Ask: What is the product of $\frac{1}{2} \times \frac{1}{6}$? $\frac{1}{12}$ So what is the product of $\frac{1}{10} \times \frac{5}{6}$? $\frac{1}{12}$

Remind students that even when they simplify before multiplying, it is best to double-check that the product cannot be simplified.

4. Have students write $3\frac{1}{8} \times 1\frac{7}{15} = ?$

Say: When we multiply mixed numbers, we must first change each mixed number to an improper fraction before we can find the product.

Ask: What is $3\frac{1}{8}$ written as an improper fraction? $\frac{25}{8}$

Ask: What is $1\frac{7}{15}$ written as an improper fraction? $\frac{22}{15}$

Say: Rewrite the problem using the improper fractions. $\frac{25}{8} \times \frac{22}{15} = ?$

Say: Now we can continue as we did before. Divide out common factors before you multiply.

Guide students through this problem as you did in Step 2. Students should answer that 5 is a common factor of 25 and 15 and that 2 is a common factor of 8 and 22.

Ask: After dividing out common factors, how can $\frac{25}{8} \times \frac{22}{15} = ?$ be rewritten? $\frac{5}{4} \times \frac{11}{3} = ?$

$$\frac{\overset{5}{\cancel{25}}}{\underset{4}{\cancel{8}}} \times \frac{\overset{11}{\cancel{22}}}{\underset{3}{\cancel{15}}} = ?$$

Multiply the numerators and then the denominators.

Ask: What is the product of $\frac{5}{4} \times \frac{11}{3}$? $\frac{55}{12}$

Say: Now let's write the product as a mixed number.

Ask: What is $\frac{7}{15}$ written as a mixed number? $4\frac{7}{12}$

Ask: Can $4\frac{7}{12}$ be simplified? No What is the product of $\frac{5}{4} \times \frac{11}{3}$? $4\frac{7}{12}$ So what is the product of $3\frac{1}{8} \times 1\frac{7}{15}$? $4\frac{7}{12}$

LEARN Steps to Solutions

Students will practice multiplying two fractions that are each less than 1 and they will practice multiplying mixed numbers.

- Use models and equations to multiply a whole number or a fraction by a fraction.

TRY IT More Fraction Multiplication

Students will practice multiplying fractions with the standard algorithm. View or print the More Fraction Multiplication activity page.

Students should copy the problems into their Math Notebook and solve them there.

- Use models and equations to multiply a whole number or a fraction by a fraction.

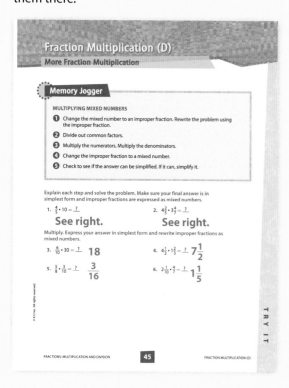

Additional Answers

1. **Example:** Multiply $\frac{4}{5} \cdot 10 = ?$

   - Change the whole number 10 to a fraction with a denominator of 1: $\frac{10}{1}$.

   - Rewrite the problem: $\frac{4}{5} \cdot \frac{10}{1} = ?$

   - Divide out the common factor 5.

   - Multiply the numerators.

   - Multiply the denominators.

   - Write the product: $\frac{4}{5} \cdot 10 = 8$.

   - Check: Can the answer be simplified? If so, simplify it. The answer is in simplest form.

   - The answer is 8.

2. **Example:** Multiply $4\frac{2}{5} \cdot 3\frac{4}{7} = ?$

   - Change the mixed numbers to improper fractions: $4\frac{2}{5} = \frac{22}{5}$ and $3\frac{4}{7} = \frac{25}{7}$.

   - Rewrite the problem: $\frac{22}{5} \cdot \frac{25}{7} = ?$

   - Divide out the common factor of 5.

   - Rewrite the problem: $\frac{22}{1} \cdot \frac{5}{7} = ?$

   - Multiply the numerators.

   - Multiply the denominators.

   - Write the product: $4\frac{2}{5} \cdot 3\frac{4}{7} = \frac{110}{7}$.

   - Check: Can the answer be simplified? If so, simplify it. $\frac{110}{7} = 15\frac{5}{7}$

   - The answer is $15\frac{5}{7}$.

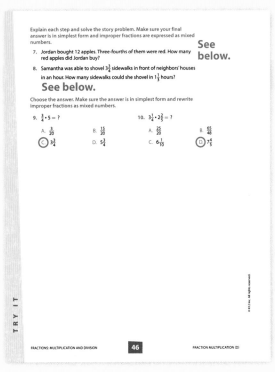

Explain each step and solve the story problem. Make sure your final answer is in simplest form and improper fractions are expressed as mixed numbers.

7. Jordan bought 12 apples. Three-fourths of them were red. How many red apples did Jordan buy? **See below.**

8. Samantha was able to shovel $3\frac{3}{4}$ sidewalks in front of neighbors' houses in an hour. How many sidewalks could she shovel in $1\frac{1}{3}$ hours?
See below.

Choose the answer. Make sure the answer is in simplest form and rewrite improper fractions as mixed numbers.

9. $\frac{3}{4} \cdot 5 = ?$
   A. $\frac{3}{20}$
   B. $\frac{15}{20}$
   (C.) $3\frac{3}{4}$
   D. $5\frac{3}{4}$

10. $3\frac{1}{4} \cdot 2\frac{2}{5} = ?$
   A. $\frac{25}{20}$
   B. $\frac{65}{48}$
   C. $6\frac{1}{10}$
   (D.) $7\frac{4}{5}$

TRY IT

7. **Example:** Multiply $\frac{3}{4} \cdot 12 = ?$ because $\frac{3}{4}$ of 12 apples were red.
   - Change the whole number 12 to a fraction with a denominator of 1: $\frac{12}{1}$.
   - Rewrite the problem: $\frac{3}{4} \cdot \frac{12}{1} = ?$
   - Divide out the common factor 4.
   - Multiply the numerators.
   - Multiply the denominators.
   - Write the product: $\frac{3}{4} \cdot 12 = 9$.
   - Check: Can the answer be simplified? If so, simplify it. The answer is in simplest form.
   - The answer is 9 apples.

8. **Example:** Multiply $3\frac{3}{4} \cdot 1\frac{1}{3} = ?$
   - Change the mixed numbers to improper fractions: $3\frac{3}{4} = \frac{15}{4}$ and $1\frac{1}{3} = \frac{4}{3}$.
   - Rewrite the problem: $\frac{15}{4} \cdot \frac{4}{3} = ?$
   - Divide out the common factor 4 and the common factor 3.
   - Rewrite the problem: $\frac{5}{1} \cdot \frac{1}{1} = ?$
   - Multiply the numerators.
   - Multiply the denominators.
   - Write the product: $3\frac{3}{4} \cdot 1\frac{1}{3} = 5$.
   - Check: Can the answer be simplified? If so, simplify it. The answer is in simplest form.
   - The answer is 5 sidewalks.

CHECKPOINT

ONLINE 15min

Students will complete an online Checkpoint. If necessary, read the directions, problems, and answer choices to students and help them with keyboard or mouse operations.

Objectives

- Use models and equations to multiply a whole number or a fraction by a fraction.

Multiplication as Scaling

Lesson Overview

LEARN Scaling Effects	20 minutes	**ONLINE**
LEARN Scaling Problems	20 minutes	**ONLINE**
TRY IT Solve Scaling Problems	20 minutes	**OFFLINE**

▶ Lesson Objectives

- Interpret multiplication as scaling.
- Compare the size of a product to the size of one factor on the basis of the size of the other factor, without multiplying.
- Explain why multiplying a given number by a fraction greater than 1 results in a product greater than the given number.
- Explain why multiplying a given number by a positive fraction less than 1 results in a product smaller than the given number.

▶ Content Background

In this lesson, students will interpret multiplication as scaling statements. A scaling effect refers to when a factor is enlarged or shrunk when it is multiplied by a positive factor greater than or less than 1.

When a factor is multiplied by a factor greater than 1, the product will be greater than the first factor. For example, $100 \times 2 = 200$. This is called an enlargement.

When a factor is multiplied by a positive fraction, or factor less than 1, the product will be less than the first factor. For example, $100 \times \frac{1}{2} = 50$. This is called shrinking.

When students interpret scaling effects, they will refer to products as "twice as large" or "half the size" of the greatest factor in the equation. For example, "200 is twice as large as 100," or "200 is double 100," and "50 is half the size of 100," or "50 is half as great as 100."

Students who understand scaling effects can compare products without multiplying the factors. Strategies for solving scaling problems involve comparing factors or drawing pictures. Students can solve scaling problems without drawing precise diagrams. Have students focus on the scale factor in each problem; that is, the amount by which a factor is increased or decreased. Students may also need reminders that improper fractions such as $\frac{8}{6}$ or $\frac{4}{3}$ are greater than 1 and will result in an enlargement.

Although students will most often see fractions written with a horizontal fraction bar in math, such as $\frac{2}{3}$ or $5\frac{5}{6}$, they will occasionally see a diagonal fraction bar, such as 2/3 or 5 5/6 . Students will very likely see the diagonal fraction bar in everyday experiences, but be sure they understand that using the horizontal fraction bar in their work will make problems involving fractions easier to interpret and solve.

Materials to Gather

SUPPLIED

Solve Scaling Problems activity page

LEARN Scaling Effects

Objectives

Students will compare a product with one of its factors by thinking of multiplication as enlarging or shrinking. They will interpret multiplication equations as scaling statements and explain the scaling effect of multiplying a given number by a positive fraction greater than 1 and by a positive fraction less than 1.

- Interpret multiplication as scaling.
- Compare the size of a product to the size of one factor on the basis of the size of the other factor, without multiplying.
- Explain why multiplying a given number by a fraction greater than 1 results in a product greater than the given number.
- Explain why multiplying a given number by a positive fraction less than 1 results in a product smaller than the given number.

LEARN Scaling Problems

Objectives

Students will explore real-world problems that involve comparing two or more products based on their factors. They will also compare products without multiplying.

- Interpret multiplication as scaling.
- Compare the size of a product to the size of one factor on the basis of the size of the other factor, without multiplying.
- Explain why multiplying a given number by a fraction greater than 1 results in a product greater than the given number.
- Explain why multiplying a given number by a positive fraction less than 1 results in a product smaller than the given number.

TRY IT Solve Scaling Problems

Objectives

Students will solve problems involving scaling effects in which a number is enlarged or shrunk based on whether it is multiplied by a factor greater than 1 or less than 1. View or print the Solve Scaling Problems activity page.

Students should copy the problems into their Math Notebook and solve them there.

- Interpret multiplication as scaling.
- Compare the size of a product to the size of one factor on the basis of the size of the other factor, without multiplying.
- Explain why multiplying a given number by a fraction greater than 1 results in a product greater than the given number.
- Explain why multiplying a given number by a positive fraction less than 1 results in a product smaller than the given number.

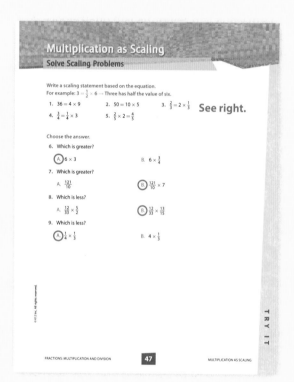

Additional Answers

1. 36 is 4 times as great as 9, or 36 is quadruple the size of 9.

2. 50 is 10 times as great as 5, or 50 is 10 times the size of 5.

3. $\frac{2}{3}$ is twice as great as $\frac{1}{3}$, or $\frac{2}{3}$ is double the size of $\frac{1}{3}$.

4. $\frac{3}{4}$ is one-fourth the size of 3, or $\frac{3}{4}$ is a quarter the size of 3.

5. $\frac{4}{5}$ is twice as great as $\frac{2}{5}$, or $\frac{4}{5}$ is double the size of $\frac{2}{5}$.

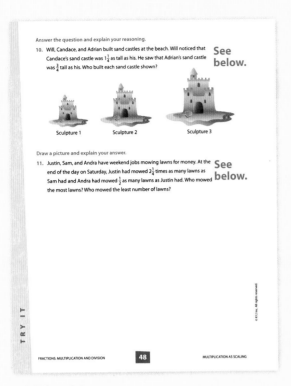

Additional Answers

10. Since Candace's sand castle is $1\frac{1}{4}$ times as tall as Will's her sculpture must be taller than Will's, since it is scaled by a factor greater than 1. Since Adrian's sand castle is $\frac{3}{4}$ as tall as Will's, Adrian's must be shorter than Will's since it is scaled by a factor less than 1. Candace's sand castle is taller than Will's and Adrian's is shorter. Adrian built Sculpture 1, Will built Sculpture 2, and Candace built Sculpture 3.

11. Sam's lawns

Justin's lawns

Andra's lawns

You can compare Andra's and Justin's mowed lawns to Sam's. Draw a picture to represent that Sam mowed "a number of lawns." To represent Justin's mowed lawns, draw another picture that is $2\frac{1}{4}$ times the size of Sam's mowed lawns. Justin's picture should be double the size of Sam's with $\frac{1}{4}$ extra. To represent Andra's mowed lawns, draw a picture that is $\frac{1}{2}$ the size of Justin's mowed lawns. Compare the pictures. Justin mowed the most lawns. Sam mowed the least number of lawns.

Fractions as Division Problems

Lesson Overview

LEARN Fractions as Division	10 minutes	ONLINE
LEARN Match Stories and Fractions	10 minutes	ONLINE
LEARN Fraction Quotients on the Number Line	15 minutes	ONLINE
TRY IT Division Problems with Fractions	15 minutes	OFFLINE
CHECKPOINT	10 minutes	ONLINE

▶ Lesson Objectives

- Explain and give examples of different interpretations of fractions.
- Divide whole numbers by unit fractions and unit fractions by whole numbers.

▶ Content Background

Students will continue to extend their knowledge of fractions, including improper fractions and mixed numbers beyond thinking of them as part of a whole, part of a set, and location on a number line to realizing that fractions can also represent division problems.

Fractions can represent equal sharing, or division. For example, if 2 people are sharing 3 granola bars equally, the fraction $\frac{3}{2}$ describes how much each person will receive. The fraction $\frac{3}{2}$ can be read *three-halves* or *3 divided by 2*. So $\frac{3}{2} = 1\frac{1}{2}$ and $3 \div 2 = 1\frac{1}{2}$.

▶ Common Errors and Misconceptions

- Students might not understand the difference between fractions and whole numbers. Fractions are parts of whole numbers. Examples of fractions include $\frac{4}{5}$, $\frac{7}{100}$, and $2\frac{1}{2}$. Examples of whole numbers include 4, 6, and 10. Whole numbers may be written as fractions, but always with a denominator of 1, such as $\frac{4}{1}$, $\frac{6}{1}$, or $\frac{10}{1}$.

- Students might have difficulty understanding how different models represent fractions because they often see fractions represented as parts of circles, such as pie and pizza illustrations. They might not recognize, for example, that the following models all represent the fraction $\frac{3}{5}$.

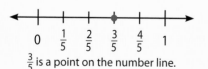

$\frac{3}{5}$ is a point on the number line.

$\frac{3}{5}$ of the shapes are triangles.

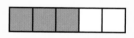

$\frac{3}{5}$ of the rectangle is shaded.

Materials to Gather

SUPPLIED

Division Problems with Fractions activity page

- Students might think that a fraction compares one part to another part, rather than recognizing that a fraction compares one part or several parts to the whole.
- Students might think that a fraction always represents the size of a part of a whole, number of items in a set, or a location on the number line, and so might not understand that a fraction can also represent a relationship, such as a quotient or a ratio of one quantity to another.

ONLINE
10min

LEARN Fractions as Division

By using models to represent fractions in division story problems, students will learn that fractions can represent a quotient.

Objectives
- Explain and give examples of different interpretations of fractions.

ONLINE
10min

LEARN Match Stories and Fractions

Students will match a fraction with the story problem that it solves.

Objectives
- Explain and give examples of different interpretations of fractions.

ONLINE
15min

LEARN Fraction Quotients on the Number Line

Students will solve fractions-as-division story problems and locate the quotients on a number line.

Objectives
- Explain and give examples of different interpretations of fractions.

OFFLINE
15min

TRY IT Division Problems with Fractions

Students will practice using fractions to solve problems involving equal sharing. Have students turn to the Division Problems with Fractions activity page in their Activity Book and read the directions with them.

Students should copy the problems from the Activity Book into their Math Notebook as necessary and solve them there.

Objectives
- Explain and give examples of different interpretations of fractions.
- Divide whole numbers by unit fractions and unit fractions by whole numbers.

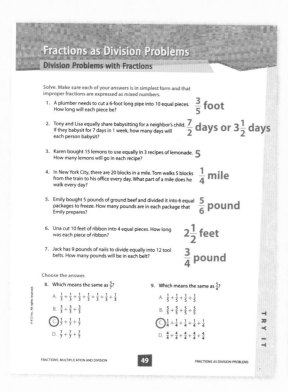

Fractions as Division Problems
Division Problems with Fractions

Solve. Make sure each of your answers is in simplest form and that improper fractions are expressed as mixed numbers.

1. A plumber needs to cut a 6-foot long pipe into 10 equal pieces. How long will each piece be? — $\frac{3}{5}$ foot

2. Tony and Lisa equally share babysitting for a neighbor's child. If they babysit for 7 days in 1 week, how many days will each person babysit? — $\frac{7}{2}$ days or $3\frac{1}{2}$ days

3. Karen bought 15 lemons to use equally in 3 recipes of lemonade. How many lemons will go in each recipe? — 5

4. In New York City, there are 20 blocks in a mile. Tom walks 5 blocks from the train to his office every day. What part of a mile does he walk every day? — $\frac{1}{4}$ mile

5. Emily bought 5 pounds of ground beef and divided it into 6 equal packages to freeze. How many pounds are in each package that Emily prepares? — $\frac{5}{6}$ pound

6. Una cut 10 feet of ribbon into 4 equal pieces. How long was each piece of ribbon? — $2\frac{1}{2}$ feet

7. Jack has 9 pounds of nails to divide equally into 12 tool belts. How many pounds will be in each belt? — $\frac{3}{4}$ pound

Choose the answer.

8. Which means the same as $\frac{3}{7}$?
   A. $\frac{1}{3}+\frac{1}{3}+\frac{1}{3}+\frac{1}{3}+\frac{1}{3}+\frac{1}{3}+\frac{1}{3}$
   B. $\frac{3}{3}+\frac{3}{3}+\frac{3}{3}$
   C. $\frac{1}{7}+\frac{1}{7}+\frac{1}{7}$ (circled)
   D. $\frac{7}{7}+\frac{7}{7}+\frac{7}{7}$

9. Which means the same as $\frac{5}{4}$?
   A. $\frac{1}{5}+\frac{1}{5}+\frac{1}{5}+\frac{1}{5}+\frac{1}{5}$
   B. $\frac{5}{5}+\frac{5}{5}+\frac{5}{5}+\frac{5}{5}$
   C. $\frac{1}{4}+\frac{1}{4}+\frac{1}{4}+\frac{1}{4}+\frac{1}{4}$ (circled)
   D. $\frac{4}{4}+\frac{4}{4}+\frac{4}{4}+\frac{4}{4}+\frac{4}{4}$

TRY IT

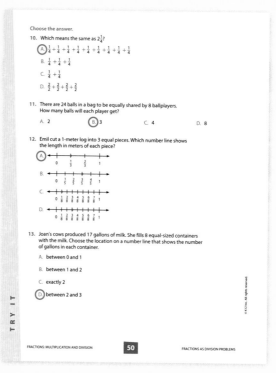

Choose the answer.

10. Which means the same as $2\frac{1}{4}$?
    A. $\frac{1}{4}+\frac{1}{4}+\frac{1}{4}+\frac{1}{4}+\frac{1}{4}+\frac{1}{4}+\frac{1}{4}+\frac{1}{4}+\frac{1}{4}$ (circled)
    B. $\frac{1}{4}+\frac{1}{4}+\frac{1}{4}$
    C. $\frac{1}{4}+\frac{1}{4}$
    D. $\frac{2}{4}+\frac{2}{4}+\frac{2}{4}+\frac{2}{4}$

11. There are 24 balls in a bag to be equally shared by 8 ballplayers. How many balls will each player get?
    A. 2   B. 3 (circled)   C. 4   D. 8

12. Emil cut a 1-meter log into 3 equal pieces. Which number line shows the length in meters of each piece?
    A. (circled)
    B.
    C.
    D.

13. Joan's cows produced 17 gallons of milk. She fills 8 equal-sized containers with the milk. Choose the location on a number line that shows the number of gallons in each container.
    A. between 0 and 1
    B. between 1 and 2
    C. exactly 2
    D. between 2 and 3 (circled)

TRY IT

CHECKPOINT

ONLINE 10 min

Students will complete an online Checkpoint. If necessary, read the directions, problems, and answer choices to students and help them with keyboard or mouse operations.

Objectives

- Explain and give examples of different interpretations of fractions.
- Divide whole numbers by unit fractions and unit fractions by whole numbers.

Fraction Division (A)

Lesson Overview

LEARN Whole Number by Unit Fraction Division	20 minutes	ONLINE
LEARN Area Models	25 minutes	ONLINE
TRY IT Fraction Division with Models	15 minutes	ONLINE

▶ Lesson Objectives

Divide whole numbers by unit fractions and unit fractions by whole numbers.

▶ Content Background

In this lesson, students will learn to understand division of fractions by studying examples of whole numbers divided by unit fractions. Students will use online models, such as number lines and fraction strips, as well as area models with pattern blocks and rectangles.

Although the traditional algorithm of changing fraction division problems to multiplication by the reciprocal certainly works, the rule gives students answers that they often do not understand. They struggle to know if their answers make sense. By modeling several problems, students begin to get an intuitive sense about the correctness of their answers. Encourage students to understand the models before moving directly into the algorithm.

Although students will most often see fractions written with a horizontal fraction bar in math, such as $\frac{2}{3}$ or $5\frac{5}{6}$, they will occasionally see a diagonal fraction bar, such as 2/3 or 5 5/6. Students will very likely see the diagonal fraction bar in everyday experiences, but be sure they understand that using the horizontal fraction bar in their work will make problems involving fractions easier to interpret and solve.

▶ Common Errors and Misconceptions

Students might have difficulty understanding that numbers can look different but still represent the same amount. For example, students might find it difficult to understand that although the numbers $\frac{1}{2}$, $\frac{3}{6}$, and $\frac{5}{10}$ look different, they are all equivalent, or represent the same part of a whole, part of a set, location on the number line, quotient, or ratio.

Materials to Gather

There are no materials to gather for this lesson.

LEARN Whole Number by Unit Fraction Division

ONLINE 20min

Students will extend their understanding of division to fraction division. They will use online models to divide whole numbers by unit fractions.

Objectives

- Divide whole numbers by unit fractions and unit fractions by whole numbers.

LEARN Area Models

ONLINE 25min

Students will investigate area models to better understand division of whole numbers by unit fractions.

Objectives

- Divide whole numbers by unit fractions and unit fractions by whole numbers.

TRY IT Fraction Division with Models

ONLINE 15min

Students will complete an online Try It. If necessary, read the directions, problems, and answer choices to students and help them with keyboard or mouse operations.

Objectives

- Divide whole numbers by unit fractions and unit fractions by whole numbers.

Fraction Division (B)

Lesson Overview

GET READY A Fraction Multiplication Story	5 minutes	**ONLINE**
LEARN Unit Fraction by Whole Number Division	20 minutes	**ONLINE**
LEARN Division as the Inverse of Multiplication	15 minutes	**ONLINE**
TRY IT Divide Fractions	10 minutes	**ONLINE**
CHECKPOINT	10 minutes	**ONLINE**

▶ ## Lesson Objectives

- Represent division of a unit fraction by a whole number such as $\frac{1}{3} \div 7$ using objects and pictorial models, including area models.
- Divide whole numbers by unit fractions and unit fractions by whole numbers.

▶ ## Prerequisite Skills

Multiply a fraction by a whole number to solve a story problem.

▶ ## Content Background

Students will learn how to model fraction division of a fraction by a whole number.

The division of fractions has often been taught as a rote manipulation of numbers. As a result, it is one of the mathematical concepts that is easily forgotten, even by adults. For this reason, it is very important to provide students with a variety of ways to visualize how a number can be divided by a fraction and to delay the introduction of specific steps for dividing fractions until students can observe and understand the underlying concepts. Students usually know $12 \div 4$ as, "How many 4s are in 12," or "What is 12 shared 4 ways?" But they do not as easily view $\frac{1}{3} \div 4$ as, "What fraction of 4 is in $\frac{1}{3}$," or "What is $\frac{1}{3}$ shared 4 ways?" It is important for students to gain this understanding before they learn division algorithms, or step-by-step procedures.

▶ ## Common Errors and Misconceptions

- Students might quickly read through a problem and immediately begin to compute with the numbers, often choosing the wrong operation because they did not take time to read through and understand the context of the problem. Students need to learn to use "slow-down" mechanisms that can help them concentrate on thoroughly understanding a problem before they solve it.
- Students might not see the relationship between the models (such as fraction strips and number lines) and the procedures for dividing fractions. Once they begin to use symbols without models, students might apply memorized rules without thinking about the reasons for the procedures.

▶ ## Advance Preparation

Print the Centimeter Grid Paper and the Whole to Twelfths Number Lines.

Materials to Gather

SUPPLIED

Centimeter Grid Paper (printout)

Whole to Twelfths Number Lines (printout)

GET READY A Fraction Multiplication Story

Objectives

Students will review fraction multiplication by solving a story problem involving the multiplication of a whole number by a unit fraction.

- Multiply a fraction by a whole number to solve a story problem.

LEARN Unit Fraction by Whole Number Division

Objectives

Students will investigate models of division of a unit fraction by a whole number. Gather the Centimeter Grid Paper and Whole to Twelfths Number Lines.

- Divide whole numbers by unit fractions and unit fractions by whole numbers.
- Represent division of a unit fraction by a whole number such as $\frac{1}{3} \div 7$ using objects and pictorial models, including area models.

LEARN Division as the Inverse of Multiplication

Objectives

Students will investigate division of a unit fraction by a whole number in the context of a division problem as the inverse of the related multiplication problem.

- Represent division of a unit fraction by a whole number such as $\frac{1}{3} \div 7$ using objects and pictorial models, including area models.

TRY IT Divide Fractions

Objectives

Students will complete an online Try It. If necessary, read the directions, problems, and answer choices to students and help them with keyboard or mouse operations.

- Represent division of a unit fraction by a whole number such as $\frac{1}{3} \div 7$ using objects and pictorial models, including area models.

Tips

Have students use sketches to help them solve each problem.

Students will complete an online Checkpoint. If necessary, read the directions, problems, and answer choices to students and help them with keyboard or mouse operations.

Objectives

- Represent division of a unit fraction by a whole number such as $\frac{1}{3} \div 7$ using objects and pictorial models, including area models.

- Divide whole numbers by unit fractions and unit fractions by whole numbers.

Fraction Division (C)

Lesson Overview

LEARN Fraction Division Stories	20 minutes	ONLINE
LEARN Write a Fraction Division Story	20 minutes	ONLINE
TRY IT Fraction Division Problems	10 minutes	ONLINE
CHECKPOINT	10 minutes	ONLINE

▶ Lesson Objectives

Divide whole numbers by unit fractions and unit fractions by whole numbers.

Materials to Gather

There are no materials to gather for this lesson.

▶ Content Background

Students will apply their knowledge of fraction division with a whole number and unit fraction to solving and writing story problems.

The division of fractions has often been taught as a rote manipulation of numbers. As a result, it is one of the mathematical concepts that is easily forgotten, even by adults. For this reason, it is important to provide students with a variety of ways to visualize how a number can be divided by a fraction and to delay the introduction of specific steps for dividing fractions until students can observe and understand the underlying concepts. Students usually know $12 \div 4$ as, "How many 4s are in 12?" But they do not as easily view $12 \div \frac{1}{3}$ as, "How many thirds are in 12?" It is important for students to gain this understanding before they learn division algorithms, or step-by-step procedures.

▶ Common Errors and Misconceptions

- Students might quickly read through a problem and immediately begin to compute with the numbers, often choosing the wrong operation because they did not take time to read through and understand the context of the problem. Students need to learn to use "slow-down" mechanisms that can help them concentrate on thoroughly understanding a problem before they solve it.

- Students might not see the relationship between the models (such as fraction strips and number lines) and the procedures for dividing fractions. Once they begin to use symbols without models, students might apply memorized rules without thinking about the reasons for the procedures.

LEARN Fraction Division Stories

Objectives

Students will use models to solve story problems in which they will divide whole numbers by unit fractions and unit fractions by whole numbers.

- Divide whole numbers by unit fractions and unit fractions by whole numbers.

LEARN Write a Fraction Division Story

ONLINE 20min

Objectives

Students will apply their knowledge and skills of fraction divsion of whole numbers and unit fractions to create their own story problems.

- Divide whole numbers by unit fractions and unit fractions by whole numbers.

TRY IT Fraction Division Problems

ONLINE 10min

Objectives

Students will complete an online Try It. If necessary, read the directions, problems, and answer choices to students and help them with keyboard or mouse operations.

- Divide whole numbers by unit fractions and unit fractions by whole numbers.

Tips Allow students to use sketches, fraction strips, number lines, or any model they choose to help them solve the problems.

CHECKPOINT

ONLINE 10min

Objectives

Students will complete an online Checkpoint. If necessary, read the directions, problems, and answer choices to students and help them with keyboard or mouse operations.

- Divide whole numbers by unit fractions and unit fractions by whole numbers.

Core Focus
Multiplication Stories

Lesson Overview

GET READY Fraction Multiplication Steps	5 minutes	ONLINE
LEARN Use a Step-by-Step Approach	15 minutes	OFFLINE
LEARN Write a Fraction Multiplication Story	15 minutes	ONLINE
TRY IT Stories with Fraction Multiplication	15 minutes	OFFLINE
CHECKPOINT	10 minutes	OFFLINE

▶ Lesson Objectives

- Use models and equations to multiply a whole number or a fraction by a fraction.
- Solve real-world problems involving multiplication of fractions and mixed numbers.

▶ Content Background

Students will apply their knowledge of fraction multiplication to solve and write story problems.

Materials to Gather

SUPPLIED

Stories with Fraction Multiplication activity page

Checkpoint (printout)

Checkpoint Answer Key (printout)

GET READY Fraction Multiplication Steps

ONLINE 5min

Students will review the steps to solving fraction multiplication computation problems.

Objectives

- Use models and equations to multiply a whole number or a fraction by a fraction.

LEARN Use a Step-by-Step Approach

OFFLINE 15min

Students will use algorithms to multiply fractions by various types of numbers. They will multiply a fraction by a fraction, a fraction by a whole number, a fraction by a mixed number, and mixed numbers by mixed numbers. Students should write the problems in their Math Notebook.

Objectives

- Use models and equations to multiply a whole number or a fraction by a fraction.

MULTIPLY FRACTION BY FRACTION

1. Read the following problem to students:
   - Inez has a stamp collection. Of the stamps she has, $\frac{3}{8}$ are from the United States. In her collection, $\frac{4}{5}$ of the stamps from the United States are from California. What part of Inez's stamp collection is from California?

Tips

Describing the steps needed to solve multiplication problems involving whole numbers, fractions, and mixed numbers helps students improve their computation skills.

2. Tell students that they need to find $\frac{4}{5}$ of $\frac{3}{8}$, or $\frac{4}{5} \times \frac{3}{8}$ to solve this problem. Have students use the multiplication dot to write the number sentence that solves the problem: $\frac{4}{5} \cdot \frac{3}{8} = ?$ Have students describe the steps they take as they find the product. Check that students say they need to divide out common factors and rewrite the number sentence if needed, multiply numerators, multiply denominators, write the product, and check to see that the answer is in simplest form and simplify if needed.

3. **Ask:** What is the product of $\frac{4}{5} \cdot \frac{3}{8} = ?$ in simplest form? $\frac{3}{10}$

   Ask: What part of Inez's stamp collection is from California? $\frac{3}{10}$

MULTIPLY FRACTION BY WHOLE NUMBER

4. Read the following problem to students:

   - Jason's dog eats $\frac{2}{3}$ pound of dog food each day. How many pounds of dog food does Jason's dog eat in 3 days?

5. **Say:** Use an algorithm to multiply $3 \cdot \frac{2}{3} = ?$

6. **Ask:** What is 3 in fraction form? $\frac{3}{1}$

7. Have students use the multiplication dot to write the number sentence that solves the problem: $3 \cdot \frac{2}{3} = ?$ Have students describe the steps they take as they find the product. Check that students say they need to rewrite the problem with the fraction form of 3, divide out common factors, multiply numerators, multiply denominators, write the product, and check to see that the answer is in simplest form and simplify if needed.

8. **Ask:** What is the product of $3 \cdot \frac{2}{3} = ?$ in simplest form? 2

   Ask: What is the answer to the problem? Jason's dog eats 2 pounds of dog food in 3 days.

9. Have students use an algorithm to solve the next three problems. Tell them to use either the multiplication symbol or the multiplication dot in their number sentences.

MULTIPLY FRACTION BY MIXED NUMBER

10. Tell students to write $\frac{5}{7} \times 2\frac{4}{5} = ?$

11. **Ask:** When you solve a problem where you multiply with a mixed number, what do you do first? Write the mixed number as an improper fraction.

12. **Ask:** What is $2\frac{4}{5}$ as an improper fraction? $\frac{14}{5}$

13. Have students rewrite the problem, replacing the mixed number with the fraction. $\frac{5}{7} \times \frac{14}{5} = ?$

14. **Ask:** Can you divide out any common factors before you multiply $\frac{5}{7} \times \frac{14}{5} = ?$

    Explain. Yes. You can divide 5 in the numerator and 5 in the denominator by a common factor of 5. You can also divide 7 in the denominator and 14 in the numerator by a common factor of 7.

15. **Ask:** What is the number sentence after you divide out the common factors?
$\frac{1}{1} \times \frac{2}{1} = ?$

16. **Ask:** What is the product of $\frac{5}{7} \times 2\frac{4}{5} = ?$ 2

MULTIPLY MIXED NUMBER BY MIXED NUMBER

17. Tell students to write $1\frac{2}{9} \times 2\frac{4}{7} = ?$

18. Have them change $1\frac{2}{9}$ and $2\frac{4}{7}$ to improper fractions and write the new number sentence. $1\frac{2}{9} = \frac{11}{9}$; $2\frac{4}{7} = \frac{18}{7}$; The new number sentence is $\frac{11}{9} \times \frac{18}{7} = ?$

19. **Ask:** What is the next step before multiplying? Divide out common factors.

20. Have students divide out a common factor of 9 in 9 and 18. $\frac{11}{1} \times \frac{2}{7} = ?$

21. **Say:** Find the product of $\frac{11}{1} \times \frac{2}{7} = ?$ and write the answer as a mixed number. Describe the steps you follow. Multiply the numerators. Then multiply the denominators. The product is $\frac{22}{7}$. Divide the product of the numerators by the product of the denominators. Write the quotient as a whole number and a fraction with the remainder as the numerator and 7 as the denominator. $1\frac{2}{9} \times 2\frac{4}{7} = 3\frac{1}{7}$

22. Tell students to write $3\frac{3}{5} \times 4\frac{1}{6} = ?$

23. Have students find the product. They will follow these steps:
    - Change each factor from a mixed number to an improper fraction.
    - Divide out common factors.
    - Multiply the numerators and multiply the denominators.
    - Check to see that the answer is in simplest form. Simplify if needed.

    Check that students found that the product of $3\frac{3}{5} \times 4\frac{1}{6} = 15$.

LEARN Write a Fraction Multiplication Story

ONLINE
15 min

Objectives

Students will use their knowledge of fraction multiplication to create story problems from a given equation and model.

- Solve real-world problems involving multiplication of fractions and mixed numbers.

TRY IT Stories with Fraction Multiplication

Objectives

- Solve real-world problems involving multiplication of fractions and mixed numbers.

Students will practice solving and creating story problems that involve fraction multiplication. View or print the Stories with Fraction Multiplication activity page. Students should copy the problems into their Math Notebook and solve them there.

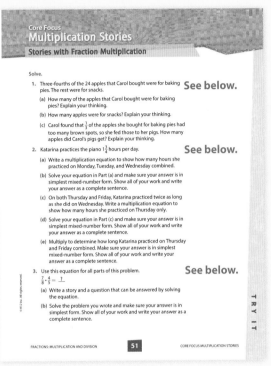

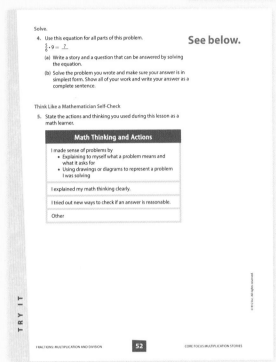

Additional Answers

1. **(a)** Carol bought 18 apples for baking pies. **Possible explanation:** Since $\frac{3}{4}$ of the apples were for baking, that's $\frac{3}{4}$ of all 24 apples: $\frac{3}{4} \times 24 = 18$.

   (b) Carol bought 6 apples for snacks. **Possible explanation:** Since 18 of the 24 apples were for baking, I subtracted 18 from 24 to find that she had 6 apples for snacks. I also could have taken $\frac{1}{4}$ of 24: $\frac{1}{4} \times 24 = 6$.

   (c) The pigs got 6 apples. **Possible explanation:** Since Carol had 18 apples for baking pies and $\frac{1}{3}$ were bad, I took $\frac{1}{3}$ of 18 to see how many the pigs got: $\frac{1}{3} \times 18 = 6$.

3. **(a) Possible problem:** Louise packaged $\frac{4}{5}$ of the muffins she baked. Seven-eighths of those muffins were blueberry and the rest of the batch were raspberry. What fraction of all the muffins were blueberry?

   (b) $\frac{7}{8} \cdot \frac{4}{5} = \frac{7}{2} \cdot \frac{1}{5} = \frac{7}{10}$; **Sample sentence:** Seven-tenths of the muffins were blueberry muffins.

2. **(a)** $1\frac{3}{4} \times 3 = ?$

   (b) $1\frac{3}{4} \times 3 = \frac{7}{4} \times \frac{3}{1} = \frac{21}{4} = 5\frac{1}{4}$; Katarina practiced a total of $5\frac{1}{4}$ hours Monday, Tuesday, and Wednesday.

   (c) $1\frac{3}{4} \times 2 = ?$

   (d) $1\frac{3}{4} \times 2 = \frac{7}{4} \times \frac{2}{1} = \frac{14}{4} = 3\frac{2}{4} = 3\frac{1}{2}$; Katarina practiced $3\frac{1}{2}$ hours on Thursday.

   (e) $3\frac{1}{2} \times 2 = \frac{7}{2} \times \frac{2}{1} = \frac{7}{1} = 7$; Katarina practiced 7 hours on Thursday and Friday combined.

4. **(a) Possible problem:** Andreas ran 9 kilometers without stopping. During $\frac{5}{6}$ of his run, he listened to music. For how many kilometers did Andreas listen to music?

   (b) $\frac{5}{6} \cdot 9 = \frac{5}{6} \cdot \frac{9}{1} = \frac{5}{2} \cdot \frac{3}{1} = \frac{15}{2} = 7\frac{1}{2}$; **Sample sentence:** Andreas listened to music for $7\frac{1}{2}$ kilometers of his run.

OFFLINE
10 min

The Checkpoint and its answer key are located in the Resources section for this unit in the Online Book Menu of *Math+ Yellow Lesson Guide*. Give students the Checkpoint. Have students complete the Checkpoint on their own. Use the answer key to score the Checkpoint, and then enter the results online.

- Use models and equations to multiply a whole number or a fraction by a fraction.

Unit Review

UNIT REVIEW Look Back	10 minutes	**ONLINE**
UNIT REVIEW Checkpoint Practice	50 minutes	**ONLINE**
▶ **UNIT REVIEW** Prepare for the Checkpoint		

▶ Unit Objectives

This lesson reviews the following objectives:

- Use models and equations to multiply a whole number or a fraction by a fraction.
- Interpret multiplication as scaling.
- Compare the size of a product to the size of one factor on the basis of the size of the other factor, without multiplying.
- Explain why multiplying a given number by a fraction greater than 1 results in a product greater than the given number.
- Explain why multiplying a given number by a positive fraction less than 1 results in a product smaller than the given number.
- Explain and give examples of different interpretations of fractions.
- Divide whole numbers by unit fractions and unit fractions by whole numbers.
- Represent division of a unit fraction by a whole number such as $\frac{1}{3} \div 7$ using objects and pictorial models, including area models.
- Solve real-world problems involving multiplication of fractions and mixed numbers.

▶ Advance Preparation

In this lesson, students will have an opportunity to review previous activities in the Fractions: Multiplication and Division unit. Look at the suggested activities in Unit Review: Prepare for the Checkpoint online and gather any needed materials.

Materials to Gather

There are no materials to gather for this lesson.

ONLINE

UNIT REVIEW Look Back   **10**min

Objectives

- Review unit objectives.

Students will review key concepts from the unit to prepare for the Unit Checkpoint.

UNIT REVIEW Checkpoint Practice

ONLINE 50min

Objectives

- Review unit objectives.

Students will complete an online Checkpoint Practice to prepare for the Unit Checkpoint. If necessary, read the directions, problems, and answer choices to students. Have students answer the problems on their own. Review any missed problems with students.

➔ UNIT REVIEW Prepare for the Checkpoint

What you do next depends on how students performed in the previous activity, Unit Review: Checkpoint Practice. If students had difficulty with any of the problems, complete the appropriate review activity listed in the table online.

Unit Checkpoint

UNIT CHECKPOINT Online ⋯⋯⋯⋯⋯⋯⋯⋯ 60 minutes ⋮ **ONLINE**

▶ Unit Objectives

- Use models and equations to multiply a whole number or a fraction by a fraction.
- Interpret multiplication as scaling.
- Compare the size of a product to the size of one factor on the basis of the size of the other factor, without multiplying.
- Explain why multiplying a given number by a fraction greater than 1 results in a product greater than the given number.
- Explain why multiplying a given number by a positive fraction less than 1 results in a product smaller than the given number.
- Explain and give examples of different interpretations of fractions.
- Divide whole numbers by unit fractions and unit fractions by whole numbers.
- Represent division of a unit fraction by a whole number such as $\frac{1}{3} \div 7$ using objects and pictorial models, including area models.
- Solve real-world problems involving multiplication of fractions and mixed numbers.

Materials to Gather

There are no materials to gather for this lesson.

ONLINE
60min

UNIT CHECKPOINT Online

Objectives

- Assess unit objectives.

Students will complete an online Checkpoint. If necessary, read the directions, problems, and answer choices to students and help them with keyboard or mouse operations.

Extended Problems: Reasoning

USE WHAT YOU KNOW Offline	60 minutes	OFFLINE

▶ Lesson Objectives

This lesson assesses the following objectives:

- Analyze complex problems using mathematical knowledge and skills.
- Compare the size of a product to the size of one factor on the basis of the size of the other factor, without multiplying.
- Use models and equations to multiply a whole number or a fraction by a fraction.
- Solve real-world problems involving multiplication of fractions and mixed numbers.
- Divide whole numbers by unit fractions and unit fractions by whole numbers.
- Explain how multiplying two fractions or multiplying a fraction and a whole number affects the size of the product.

Materials to Gather

SUPPLIED

Extended Problems: Reasoning (printout)

Extended Problems: Reasoning Answer Key (printout)

OFFLINE
60 min

USE WHAT YOU KNOW Offline

The Extended Problems: Reasoning and its answer key are located in the Resources section for this unit in the Online Book Menu of *Math+ Yellow Lesson Guide*. Give students the Extended Problems: Reasoning. Read the directions, problems, and answer choices to students, if necessary.

You will grade this assignment.

- Students should complete the assignment on their own.
- Students should submit the completed assignment to you.

Objectives

- Analyze complex problems using mathematical knowledge and skills.

Problems Involving Fractions

▶ Unit Objectives

- Solve real-world problems involving multiplication of fractions and mixed numbers.

- Solve a simple problem involving addition or subtraction of fractions.

▶ Big Ideas

Fractions can be added, subtracted, multiplied, and divided.

▶ Unit Introduction

In this unit, students will use what they know about multiplication of fractions and mixed numbers to solve story problems. They will learn how to decide what operation would be used to solve a fraction or mixed number story problem. They also will learn how to write number sentences to set up the solution to a fraction or mixed number problem. Students will learn how to add and subtract mixed numbers and fractions with like and unlike denominators.

▶ Keywords

common factor
denominator
divide out a common factor
factor
fraction
greatest common factor (GCF)

least common denominator (LCD)
least common multiple (LCM)
like denominators
mixed number

numerator
reciprocal
regrouping
remainder
unlike denominators

Fraction Multiplication Story Problems (A)

Lesson Overview

GET READY Review Multiplying Fractions	10 minutes	ONLINE
LEARN Understand Multiplication Story Problems	20 minutes	OFFLINE
LEARN Solve Story Problems	20 minutes	OFFLINE
TRY IT Practice Solving Story Problems	10 minutes	OFFLINE

▶ Lesson Objectives

Solve real-world problems involving multiplication of fractions and mixed numbers.

▶ Prerequisite Skills

Multiply fractions and explain a step-by-step approach.

▶ Content Background

MULTIPLY A FRACTION BY A FRACTION

After students use models to multiply a fraction by a fraction, they will use a step-by-step approach. The steps of the traditional approach are as follows: First divide out common factors before multiplying. Then express the answer in its simplest form.

MULTIPLY A FRACTION BY A MIXED NUMBER

After students use models to multiply a fraction by a mixed number, they will use a step-by-step approach. The steps of the traditional approach are as follows: First change mixed numbers into improper fractions. Then divide out common factors before multiplying. Next express the answer in its simplest form by dividing the numerator by the denominator. If the answer is an improper fraction, the quotient is the whole-number part of the mixed number. The remainder is the numerator of the fractional part, and the divisor is the denominator of the fractional part.

MULTIPLY A MIXED NUMBER BY A MIXED NUMBER

Once students have worked with models that show how to multiply a mixed number by a mixed number, they will use a step-by-step approach. To find the product of two mixed numbers, the steps of the traditional approach are as follows: First change mixed numbers to improper fractions. Then divide out common factors before multiplying. Next express the answer in its simplest form by dividing the numerator by the denominator. The quotient is the whole-number part of the mixed number. The remainder is the numerator of the fractional part, and the divisor is the denominator of the fractional part.

Materials to Gather

SUPPLIED

Understand Multiplication Story Problems activity page

Practice Solving Story Problems activity page

▶ Common Errors and Misconceptions

Students might view the numerator and denominator of a fraction as separate, isolated numbers that can be operated on independently. This may lead to students "memorizing" rather than understanding fraction algorithms, and then using them incorrectly.

ONLINE
10 min

GET READY Review Multiplying Fractions

Students will review the steps to solve a multiplication problem with mixed numbers. Then they will practice solving multiplication problems with fractions, whole numbers, and mixed numbers.

Objectives

- Multiply fractions and explain a step-by-step approach.

OFFLINE
20 min

LEARN Understand Multiplication Story Problems

Students will explain how to answer story problems. They will write number sentences to set up the solutions to multiplication story problems with fractions, whole numbers, and mixed numbers. Students will write the number sentences but will not solve them in this activity. Keep their number sentences for later use. Students will write these number sentences in their Math Notebook.

View or print the Understand Multiplication Story Problems activity page.

1. Tell students that in this activity, they will write number sentences that set up the solution to a multiplication story problem.

2. Read and discuss Problem 1, including the Solution and the Answer, in Worked Examples with students.

3. Read Problem 1 in the problem set with students. Discuss what the problem is asking (the length of the side of the toy box).

4. Tell students that the problem states that the paintbrush is $\frac{3}{10}$ feet wide, and it takes 9 brushstrokes to paint the side. Tell students they can use a model to set up the number sentence needed to solve the problem.

5. Draw a rectangle and divide it into 9 equal sections. Tell students that the 9 sections represent the 9 brushstrokes. Label each section $\frac{3}{10}$.

$\frac{3}{10}$	$\frac{3}{10}$	$\frac{3}{10}$	$\frac{3}{10}$	$\frac{3}{10}$	$\frac{3}{10}$	$\frac{3}{10}$	$\frac{3}{10}$	$\frac{3}{10}$

6. Explain that multiplication can be used to solve this problem because $\frac{3}{10}$ is painted 9 times to cover the side of the toy box. The $\frac{3}{10}$ measurement remains the same and occurs over and over again. Point to each section and tell students that $\frac{3}{10} + \frac{3}{10} + \frac{3}{10} + \frac{3}{10} + \frac{3}{10} + \frac{3}{10} + \frac{3}{10} + \frac{3}{10} + \frac{3}{10}$ is the same as $\frac{3}{10} \times 9$. The product of $\frac{3}{10} \times 9$ gives the length of the side.

7. Have students write the number sentence $\frac{3}{10} \times 9 = ?$ near the model. Tell them they will use the number sentences they write in this activity to solve the problems later.

8. Read Problem 2 in the problem set with students.

   Ask: What are you asked to find? the length of the glass inserts

Objectives

- Solve real-world problems involving multiplication of fractions and mixed numbers.

Tips

If students are having trouble understanding the problem, have them draw a model to represent the parts that they know in the story problem.

Ask: What facts are given? the length of the table and the portion the inserts will be

9. Draw a rectangle that is longer horizontally than vertically. Label the length $2\frac{1}{4}$ yards. Divide the rectangle into 6 equal sections. Explain to students that each of these sections is $\frac{1}{6}$ of the table's length.

10. Refer to the problem. Explain that the inserts are $\frac{4}{6}$ of the length, so 4 sections of the rectangle need to be shaded.

$\frac{1}{6}$	$\frac{1}{6}$	$\frac{1}{6}$	$\frac{1}{6}$	$\frac{1}{6}$	$\frac{1}{6}$

$$\text{length} = 2\frac{1}{4} \text{ yards}$$

11. Discuss why multiplication is used to solve the problem. Explain that $2\frac{1}{4}$ is the entire length of the table, and $\frac{1}{6}$ of it is multiplied 4 times.

12. Have students write the number sentence $2\frac{1}{4} \times \frac{4}{6} = ?$ near the model.

13. Read Problem 3 with students.

14. Guide students to understand the problem and write the number sentence to solve it.

    Ask: What are you asked to find? the length of the design in the door

    Ask: What facts are given? The length of the door is $2\frac{6}{9}$ feet. The design on the door is $\frac{3}{4}$ of this length.

15. Have students review the models they used to set up the first two problems. Tell students that they could make a model like the ones used for the previous two problems to solve this problem.

    Ask: What number sentence will you use to solve this problem? $2\frac{6}{9} \times \frac{3}{4} = ?$

16. Have students write the number sentence $2\frac{6}{9} \times \frac{3}{4} = ?$ in their Math Notebook.

17. Repeat Steps 13–16 for the remaining problems on the page.

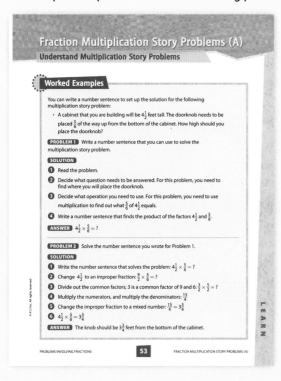

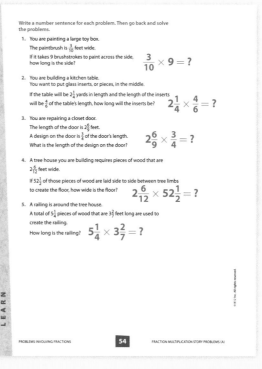

LEARN Solve Story Problems

Students will solve story problems that they explained and set up in the Understand Multiplication Story Problems activity. Students will write their answers in their Math Notebook.

- Solve real-world problems involving multiplication of fractions and mixed numbers.

View or print the Understand Multiplication Story Problems activity page. Gather the number sentences that students wrote for that activity.

1. Read and discuss Problem 2, including the Solution and Answer, in Worked Examples with students.

2. Have students review the number sentence they wrote for Problem 1 in the problem set. Remind students that the number sentence $\frac{3}{10} \times 9 = ?$ solves this story problem.

3. Remind students that when they multiply a fraction and a whole number, the first step is to change the whole number to fraction with a denominator of 1. Have students write $\frac{3}{10} \times \frac{9}{1} = ?$ below the original problem.

4. **Say:** There are no common factors to divide out in this problem, so multiply the numerators. $3 \times 9 = 27$. Write 27 as the numerator of the product.

5. **Say:** Multiply the denominators. $10 \times 1 = 10$. Write 10 as the denominator of the product.

6. Point to the product, $\frac{27}{10}$. Explain to students that since the product is an improper fraction, it should be changed to a mixed number. Tell students to divide 27 by 10. The quotient is 2, which is the whole-number part of the mixed number. The remainder is the numerator of the fractional part, and the divisor is the denominator of the fractional part. So the improper fraction $\frac{27}{10}$ becomes the mixed number $2\frac{7}{10}$.

7. Tell students that the product of $\frac{3}{10} \times 9$ is $2\frac{7}{10}$. Discuss with them that in this problem, multiplying a fraction by a whole number results in a product greater than one of the factors.

8. Remind students that the story problem asks how long the side of the toy box is. The product of $\frac{3}{10} \times 9$ shows that the side of the toy box is $2\frac{7}{10}$ feet long.

9. Have students review the number sentence they wrote for Problem 2 in the problem set.

10. Explain that the first step in multiplying with mixed numbers is to make each mixed number into an improper fraction. Have students change $2\frac{1}{4}$ to an equivalent improper fraction, $\frac{9}{4}$.

11. Have students rewrite the problem as $\frac{9}{4} \times \frac{4}{6} = ?$

12. **Say:** Divide out common factors: 3 is a common factor of 9 and 6, and 4 is a common factor of 4 and 4. Rewrite the problem as $\frac{3}{1} \times \frac{1}{2} = ?$ underneath the original problem.

13. **Say:** Multiply the numerators. $3 \times 1 = 3$. Write 3 as the numerator of the product.

14. **Say:** Multiply the denominators. $1 \times 2 = 2$. Write 2 as the denominator of the product.

15. Have students change the product, $\frac{3}{2}$, into a mixed number. Tell students to divide 3 by 2. The quotient is 1, which is the whole-number part of the mixed number. The remainder is the numerator of the fractional part, and the divisor is the denominator of the fractional part. The product is $1\frac{1}{2}$.

16. Have students read the problem and write the answer in the number sentence: $2\frac{1}{4} \times \frac{4}{6} = 1\frac{1}{2}$

17. **Say:** This problem multiplies a mixed number and fraction. The product, $1\frac{1}{2}$, is greater than one of the factors, $\frac{4}{6}$.

    Ask: What does this answer mean in terms of solving the problem? The glass inserts for the table are $1\frac{1}{2}$ yards long.

18. Repeat Steps 9–17 for the rest of the problems. It is important that students review the answer that they find by using multiplication and relate that answer to the story problem. Students should return to the problem to answer the question.

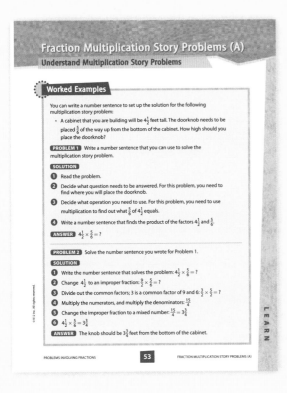

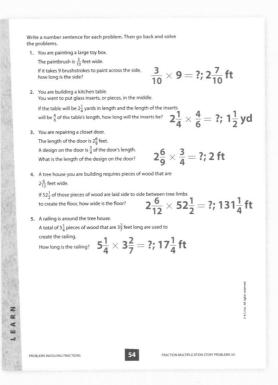

TRY IT Practice Solving Story Problems

Objectives

Students will practice solving multiplication story problems with fractions, whole numbers, and mixed numbers. View or print the Practice Solving Story Problems activity page and read the directions with students.

Students should copy the problems from the Activity Book into their Math Notebook as necessary and solve them there.

- Solve real-world problems involving multiplication of fractions and mixed numbers.

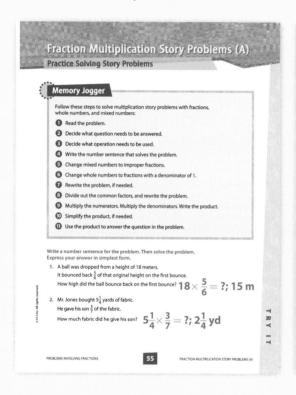

Fraction Multiplication Story Problems (B)

Lesson Overview

GET READY Review Fraction Multiplication	5 minutes	ONLINE
LEARN Understand Fraction Story Problems	15 minutes	OFFLINE
LEARN Apply Fractions to Story Problems	15 minutes	OFFLINE
TRY IT Multiplication Story Problems with Fractions	15 minutes	OFFLINE
CHECKPOINT	10 minutes	ONLINE

▶ Lesson Objectives

Solve real-world problems involving multiplication of fractions and mixed numbers.

▶ Prerequisite Skills

Multiply fractions and explain a step-by-step approach.

▶ Content Background

MULTIPLY A FRACTION BY A FRACTION

After students use models to multiply a fraction by a fraction, they will use a step-by-step approach. The steps of the traditional approach are as follows: First divide out common factors before multiplying. Then express the answer in i ts simplest form.

MULTIPLY A FRACTION BY A MIXED NUMBER

After students use models to multiply a fraction by a mixed number, they will use a step-by-step approach. The steps of the traditional approach are as follows: First change mixed numbers into improper fractions. Then divide out common factors before multiplying. Next, express the answer in its simplest form by dividing the numerator by the denominator. If the answer is an improper fraction, the quotient is the whole-number part of the mixed number. The remainder is the numerator of the fractional part, and the divisor is the denominator of the fractional part.

MULTIPLY A MIXED NUMBER BY A MIXED NUMBER

Once students have worked with models that show how to multiply a mixed number by a mixed number, they will use a step-by-step approach. To find the product of two mixed numbers, the steps of the traditional approach are as follows: First change mixed numbers to improper fractions. Then divide out common factors before multiplying. Next, express the answer in its simplest form by dividing the numerator by the denominator. The quotient is the whole-number part of the mixed number. The remainder is the numerator of the fractional part, and the divisor is the denominator of the fractional part.

Materials to Gather

SUPPLIED

Understand Fraction Story Problems
    activity page

Multiplication Story Problems with
    Fractions activity page

▶ Common Errors and Misconceptions

Students might view the numerator and denominator of a fraction as separate, isolated numbers that can be operated on independently. This may lead to students "memorizing" rather than understanding fraction algorithms, and then using them incorrectly.

GET READY Review Fraction Multiplication

ONLINE
5 min

Objectives

- Multiply fractions and explain a step-by-step approach.

Students will practice multiplying fractions and mixed numbers.

LEARN Understand Fraction Story Problems

OFFLINE
15 min

Objectives

- Solve real-world problems involving multiplication of fractions and mixed numbers.

Students will explain how to answer story problems. They will write equations to set up the solutions to multiplication story problems with fractions, whole numbers, and mixed numbers. Students will write the equations but will not solve them in this activity. Keep their equations for later use. Students will write these equations in their Math Notebook.

View or print the Understand Fraction Story Problems activity page.

1. Discuss Problems 1 and 3 in Worked Examples with students. Explain that in this activity, they will write equations that set up the solution to multiplication story problems.

2. Read Problem 1 in the Worked Examples with students. Discuss what the problem is asking (how many cups of sauce are needed).

3. Tell students that the problem states that $1\frac{1}{6}$ cups of sauce are needed for each of the 8 pizzas. Tell students that they will set up the equation needed to solve the problem.

4. Explain to students that multiplication is used to solve this problem because each of the 8 pizzas needs $1\frac{1}{6}$ cups of sauce. The product of $1\frac{1}{6} \times 8$ gives the number of cups of sauce needed, which is the solution to the problem.

5. Have students write the equation $1\frac{1}{6} \times 8 = ?$ in their Math Notebook.

6. Read Problem 3 in the Worked Examples with students.

7. Guide students to understand the problem and write the equation to solve it.
   Ask: What are you asked to find? how much flour is needed
   Ask: What facts are given? A single recipe requires $2\frac{5}{6}$ cups of flour and they are making $1\frac{1}{2}$ times the recipe.

8. Discuss why multiplication is used to solve the problem. Explain that Avery and his father need $1\frac{1}{2}$ times as much flour as the original recipe requires.
   Ask: How are you going to solve this problem? $2\frac{5}{6} \times 1\frac{1}{2} = ?$

9. Have students explain why multiplication would be used instead of division. The recipe is not divided into equal groups, so we would not use division. Instead, we need to multiply ingredients in the recipe.

10. Have students write the equation $2\frac{5}{6} \times 1\frac{1}{2} = ?$ in their Math Notebook

11. Read Problem 3 in the problem set with students.

    Ask: What are you asked to find? the number of customers who ordered cheeseburgers and french fries

    Ask: What facts are given? During lunch, $\frac{3}{10}$ of the customers order cheeseburgers and french fries. There are 70 customers in the restaurant.

12. Discuss with students why multiplication would be used to solve this problem. Explain that $\frac{3}{10}$ of the orders would be multiplied by 70 customers to find how many customers order cheeseburgers and french fries.

13. Have students write the equation $\frac{3}{10} \times 70 = ?$ in their Math Notebook.

14. Have students try the remaining story problems on their own, but be available to answer questions. Check students' equations for accuracy when they have finished and go over any incorrect equations.

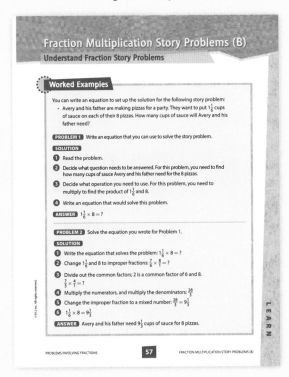

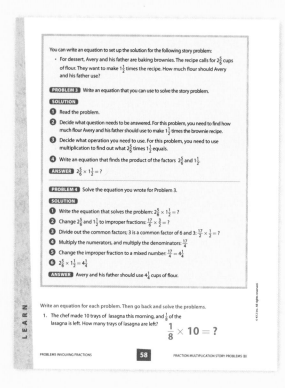

You can write an equation to set up the solution for the following story problem:

- For dessert, Avery and his father are baking brownies. The recipe calls for $2\frac{5}{6}$ cups of flour. They want to make $1\frac{1}{2}$ times the recipe. How much flour should Avery and his father use?

PROBLEM 3 Write an equation that you can use to solve the story problem.

SOLUTION

1 Read the problem.

2 Decide what question needs to be answered. For this problem, you need to find how much flour Avery and his father should use to make $1\frac{1}{2}$ times the brownie recipe.

3 Decide what operation you need to use. For this problem, you need to use multiplication to find out what $2\frac{5}{6}$ times $1\frac{1}{2}$ equals.

4 Write an equation that finds the product of the factors $2\frac{5}{6}$ and $1\frac{1}{2}$.

ANSWER $2\frac{5}{6} \times 1\frac{1}{2} = ?$

PROBLEM 4 Solve the equation you wrote for Problem 3.

SOLUTION

1 Write the equation that solves the problem: $2\frac{5}{6} \times 1\frac{1}{2} = ?$

2 Change $2\frac{5}{6}$ and $1\frac{1}{2}$ to improper fractions: $\frac{17}{6} \times \frac{3}{2} = ?$

3 Divide out the common factors; 3 is a common factor of 6 and 3: $\frac{17}{2} \times \frac{1}{2} = ?$

4 Multiply the numerators, and multiply the denominators: $\frac{17}{4}$

5 Change the improper fraction to a mixed number: $\frac{17}{4} = 4\frac{1}{4}$

6 $2\frac{5}{6} \times 1\frac{1}{2} = 4\frac{1}{4}$

ANSWER Avery and his father should use $4\frac{1}{4}$ cups of flour.

Write an equation for each problem. Then go back and solve the problems.

1. The chef made 10 trays of lasagna this morning, and $\frac{1}{8}$ of the lasagna is left. How many trays of lasagna are left? $\frac{1}{8} \times 10 = ?$

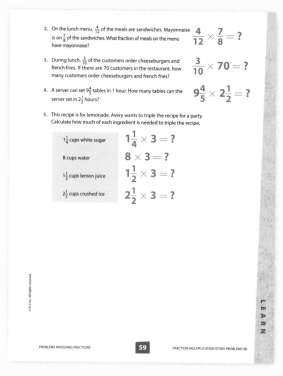

2. On the lunch menu, $\frac{4}{12}$ of the meals are sandwiches. Mayonnaise is on $\frac{7}{8}$ of the sandwiches. What fraction of meals on the menu have mayonnaise? $\frac{4}{12} \times \frac{7}{8} = ?$

3. During lunch, $\frac{3}{10}$ of the customers order cheeseburgers and french fries. If there are 70 customers in the restaurant, how many customers order cheeseburgers and french fries? $\frac{3}{10} \times 70 = ?$

4. A server can set $9\frac{4}{5}$ tables in 1 hour. How many tables can the server set in $2\frac{1}{2}$ hours? $9\frac{4}{5} \times 2\frac{1}{2} = ?$

5. This recipe is for lemonade. Avery wants to triple the recipe for a party. Calculate how much of each ingredient is needed to triple the recipe.

$1\frac{1}{4}$ cups white sugar	$1\frac{1}{4} \times 3 = ?$
8 cups water	$8 \times 3 = ?$
$1\frac{1}{2}$ cups lemon juice	$1\frac{1}{2} \times 3 = ?$
$2\frac{1}{2}$ cups crushed ice	$2\frac{1}{2} \times 3 = ?$

LEARN Apply Fractions to Story Problems

OFFLINE 15 min

Objectives

- Solve real-world problems involving multiplication of fractions and mixed numbers.

Students will solve story problems that they explained and set up in the Understand Fraction Story Problems activity. Students will write their answers in their Math Notebook.

View or print the Understand Fraction Story Problems activity page. Gather the equations that students wrote for the problems in that activity.

1. Discuss Problems 2 and 4 in Worked Examples with students. Explain that in this activity, students will use the equations they wrote to solve the multiplication story problems.

2. Have students review the equation they wrote for Problem 1 in the problem set. Remind students the number sentence $\frac{1}{8} \times 10 = ?$ solves this story problem.

3. Remind students that to multiply a fraction by a fraction, the first steps are to write the whole number as a fraction and check for any common factors that can be divided out to simplify the problem. In this case, students can divide out the common factor of 2 for 8 and 10. Have students rewrite the problem as $\frac{1}{4} \times \frac{5}{1} = ?$ below the original problem.

4. Guide students through the remaining steps of the problem (see Worked Examples for assistance). When students have finished the problem, emphasize that the product is $\frac{5}{4} = 1\frac{1}{4}$.

5. Explain that the story problem asks how many trays of lasagna are left. Discuss the equation and the answer in terms of the problem. The product tells us there are $1\frac{1}{4}$ trays left.

6. Have students review the equation they wrote for Problem 2 in the problem set.

Ask: What equation solves this problem? $\frac{4}{12} \times \frac{7}{8} = ?$

7. Guide students through the remaining steps of the problem (see Worked Examples for assistance).

Ask: What does the answer $\frac{7}{24}$ mean in terms of solving the problem? $\frac{7}{24}$ of the meals on the menu have mayonnaise.

8. Have students review the equation they wrote for Problem 3 in the problem set. Remind students the equation $\frac{3}{10} \times 70 = ?$ solves this story problem.

9. Explain to students that to multiply a fraction by a whole number, the first step is to change the whole number to a fraction with a denominator of 1.

10. Guide students through the steps to solve the problem. Then have students explain how they found the answer.

Ask: What does the answer 21 mean in terms of solving the problem? 21 customers ordered cheeseburgers and french fries.

11. Repeat Steps 8–10 for the rest of the problems on the page. Remind students to refer to Worked Examples for the steps for multiplying mixed numbers by mixed numbers. These steps will help them calculate the answers. Make sure that students review the answer that they find and relate it to the story problem. Students should return to the problem to answer the question.

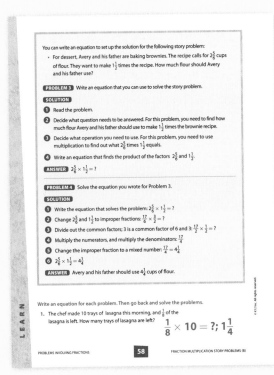

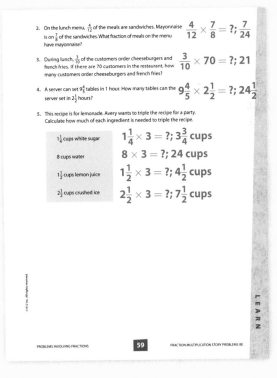

TRY IT Multiplication Story Problems with Fractions

OFFLINE 15 min

Objectives

- Solve real-world problems involving multiplication of fractions and mixed numbers.

Students will practice solving multiplication story problems with fractions, whole numbers, and mixed numbers. View or print the Multiplication Story Problems with Fractions activity page and read the directions with students.

Students should copy the problems from the Activity Book into their Math Notebook as necessary and solve them there.

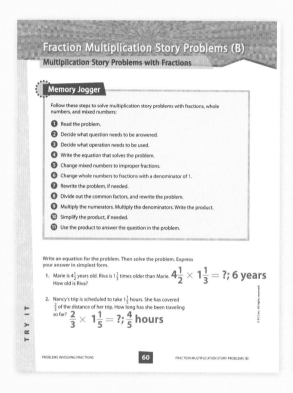

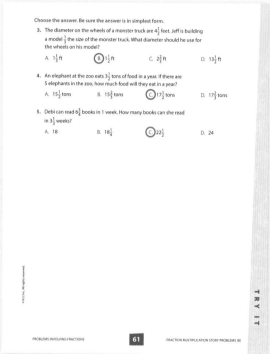

ONLINE 10 min

CHECKPOINT

Objectives

- Solve real-world problems involving multiplication of fractions and mixed numbers.

Students will complete an online Checkpoint. If necessary, read the directions, problems, and answer choices to students and help them with keyboard or mouse operations.

Add and Subtract Fractions (A)

Lesson Overview		
LEARN Add Fractions with Like Denominators	20 minutes	OFFLINE
LEARN Subtract Fractions with Like Denominators	20 minutes	ONLINE
TRY IT Subtract and Add Fractions	10 minutes	ONLINE
CHECKPOINT	10 minutes	ONLINE

▶ Lesson Objectives

Solve a simple problem involving addition or subtraction of fractions.

▶ Content Background

Students will add and subtract fractions, including mixed numbers, that have like denominators.

The traditional approach to finding the sums or differences of fractions or mixed numbers, with or without like denominators, is to use regrouping. The steps are:

- Leave mixed numbers as mixed numbers. Add or subtract the fractions and add or subtract the whole numbers in either order. When subtracting, students may need to regroup a whole number as a fraction with the like denominator to subtract the fraction parts.

- If the fraction portion of the sum is an improper fraction, change the improper fraction to a mixed number, shown as a whole-number and fraction.

- Combine the whole-number portion of the sum or difference and the whole number from the improper fraction with the fraction to express the answer in the simplest form, as a mixed number.

Although students will most often see fractions written with a horizontal fraction bar in math, such as $\frac{2}{3}$ or $5\frac{5}{6}$, they will occasionally see a diagonal fraction bar, such as 2/3 or 5 5/6. They will very likely see the diagonal fraction bar in everyday experiences, but be sure they understand that using the horizontal fraction bar in their work will make problems involving fractions easier to interpret and solve.

▶ Common Errors and Misconceptions

- Students might have difficulty understanding how different models represent fractions because they often see fractions represented as parts of circles—for example, pie and pizza illustrations. They might not recognize, for example, that the following models all represent the fraction $\frac{3}{5}$:

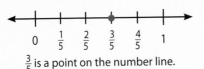

$\frac{3}{5}$ is a point on the number line.

$\frac{3}{5}$ of the shapes are triangles.

$\frac{3}{5}$ of the rectangle is shaded.

Materials to Gather

SUPPLIED
Fraction Models (printout)

ALSO NEEDED
pencils, coloring

- Students might not understand that for a model to accurately represent a fraction as a part of a whole, the model must show a whole divided into equally sized parts.

- Students might not see the relationship between the models (such as fraction strips and number lines) and the procedures for adding and subtracting fractions. Once they begin to use symbols without models, students might apply memorized rules without thinking about the reasons for the procedures.

▶ Advance Preparation

Print one copy of the Fraction Models.

LEARN Add Fractions with Like Denominators

OFFLINE
20min

Objectives

- Solve a simple problem involving addition or subtraction of fractions.

Students will learn how to add fractions with like denominators. Have them write and draw their answers in their Math Notebook. Gather the Fraction Models printout and coloring pencils.

1. Tell students to write $\frac{3}{10} + \frac{4}{10} = ?$

   Ask: What is the denominator of both fractions? 10

2. Have them use the fraction strip divided into tenths on the printout. This model uses tenths because the common denominator of the fractions being added is 10.

$$\frac{3}{10} + \frac{4}{10} = ?$$

Tell students to model $\frac{3}{10} + \frac{4}{10}$ by shading the first 3 tenths in one color and the next 4 tenths in another color.

$$\frac{3}{10} + \frac{4}{10} = ?$$

Tips

If students have difficulty adding fractions without models, have them use fraction strips, number lines, or other models to solve problems.

   Ask: How many tenths did you shade in all? 7 tenths

   Ask: What is the sum of $\frac{3}{10} + \frac{4}{10}$? $\frac{7}{10}$

3. Have students write the number sentence $\frac{3}{10} + \frac{4}{10} = \frac{7}{10}$ below the fraction strip.

4. Use a number line to model the second problem. Tell students to write $1\frac{3}{8} + \frac{2}{8} = ?$ in their Math Notebook.

   Ask: What is the denominator of both fractions? 8

5. Have students use the number line divided into eighths on the printout. Tell students that the number line is marked in eighths because the common denominator of the fractions being added is 8.

6. Have students mark a point at 0 and $1\frac{3}{8}$ on the number line. Start at 0 and "hop" 1 whole and 3 eighths to the right of 0. Show an arc between 0 and $1\frac{3}{8}$. Then have students "hop" 2 eighths to the right of $1\frac{3}{8}$ to $1\frac{5}{8}$. Have students mark a point at $1\frac{5}{8}$.

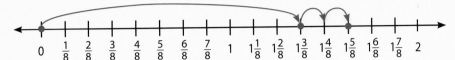

Ask: What is the sum of $1\frac{3}{8} + \frac{2}{8}$? $1\frac{5}{8}$

7. Have students write the number sentence $1\frac{3}{8} + \frac{2}{8} = 1\frac{5}{8}$ below the number line.

8. Use a step-by-step approach to solve the last two problems. Explain to students that when fractions have like denominators, they can add the numerators. The denominator stays the same. For each problem, encourage students to use the number lines on the printout to check their answers.

9. Have students write $\frac{2}{9} + \frac{4}{9} = ?$ in their Math Notebook.

   Ask: What is the sum of the numerators? 6

   Ask: What is the denominator in both fractions? 9

   Ask: What is the denominator for the sum? 9

   Ask: What is the sum of $\frac{2}{9} + \frac{4}{9}$? $\frac{6}{9}$

   Ask: How do you simplify $\frac{6}{9}$? Divide $\frac{6}{9}$ by a value of 1 in fraction form. In this case, use $\frac{3}{3}$.

   Ask: What is the sum of $\frac{2}{9} + \frac{4}{9}$ in simplest form? $\frac{2}{3}$

10. Have students write the number sentence $\frac{2}{9} + \frac{4}{9} = \frac{6}{9} = \frac{2}{3}$ in their Math Notebook.

11. Repeat Steps 9 and 10 with $\frac{5}{6} + \frac{2}{6} = ?$ Have students find the answer and explain how to simplify it from an improper fraction into a mixed number. $\frac{5}{6} + \frac{2}{6} = \frac{7}{6}$. To simplify the answer, divide the numerator by the denominator. The quotient is the whole number part of the mixed number. The remainder is the numerator of the fractional part and the divisor, 6, is the denominator of the fractional part $\left(1\frac{1}{6}\right)$.

12. Tell students to write $1\frac{3}{5} + \frac{1}{5} = ?$ in their Math Notebook.

    Ask: What is the denominator of both fractions? 5

13. Have students use the fraction strips divided into fifths on the printout. The model uses fifths because the common denominator of the fractions being added is 5. Tell them to shade all of the first fraction strip, and 3 fifths of the second fraction strip, in one color, to model $1\frac{3}{5}$. Have students shade the next fifth on the second fraction strip in a different color to model adding $\frac{1}{5}$ to $1\frac{3}{5}$.

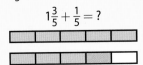

Ask: How many whole fraction strips did you shade? 1

Ask: How many fifths did you shade in the second fraction strip? 4 fifths

Ask: What is the sum of $1\frac{3}{5} + \frac{1}{5}$? $1\frac{4}{5}$

14. Have students write the number sentence $1\frac{3}{5} + \frac{1}{5} = 1\frac{4}{5}$ below the fraction strips.

15. Use a step-by-step approach to solve the last problem. Tell students that to add mixed numbers, they add the whole number and then add the fractions in any order.

16. Have students write $3\frac{7}{10} + 2\frac{8}{10} + 1\frac{3}{10} = ?$ in their Math Notebook.

    Ask: What is the sum of the whole numbers? 6

    Ask: What is the sum of the fractions? $\frac{18}{10}$

    Ask: What is $\frac{18}{10}$ as a mixed number? $1\frac{8}{10}$

    Ask: What is $1\frac{8}{10}$ in simplest form? $1\frac{4}{5}$

    Say: Combine the sum of the whole numbers with the sum of the fractions.

    Ask: What is $6 + 1\frac{4}{5}$? $7\frac{4}{5}$

    Ask: What is the sum of $3\frac{7}{10} + 2\frac{8}{10} + 1\frac{3}{10}$ in simplest form? $7\frac{4}{5}$

17. Have students write the number sentence $3\frac{7}{10} + 2\frac{8}{10} + 1\frac{3}{10} = 7\frac{4}{5}$ in their Math Notebook.

ONLINE 20min

LEARN Subtract Fractions with Like Denominators

Students will learn and practice subtraction of fractions and mixed numbers with like denominators to solve story problems. Some problems with mixed numbers involve regrouping.

Objectives

- Solve a simple problem involving addition or subtraction of fractions.

ONLINE 10min

TRY IT Subtract and Add Fractions

Students will complete an online Try It. If necessary, read the directions, problems, and answer choices to students and help them with keyboard or mouse operations.

Objectives

- Solve a simple problem involving addition or subtraction of fractions.

ONLINE 10min

CHECKPOINT

Students will complete an online Checkpoint. If necessary, read the directions, problems, and answer choices to students and help them with keyboard or mouse operations.

Objectives

- Solve a simple problem involving addition or subtraction of fractions.

Add and Subtract Fractions (B)

Lesson Overview

LEARN Use Models to Add Fractions	20 minutes	OFFLINE
LEARN Least Common Denominator	10 minutes	ONLINE
LEARN Add Mixed Numbers with Unlike Denominators	15 minutes	OFFLINE
TRY IT Fraction Subtraction and Addition	15 minutes	ONLINE

▶ ## Lesson Objectives

Solve a simple problem involving addition or subtraction of fractions.

▶ ## Prerequisite Skills

- Use objects or sketches to solve a story problem that involves addition or subtraction of fractions.
- Solve and simplify a problem that involves addition or subtraction of fractions with unlike denominators.

▶ ## Content Background

Students will add fractions and mixed numbers with unlike denominators.

Students will follow multiple steps to add fractions and mixed numbers with unlike denominators. The first step is to find the least common denominator of the fraction or fraction part of a mixed number and use the least common denominator to write equivalent fractions with like denominators. Then they add the like fraction parts and add the whole-number parts. Adding the fraction parts before the whole-number parts is important if the fraction parts of the sum add to an improper fraction. If the fraction part of the sum is an improper fraction, students change the improper fraction to a mixed number and combine the mixed number with the whole-number part of the sum. If the sum is not in simplest form, they simplify the sum.

Although students will most often see fractions written with a horizontal fraction bar in math, such as $\frac{2}{3}$ or $5\frac{5}{6}$, they will occasionally see a diagonal fraction bar, such as 2/3 or 5 5/6. They will very likely see the diagonal fraction bar in everyday experiences, but be sure they understand that using the horizontal fraction bar in their work will make problems involving fractions easier to interpret and solve.

▶ ## Common Errors and Misconceptions

- Students might have difficulty understanding how different models represent fractions because they often see fractions represented as parts of circles—for example, pie and pizza illustrations. They might not recognize, for example, that the following models all represent the fraction $\frac{3}{5}$:

Materials to Gather

SUPPLIED
Fraction Circles (printout)
Centimeter Grid Paper (printout)

ALSO NEEDED
ruler, dual-scale

$\frac{3}{5}$ is a point on the number line.

$\frac{3}{5}$ of the shapes are triangles.

$\frac{3}{5}$ of the rectangle is shaded.

- Students might not understand that for a model to accurately represent a fraction as a part of a whole, the model must show a whole divided into equally sized parts.

- Students might not see the relationship between the models (such as fraction strips and number lines) and the procedures for adding and subtracting fractions. Once they begin to use symbols without models, students might apply memorized rules without thinking about the reasons for the procedures.

▶ **Advance Preparation**

Print one copy each of the Fraction Circles and Centimeter Grid Paper.

LEARN Use Models to Add Fractions

OFFLINE
20min

Objectives

- Solve a simple problem involving addition or subtraction of fractions.

Students will use models to add fractions and mixed numbers with unlike denominators.

Gather the ruler and the Fraction Circles and Centimeter Grid Paper printouts.

1. Give students the Fraction Circles printout. Tell them to write $\frac{1}{2} + \frac{1}{4} = ?$ on the printout, beneath the first two circles on the first row.

2. Have students shade $\frac{1}{2}$ of the first circle and label it $\frac{1}{2}$. Then have them use a ruler to draw a straight line through the next fraction circle to divide it into fourths. Have students shade $\frac{1}{4}$ and label it $\frac{1}{4}$. Tell students the half circle and one-fourth circle represent the two fractions.

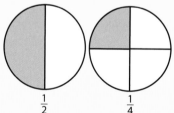

Ask: Look at the fractions. Do $\frac{1}{2}$ and $\frac{1}{4}$ have like denominators? No

Say: To add these fractions, the fractions need to have like denominators.

3. Tell students to use a ruler to draw a straight line through the first fraction circle to divide it into fourths. Then have students count the number of shaded fourths and add "$= \frac{2}{4}$" to the label $\frac{1}{2}$.

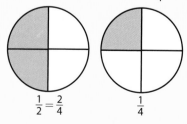

Ask: How many fourths is $\frac{1}{2}$ equal to? $\frac{2}{4}$

Ask: Look at the fractions. Do the $\frac{2}{4}$ and $\frac{1}{4}$ have like denominators now? Yes

Ask: What is the sum of $\frac{2}{4} + \frac{1}{4}$? $\frac{3}{4}$

Ask: What is the sum of $\frac{1}{2} + \frac{1}{4}$? $\frac{3}{4}$

4. Give students the grid paper and tell them to write $\frac{1}{6} + \frac{2}{3} = ?$ on it.

   Tell students they will draw rectangular models to solve this problem.

5. Have students outline two 3 by 2 rectangles side by side on the grid paper. Each rectangle will represent a fraction.

6. Tell students to draw 2 vertical lines and 1 horizontal line in the first rectangle to divide it into sixths. Have students shade $\frac{1}{6}$ and label it $\frac{1}{6}$.

7. Tell students to draw 2 vertical lines in the second rectangle to divide it into thirds. Have students shade $\frac{2}{3}$ and label it $\frac{2}{3}$.

 $\frac{1}{6}$ 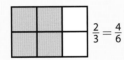 $\frac{2}{3}$

   Ask: Look at the fractions. Do $\frac{1}{6}$ and $\frac{2}{3}$ have like denominators? No

8. Tell students to draw 1 horizontal line in the second rectangle to divide it into sixths. Then have students count the number of shaded sixths in the second rectangle. Have students add "$= \frac{4}{6}$" to the label $\frac{2}{3}$.

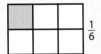 $\frac{1}{6}$ 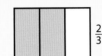 $\frac{2}{3} = \frac{4}{6}$

   Ask: How many sixths is $\frac{2}{3}$ equal to? $\frac{4}{6}$

   Ask: Look at the fractions. Do $\frac{1}{6}$ and $\frac{4}{6}$ have like denominators now? Yes

   Ask: What is the sum of $\frac{1}{6} + \frac{4}{6}$? $\frac{5}{6}$

   Ask: What is the sum of $\frac{1}{6} + \frac{2}{3}$? $\frac{5}{6}$

9. Have students find the circles divided into fourths on the Fraction Circles printout. Have them write this number sentence on the printout: $1\frac{2}{4} + \frac{3}{8} = ?$

10. Have students shade all of the first circle and $\frac{2}{4}$ of the second circle to show $1\frac{2}{4}$ and label them $1\frac{2}{4}$. Then have students draw 2 diagonal lines through the third fraction circle to divide it into eighths. Have students shade $\frac{3}{8}$ and label it $\frac{3}{8}$.

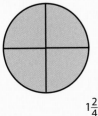 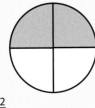 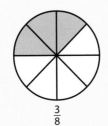

$1\frac{2}{4}$ $\frac{3}{8}$

Ask: Look at the fractions. Do $1\frac{2}{4}$ and $\frac{3}{8}$ have like denominators? No

Say: When you add mixed numbers, the fraction parts need to have like denominators.

11. Have students draw 2 diagonal lines through the fraction circle that shows $\frac{2}{4}$ to divide it into eighths. Then have them count the number of shaded eighths. Have them add "$= 1\frac{4}{8}$" to the label $1\frac{2}{4}$.

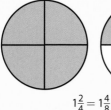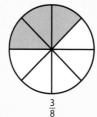

$$1\frac{2}{4} = 1\frac{4}{8} \qquad\qquad \frac{3}{8}$$

Ask: How many eighths is $\frac{2}{4}$ equal to? $\frac{4}{8}$

Ask: Look at the fractions. Do the fraction part of $1\frac{4}{8}$ and the fraction $\frac{3}{8}$ have like denominators now? Yes

Ask: What is the sum of $\frac{4}{8} + \frac{3}{8}$? $\frac{7}{8}$

Ask: What is the sum of $\frac{2}{4} + \frac{3}{8}$? $\frac{7}{8}$

Ask: What is the sum of $1\frac{2}{4} + \frac{3}{8}$? $1\frac{7}{8}$

12. Tell students they will draw rectangular models on Centimeter Grid Paper to solve this problem: $1\frac{2}{5} + 1\frac{3}{10} = ?$

13. Have students outline two 5 by 2 rectangles side by side on the grid paper.

14. Tell students to draw 4 vertical lines in the second rectangle to divide it into fifths. Have students shade all of the first rectangle and $\frac{2}{5}$ of the second rectangle to show $1\frac{2}{5}$ and label them $1\frac{2}{5}$.

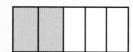 $1\frac{2}{5}$

15. Have students outline two more 5 by 2 rectangles side by side below the other rectangles.

16. Tell students to draw 4 vertical lines and 1 horizontal line in the second rectangle to divide it into tenths. Have students shade all of the first rectangle and $\frac{3}{10}$ of the second rectangle to show $1\frac{3}{10}$ and label them $1\frac{3}{10}$.

 $1\frac{3}{10}$

Ask: Look at the fractions. Do $1\frac{2}{5}$ and $1\frac{3}{10}$ have like denominators? No

17. Have students explain how to change the model of $1\frac{2}{5}$ so that the two fraction parts of the mixed numbers have the same denominator. Draw 1 horizontal line in the rectangle that shows $\frac{2}{5}$ to divide it into tenths.

18. Have students count the number of shaded tenths.

 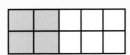 $1\frac{2}{5} = ?$

Ask: How many tenths is $\frac{2}{5}$ equal to? $\frac{4}{10}$

Ask: Look at the fractions. Do the fraction parts $\frac{3}{10}$ and $\frac{4}{10}$ have like denominators now? Yes

Ask: What is the sum of the fraction parts of $\frac{4}{10} + \frac{3}{10}$? $\frac{7}{10}$

Ask: What is the sum of the fraction parts of $\frac{2}{5} + \frac{3}{10}$? $\frac{7}{10}$

Ask: What is the sum of the whole-number parts in $1\frac{2}{5} + 1\frac{3}{10}$? 2

Ask: What is the sum of $1\frac{2}{5} + 1\frac{3}{10}$? Explain how you found the sum. $2\frac{7}{10}$;
I changed the fraction parts of the mixed numbers to like denominators.
I added the fraction parts and the whole-number parts.

LEARN Least Common Denominator	ONLINE 10min	Objectives

Students will learn a method for finding a least common denominator and will use this skill to solve problems.

- Solve a simple problem involving addition or subtraction of fractions.

LEARN Add Mixed Numbers with Unlike Denominators	OFFLINE 15min	Objectives

Students will practice adding mixed numbers with unlike denominators using a step-by-step method.

- Solve a simple problem involving addition or subtraction of fractions.

1. Have students write in their Math Notebook.

Say: Write $3\frac{1}{2} + 2\frac{7}{8} + 1\frac{1}{8} = ?$ You will add the fraction parts of the mixed numbers first. That's important if the fractions parts of the sum add to an improper fraction. The improper fraction can be changed to a mixed number and simplified. The fractions have unlike denominators, so you need to change the fraction parts $\frac{1}{2}, \frac{7}{8}$, and $\frac{1}{8}$ to fractions with like denominators.

2. Tell students that sometimes the denominator of one fraction is a multiple of the denominator of the other fractions.

Ask: What are the first four multiples of 2? 2, 4, 6, 8

Say: Eight is a multiple of 2 and it is the denominator of $\frac{7}{8}$, so the least common denominator of $\frac{1}{2}, \frac{7}{8}$, and $\frac{1}{8}$ is 8.

3. Have students write a fraction equivalent to $\frac{1}{2}$ that has a denominator of 8.

Ask: What number times 2 equals 8? 4

Say: Multiply $\frac{1}{2}$ by $\frac{4}{4}$ because $\frac{4}{4}$ is equal to 1. $\frac{4}{8}$

Say: The fractions now have the same denominator, so you can add.

4. Have students write the sum of the fraction parts: $\frac{4}{8} + \frac{7}{8} + \frac{1}{8} = ?$

Ask: What is the sum of $\frac{4}{8} + \frac{7}{8} + \frac{1}{8}$? $\frac{12}{8}$

Ask: How do you change $\frac{12}{8}$ to a mixed number? Divide 12 by 8. The quotient is the whole-number part of the mixed number. The remainder is the numerator of the fractional part, and the divisor is the denominator of the fractional part, which is 8.

Ask: What is $\frac{12}{8}$ as a mixed number? $1\frac{4}{8}$

Ask: Is $1\frac{4}{8}$ in simplest form? No

Ask: What is $1\frac{4}{8}$ in simplest form? $1\frac{1}{2}$

Ask: What is the sum of the fraction parts of the mixed numbers? $1\frac{1}{2}$

5. Tell students the next step is to find the sum of the whole-number parts of $3\frac{1}{2} + 2\frac{7}{8} + 1\frac{1}{8} = ?$

Ask: What is the sum of $3 + 2 + 1$? 6

Ask: What is the sum of $6 + 1\frac{1}{2}$? $7\frac{1}{2}$

Ask: What is the sum of $3\frac{1}{2} + 2\frac{7}{8} + 1\frac{1}{8} = ?$ $7\frac{1}{2}$

6. Repeat Steps 1–5 for $2\frac{3}{4} + 1\frac{3}{6} = ?$ Change the fractions to have a common denominator, which is 12. Rewrite the problem to $2\frac{9}{12} + 1\frac{6}{12} = ?$ The sum of the fraction parts is $\frac{15}{12}$. Change $\frac{15}{12}$ to the mixed number $1\frac{3}{12}$. Simplify $1\frac{3}{12}$ to $1\frac{1}{4}$. Add the whole-number parts: $2 + 1 = 3$. Add the whole-number parts and the fraction parts: $3 + 1\frac{1}{4} = 4\frac{1}{4}$.

ONLINE

15 min

TRY IT Fraction Subtraction and Addition

Students will complete an online Try It. If necessary, read the directions, problems, and answer choices to students and help them with keyboard or mouse operations.

Objectives

- Solve a simple problem involving addition or subtraction of fractions.

Add and Subtract Fractions (C)

Lesson Overview

GET READY Regroup Whole Numbers as Fractions	10 minutes	ONLINE
LEARN Subtract Mixed Numbers with Unlike Denominators	15 minutes	OFFLINE
LEARN Mixed-Number Addition and Subtraction	15 minutes	ONLINE
TRY IT More Fraction Addition and Subtraction	10 minutes	ONLINE
CHECKPOINT	10 minutes	ONLINE

▶ Lesson Objectives

Solve a simple problem involving addition or subtraction of fractions.

▶ Content Background

Students will subtract fractions and mixed numbers with like denominators.

The traditional approach to subtracting mixed numbers with like denominators is to leave the mixed numbers and not change them to improper fractions. The first step in subtracting mixed numbers is to subtract the fraction part of the mixed numbers. Students may need to regroup a whole number as a fraction with the like denominator to subtract the fraction parts. Then they subtract the whole-number parts of the mixed numbers. If the fraction part of the difference is an improper fraction, students change the improper fraction to a mixed number and combine it with the whole-number difference. This is the place where they might struggle. They add the fraction part and the whole-number part of the difference. Finally students write the difference in simplest form.

Although students will most often see fractions written with a horizontal fraction bar in math, such as $\frac{2}{3}$ or $5\frac{5}{6}$, they will occasionally see a diagonal fraction bar, such as 2/3 or 5 5/6. They will very likely see the diagonal fraction bar in everyday experiences, but be sure they understand that using the horizontal fraction bar in their work will make problems involving fractions easier to interpret and solve.

▶ Common Errors and Misconceptions

- Students might have difficulty understanding how different models represent fractions because they often see fractions represented as parts of circles—for example, pie and pizza illustrations. They might not recognize, for example, that the following models all represent the fraction $\frac{3}{5}$:

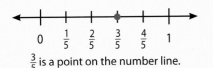

$\frac{3}{5}$ is a point on the number line.

$\frac{3}{5}$ of the shapes are triangles.

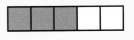

$\frac{3}{5}$ of the rectangle is shaded.

- Students might not understand that for a model to accurately represent a fraction as a part of a whole, the model must show a whole divided into equally sized parts.
- Students might not see the relationship between the models (such as fraction strips and number lines) and the procedures for adding and subtracting fractions. Once they begin to use symbols without models, students might apply memorized rules without thinking about the reasons for the procedures.

▶ Advance Preparation

Print the Fraction Circles.

GET READY Regroup Whole Numbers as Fractions 10 min

Objectives

Students will review regrouping when subtracting whole numbers and mixed numbers.

- Solve a simple problem involving addition or subtraction of fractions.

LEARN Subtract Mixed Numbers with Unlike Denominators 15 min

Objectives

Students will first use a model to show subtracting of mixed numbers with unlike denominators. Then they will use a step-by-step approach to subtract mixed numbers with unlike denominators.

Gather the Fraction Circles printout. Students should write the steps for the step-by-step approach in their Math Notebook.

- Solve a simple problem involving addition or subtraction of fractions.

PROBLEM 1

1. Tell students they will solve the problem $5\frac{1}{2} - 3\frac{3}{4} = ?$ using fraction circles to model the problem.

2. Have students locate the row of halves fraction circles on the printout. Have them write $5\frac{1}{2} - 3\frac{3}{4} = ?$ above the fraction circles.

3. Tell students to model $5\frac{1}{2}$ by shading 5 circles, to show 5 wholes, and 1 of 2 halves of the sixth circle to show $\frac{1}{2}$.

$$5\frac{1}{2} - 3\frac{3}{4} = ?$$

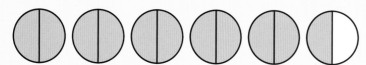

4. **Say:** You need like denominators to be able to find the answer to $5\frac{1}{2} - 3\frac{3}{4}$.
You will subtract the fraction parts of the mixed numbers first.

Ask: Do $\frac{1}{2}$ and $\frac{3}{4}$ have like denominators? No

Say: When fractions are being subtracted, the fractions need to have like denominators. Draw one horizontal line in the half-shaded circle, and one horizontal line in one whole circle, so that 1 whole becomes $\frac{4}{4}$.

$$5\frac{1}{2} - 3\frac{3}{4} = \;?$$

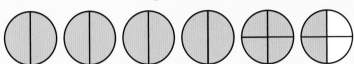

Ask students these questions:

- How many fourths is $\frac{1}{2}$ equal to? $\frac{2}{4}$

- How many fourths are you subtracting from $\frac{2}{4}$? $\frac{3}{4}$

- Before you subtract $\frac{3}{4}$ from $\frac{2}{4}$, what should you do? regroup

5. Tell students they can regroup a whole number.

Ask: How many shaded fourths are in the whole circle next to the circle that shows $\frac{2}{4}$? $\frac{4}{4}$

Ask: When you regroup the shaded fourths in the whole circle with the shaded fourths in the last circle, how many shaded fourths are there in all? $\frac{6}{4}$

6. **Say:** Now subtract $\frac{3}{4}$. Mark an **X** on 1 shaded fourth in the whole circle and 2 shaded fourths in the circle that shows $\frac{2}{4}$.

$$5\frac{1}{2} - 3\frac{3}{4} = \;?$$

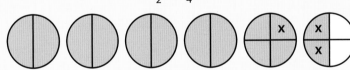

Ask students these questions:

- How many shaded fourths in the last two circles do not have an **X**? 3

- What is $\frac{6}{4} - \frac{3}{4}$? $\frac{3}{4}$

7. Tell students to subtract the whole-number parts of the mixed numbers next. Have them mark an **X** on each of 3 of the circles that represent 3 wholes, to complete the subtraction $5\frac{1}{2} - 3\frac{3}{4} = \;?$

$$5\frac{1}{2} - 3\frac{3}{4} = \;?$$

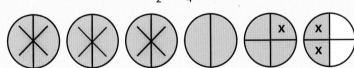

Ask: How many whole circles are left? Remember not to count the circle you used for regrouping. 1

Say: Remember that we are solving a subtraction problem. But at this step, we combine the whole-number difference with the difference of the fractions.

Ask: Combine the whole-number difference and the fraction difference. What is 1 and $\frac{3}{4}$? $1\frac{3}{4}$

Ask: What is $5\frac{1}{2} - 3\frac{3}{4}$? $1\frac{3}{4}$

Have students write the number sentence $5\frac{1}{2} - 3\frac{3}{4} = 1\frac{3}{4}$ below the fraction circles.

PROBLEM 2

8. Tell students they will use a step-by-step approach to subtract mixed numbers.

9. Remind students that when subtracting mixed numbers, they subtract the fraction parts first, then the whole-number parts.

10. Have students write $4\frac{7}{12} - 2\frac{1}{4} = ?$ in their Math Notebook.

    Say: Look at the fraction parts of the mixed numbers. You need to find the least common denominator of $\frac{7}{12}$ and $\frac{1}{4}$ in order to subtract the fraction parts.

11. **Ask:** How do you find the least common denominator of two fractions? Find the least common multiple of the denominators. Think about the multiples of 12: 12, 24, 36, 48.Think about the multiples of 4: 4, 8, 12, 16.

    Ask: What is the least common multiple of 12 and 4? 12

    Ask: What is the least common denominator of $\frac{7}{12}$ and $\frac{1}{4}$? 12

12. **Ask:** What fraction with a denominator of 12 is equivalent to $\frac{1}{4}$? $\frac{3}{12}$

    Have students write $\frac{7}{12} - \frac{3}{12} = ?$ in their Math Notebook.

    Ask: What is $\frac{7}{12} - \frac{3}{12}$ in simplest form? $\frac{1}{3}$

13. **Say:** Now subtract the whole-number parts. What is $4 - 2$? 2

    Ask: Combine the whole-number difference and the fraction difference. What is 2 and $\frac{1}{3}$? $2\frac{1}{3}$

    Ask: What is $4\frac{7}{12} - 2\frac{1}{4}$? $2\frac{1}{3}$

    Have students write the number sentence $4\frac{7}{12} - 2\frac{1}{4} = 2\frac{1}{3}$ in their Math Notebook.

PROBLEM 3

14. Tell students they will use a step-by-step approach to subtract mixed numbers.

15. Remind students that when subtracting mixed numbers, they subtract the fraction parts first, then the whole-number parts.

16. Have students write $7\frac{1}{3} - 3\frac{3}{4} = ?$ in their Math Notebook.

    Say: Look at the fraction parts of the mixed numbers. You need to find the least common denominator of $\frac{1}{3}$ and $\frac{3}{4}$ in order to subtract the fraction parts.

17. **Ask:** How do you find the least common denominator of two fractions? Find the least common multiple of the denominators. Think about the multiples of 3: 3, 6, 9, 12, 15. Think about the multiples of 4: 4, 8, 12, 16.

    Ask: What is the least common multiple of 3 and 4? 12

    Ask: What is the least common denominator of $\frac{1}{3}$ and $\frac{3}{4}$? 12

18. **Ask:** What fraction with a denominator of 12 is equivalent to $\frac{1}{3}$? $\frac{4}{12}$

    Ask: What fraction with a denominator of 12 is equivalent to $\frac{3}{4}$? $\frac{9}{12}$

    Ask: Before you subtract $\frac{9}{12}$ from $\frac{4}{12}$, what should you do? regroup

19. Tell students they need to regroup a whole number in order to subtract the fraction parts of the mixed numbers.

    Say: Regroup 1 whole as $\frac{12}{12}$. $7\frac{1}{3}$ is equivalent to $7\frac{4}{12}$. The mixed number in the original problem changes to $6\frac{16}{12}$. Write $6\frac{16}{12} - 3\frac{9}{12} = ?$ in your Math Notebook.

    Ask: When we regrouped, we added $\frac{12}{12}$ to $\frac{4}{12}$. What is the improper fraction you are subtracting from now? $\frac{16}{12}$

    Ask: Now subtract to find the fraction part difference. What is $\frac{16}{12} - \frac{9}{12}$ in simplest form? $\frac{7}{12}$

20. **Say:** Now subtract the whole-number parts. We rewrote the problem when we regrouped to $6\frac{16}{12} - 3\frac{9}{12} = ?$ What is $6 - 3$? 3

    Ask: Combine the whole-number difference and the fraction difference. What is 3 and $\frac{7}{12}$? $3\frac{7}{12}$

    Ask: What is $7\frac{1}{3} - 3\frac{3}{4}$? $3\frac{7}{12}$

    Have students write the number sentence is $7\frac{1}{3} - 3\frac{3}{4} = 3\frac{7}{12}$ in their Math Notebook.

PROBLEM 4

21. Have students write the problem in their Math Notebook and use a step-by-step approach to solve it on their own. Have them explain the steps they followed to solve the following problem: $8\frac{1}{5} - 4\frac{1}{4} = ?$

22. Students should follow these steps to find the answer:
    - Subtract fraction parts of mixed numbers first, and then whole-number parts.
    - Look at the fraction parts of the mixed numbers. Find the least common denominator of the fractions $\frac{1}{5}$ and $\frac{1}{4}$. To do this, find the least common multiple of the denominators 5 and 4.

      Think about the multiples of 5: 5, 10, 15, 20, 25.

      Think about the multiples of 4: 4, 8, 12, 16, 20, 24.

      The least common multiple of 5 and 4 is 20. The least common denominator of $\frac{1}{5}$ and $\frac{1}{4}$ is 20.

      The fraction with a denominator of 20 that is equivalent to $\frac{1}{5}$ is $\frac{4}{20}$.

      The fraction with a denominator of 20 that is equivalent to $\frac{1}{4}$ is $\frac{5}{20}$.

    - Before you subtract the fraction parts of the mixed numbers, $\frac{4}{20} - \frac{5}{20}$, regroup a whole number from the mixed number $8\frac{1}{5}$.

    - Regroup 1 whole as $\frac{20}{20}$. $8\frac{1}{5}$ is equivalent to $8\frac{4}{20}$.

    - Add $\frac{20}{20}$ to $\frac{4}{20}$ to find the improper fraction $\frac{24}{20}$ to subtract $\frac{5}{20}$ from.

The mixed number in the original problem changes to $7\frac{24}{20}$. Write the problem as $7\frac{24}{20} - 4\frac{5}{20} = ?$

- Subtract to find the fraction part difference. $\frac{24}{20} - \frac{5}{20} = \frac{19}{20}$

- Subtract to find the whole-number difference. The problem was rewritten when regrouped to $7\frac{24}{20} - 4\frac{5}{20} = ?$ So $7 - 4 = 3$.

- Combine the whole-number difference and the fraction difference. 3 and $\frac{19}{20}$ is $3\frac{19}{20}$.

- Write the number sentence with the answer: $8\frac{1}{5} - 4\frac{1}{4} = 3\frac{19}{20}$.

ONLINE 15 min

LEARN Mixed-Number Addition and Subtraction

Students will practice subtracting fractions and mixed numbers with like denominators to solve story problems.

Objectives

- Solve a simple problem involving addition or subtraction of fractions.

ONLINE 10 min

TRY IT More Fraction Addition and Subtraction

Students will complete an online Try It. If necessary, read the directions, problems, and answer choices to students and help them with keyboard or mouse operations.

Objectives

- Solve a simple problem involving addition or subtraction of fractions.

ONLINE 10 min

CHECKPOINT

Students will complete an online Checkpoint. If necessary, read the directions, problems, and answer choices to students and help them with keyboard or mouse operations.

Objectives

- Solve a simple problem involving addition or subtraction of fractions.

Add and Subtract Fractions (D)

Lesson Overview

LEARN Fraction Story Problems	20 minutes	**ONLINE**
LEARN Reasonable or Not?	10 minutes	**ONLINE**
TRY IT Fraction Addition and Subtraction	15 minutes	**ONLINE**
CHECKPOINT	15 minutes	**ONLINE**

▶ Lesson Objectives

Solve a simple problem involving addition or subtraction of fractions.

▶ Content Background

Students will apply their knowledge and skills of adding and subtracting fractions to solve practical problems. Make sure students realize that one reason they learn computation in math is so that they can apply that understanding to solve actual problems in everyday life.

Students will also be encouraged to think about whether answers make sense by estimating fraction solutions mentally. This skill will serve them well as they make sense of their work and also in everyday experiences.

Although students will most often see fractions written with a horizontal fraction bar in math, such as $\frac{2}{3}$ or $5\frac{5}{6}$, they will occasionally see a diagonal fraction bar, such as 2/3 or 5 5/6. They will very likely see the diagonal fraction bar in everyday experiences, but be sure they understand that using the horizontal fraction bar in their work will make problems involving fractions easier to interpret and solve.

▶ Common Errors and Misconceptions

- Students might have difficulty understanding how different models represent fractions because they often see fractions represented as parts of circles—for example, pie and pizza illustrations. They might not recognize, for example, that the following models all represent the fraction $\frac{3}{5}$:

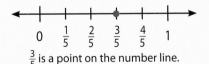

$\frac{3}{5}$ is a point on the number line.

$\frac{3}{5}$ of the shapes are triangles.

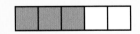

$\frac{3}{5}$ of the rectangle is shaded.

- Students might not understand that for a model to accurately represent a fraction as a part of a whole, the model must show a whole divided into equally sized parts.

- Students might not see the relationship between the models (such as fraction strips and number lines) and the procedures for adding and subtracting fractions. Once they begin to use symbols without models, students might apply memorized rules without thinking about the reasons for the procedures.

Materials to Gather

There are no materials to gather for this lesson.

LEARN Fraction Story Problems

Objectives

Students will learn techniques for solving story problems that involve addition and subtraction of fractions with unlike denominators. They will be encouraged to think about the reasonableness of their answers as they solve problems on their own.

- Solve a simple problem involving addition or subtraction of fractions.

LEARN Reasonable or Not?

Objectives

Students will determine the reasonableness of the answer to a given story problem.

- Solve a simple problem involving addition or subtraction of fractions.

TRY IT Fraction Addition and Subtraction

Objectives

Students will complete an online Try It. If necessary, read the directions, problems, and answer choices to students and help them with keyboard or mouse operations.

- Solve a simple problem involving addition or subtraction of fractions.

CHECKPOINT

Objectives

Students will complete an online Checkpoint. If necessary, read the directions, problems, and answer choices to students and help them with keyboard or mouse operations.

- Solve a simple problem involving addition or subtraction of fractions.

Core Focus
Fraction Addition and Subtraction Stories

Lesson Overview

GET READY Fraction Addition and Subtraction Review	10 minutes	ONLINE
LEARN Solve a Popcorn Story Problem	10 minutes	ONLINE
LEARN Applications of Fraction Addition and Subtraction	10 minutes	ONLINE
TRY IT Fraction Stories with Addition and Subtraction	15 minutes	OFFLINE
CHECKPOINT	15 minutes	OFFLINE

▶ Lesson Objectives

Solve a simple problem involving addition or subtraction of fractions.

▶ Content Background

Students will apply their understanding of fraction addition and subtraction to new and practical situations. In this lesson, students will use what they know about adding and subtracting fractions to solve problems related to distance and other applications of fractions.

▶ Safety

If students make a recipe, have them follow kitchen safety rules. Be aware of any food allergies students might have.

Materials to Gather

SUPPLIED

Fraction Stories with Addition and Subtraction activity page

Checkpoint (printout)

Checkpoint Answer Key (printout)

GET READY Fraction Addition and Subtraction Review

ONLINE 10min

Students will use online flip cards to practice solving problems involving addition and subtraction of fractions and mixed numbers. Encourage students to test themselves by working each problem carefully before flipping the card to reveal the answer. Tell them watch for problems that do not have a common denominator and also to make sure their answers are in simplest form.

Objectives

- Solve a simple problem involving addition or subtraction of fractions.

LEARN Solve a Popcorn Story Problem

Students will subtract fractions and mixed numbers with unlike denominators to solve story problems about recipes. This activity can be extended if you and students make one or both of the recipes. Have students compare the ingredient amounts in the recipes to practice subtracting fractions and mixed numbers.

Winnie's Popcorn Snack

$8\frac{1}{2}$ cups popped popcorn

$\frac{2}{3}$ cup dried apples

$2\frac{3}{4}$ cups pine nuts

$\frac{1}{4}$ teaspoon dry mustard

Ron's Popcorn Snack

$9\frac{2}{3}$ cups popped popcorn

$\frac{5}{8}$ cup raisins

$1\frac{5}{12}$ cups toasted walnuts

$\frac{1}{8}$ teaspoon dry mustard

Objectives

- Solve a simple problem involving addition or subtraction of fractions.

Tips

Have students write their own popcorn snack recipe using fractions and mixed numbers.

LEARN Applications of Fraction Addition and Subtraction

Students will use their knowledge and skills in adding and subtracting fractions to solve problems related to the planning, preparation, and planting of a vegetable garden.

Objectives

- Solve a simple problem involving addition or subtraction of fractions.

TRY IT Fraction Stories with Addition and Subtraction

Objectives

Students will solve story problems that apply addition and subtraction of fractions.
View or print the Fraction Stories with Addition and Subtraction activity page.
Students should copy the problems into their Math Notebook and solve them there.

- Solve a simple problem involving addition or subtraction of fractions.

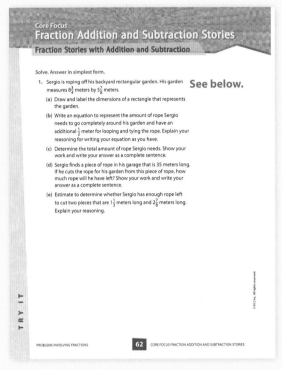

See below.

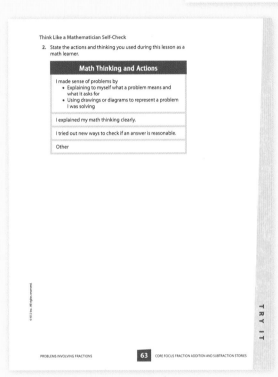

Additional Answers

1. **(a)**

$8\frac{3}{4}$ m

$5\frac{7}{8}$ m

(b) $8\frac{3}{4} + 5\frac{7}{8} + 8\frac{3}{4} + 5\frac{7}{8} + \frac{1}{2} = r$; The equation shows all 4 dimensions around the garden plus the additional rope Sergio needs to use for looping and tying. I used r to represent the total amount of rope.

(c) Sergio needs $29\frac{3}{4}$ meters of rope.

$8\frac{3}{4} + 5\frac{7}{8} + 8\frac{3}{4} + 5\frac{7}{8} + \frac{1}{2} = r$

$8\frac{6}{8} + 5\frac{7}{8} + 8\frac{6}{8} + 5\frac{7}{8} + \frac{4}{8} = r$

$26\frac{30}{8} = 29\frac{6}{8} = 29\frac{3}{4} = r$

(d) Sergio will have $5\frac{1}{4}$ meters of rope left.

$35 - 29\frac{3}{4} = l$

$5\frac{1}{4} = l$

(e) The two pieces Sergio wants to cut are $1\frac{1}{3}$ meters long and $2\frac{7}{8}$ meters long, or about 1 meter + 3 meters = 4 meters long. Since Sergio has $5\frac{1}{4}$ meters of rope left, he should have enough for the two pieces.

OFFLINE
15min

Objectives

The Checkpoint and its answer key are located in the Resources section for this unit in the Online Book Menu of *Math+ Yellow Lesson Guide*. Give students the Checkpoint. Have students complete the Checkpoint on their own. Use the answer key to score the Checkpoint, and then enter the results online.

- Solve a simple problem involving addition or subtraction of fractions.

Unit Review

UNIT REVIEW Look Back	10 minutes	**ONLINE**
UNIT REVIEW Checkpoint Practice	50 minutes	**ONLINE**
▶ **UNIT REVIEW** Prepare for the Checkpoint		

▶ Unit Objectives

This lesson reviews the following objectives:

- Solve real-world problems involving multiplication of fractions and mixed numbers.
- Solve a simple problem involving addition or subtraction of fractions.

▶ Advance Preparation

In this lesson, students will have an opportunity to review previous activities in the Problems Involving Fractions unit. Look at the suggested activities in Unit Review: Prepare for the Checkpoint online and gather any needed materials.

Materials to Gather

There are no materials to gather for this lesson.

ONLINE

10 min

UNIT REVIEW Look Back

Objectives

- Review unit objectives.

Students will review key concepts from the unit to prepare for the Unit Checkpoint.

ONLINE

50 min

UNIT REVIEW Checkpoint Practice

Objectives

- Review unit objectives.

Students will complete an online Checkpoint Practice to prepare for the Unit Checkpoint. If necessary, read the directions, problems, and answer choices to students. Have students answer the problems on their own. Review any missed problems with students.

▶ UNIT REVIEW Prepare for the Checkpoint

What you do next depends on how students performed in the previous activity, Unit Review: Checkpoint Practice. If students had difficulty with any of the problems, complete the appropriate review activity listed in the table online.

Unit Checkpoint

UNIT CHECKPOINT Online	60 minutes	**ONLINE**

▶ Unit Objectives

This lesson assesses the following objectives:

- Solve real-world problems involving multiplication of fractions and mixed numbers.
- Solve a simple problem involving addition or subtraction of fractions.

Materials to Gather

There are no materials to gather for this lesson.

UNIT CHECKPOINT Online

ONLINE 60min

Students will complete the Unit Checkpoint online. If necessary, read the directions, problems, and answer choices to students and help them with keyboard or mouse operations.

Objectives

- Assess unit objectives.

Extended Problems: Real-World Application

USE WHAT YOU KNOW Offline	60 minutes : **OFFLINE**

▶ Lesson Objectives

This lesson assesses the following objectives:

- Solve real-world problems involving multiplication of fractions and mixed numbers.
- Solve a simple problem involving addition or subtraction of fractions.
- Represent a data set of measurements in fractions of a unit on a line plot $\left(\text{limited to } \frac{1}{2}, \frac{1}{4}, \text{ and } \frac{1}{8}\right)$.
- Solve problems involving addition of fractions using information recorded in line plots $\left(\text{limited to } \frac{1}{2}, \frac{1}{4}, \text{ and } \frac{1}{8}\right)$.
- Solve problems involving subtraction of fractions using information recorded in line plots $\left(\text{limited to } \frac{1}{2}, \frac{1}{4}, \text{ and } \frac{1}{8}\right)$.
- Apply mathematical knowledge and skills to evaluate and analyze real-world situations.

Materials to Gather

SUPPLIED

Extended Problems: Real-World Application (printout)

USE WHAT YOU KNOW Offline

Objectives

Open the Extended Problems: Real-World Application. Read the directions, problems, and answer choices to students, if necessary.

The teacher will grade this assignment.

- Students should save the graded assignment to their computer. In the filename, they should replace "studentname" with their last name followed by their first initial.
- Students should complete the assignment on their own.
- Students should submit the completed assignment according to the teacher's instructions.

- Apply mathematical knowledge and skills to evaluate and analyze real-world situations.

Decimals: Addition and Subtraction

26.22
miles to go

▶ Unit Objectives

- Compare decimal numbers.
- Order three or more decimal numbers.
- Read, write, compare, and order decimals to thousandths.
- Write decimals in expanded form.
- Recognize that in a multidigit number, a digit in one place represents 10 times as much as it represents in the place to its right and $\frac{1}{10}$ of what it represents in the place to its left.
- Round a decimal number to any place through hundredths.
- Add or subtract decimals to hundredths, using models or drawings and strategies based on place value.
- Solve a story problem involving addition or subtraction of decimal numbers.
- Estimate the sum or difference of positive decimal numbers.
- Use estimation to predict a solution to a story problem and to verify the reasonableness of the calculated result.
- Estimate the sum or difference in a problem involving decimal numbers.
- Solve an addition or subtraction problem involving decimal numbers.

▶ Big Ideas

- Ratios, fractions, percents, and decimals can be used to compare one value to another, or through models, to compare properties of two things or situations.
- Equivalence is a fundamental property of rational numbers; equivalent fractions, percents, and decimals all name the same relationship between two values.
- Any integer or rational number can be plotted on a number line.

▶ Unit Introduction

This unit builds upon students' prior knowledge of whole number and decimal place value, decimal numbers in money, and fractions as rational numbers along a number line. In this unit, students will learn to relate a decimal number to a familiar fraction on a number line and will use this understanding to compare and order decimal numbers with renewed emphasis on correct usage of the less-than symbol (<) and the greater-than symbol (>). They will review the underlying concept behind rounding numbers and apply it to rounding decimal numbers through the hundredths place by using a number line, rounding to a given place, and judging the appropriate uses of rounded numbers. Next, students will round decimal addends, minuends, and subtrahends to estimate sums and differences. They will then learn to find the actual sum or difference of decimal numbers and compare an estimate of the sum or difference to the actual answer to verify that their solution is reasonable. To reinforce newly acquired understanding of a decimal number and a fraction as two ways to express the same value, students will have the opportunity to write tenths and hundredths in decimal and fraction notation and show that the representations are equivalent.

▶ Keywords

algorithm	equivalent decimals	round
decimal number	estimate	tenths
decimal place-value chart	hundredths	thousandths
	place value	

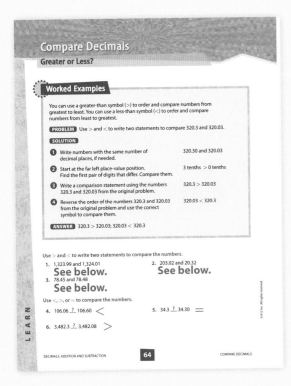

Compare Decimals
Greater or Less?

Worked Examples

You can use a greater-than symbol (>) to order and compare numbers from greatest to least. You can use a less-than symbol (<) to order and compare numbers from least to greatest.

PROBLEM Use > and < to write two statements to compare 320.3 and 320.03.

SOLUTION

1. Write numbers with the same number of decimal places, if needed.   320.30 and 320.03

2. Start at the far left place-value position. Find the first pair of digits that differ. Compare them.   3 tenths > 0 tenths

3. Write a comparison statement using the numbers 320.3 and 320.03 from the original problem.   320.3 > 320.03

4. Reverse the order of the numbers 320.3 and 320.03 from the original problem and use the correct symbol to compare them.   320.03 < 320.3

ANSWER 320.3 > 320.03; 320.03 < 320.3

Use > and < to write two statements to compare the numbers.

1. 1,323.99 and 1,324.01
   See below.
2. 203.02 and 20.32
   See below.
3. 78.45 and 78.48
   See below.

Use <, >, or = to compare the numbers.

4. 106.06 __?__ 106.60   **<**

5. 34.3 __?__ 34.30   **=**

6. 3,482.3 __?__ 3,482.08   **>**

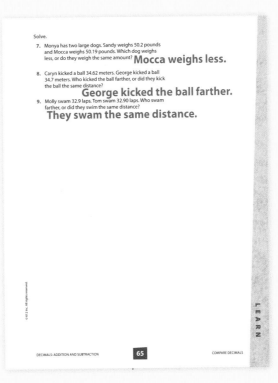

Solve.

7. Monya has two large dogs. Sandy weighs 50.2 pounds and Mocca weighs 50.19 pounds. Which dog weighs less, or do they weigh the same amount? **Mocca weighs less.**

8. Caryn kicked a ball 34.62 meters. George kicked a ball 34.7 meters. Who kicked the ball farther, or did they kick the ball the same distance? **George kicked the ball farther.**

9. Molly swam 32.9 laps. Tom swam 32.90 laps. Who swam farther, or did they swim the same distance? **They swam the same distance.**

Additional Answers

1. 1,323.99 < 1,324.01; 1,324.01 > 1,323.99

2. 203.02 > 20.32; 20.32 < 203.02

3. 78.45 < 78.48; 78.48 > 78.45

ONLINE
10 min

TRY IT Compare Decimals

Objectives

- Compare decimal numbers.

Students will complete an online Try It. If necessary, read the directions, problems, and answer choices to students and help them with keyboard or mouse operations.

Compare and Expand Decimals

Lesson Overview

LEARN Read, Write, and Expand Decimals	30 minutes	OFFLINE
LEARN Patterns in Place Value	30 minutes	ONLINE

▶ Lesson Objectives

- Read, write, compare, and order decimals to thousandths.
- Write decimals in expanded form.
- Recognize that in a multidigit number, a digit in one place represents 10 times as much as it represents in the place to its right and $\frac{1}{10}$ of what it represents in the place to its left.

Materials to Gather

SUPPLIED

Read, Write, and Expand Decimals activity page

LEARN Read, Write, and Expand Decimals

OFFLINE
30 min

Objectives

- Read, write, compare, and order decimals to thousandths.
- Write decimals in expanded form.

Students will learn to read decimals and write decimals in verbal form and expanded form. View or print the Read, Write, and Expand Decimals activity page. Students should copy the problems into their Math Notebook and solve them there.

1. Have students read Problem 1 in the Worked Examples and place the number in their own place-value chart in their Math Notebook.
2. Have students read the number aloud, as the answer indicates. Before they read the answer, encourage them to say it aloud slowly. Check their oral answer with the written words and provide correction, if necessary.
3. Have them write out the words before they check the written answer.
4. Have students read Problem 2 in the Worked Examples. Guide students to read the words aloud, with extra emphasis on the *and*, before attempting to write.

   Ask: Why is the *and*, important? What does it indicate? The *and*, indicates the location of the decimal point.
5. Have students follow Steps 1 and 2 before looking at the answer. If necessary, have them refer to their place-value chart. Emphasize that the *–ths* at the end of hundredths indicates that the place value is the decimal portion to the right of the decimal point.
6. Have students read Problem 3 and Step 1 in the Worked Examples and place the number in their own place-value chart in their Math Notebook.
7. Guide students as they label each column, as indicated in Step 2.
8. Have them read Step 3 and try to write out the expanded form on their own. Emphasize that the expanded form shows the place value for each digit.

9. Have students read through Problem 4 in the Worked Examples. Emphasize that because the hundreds place shows a zero, 0×100 is shown in the expanded form. Even though the value is 0, encourage students to include this digit and its place value, since the expanded form needs to show every digit. The same is true in the hundredths place.

10. Have students complete Problems 1–6, and assist them as necessary.

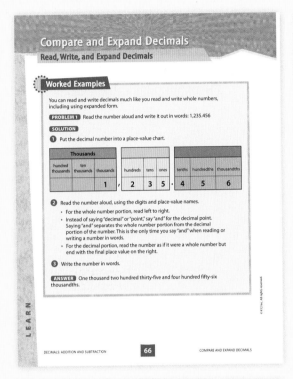

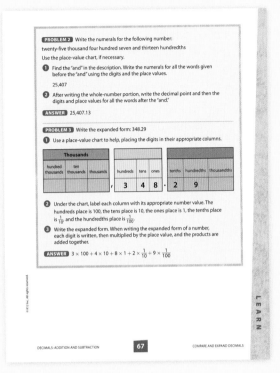

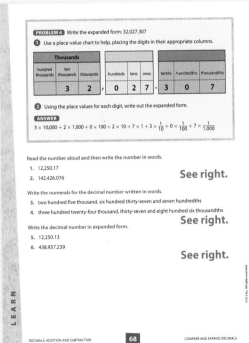

Additional Answers

1. twelve thousand two hundred fifty and seventeen hundredths

2. one hundred forty-two thousand, four hundred twenty-six and seventy-six thousandths

3. 205,637.07

4. 324,037.806

5. $1 \times 10{,}000 + 2 \times 1{,}000 + 2 \times 100 + 5 \times 10 + 0 \times 1 + 1 \times \frac{1}{10} + 3 \times \frac{1}{100}$

6. $4 \times 100{,}000 + 3 \times 10{,}000 + 8 \times 1{,}000 + 9 \times 100 + 5 \times 10 + 7 \times 1 + 2 \times \frac{1}{10} + 3 \times \frac{1}{100} + 9 \times \frac{1}{1{,}000}$

Students will compare adjacent place values in decimal numbers to discover a place-value pattern.

Objectives

- Recognize that in a multidigit number, a digit in one place represents 10 times as much as it represents in the place to its right and $\frac{1}{10}$ of what it represents in the place to its left.

Order Three Decimal Numbers

Lesson Overview

GET READY Use $<$, $>$, and $=$ to Compare	5 minutes	ONLINE
LEARN Use Symbols to Order	10 minutes	ONLINE
LEARN Order Numbers	15 minutes	OFFLINE
TRY IT Write Comparison Statements	20 minutes	OFFLINE
CHECKPOINT	10 minutes	ONLINE

▶ **Lesson Objectives**

Order three or more decimal numbers.

▶ **Prerequisite Skills**

Compare decimal numbers.

▶ **Content Background**

Students will learn to compare three decimal numbers and write comparison statements with comparison symbols ($<$ or $>$). They will learn that there are two comparison statements that they can write to order numbers; for example, if $3 < 9 < 12$, then $12 > 9 > 3$.

Avoid using the word *point* with students when reading decimals. For example, encourage students to think and say "thirty-five and nineteen hundredths" when they see 35.19, rather than "thirty-five point nineteen."

Students will compare three decimal numbers by comparing place-value positions. They will determine which number is greatest, which is least, and which is between the greatest number and the least number. Students will use two less-than symbols ($<$) or two greater-than symbols ($>$) to write comparison statements. Reinforce the words that are associated with each symbol—for example, *is greater than* for $>$ and *is less than* for $<$. This knowledge of the words will enable students, when they see $89.3 > 89.17 > 89.09$, to say "eighty-nine and three tenths is greater than eighty-nine and seventeen hundredths, which is greater than eighty-nine and nine hundredths." Help students understand that $89.3 = 89.30$ and $89.30 > 89.17 > 89.09$, so $89.3 > 89.17 > 89.09$. Likewise when they see $89.09 < 89.17 < 89.3$, they will say, "eighty-nine and nine hundredths is less than eighty-nine and seventeen hundredths, which is less than eighty-nine and three tenths." Help students understand that $89.3 = 89.30$ and $89.09 < 89.17 < 89.30$, so $89.09 < 89.17 < 89.3$.

▶ **Advance Preparation**

Print the Decimal Number Place-Value Chart.

Number three separate index cards with the following decimal numbers: 176.05, 176.45, and 176.5. Label two index cards with the less-than symbol ($<$) and two index cards with the greater-than symbol ($>$).

Materials to Gather

SUPPLIED

Decimal Number Place-Value Chart (printout)

Order Numbers activity page

Write Comparison Statements activity page

ALSO NEEDED

index cards – labeled

GET READY Use <, >, and = to Compare

Students will use <, >, and = to compare decimal numbers. As they work through the activity, have them read each decimal number aloud.

Objectives

• Compare decimal numbers.

LEARN Use Symbols to Order

Students will order three decimal numbers. They will write and say the comparison statements.

Gather the Decimal Number Place-Value Chart. Students may wish to refer to the place-value chart as they work through the activity online.

Objectives

• Order three or more decimal numbers.

LEARN Order Numbers

Students will order three or more decimal numbers from greatest to least or least to greatest. Gather the number and symbol cards and the Decimal Number Place-Value Chart. View or print the Order Numbers activity page.

Students should copy the problems from the Activity Book into their Math Notebook as necessary and solve them there.

1. Give students the number cards (176.5, 176.05, and 176.45) and the less-than symbol (<) cards.

   Say: Place the less-than symbols between the numbers to make a comparison statement. Since 176.5 has nothing in the hundredths place, it may help to write or visualize 0 in the hundredths place to remind you that 176.5 = 176.50. 176.05 < 176.45 < 176.5

   Allow students to use the decimal place-value chart if they wish. Alternatively, show students how they can turn their Math Notebook sideways to create vertical lines to align digits as in a decimal place-value chart. Have students leave enough space above and below the first two numbers they write in their chart, so that they can insert the third number if it belongs between the least and greatest numbers. For example,

Hundreds	Tens	Ones	.	Tenths	Hundredths
1	7	6	.	0	5
1	7	6	.	4	5
1	7	6	.	5	0

2. Have students read the statement aloud and explain how they arrived at their answer. **Sample explanation:** I compared digits in each place-value position from left to right. All the numbers had one hundred seventy-six, so I compared the values of the tenths digits. Since 0 tenths is less than 4 tenths and 5 tenths, I knew 176.05 was the least number. Then I compared 176.5 and 176.45. Since 5 tenths is greater than 4 tenths, 176.5 is greater than 176.45. So 176.05 is the least number, 176.5 is the greatest number, and 176.45 is between 176.05 and 176.5.

3. Repeat Steps 1 and 2 with the greater-than symbol (>) cards.
   176.5 > 176.45 > 176.05

4. Direct students' attention to the activity page. Read the Worked Examples and go through the solution with them. Show them how to write 5.7 in the chart as 5.70. Explain that 5.70 > 5.34 and 4.98, so 5.70, or 5.7, is the greatest number.

5. Have students complete Problems 1–6. Allow them to use the decimal place-value chart if they wish. Remind them that it may be helpful to write or visualize a 0 in the hundredths place of any number shown in tenths *if* the other numbers are expressed in hundredths.

   Say: Pay close attention to whether the problem asks for greatest to least or least to greatest.

6. When students reach Problem 7, point out that they need to use the data in the table to solve the problem. Because students are familiar with many sports in which the "highest number wins," remind them that the fastest time in a race means the athlete spent the least amount of time to complete the race.

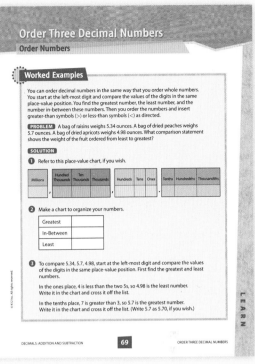

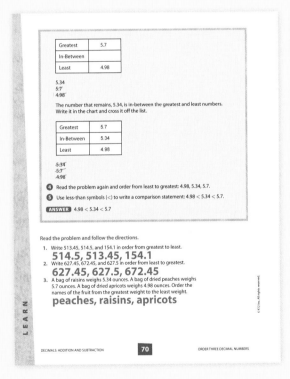

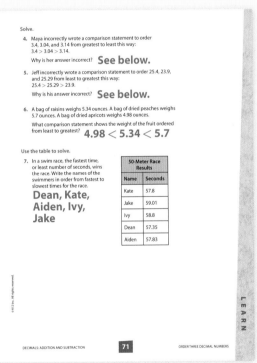

Additional Answers

4. 3.04 is not greater than 3.14. Correct comparison statement:
   3.4 > 3.14 > 3.04

5. He wrote them from greatest to least. Correct comparison statement:
   23.9 < 25.29 < 25.4

TRY IT Write Comparison Statements

OFFLINE
20min

Objectives

- Order three or more decimal numbers.

Students will practice ordering three decimal numbers. View or print the Write Comparison Statements activity page and read the directions with students.

Students should copy the problems from the Activity Book into their Math Notebook as necessary and solve them there.

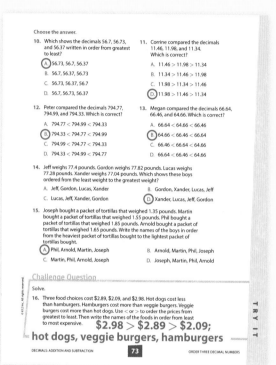

ONLINE
10min

CHECKPOINT

Objectives

- Compare decimal numbers.

Students will complete an online Checkpoint. If necessary, read the directions, problems, and answer choices to students and help them with keyboard or mouse operations.

Round Decimals Through Hundredths

Lesson Overview

LEARN Model Decimal Numbers	10 minutes	ONLINE
LEARN Find Rounded Decimals	15 minutes	ONLINE
LEARN Round Decimals in Stories	15 minutes	ONLINE
TRY IT Practice Rounding Decimals	10 minutes	OFFLINE
CHECKPOINT	10 minutes	ONLINE

▶ ## Lesson Objectives

Round a decimal number to any place through hundredths.

▶ ## Content Background

Students will round decimals to the hundredths place. Decimal numbers name wholes and parts of a whole. The names of the parts of a whole are tenths, hundredths, thousandths, and so on.

Rounding numbers in a problem can make finding an estimate easier. Decimals can be rounded to friendly numbers such as 0.05, 0.10, 0.25, 0.50, or 1. They can also be rounded to a specific place. For example, if people buy 4.381 gallons of gasoline, they could round the number of gallons to the nearest hundredth. Since 4.381 is between 4.38 and 4.39, but closer to 4.38, 4.381 rounds to 4.38.

When students round a number ending in a 5, they cannot round to the nearer number, since the 5 is halfway between two boundary numbers. For instance, 1.25 is halfway between 1.2 and 1.3. In this math course, numbers ending in 5 are rounded to the greater number. So 1.25 rounded to the nearest tenth is 1.3. There are other situations in which you might round numbers ending in 5 to the lesser number, but those situations are rare and will be discussed as specific cases.

When students write and compute with decimal numbers, they often use numbers that are between 0 and 1—for example, 0.1. While it is acceptable to write this number as .1, mathematicians usually write the leading zero, to show that the decimal number has zero for the part that is the whole number and to avoid confusion about the value of the number.

When students use a number line to help them round decimal numbers, all the numbers will show the same number of decimal places. For example, on a number line showing numbers in hundredths, numbers such as 42.80 will appear, rather than the equivalent value 42.8. When students find the rounded value of a number, they should give their answer to the decimal place being rounded. For example, when rounding 42.78 to the nearest tenth, they would answer 42.8, emphasizing the tenths place, even though the number line shows 42.80. Be sure that students understand that numbers such as 42.8 and 42.80 show the same value and position on the number line but emphasize different place values.

Materials to Gather

SUPPLIED

Round Decimals in Stories (printout)

Practice Rounding Decimals activity page

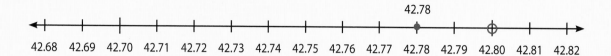

42.78

42.68 42.69 42.70 42.71 42.72 42.73 42.74 42.75 42.76 42.77 42.78 42.79 42.80 42.81 42.82

▶ Common Errors and Misconceptions

- Students might become so concerned about getting the correct answer when estimating that they first find the exact answer and then round it. For example, when asked to estimate 348 + 176, students might find the sum (524), and then round it to the nearest hundred (500).

- Students might have difficulty accepting that there is more than one correct approach and answer to an estimation problem.

- Students might have difficulty understanding rounding because traditional teaching focuses on how to round, not why to round. For example, students might have been taught to "round up" to the nearest ten if the digit in the ones place is 5 or greater. There are some situations, however, in which "rounding down" would be more appropriate—having an understanding of why to round might help students identify these situations.

▶ Advance Preparation

Print the Round Decimals in Stories printout.

LEARN Model Decimal Numbers

ONLINE
10 min

Students will use the online Grid Learning Tool to model decimal numbers through the hundreths place.

DIRECTIONS FOR USING THE GRID LEARNING TOOL

1. Review the Grid Learning Tool with students. Tell students that when they use the grid to represent decimals, the whole grid represents 1 whole (1.0), each column represents 1 tenth (0.1), and each small square represents 1 hundredth (0.01). See the example grid that follows.

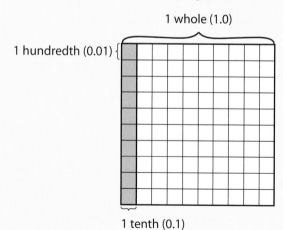

1 whole (1.0)

1 hundredth (0.01) {

1 tenth (0.1)

2. Have students say 0.08 (eight hundredths). Then have students shade 0.08 with the learning tool. See the example answer.

3. Have students repeat Step 2 with the following decimal numbers. Use the arrows to scroll to screens that have more than one whole grid. Have students clear the grid between problems.

- 0.6
- 0.41
- 1.53
- 1.9

After students model each decimal number, have them explain how the model shows each place value. For example, the model for 1.53 shows 1 whole, 5 tenths, and 3 hundredths. The model for 1.9 shows 1 whole and 9 tenths.

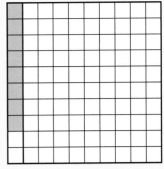

0.08

4. Use the arrows to scroll to the screen that has three whole grids. Now have students shade 2.90 with the learning tool.

2.90

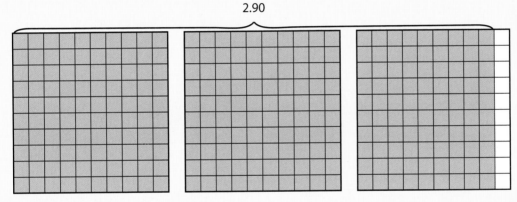

Ask: How many whole grids did you shade? 2

Ask: How many hundredths did you shade? 90

Ask: When you shaded 90 hundredths, how many tenths did you shade? 9

Ask: What decimal number is equivalent to 2.90? 2.9

5. Use the arrows to scroll to the screen that has one whole grid. Introduce students to thousandths. Explain to students that if they divided one whole grid by a thousand, each small square in the grid would have 10 equal parts, and the total grid would have 1,000 equal parts. Tell students that when they divide one hundredth into 10 equal parts, each part is one thousandth.

6. Use the arrows to scroll to the screen that has two whole grids. Have students shade 1.62 by shading one whole grid, then the left six columns and two squares at the top of the seventh column on the second grid. Ask them to name the decimal number shaded. 1.62

Tell students that 1.627 is greater than 1.62 because 1.627 has 7 in the thousandths place and 1.62 has 0 in the thousandths place. Show students the following example of how 1.627 would be shaded on the grid if it showed thousandths. Be sure to let students see the magnified part of one small square on one whole grid that shows 7 thousandths shaded.

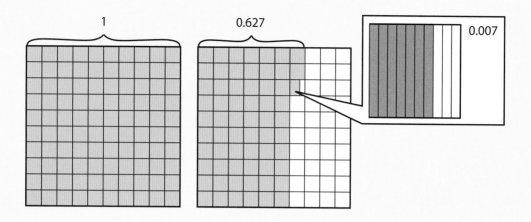

1   0.627   0.007

LEARN Find Rounded Decimals

ONLINE 15 min

Students will use number lines to round decimal numbers through hundredths. The activity will show students how one number can be rounded to different place values, which results in different rounded numbers for the original number.

Objectives

- Round a decimal number to any place through hundredths.

LEARN Round Decimals in Stories

ONLINE 15 min

Students will round decimal numbers to solve story problems. Gather the Round Decimals in Stories printout. Students will write some answers in their Math Notebook.

1. Have students read the first on-screen problem.
2. Have students write 12.394 above the top two number lines on the printout. Have them count aloud from 12.390 to 12.400 using the top number line.

   Say: Let's use a number line to round numbers and solve the problem. What place does the question ask you to round 12.394 to? tenths

   Ask: Use the number line that is marked from 12.390 to 12.400. Mark 12.394 with a dot. Is 12.394 closer to 12.390 or 12.400? 12.390

   Say: We can write 12.390 and 12.400 as equivalent decimal numbers that have digits in the tenths and hundredths places. 12.390 is equivalent to 12.39 and 12.400 is equivalent to 12.40. So 12.394 rounded to the nearest hundredth is 12.39.

   Have students count aloud from 12.30 to 12.40 using the second number line.

   Ask: Use the number line that is marked from 12.30 to 12.40. Mark the approximate location of 12.394 with a dot. Is 12.394 closer to 12.30 or 12.40? 12.40

   Say: We can write 12.30 and 12.40 as equivalent decimal numbers that have digits in the tenths places. 12.30 is equivalent to 12.3 and 12.40 is equivalent to 12.4. So 12.394 rounded to the nearest tenth is 12.4.

Objectives

- Round a decimal number to any place through hundredths.

Tips

Tell students that when they need to round a number ending in 5, they should round to the greater number. For instance, 1.25 rounded to the nearest tenth is 1.3.

Say: What is the answer to the original problem? Nancy put about 12.4 gallons of gas in her car, rounded to the nearest tenth of a gallon.

3. Have students read the second on-screen problem.

4. Have students write 2.465 above the bottom three number lines on the printout. Have them count aloud from 2.460 to 2.470 using the top number line.

   Say: Let's use a number line to round numbers and solve the problem. What place does the question ask you to round 2.465 to? whole number

   Ask: Use the number line that is marked from 2.460 to 2.470. Mark the approximate location of 2.465 with a dot. Since 2.465 is halfway between 2.460 and 2.470, round 2.465 to the greater number. What is 2.465 rounded to the hundredths place? 2.470

   Say: We can write 2.460 and 2.470 as equivalent decimal numbers that have digits in the tenths and hundredths places. 2.460 is equivalent to 2.46 and 2.470 is equivalent to 2.47. So 2.465 rounded to the nearest hundredth is 2.470.

   Have students count aloud from 2.40 to 2.50 using the middle number line.

   Ask: Use the number line that is marked from 2.40 to 2.50. Mark the approximate location of 2.465 with a dot. Is 2.465 closer to 2.40 or 2.50? 2.50

   Say: We can write 2.40 and 2.50 as equivalent decimal numbers that have digits in the tenths place. 2.40 is equivalent to 2.4 and 2.50 is equivalent to 2.5. So 2.465 rounded to the nearest tenth is 2.5.

   Have students count aloud from 2.0 to 3.0 using the bottom number line.

   Ask: Use the number line that is marked from 2.0 to 3.0. Mark the approximate location of 2.465 with a dot. Is 2.465 closer to 2.0 or 3.0? 2.0

   Say: We can write 2.0 and 3.0 as equivalent decimal numbers that have digits in the ones place. 2.0 is equivalent to 2 and 3.0 is equivalent to 3. So 2.465 rounded to the nearest whole number is 2.

   Say: What is the answer to the original problem? Denny put about 2 gallons of gas in his riding lawn mower, rounded to the nearest gallon.

5. Have students read the third on-screen problem. They will not use a number line for this problem and the last problem.

6. Have students write 42.385 in their Math Notebook and round the number to the nearest hundredth of a gallon. They will write the answer in their Math Notebook.

   Ask: What is the closest hundredth that is less than 42.385? 42.38

   Ask: What is the closest hundredth that is greater than 42.385? 42.39

   Say: Since 42.385 is halfway between 42.38 and 42.39, round 42.385 to the greater number.

   Ask: What is the 42.385 rounded to the nearest hundredth? 42.39

   Say: What is the answer to the original problem? The trucker put about 42.39 gallons of diesel fuel in the truck, rounded to the nearest hundredth of a gallon.

7. Have students read the fourth on-screen problem.

8. Have students write 9.27 in their Math Notebook and round the number to the nearest tenth of a gallon. They will write the answer in their Math Notebook.

   Ask: What is the closest tenth that is less than 9.27? 9.2

   Ask: What is the closest tenth that is greater than 9.27? 9.3

Ask: Look at the 7 in the hundredths place in 9.27. Which tenth is 9.27 closer to, 9.2 or 9.3? 9.3

Ask: What is the 9.27 rounded to the nearest tenth? 9.3

Say: What is the answer to the original problem? The farmer put about 9.3 gallons of fuel in the tractor, rounded to the nearest tenth of a gallon.

TRY IT Practice Rounding Decimals

OFFLINE
10 min

Objectives

- Round a decimal number to any place through hundredths.

Students will practice rounding decimal numbers. View or print the Practice Rounding Decimals activity page and read the directions with students.

Students should copy the problems from the Activity Book into their Math Notebook as necessary and solve them there.

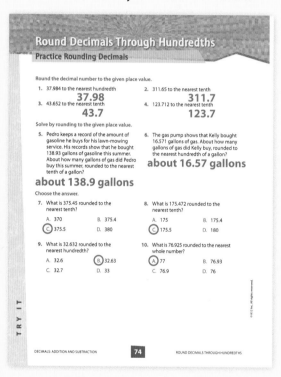

CHECKPOINT

ONLINE
10 min

Objectives

- Round a decimal number to any place through hundredths.

Students will complete an online Checkpoint. If necessary, read the directions, problems, and answer choices to students and help them with keyboard or mouse operations.

Decimal Addition

GET READY Model Decimals	10 minutes	ONLINE
LEARN Model Decimal Addition	20 minutes	ONLINE
LEARN Use the Algorithm for Decimal Addition	15 minutes	ONLINE
TRY IT Addition with Decimals	15 minutes	OFFLINE

▶ Lesson Objectives

Add or subtract decimals to hundredths, using models or drawings and strategies based on place value.

▶ Prerequisite Skills

Identify decimal place values through thousandths.

▶ Content Background

Students will use models to gain greater understanding of place value and the role of place value in addition of decimal numbers. When learning both addition and subtraction of decimal numbers, many adults and students have simply been told "line up the decimals," but that direction does not promote a true understanding of decimal addition and subtraction. Encourage students to work through the examples with models before applying the standard algorithm for both addition and subtraction.

▶ Advance Preparation

Print two copies each of the 10-by-10 Grid and the Centimeter Grid Paper.

Materials to Gather

SUPPLIED
10-by-10 Grid Paper (printout)
Centimeter Grid Paper (printout)
Addition with Decimals activity page

ALSO NEEDED
pencil, coloring – 3 colors

GET READY Model Decimals

ONLINE **10**min

Students will review models for decimal numbers.

Objectives

- Identify decimal place values through thousandths.

LEARN Model Decimal Addition

ONLINE **20**min

Students will investigate grid models to better understand place value in decimal addition.
Gather the two copies of the 10-by-10 Grid Paper. Students will write some answers in their Math Notebook.

Objectives

- Add or subtract decimals to hundredths, using models or drawings and strategies based on place value.

LEARN Use the Algorithm for Decimal Addition

Objectives

- Add or subtract decimals to hundredths, using models or drawings and strategies based on place value.

Students will transition from modeling decimal addition problems to using the standard algorithm. Students need to be able to explain the process of adding decimal numbers.

Gather the two copies of the Centimeter Grid Paper and the coloring pencils. Students will write some answers in their Math Notebook.

TRY IT Addition with Decimals

Objectives

- Add or subtract decimals to hundredths, using models or drawings and strategies based on place value.

Students will practice decimal addition and explain their processes. View or print the Addition with Decimals activity page and read the directions with students.

Students should copy the problems from the Activity Book into their Math Notebook as necessary and solve them there.

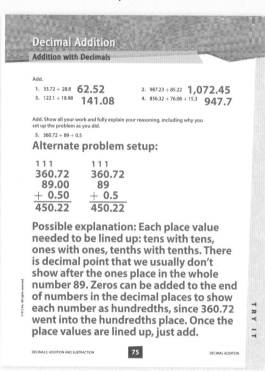

Decimal Addition
Addition with Decimals

Add.
1. 33.72 + 28.8 **62.52**
2. 987.23 + 85.22 **1,072.45**
3. 122.1 + 18.98 **141.08**
4. 856.32 + 76.08 + 15.3 **947.7**

Add. Show all your work and fully explain your reasoning, including why you set up the problem as you did.
5. 360.72 + 89 + 0.5

Alternate problem setup:

```
  1 1 1           1 1 1
  360.72          360.72
   89.00           89
+  0.50        +   0.5
─────────      ─────────
  450.22          450.22
```

Possible explanation: Each place value needed to be lined up: tens with tens, ones with ones, tenths with tenths. There is decimal point that we usually don't show after the ones place in the whole number 89. Zeros can be added to the end of numbers in the decimal places to show each number as hundredths, since 360.72 went into the hundredths place. Once the place values are lined up, just add.

DECIMALS: ADDITION AND SUBTRACTION 75 DECIMAL ADDITION

TRY IT

Decimal Subtraction

Lesson Overview

LEARN Model Decimal Subtraction	15 minutes	ONLINE
LEARN Use the Algorithm for Decimal Subtraction	15 minutes	ONLINE
TRY IT Subtracting with Decimals	15 minutes	OFFLINE
CHECKPOINT	15 minutes	ONLINE

▶ Lesson Objectives

Add or subtract decimals to hundredths, using models or drawings and strategies based on place value.

▶ Content Background

Students will use models to gain greater understanding of place value and the role of place value in subtraction of decimal numbers. When learning both addition and subtraction of decimal numbers, many adults and students have simply been told "line up the decimals," but that direction does not promote a true understanding of decimal addition and subtraction. Encourage students to work through the examples with models before applying the standard algorithm for both addition and subtraction.

Students will also gain a greater understanding of the inverse relationship between addition and subtraction as related to decimal numbers.

▶ Advance Preparation

Print two copies each of the 10-by-10 Grid Paper and the Centimeter Grid Paper.

Materials to Gather

SUPPLIED

10-by-10 Grid Paper (printout)

Centimeter Grid Paper (printout)

Subtracting with Decimals activity page

ALSO NEEDED

pencils, coloring - 3 colors

LEARN Model Decimal Subtraction

ONLINE 15min

Students will investigate grid models to better understand place value in decimal subtraction. Gather the two copies of the 10-by-10 Grid Paper.

Tips If students are having trouble determining whether the place values are lined up, have them write an abbreviation for each place, such as O for ones, Te for tenths, and Hu for hundredths.

Objectives

- Add or subtract decimals to hundredths, using models or drawings and strategies based on place value.

LEARN Use the Algorithm for Decimal Subtraction

Students will transition from modeling decimal subtraction problems to using the standard algorithm. Students need to be able to explain the process of subtracting decimal numbers and check their work by using addition.

Gather the two copies of the Centimeter Grid Paper and coloring pencils. Students will write some answers in their Math Notebook.

Objectives

- Add or subtract decimals to hundredths, using models or drawings and strategies based on place value.

TRY IT Subtracting with Decimals

Students will practice decimal subtraction and explain their processes, including how to check their work by using addition. View or print the Subtracting with Decimals activity page and read the directions with students.

Students should copy the problems from the Activity Book into their Math Notebook as necessary and solve them there.

Objectives

- Add or subtract decimals to hundredths, using models or drawings and strategies based on place value.

Decimal Subtraction

Subtracting with Decimals

Solve.

1. 98.4 − 23.65 = ?   **74.75**
2. 77.63 − 9.3 = ?   **68.33**
3. 639.2 − 42.12 = ?   **597.08**
4. 123.43 − 3.4 = ?   **120.03**

Subtract. Show all work and fully explain your reasoning, including why you set up the problem as you did.

5. 856 − 73.78 = ?   **See right.**

Show how to use addition to check the answer to this problem. Explain why this method of checking works.

6. 15.63 − 6.7 = 8.93   **See right.**

TRY IT

DECIMALS: ADDITION AND SUBTRACTION   76   DECIMAL SUBTRACTION

Additional Answers

5.

$$
\begin{array}{r}
{}^{7\ 15\ 5\ \overset{9}{\cancel{10}}10} \\
8\cancel{56.00} \\
-\ 73.78 \\
\hline
782.22
\end{array}
$$

Possible explanation: Each place value needed to be lined up: tens with tens, ones with ones, tenths with tenths. There is a decimal point that we usually don't show after the ones place in the whole number 856, but we need to put the decimal after 856 and annex 2 zeroes to be able to regroup. Once the place values are lined up, regroup and subtract.

6.

$$
\begin{array}{r}
{}^{0\ 14\ 16} \\
\cancel{15.63} \\
-\ 6.70 \\
\hline
8.93
\end{array}
$$

Possible explanation: When adding the difference to the second number, the sum should be the first number if the problem has been worked correctly. In this problem 8.93 + 6.7 does equal 15.63, so the subtraction was done correctly. This works because addition and subtraction are inverse operations. Subtracting 6.7 from the starting number, 15.63, and then adding 6.7 to the result undoes the operation and results in the starting number.

CHECKPOINT

Students will complete an online Checkpoint. If necessary, read the directions, problems, and answer choices to students and help them with keyboard or mouse operations.

Objectives

- Add or subtract decimals to hundredths, using models or drawings and strategies based on place value.

Solve Story Problems with Decimals

Lesson Overview

GET READY Review Decimal Addition and Subtraction	10 minutes	ONLINE
LEARN Solve Decimal Stories	20 minutes	ONLINE
TRY IT Solve Problems with Decimals	15 minutes	OFFLINE
CHECKPOINT	15 minutes	ONLINE

▶ Lesson Objectives

Solve a story problem involving addition or subtraction of decimal numbers.

▶ Prerequisite Skills

Add or subtract decimals to hundredths, using models or drawings and strategies based on place value.

▶ Content Background

Students may already have a basic understanding of adding and subtracting decimal numbers. They will solve addition and subtraction story problems with decimal numbers.

When students write and compute with decimal numbers, they often use numbers that are between 0 and 1—for example, 0.1. While it is acceptable to write this number as .1, mathematicians usually write the leading zero, to show that the decimal number has zero for the part that is the whole number and to avoid confusion about the value of the number.

▶ Advance Preparation

Print the Decimal Addition and Subtraction Stories printout.

Materials to Gather

SUPPLIED

Decimal Addition and Subtraction Stories (printout)

Solve Problems with Decimals activity page

ONLINE
10min

GET READY Review Decimal Addition and Subtraction

Objectives

Students will solve decimal addition and subtraction problems. The problems will require students to add or subtract decimal numbers of different places. For instance, they may add or subtract a number in the tenths and a number in the hundredths.

- Add or subtract decimals to hundredths, using models or drawings and strategies based on place value.

LEARN Solve Decimal Stories

ONLINE **20**min

Students will solve addition and subtraction story problems. Students also will solve problems using the algorithm, or step-by-step method, and for some problems they will use number lines to check their work.

Gather the Solve Decimal Addition and Subtraction Stories printout. Students will write in their Math Notebook.

Objectives

- Solve a story problem involving addition or subtraction of decimal numbers.

TRY IT Solve Problems with Decimals

OFFLINE **15**min

Students will practice solving addition and subtraction story problems with decimal numbers. View or print the Solve Problems with Decimals activity page and read the directions with students.

Students should copy the problems from the Activity Book into their Math Notebook as necessary and solve them there.

Objectives

- Solve a story problem involving addition or subtraction of decimal numbers.

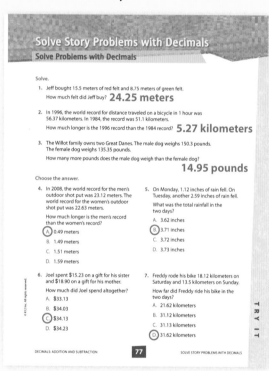

CHECKPOINT

ONLINE **15**min

Students will complete an online Checkpoint. If necessary, read the directions, problems, and answer choices to students and help them with keyboard or mouse operations.

Objectives

- Solve a story problem involving addition or subtraction of decimal numbers.

Estimate Decimal Sums and Differences

Lesson Overview

GET READY Round Decimal Numbers	5 minutes	ONLINE
LEARN Round to Estimate Sums and Differences	20 minutes	ONLINE
LEARN Estimate with Story Problems	10 minutes	OFFLINE
TRY IT Decimal Sum and Difference Estimation	15 minutes	OFFLINE
CHECKPOINT	10 minutes	ONLINE

▶ Lesson Objectives

- Estimate the sum or difference of positive decimal numbers.
- Add or subtract decimals to hundredths, using models or drawings and strategies based on place value.
- Use estimation to predict a solution to a story problem and to verify the reasonableness of the calculated result.
- Estimate the sum or difference in a problem involving decimal numbers.

▶ Prerequisite Skills

Round a decimal number.

▶ Content Background

One way to solve a problem is to use estimation. Students will estimate the sums and differences. To estimate, they will round each number and then add or subtract the rounded numbers.

When students write and compute with decimal numbers, they often use numbers that are between 0 and 1—for example, 0.1. While it is acceptable to write this number as .1, mathematicians usually write the leading zero to show that the decimal number has zero for the part that is the whole number and to avoid confusion about the value of the number.

▶ Common Errors and Misconceptions

- Students might become so concerned about getting the correct answer when estimating that they first find the exact answer and then round it. For example, when asked to estimate $348 + 176$, students might find the sum (524) and then round it to the nearest hundred (500).
- Students might have difficulty accepting that there is more than one correct approach and answer to an estimation problem.

> ### Materials to Gather
>
> **SUPPLIED**
>
> Decimal Sum and Difference Estimation activity page

GET READY Round Decimal Numbers

Students will use data about the wingspans of birds to round decimal numbers to whole numbers and tenths.

- Round a decimal number.

LEARN Round to Estimate Sums and Differences

Students will round numbers to estimate sums and differences in story problems.

- Estimate the sum or difference of positive decimal numbers.

LEARN Estimate with Story Problems

Students will estimate and solve addition and subtraction story problems with decimal numbers. Have students show their work and write their answers in their Math Notebook.

- Estimate the sum or difference of positive decimal numbers.
- Use estimation to predict a solution to a story problem and to verify the reasonableness of the calculated result.
- Add or subtract decimals to hundredths, using models or drawings and strategies based on place value.

1. Read this story problem to students.
   - Yuki is buying two bags of apples at the store. The first bag weighs 3.12 pounds. The second bag weighs 2.65 pounds. How much do both bags weigh together?

2. **Ask:** Should addition or subtraction be used to solve this problem? addition

3. Have students estimate the sum by rounding each number to the nearest tenth and then adding the rounded numbers. Have students write the sum in their Math Notebook. $3.1 + 2.7 = 5.8$; about 5.8 pounds

4. Have students calculate the exact answer. Remind them to line up the decimal numbers by place values and start by adding the numbers in the hundredths place. $3.12 + 2.65 = 5.77$; 5.77 pounds

5. Have students look at the estimate. Ask them if the calculated answer is reasonable. Yes

   If students decide the calculated answer is not reasonable, they should check their addition and decide if the new answer is reasonable.

6. **Ask:** Why is the answer reasonable? The exact answer, 5.77, is close to the estimated answer, 5.8. In fact, 5.77 rounded to the nearest tenth is 5.8, which is the estimated answer.

   Have students write the answer to the problem. The two bags weigh 5.77 pounds together.

7. Read this story problem to students.
   - José was going to buy four bags of carrots that weighed 8.7 pounds, but decided to put one bag back. That bag weighed 2.2 pounds. How many pounds of carrots are in the three bags José is buying?

8. **Ask:** Should addition or subtraction be used to solve this problem? subtraction

9. Have students estimate the difference by rounding each number to the nearest whole number and then subtracting the rounded numbers. Have students write the difference in their Math Notebook. $9 - 2 = 7$; about 7 pounds

10. Have students calculate the exact answer. Remind them to line up the decimal numbers by place values and start by subtracting the number in the tenths place. 8.7 − 2.2 = 6.5; 6.5 pounds

11. Have students look at the estimate. Ask them if the calculated answer is reasonable. Yes

If students decide the calculated answer is not reasonable, have them check their subtraction and decide if the new answer is reasonable.

12. **Ask:** Why is the answer reasonable? The exact answer, 6.5, is close to the estimated answer, 7. In fact, rounding 6.5 to the greater whole number equals 7, which is the estimated answer.

Have students write the answer to the problem. There are 6.5 pounds of carrots in the three bags.

OFFLINE
15min

TRY IT Decimal Sum and Difference Estimation

Students will practice rounding and estimation to solve addition and subtraction story problems with decimal numbers. View or print the Decimal Sum and Difference Estimation activity page and read the directions with students.

Students should copy the problems from the Activity Book into their Math Notebook as necessary and solve them there.

Objectives

- Estimate the sum or difference in a problem involving decimal numbers.

ONLINE
10min

CHECKPOINT

Students will complete an online Checkpoint. If necessary, read the directions, problems, and answer choices to students and help them with keyboard or mouse operations.

Objectives

- Estimate the sum or difference in a problem involving decimal numbers.

Core Focus
Decimal Addition and Subtraction

Lesson Overview

LEARN Place Value to Thousandths	10 minutes	ONLINE
LEARN Decimal Sums and Differences	20 minutes	ONLINE
TRY IT Add and Subtract with Decimals	15 minutes	OFFLINE
CHECKPOINT	15 minutes	ONLINE

▶ Lesson Objectives

- Recognize that in a multidigit number, a digit in one place represents 10 times as much as it represents in the place to its right and $\frac{1}{10}$ of what it represents in the place to its left.
- Round a decimal number to any place through hundredths.
- Estimate the sum or difference of positive decimal numbers.
- Solve an addition or subtraction problem involving decimal numbers.
- Add or subtract decimals to hundredths, using models or drawings and strategies based on place value.

▶ Content Background

Students have learned many topics related to decimal numbers including the meaning of the place values and how to find both estimated and exact sums and differences. In this lesson, students will review the relationship among place values and solve addition and subtraction computation and story problems.

Materials to Gather

SUPPLIED

Add and Subtract with Decimals activity page

LEARN Place Value to Thousandths

ONLINE **10** min

Students will review place values and the relationship among the values.

Objectives

- Recognize that in a multidigit number, a digit in one place represents 10 times as much as it represents in the place to its right and $\frac{1}{10}$ of what it represents in the place to its left.

LEARN Decimal Sums and Differences

Students will estimate and find exact solutions to addition and subtraction problems involving decimal numbers.

Objectives

- Round a decimal number to any place through hundredths.
- Estimate the sum or difference of positive decimal numbers.
- Solve an addition or subtraction problem involving decimal numbers.
- Add or subtract decimals to hundredths, using models or drawings and strategies based on place value.

TRY IT Add and Subtract with Decimals

Students will complete problems that require them to explain place value relationships. Students will also analyze and solve decimal addition and subtraction problems giving both estimates and exact answers. View or print the Add and Subtract with Decimals activity page. Students should copy the problems into their Math Notebook and solve them there.

Objectives

- Recognize that in a multidigit number, a digit in one place represents 10 times as much as it represents in the place to its right and $\frac{1}{10}$ of what it represents in the place to its left.
- Round a decimal number to any place through hundredths.
- Estimate the sum or difference of positive decimal numbers.
- Solve an addition or subtraction problem involving decimal numbers.
- Add or subtract decimals to hundredths, using models or drawings and strategies based on place value.

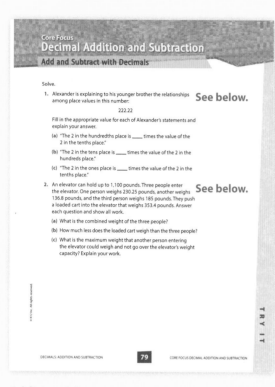

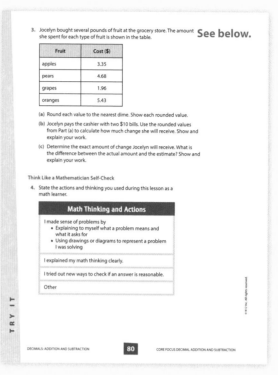

Additional Answers

1. **(a)** $\frac{1}{10}$; **Possible explanation:** Since 10 hundredths equals 1 tenth, 2 hundredths is $\frac{1}{10}$ times the value of 2 tenths.

   (b) $\frac{1}{10}$; **Possible explanation:** Since 10 tens equals 1 hundred, 2 tens is $\frac{1}{10}$ times the value of 2 hundreds.

   (c) 10; **Possible explanation:** Since 10 tenths equals 1 one, 2 ones is 10 times the value of 2 tenths.

3. **(a)** apples: \$3.40; pears: \$4.70; grapes: \$2.00; oranges: \$5.40

   (b) She will receive about \$4.50 in change.
   The approximate cost of the fruit is \$15.50.
   $3.40 + 4.70 + 2.00 + 5.40 = 15.50$
   Jocelyn gave the cashier \$20.00,
   so \$20.00 − \$15.50 = \$4.50.

   (c) She will receive exactly \$4.58 in change.
   The difference between the actual amount of change and the estimated amount is \$0.08. The exact cost of the fruit is \$15.42.
   $3.35 + 4.68 + 1.96 + 5.43 = 15.42$
   Jocelyn gave the cashier \$20.00, so
   \$20.00 − \$15.42 = \$4.58.
   The actual amount of change minus the estimated amount is \$4.58 − \$4.50 = \$0.08.

2. **(a)** The three people weigh 552.05 pounds.
   $230.25 + 136.8 + 185 = 552.05$

   (b) The cart weighs 198.65 pounds less than the people do. $552.05 − 353.4 = 198.65$

   (c) The maximum weight for another person is 194.55 pounds.
   The three people and the cart weigh 905.45 pounds.
   $230.25 + 136.8 + 185 + 353.4 = 905.45$
   The elevator can hold up to 1,100 pounds, so $1,100 − 905.45 = 194.55$ pounds.

CHECKPOINT

Objectives

Students will complete an online Checkpoint. If necessary, read the directions, problems, and answer choices to students and help them with keyboard or mouse operations.

- Recognize that in a multidigit number, a digit in one place represents 10 times as much as it represents in the place to its right and $\frac{1}{10}$ of what it represents in the place to its left.

- Estimate the sum or difference of positive decimal numbers.

- Solve an addition or subtraction problem involving decimal numbers.

- Add or subtract decimals to hundredths, using models or drawings and strategies based on place value.

Unit Review

Lesson Overview

UNIT REVIEW Look Back	10 minutes	**ONLINE**
UNIT REVIEW Checkpoint Practice	50 minutes	**ONLINE**
▣ **UNIT REVIEW** Prepare for the Checkpoint		

▶ Unit Objectives

This lesson reviews the following objectives:

- Compare decimal numbers.
- Order three or more decimal numbers.
- Read, write, compare, and order decimals to thousandths.
- Write decimals in expanded form.
- Recognize that in a multidigit number, a digit in one place represents 10 times as much as it represents in the place to its right and $\frac{1}{10}$ of what it represents in the place to its left.
- Round a decimal number to any place through hundredths.
- Add or subtract decimals to hundredths, using models or drawings and strategies based on place value.
- Solve a story problem involving addition or subtraction of decimal numbers.
- Estimate the sum or difference of positive decimal numbers.
- Use estimation to predict a solution to a story problem and to verify the reasonableness of the calculated result.
- Estimate the sum or difference in a problem involving decimal numbers.
- Solve an addition or subtraction problem involving decimal numbers.

Materials to Gather

There are no materials to gather for this lesson.

▶ Advance Preparation

In this lesson, students will have an opportunity to review previous activities in the Decimals: Addition and Subtraction unit. Look at the suggested activities in Unit Review: Prepare for the Checkpoint online and gather any needed materials.

UNIT REVIEW Look Back

ONLINE 10 min

Objectives

- Review unit objectives.

Students will review key concepts from the unit to prepare for the Unit Checkpoint.

UNIT REVIEW Checkpoint Practice

ONLINE 50 min

Objectives

- Review unit objectives.

Students will complete an online Checkpoint Practice to prepare for the Unit Checkpoint. If necessary, read the directions, problems, and answer choices to students. Have students answer the problems on their own. Review any missed problems with students.

⇥ UNIT REVIEW Prepare for the Checkpoint

What you do next depends on how students performed in the previous activity, Unit Review: Checkpoint Practice. If students had difficulty with any of the problems, complete the appropriate review activity listed in the table online.

Unit Checkpoint

UNIT CHECKPOINT Online | 60 minutes | **ONLINE**

▶ Unit Objectives

This lesson assesses the following objectives:

- Compare decimal numbers.
- Order three or more decimal numbers.
- Read, write, compare, and order decimals to thousandths.
- Write decimals in expanded form.
- Recognize that in a multidigit number, a digit in one place represents 10 times as much as it represents in the place to its right and $\frac{1}{10}$ of what it represents in the place to its left.
- Round a decimal number to any place through hundredths.
- Add or subtract decimals to hundredths, using models or drawings and strategies based on place value.
- Solve a story problem involving addition or subtraction of decimal numbers.
- Estimate the sum or difference of positive decimal numbers.
- Use estimation to predict a solution to a story problem and to verify the reasonableness of the calculated result.
- Estimate the sum or difference in a problem involving decimal numbers.
- Solve an addition or subtraction problem involving decimal numbers.

Materials to Gather

There are no materials to gather for this lesson.

UNIT CHECKPOINT Online

ONLINE 60 min

Students will complete the Unit Checkpoint online. If necessary, read the directions, problems, and answer choices to students and help them with keyboard or mouse operations.

Objectives

- Assess unit objectives.

Extended Problems: Reasoning

USE WHAT YOU KNOW Offline   60 minutes | OFFLINE

▶ Lesson Objectives

This lesson assesses the following objectives:

- Compare decimal numbers.
- Round a decimal number to any place through hundredths.
- Solve an addition or subtraction problem involving decimal numbers.
- Verify that the calculated result of a problem involving addition or subtraction of decimal numbers is reasonable.
- Solve a story problem involving addition or subtraction of decimal numbers.
- Analyze complex problems using mathematical knowledge and skills.

Materials to Gather

SUPPLIED

Extended Problems: Reasoning (printout)

Extended Problems: Reasoning Answer Key (printout)

USE WHAT YOU KNOW Offline

OFFLINE 60 min

Objectives

- Analyze complex problems using mathematical knowledge and skills.

The Extended Problems: Reasoning and its answer key are located in the Resources section for this unit in the Online Book Menu of *Math+ Yellow Lesson Guide*. Give students the Extended Problems: Reasoning. Read the directions, problems, and answer choices to students, if necessary.

You will grade this assignment.

- Students should complete the assignment on their own.
- Students should submit the completed assignment to you.

Decimals: Multiplication and Division

▶ Unit Objectives

- Multiply or divide by a multiple or power of 10.
- Write decimals in expanded form.
- Compare decimal numbers.
- Use place value to round decimals to any place.
- Estimate the product or quotient of a computation problem involving decimal numbers.
- Solve a multiplication or division problem that involves decimal numbers.
- Verify that the calculated result of a problem involving multiplication or division of decimal numbers is reasonable.
- Solve a story problem that involves multiplication or division of decimal numbers.
- Read, write, compare, and order decimals to thousandths.

▶ Big Ideas

- Estimation is a useful tool in problem solving.
- Multiplication and division can be represented by models and by using math symbols.

▶ Unit Introduction

Students will continue to develop number sense and computation skills with decimal numbers in this unit. They will learn how to mentally multiply and divide by multiples and powers of 10. Students will also estimate and find exact answers to computation and story problems involving products and quotients with decimal numbers.

▶ Keywords

addend	estimate (v.)	power of 10
algorithm	expanded form	product
boundary number	hundredths	quotient
decimal number	multiple	round
decimal place-value chart	number line	tenths
estimate (n.)	power	thousandths

Multiply and Divide by Powers of 10

▶ Lesson Objectives

Multiply or divide by a multiple or power of 10.

▶ Prerequisite Skills

Estimate or calculate a product or a quotient in a whole-number problem.

▶ Content Background

Students may already understand multiplication and division by powers of 10 with whole numbers. In this lesson, they will investigate the patterns that arise when multiplying and dividing decimal numbers by multiples and powers of 10. Students will be encouraged to compute most of the problems mentally.

When students write and compute with decimal numbers, they often use numbers that are between 0 and 1—for example, 0.1. While it is acceptable to write this number as .1, mathematicians usually write the leading zero, to show that the whole-number value for the decimal number is zero and to avoid confusion about the value of the number.

Materials to Gather

SUPPLIED

Multiply and Divide Decimals by Powers of 10 activity page

ONLINE

5 min

GET READY Multiply and Divide Whole Numbers

Students will estimate the product of multiplication problems and the quotient of division problems that involve whole numbers.

Objectives

- Estimate or calculate a product or a quotient in a whole-number problem.

LEARN Multiply and Divide Decimals by Multiples of 10 **20 min**

Objectives

Students will investigate the patterns that arise when multiplying and dividing by multiples of 10.

- Multiply or divide by a multiple or power of 10.

Tips Encourage students to learn the patterns in multiplying and dividing by multiples of 10 and work the problems mentally.

LEARN Multiply and Divide Decimals by Powers of 10 **10 min**

Objectives

Students will investigate the patterns that arise when multiplying and dividing by powers of 10.

View or print the Multiply and Divide Decimals by Powers of 10 activity page. Encourage students to study each Worked Example before working the practice problems. Students will write the problems and their answers in their Math Notebook.

- Multiply or divide by a multiple or power of 10.

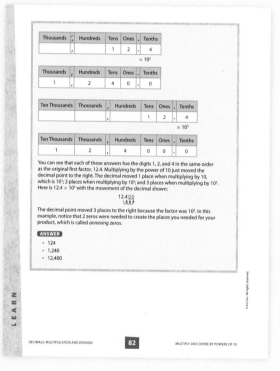

Multiply and Divide by Powers of 10

Multiply and Divide Decimals by Powers of 10

Worked Examples

The place-value system is based on powers of 10:

$10^0 = 1$ (ones place)
$10^1 = 10$ (tens place)
$10^2 = 100$ (hundreds place)
$10^3 = 1,000$ (thousands place)
and so on…

Notice that the exponent in the power of 10 matches the number of zeros in the value of the number. For example, 100 has 2 zeros, and the exponent on 10^2 is 2.

When you multiply or divide by powers of 10, you just change the location of the decimal point. You can multiply by powers of 10 simply by moving the decimal point to the right the number of places shown by the exponent on the 10 (or the number of zeros in the power of 10, if written out). When dividing, move the decimal point to the left the number of places shown by the power of 10. Remember that the decimal point is always located after the ones place, so in the whole number 23, the decimal point is located after the 3 ones.

PROBLEM 1 Find the following products:

- 12.4×10^1
- 12.4×10^2
- 12.4×10^3

SOLUTION When you multiply by a power of 10, you increase the place value of each digit by that power as you move the decimal to the right.

Hundreds	Tens	Ones	.	Tenths
	1	2	.	4

$\times 10^1$

Hundreds	Tens	Ones	.	Tenths
1	2	4	.	0

Thousands	,	Hundreds	Tens	Ones	.	Tenths
	,		1	2	.	4

$\times 10^2$

Thousands	,	Hundreds	Tens	Ones	.	Tenths
1	,	2	4	0	.	0

Ten Thousands	Thousands	,	Hundreds	Tens	Ones	.	Tenths
		,		1	2	.	4

$\times 10^3$

Ten Thousands	Thousands	,	Hundreds	Tens	Ones	.	Tenths
1	2	,	4	0	0	.	0

You can see that each of these answers has the digits 1, 2, and 4 in the same order as the original first factor, 12.4. Multiplying by the power of 10 just moved the decimal point to the right. The decimal moved 1 place when multiplying by 10, which is 10^1; 2 places when multiplying by 10^2; and 3 places when multiplying by 10^3. Here is 12.4×10^3 with the movement of the decimal shown:

12.400

The decimal point moved 3 places to the right because the factor was 10^3. In this example, notice that 2 zeros were needed to create the places you needed for your product, which is called *annexing* zeros.

ANSWER

- 124
- 1,240
- 12,400

LEARN

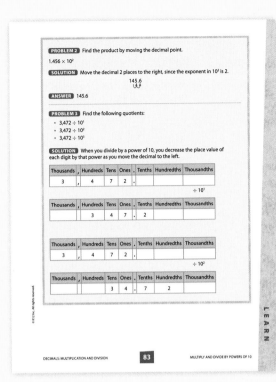

PROBLEM 2 Find the product by moving the decimal point.

1.456×10^2

SOLUTION Move the decimal 2 places to the right, since the exponent in 10^2 is 2.

145.6

ANSWER 145.6

PROBLEM 3 Find the following quotients:

- $3{,}472 \div 10^1$
- $3{,}472 \div 10^2$
- $3{,}472 \div 10^3$

SOLUTION When you divide by a power of 10, you decrease the place value of each digit by that power as you move the decimal to the left.

Thousands	,	Hundreds	Tens	Ones	.	Tenths	Hundredths	Thousandths
3		4	7	2				

$\div 10^1$

Thousands	,	Hundreds	Tens	Ones	.	Tenths	Hundredths	Thousandths
		3	4	7		2		

Thousands	,	Hundreds	Tens	Ones	.	Tenths	Hundredths	Thousandths
3		4	7	2				

$\div 10^2$

Thousands	,	Hundreds	Tens	Ones	.	Tenths	Hundredths	Thousandths
			3	4		7	2	

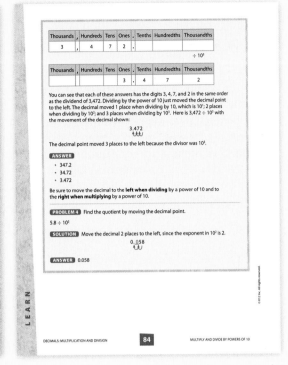

Thousands	,	Hundreds	Tens	Ones	.	Tenths	Hundredths	Thousandths
3		4	7	2				

$\div 10^3$

Thousands	,	Hundreds	Tens	Ones	.	Tenths	Hundredths	Thousandths
				3		4	7	2

You can see that each of these answers has the digits 3, 4, 7, and 2 in the same order as the dividend of 3,472. Dividing by the power of 10 just moved the decimal point to the left. The decimal moved 1 place when dividing by 10, which is 10^1; 2 places when dividing by 10^2; and 3 places when dividing by 10^3. Here is $3{,}472 \div 10^3$ with the movement of the decimal shown:

3.472

The decimal point moved 3 places to the left because the divisor was 10^3.

ANSWER

- 347.2
- 34.72
- 3.472

Be sure to move the decimal to the **left when dividing** by a power of 10 and to the **right when multiplying** by a power of 10.

PROBLEM 4 Find the quotient by moving the decimal point.

$5.8 \div 10^2$

SOLUTION Move the decimal 2 places to the left, since the exponent in 10^2 is 2.

0.058

ANSWER 0.058

Determine the product or quotient by moving the decimal.

1. 56.34×10^2 **5,634**
2. 3.06×10 **30.6**
3. $8.2 \div 10^2$ **0.082**
4. 99×10^4 **990,000**
5. 0.42×10^3 **420**
6. 0.07×10^5 **7,000**
7. $300.06 \div 10$ **30.006**
8. $86{,}743.2 \div 10^2$ **867.432**

LEARN Decimal Products and Quotients

Objectives

- Multiply or divide by a multiple or power of 10.

Students will multiply and divide numbers by powers of 10. They will see that when a decimal number is multiplied by a number greater than or equal to 1, the product is greater than or equal to the decimal number. They will also see that when a decimal number is multiplied by a number less than 1, the product is less than the decimal number. Similarly, they will see that when a decimal number is divided by a number greater than or equal to 1, the quotient is less than or equal to the decimal number. And lastly, when a decimal number is divided by a number less than 1, the quotient is greater than the decimal number.

TRY IT Multiply and Divide by Powers of 10

Objectives

- Multiply or divide by a multiple or power of 10.

Students will complete an online Try It. If necessary, read the directions, problems, and answer choices to students and help them with keyboard or mouse operations.

CHECKPOINT

Objectives

- Multiply or divide by a multiple or power of 10.

Students will complete an online Checkpoint. If necessary, read the directions, problems, and answer choices to students and help them with keyboard or mouse operations.

Expand and Compare Decimal Numbers

▶ ## Lesson Objectives

- Write decimals in expanded form.
- Compare decimal numbers.

▶ ## Prerequisite Skills

Identify decimal place values through thousandths.

▶ ## Content Background

Students may know how to write whole numbers in expanded form using words and multiples of 10. In this lesson, they will write decimal numbers in expanded form using powers of 10. With this greater understanding of place value, students will be prepared to compare decimal numbers to the thousandths place.

Materials to Gather

SUPPLIED

Compare Decimals by Place Value activity page

ONLINE
10 min

GET READY Decimal Place Value

Students will identify decimal place values through the thousandths place.

Objectives

- Identify decimal place values through thousandths.

LEARN Write Decimal Numbers in Expanded Form

ONLINE 10 min

Objectives

- Write decimals in expanded form.

Students will build on their knowledge of expanded form with whole numbers to write decimal numbers to thousandths in expanded form. Students may only have experience writing expanded form using place value words or multiples of 10. In this activity, students will use powers of 10 to write decimal numbers in expanded form.

Tips

If students have trouble writing decimal powers of 10, have them say the place value, such as "hundredths," and then write one-hundredth as a fraction.

LEARN Compare Decimal Numbers

ONLINE 10 min

Objectives

- Compare decimal numbers.

Students will place value to compare decimal numbers through the thousandths place.

LEARN Compare Decimals by Place Value

OFFLINE 10 min

Objectives

- Compare decimal numbers.

Students will review and practice comparing two decimal numbers through the thousandths place. View or print the Compare Decimals by Place Value activity page and read the directions with students. The problems will help students compare the values of decimal numbers by focusing on place value.

Students should copy the problems from the Activity Book into their Math Notebook as necessary and solve them there.

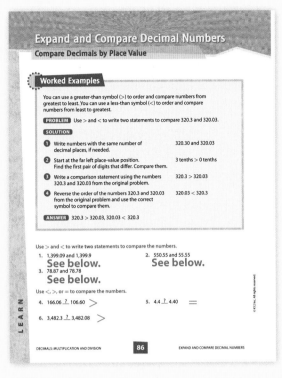

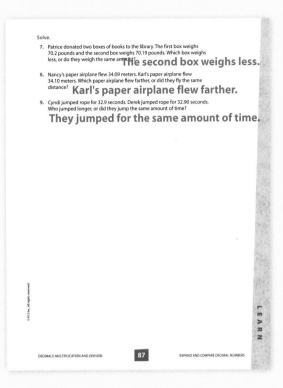

Additional Answers

1. $1,399.09 < 1,399.9$; $1,399.9 > 1,399.09$

2. $550.55 > 55.55$; $55.55 < 550.55$

3. $78.87 > 78.78$; $78.78 < 78.87$

TRY IT Expand and Compare Decimals

ONLINE **10** min

Objectives

Students will complete an online Try It. If necessary, read the directions, problems, and answer choices to students and help them with keyboard or mouse operations.

- Write decimals in expanded form.
- Compare decimal numbers.

CHECKPOINT

ONLINE **10** min

Objectives

Students will complete an online Checkpoint. If necessary, read the directions, problems, and answer choices to students and help them with keyboard or mouse operations.

- Write decimals in expanded form.
- Compare decimal numbers.

Round to Estimate Decimal Products and Quotients

▶ Lesson Objectives

- Use place value to round decimals to any place.
- Estimate the product or quotient of a computation problem involving decimal numbers.

▶ Prerequisite Skills

Round numbers through 10,000.

▶ Content Background

Students may already understand estimating products and quotients of whole numbers. In this lesson, they will learn to estimate the product or quotient in a division problem with decimal numbers.

When students write and compute with decimal numbers, they often use numbers that are between 0 and 1—for example, 0.1. While it is acceptable to write this number as .1, mathematicians usually write the leading zero, to show that the whole-number value for the decimal number is zero and to avoid confusion about the value of the number.

When students use a number line to help them round decimal numbers, all the numbers will show the same number of decimal places. For example, on a number line showing numbers in hundredths, numbers such as 42.80 will appear, rather than the equivalent value 42.8. When students find the rounded value of a number, they should give their answer to the decimal place being rounded. For example, when rounding 42.78 to the nearest tenth, they would answer 42.8, emphasizing the tenths place, even though the number line shows 42.80. Be sure that students understand that numbers such as 42.8 and 42.80 show the same value and position on the number line, but emphasize different place values.

Materials to Gather

SUPPLIED

Round to Estimate Products (printout)

Round to Estimate Quotients (printout)

Round to Estimate Products and Quotients activity page

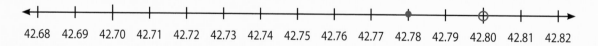

42.68 42.69 42.70 42.71 42.72 42.73 42.74 42.75 42.76 42.77 42.78 42.79 42.80 42.81 42.82

▶ Common Errors and Misconceptions

- Students might become so concerned about getting the correct answer when estimating that they first find the exact answer, and then round it. For example, when asked to estimate $348 + 176$, students might find the sum (524), and then round it to the nearest hundred (500).
- Students might have difficulty accepting that there is more than one correct approach and answer to an estimation problem.

▶ Advance Preparation

Print Round to Estimate Products and Round to Estimate Quotients.

GET READY Round Numbers Through 10,000

ONLINE 10 min

Students will round whole numbers to 10,000 using boundary numbers.

Objectives

- Round numbers through 10,000.

LEARN Round to Estimate Products

OFFLINE 15 min

Students will estimate products of decimal numbers by first rounding the decimal numbers in the problem and then multiplying the rounded numbers as fractions. Using the fraction values will allow students to not only practice fraction multiplication, but also give them a better understanding of the rules they will learn for multiplying decimals. They will use number lines to round numbers in the first set of problems. Then they will round numbers without using number lines.

Gather the Round to Estimate Products printout. Students will write some answers in their Math Notebook.

Objectives

- Use place value to round decimals to any place.
- Estimate the product or quotient of a computation problem involving decimal numbers.

Tips

If students have trouble writing equivalent fractions for decimals, make a number line from 1 to 2, marking tenths and quarters. Write the fraction equivalent below each decimal on the number line.

ROUND NUMBERS WITH A NUMBER LINE AND MULTIPLY

1. Tell students they will use number lines to estimate the product of decimal numbers. Point out the first problem—$302 \times 175 = ?$—and the first two number lines on the printout.

2. **Say:** Use a number line to round each number, 302 and 175, to the nearest ten. Then use the rounded numbers to estimate the product.

3. Point to the number line showing 290 to 320 in whole numbers.

   Say: Mark 302 with a dot.

   Ask: Is 302 closer to 300 or 310? 300

   Have students circle 300 on the number line.

   Ask: What is 302 rounded to the nearest ten? 300

4. Point to the number line showing 160 to 190 in whole numbers.

   Say: Mark 175 with a dot.

   Ask: What is 175 rounded to the tens place? 180

   Have students circle 180 on the number line.

5. Have students use the rounded numbers and write the number sentence on the printout. Have them multiply the numbers. $300 \times 180 = 54{,}000$

Ask: When you round the addends to the nearest ten, what is the estimated product of 302×175? about 54,000

6. Repeat Steps 2–5 to guide students to estimate 200×37.29 by rounding 37.29 to the nearest whole number. They will use the number lines on the printout.

7. As they estimate, have students mark the number line to show that 37.29 rounded to the nearest whole number is 37.

Say: 37.29 is one factor needed to find the product. Since 37.29 doesn't have a tick mark on the number line, you'll mark a dot that's between 37.2 and 37.3. When you do that, you're finding the *approximate* location for the point for 37.29 on the number line.

Ask: If we're rounding to the nearest whole number, what do you need to do to round 200? Since 200 is a whole number, it does not need to be rounded.

Ask: When you round the factors to the nearest whole number, what is the estimated product of 200×37.29? about 7,400

ROUND NUMBERS WITHOUT A NUMBER LINE AND MULTIPLY

8. Have students write $0.846 \times 0.723 = ?$ in their Math Notebook.

9. Tell students they will estimate the product of 0.846×0.723. They will round the addends to the nearest tenth without a number line.

10. **Ask:** Think about the number lines you used to round numbers in the first two problems. What is 0.846 rounded to the nearest tenth? 0.8

Ask: What is 0.8 in fraction form? $\frac{8}{10}$

Ask: What is 0.723 rounded to the nearest tenth? 0.7

Ask: What is 0.7 in fraction form? $\frac{7}{10}$

11. Have students find the estimated product by multiplying $\frac{8}{10} \times \frac{7}{10}$. $\frac{56}{100}$

Ask: What is $\frac{56}{100}$ in decimal form? 0.56

Ask: When you round the factors to the nearest tenth, what is the estimated product of 0.846×0.723? about 0.56

12. Have students write $1.47 \times 0.381 = ?$ in their Math Notebook.

13. Tell students they will estimate the product of 1.47×0.381 to the nearest tenth.

Ask: Think about the number lines you used to round numbers in the first two problems. What is 1.47 rounded to the nearest tenth? 1.5

Ask: What is 1.5 in mixed number form and as an improper fraction? $1\frac{5}{10} = \frac{15}{10}$

Ask: What is 0.381 rounded to the nearest tenth? 0.4

Ask: What is 0.4 in fraction form? $\frac{4}{10}$

14. Have students find the estimated product by multiplying $\frac{15}{10} \times \frac{4}{10}$. $\frac{60}{100}$

Ask: What is $\frac{60}{100}$ in decimal form? 0.6

Ask: When you round the factors to the nearest tenth, what is the estimated product of 1.47×0.381? about 0.6

LEARN Round to Estimate Quotients

Students will estimate quotients of decimal numbers by first rounding the decimal numbers for the dividend and the divisor in the problem and then dividing the rounded numbers as fractions. Using the fraction values will allow students to not only practice fraction division, but also give them a better understanding of the rules they will learn for multiplying decimals. They will use number lines to round numbers in the first set of problems. Then they will round numbers without using number lines.

Gather the Round to Estimate Quotients printout. Students will write some answers in their Math Notebook.

ROUND NUMBERS WITH A NUMBER LINE AND DIVIDE

1. Tell students they will use number lines to estimate the quotient of decimal numbers. Point out the first problem—802 ÷ 22 = ?—and the first two number lines on the printout.

2. **Say:** Use a number line to round the dividend (802) and the divisor (22) to the nearest ten. Then use the rounded numbers to estimate the quotient.

3. Point to the number line showing 790 to 820 in whole numbers.

   Say: Mark 802 with a dot.

   Ask: Is 802 closer to 800 or 810? 800

   Have students circle 800 on the number line.

   Ask: What is 802 rounded to the nearest ten? 800

4. Point to the number line showing 10 to 40 in whole numbers.

   Say: Mark 22 with a dot.

   Ask: Is 22 closer to 20 or 30? 20

   Have students circle 20 on the number line.

   Ask: What is 22 rounded to the nearest ten? 20

5. Have students use the rounded numbers and write the number sentence on the printout to estimate the quotient. Have them divide the numbers. 800 ÷ 20 = 40

   Ask: When you round the dividend and the divisor to the nearest ten, what is the estimated quotient of 802 ÷ 22? about 40

6. Point out the second problem—6.0 ÷ 0.51 = ?—and the number line on the printout.

7. **Say:** Round the dividend (6.0) and the divisor (0.51) to the nearest tenth. Then use the rounded numbers to estimate the quotient.

8. **Ask:** If we're rounding to the nearest tenth, what do you need to do to round 6.0? Since 6.0 is a whole number, it does not need to be rounded.

9. Point to the number line showing 0.40 to 0.70 in tenths.

   Say: Mark 0.51 with a dot.

   Ask: Is 0.51 closer to 0.50 or 0.60? 0.50

   Have students circle 0.50 on the number line.

   Ask: What is 0.51 rounded to the nearest tenth? 0.5

   Ask: What is 0.5 in fraction form? $\frac{5}{10}$

10. Have students find the estimated quotient of $6.0 \div \frac{5}{10}$.

$$\frac{6}{1} \div \frac{5}{10} = \frac{6}{1} \times \frac{10}{5} = \frac{60}{5} = 12$$

Ask: When you round the dividend and the divisor to the nearest tenth, what is the estimated quotient of $6.0 \div 0.51$? about 12

ROUND NUMBERS WITHOUT A NUMBER LINE AND DIVIDE

11. Have students write $0.268 \div 0.603 = ?$ in their Math Notebook.

12. Tell students they will estimate the quotient of $0.268 \div 0.603$. They will round the dividend and divisor to the nearest tenth without a number line.

13. **Ask:** Think about the number lines you used to round numbers in the last two problems. What is 0.268 rounded to the nearest tenth? 0.3

Ask: What is 0.3 in fraction form? $\frac{3}{10}$

Ask: What is 0.603 rounded to the nearest tenth? 0.6

Ask: What is 0.6 in fraction form? $\frac{6}{10}$

14. Have students find the estimated quotient by dividing $\frac{3}{10} \div \frac{6}{10}$. Remind students to divide out common factors when multiplying by the reciprocal of the divisor.

$$\frac{3}{10} \div \frac{6}{10} = \frac{3}{\cancel{10}} \times \frac{\cancel{10}^{1}}{6} = \frac{3}{6} = \frac{1}{2}$$

Ask: What is $\frac{1}{2}$ in decimal form? 0.5

Ask: When you round the dividend and the divisor to the nearest tenth, what is the estimated quotient of $0.268 \div 0.603$? about 0.5

15. Have students write $0.246 \div 2.501 = ?$ in their Math Notebook.

16. Have students find the estimated quotient by dividing $\frac{25}{100} \div \frac{250}{100}$. Remind students to divide out common factors when multiplying by the reciprocal of the divisor.

$$\frac{25}{100} \div \frac{250}{100} = \frac{\cancel{25}^{1}}{\cancel{100}_{1}} \div \frac{\cancel{100}^{1}}{\cancel{250}_{10}} = \frac{1}{10}$$

Ask: What is $\frac{1}{10}$ in decimal form? 0.1

Ask: When you round the dividend and the divisor to the nearest hundredth, what is the estimated quotient of $0.246 \div 2.501$? about 0.1

TRY IT Round to Estimate Products and Quotients

Objectives

- Use place value to round decimals to any place.
- Estimate the product or quotient of a computation problem involving decimal numbers.

Students will practice estimating quotients with decimal numbers. View or print the Round to Estimate Products and Quotients activity page and read the directions with students.

Students should copy the problems from the Activity Book into their Math Notebook as necessary and solve them there.

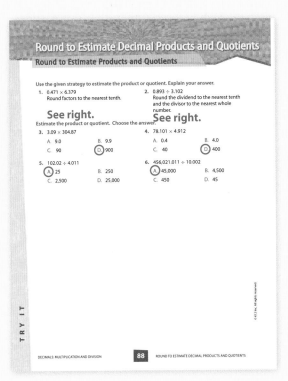

Additional Answers

1. Answers will vary. **Example explanation:** 0.471 rounded to the nearest tenth is 0.5. 6.379 rounded to the nearest tenth is 6.4.

$$0.5 \times 6.4 = \frac{5}{10} \times 6\frac{4}{10} = \frac{1}{2} \times \frac{64}{10} = \frac{32}{10} = 3\frac{2}{10} = 3.2$$

The estimated product of 0.471×6.379 is about 3.2.

2. Answers will vary. **Example explanation:** 0.893 can be rounded to the friendly number 0.9. 3.102 can be rounded to the friendly number 3.0.

$$0.9 \div 3.0 = \frac{9}{10} \div \frac{3}{1} = \frac{9}{10} \times \frac{1}{3} = \frac{3}{10} = 0.3$$

The estimated quotient of $0.893 \div 3.102$ is about 0.3.

CHECKPOINT

Objectives

- Use place value to round decimals to any place.
- Estimate the product or quotient of a computation problem involving decimal numbers.

Students will complete an online Checkpoint. If necessary, read the directions, problems, and answer choices to students and help them with keyboard or mouse operations.

Multiply and Divide Decimals (A)

Lesson Overview

GET READY Multiply Whole Numbers	5 minutes	ONLINE
LEARN Multiply a Whole Number by a Decimal	20 minutes	OFFLINE
LEARN Multiply a Decimal by a Decimal	20 minutes	OFFLINE
TRY IT Practice Multiplying Decimals	15 minutes	OFFLINE

▶ Lesson Objectives

Solve a multiplication or division problem that involves decimal numbers.

▶ Prerequisite Skills

Estimate or calculate a product or a quotient in a whole-number problem.

▶ Content Background

Decimal numbers and whole numbers can be factors when finding products. Students will learn to use a step-by-step algorithm to multiply decimal numbers by whole numbers and decimal numbers by decimal numbers.

When students write and compute with decimal numbers, they often use numbers that are between 0 and 1—for example, 0.1. While it is acceptable to write this number as .1, mathematicians usually write the leading zero, to show that the whole-number value for the decimal number is zero and to avoid confusion about the value of the number.

▶ Advance Preparation

Print two copies of the Hundredths Decimal Squares.

> ### Materials to Gather
>
> **SUPPLIED**
>
> Hundredths Decimal Squares (printout)
>
> Multiply a Whole Number by a Decimal activity page
>
> Multiply a Decimal by a Decimal activity page
>
> Practice Multiplying Decimals activity page
>
> **ALSO NEEDED**
>
> markers, coloring

GET READY Multiply Whole Numbers

ONLINE 5 min

Students will practice estimating and computing products of whole numbers in a game setting. They will use rounding to the nearest ten and friendly numbers.

Objectives

- Estimate or calculate a product or a quotient in a whole-number problem.

LEARN Multiply a Whole Number by a Decimal

Objectives

- Solve a multiplication or division problem that involves decimal numbers.

Students will learn how to multiply a whole number by various decimal numbers. First they will estimate products. Then they will use models to multiply. They will check the reasonableness of their answers by comparing the exact answers to their estimates.

Gather the Hundredths Decimal Squares printout and markers. The small squares on the decimal grids represent hundredths. The columns represent tenths.

View or print the Multiply a Whole Number by a Decimal activity page and read the directions with students. They should copy the problems from the Activity Book into their Math Notebook as necessary and solve them there.

1. Tell students they will start by estimating the product of 0.9×3. Ask them how to estimate each factor to the nearest whole number. 0.9 rounds to 1, and 3 is a whole number and doesn't need to be rounded.

   Say: Write the number sentence to estimate the product in your Math Notebook. Estimate: $1 \times 3 = ?$

   Ask: What is the estimated product of 0.9×3? 3

   Have students write the answer to the number sentence for the estimate.

   Say: An estimate can help you later. After you solve the problem, you can compare the exact answer to the estimate to see if your exact answer is reasonable.

   In their Math Notebook, have students write the following:

   Exact answer: $3 \times 0.9 = ?$
   An estimate of 0.9×3 is about 3.

2. Tell students they will now model the expression 0.9×3 on the printout to see how a whole number is multiplied by a decimal number. Explain that it is easier to model an expression when the whole number is the first factor.

   Ask: If you change the order of the factors in 0.9×3, what is the new problem? 3×0.9

   Ask: What property did you use to change the order of the factors? commutative property

3. Give students a copy of the printout. Have them write the number sentence $3 \times 0.9 = ?$ above a 10 by 10 grid.

4. Tell students to shade 0.9 three times on adjoining 10 by 10 grids with a different color each time.

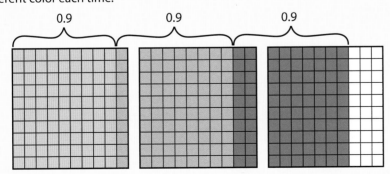

0.9   0.9   0.9

Ask: Count the shaded tenths in the decimal grids. The tenths are the columns in each grid. How many tenths did you shade in all? 27 tenths

Ask: What is 27 tenths in improper fraction form? $\frac{27}{10}$

Ask: What is $\frac{27}{10}$ as a mixed number? $2\frac{7}{10}$

Ask: What is $2\frac{7}{10}$ in decimal form? 2.7

Ask: What is 3×0.9? 2.7

Have students write $3 \times 0.9 = 2.7$ as the exact answer in their Math Notebook.

5. Tell students they can also use a step-by-step approach, or algorithm, to find the product of 3×0.9. Have students read the first problem in the Worked Examples on the activity page. Guide them to follow the steps for multiplying a decimal number by a whole number.

6. Be sure students understand that they are not "bringing the decimal point straight down into the answer" even though that appears to be the case here. It will not be the case when they multiply a decimal number by another decimal number. They are using place value to determine the placement of the decimal point.

7. Have students review the exact answer ($3 \times 0.9 = 2.7$) in their Math Notebook under their estimate and compare the two answers.

   Ask: How do you know that 2.7 is a reasonable answer? The exact answer, 2.7, rounded to the nearest whole number, is 3, which is the same as the estimated answer. So the exact answer, 2.7, is reasonable.

8. Have students write $2 \times 0.87 = ?$ above another 10 by 10 grid on the printout.

   Say: Write another number sentence to estimate 2×0.87. Round 0.87 to the nearest whole number and find the estimated product. $2 \times 1 = 2$

9. Have students model the exact answer to the problem on adjoining 10 by 10 grids, telling them that the squares are the hundredths on the grids. Tell them to shade 0.87 two times with a different color each time.

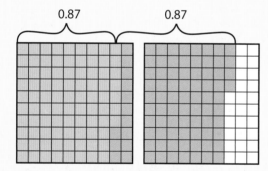

   Ask: Count the shaded hundredths on the grids. How many hundredths did you shade in all? 174 hundredths

   Have students write 174 hundredths as a fraction, mixed number, and decimal. $\frac{174}{100}$, $1\frac{74}{100}$, 1.74

10. **Ask:** What is the product of 2×0.87 written as a decimal number? 1.74

    Have students write 1.74 as the exact answer on their decimal grid.

11. Have students read the second problem in the Worked Examples on the activity page to see how to find the product using a an algorithm.

12. Have students compare their decimal grids to the product.

    Ask: How does your model show 1 one, 7 tenths, and 4 hundredths? One whole grid shows 1 one. Seven shaded columns show 7 tenths. Four shaded squares show 4 hundredths.

Have students use their estimate to explain whether the exact answer of 1.74 is reasonable. The exact answer, 1.74, rounded to the nearest whole number, is 2, which is the same as the estimated answer. So the exact answer, 1.74, is reasonable.

13. Tell students they will solve the next problem without decimal grids.

    Have students write $5.231 \times 3 = ?$ in their Math Notebook.

    Say: What is the estimated product of 5.231×3, with factors rounded to whole numbers? Write a number sentence in the Math Notebook to estimate 5.231×3. Round 5.231 to the nearest whole number and find the estimated product. $5 \times 3 = 15$

14. Have students read the third problem in the Worked Examples on the activity page. Guide them to follow the steps for multiplying a whole number by a decimal number. Then have them write $5.231 \times 3 = 15.693$ in their Math Notebook.

15. Have students use their estimate to explain whether the exact answer of 15.693 is reasonable. The estimate, 15, rounded to the nearest ten, is 20. The exact answer, 15.693, rounded to the nearest ten, is 20. Both answers can be rounded to the same number. So the exact answer, 15.693, is reasonable.

16. Have students complete the activity page problems in their Math Notebook.

Tips

Have students explain how their models relate to the steps of the algorithm.

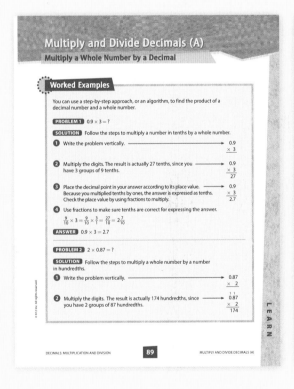

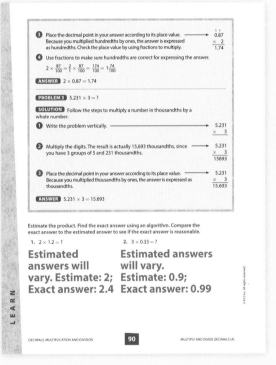

LEARN Multiply a Decimal by a Decimal

Students will learn to multiply decimal numbers by decimal numbers. First they will estimate products. Then they will use models to multiply. They will compare their estimates to their exact answers to check the reasonableness of their answers.

Gather the Hundredths Decimal Squares printout and markers.

View or print the Multiply a Decimal by a Decimal activity page and read directions with students. They should copy the problems from the Activity Book into their Math Notebook as necessary and solve them there.

- Solve a multiplication or division problem that involves decimal numbers.

Tips

Have students describe each step they take as they use an algorithm to multiply.

MULTIPLY BY TENTHS AND HUNDREDTHS

1. Tell students they will use friendly numbers to estimate the product of 0.8×0.4 before they model the problem.

   Ask: What are the friendly numbers closest to 0.8 and 0.4? A friendly number for 0.8 is 1, and a friendly number for 0.4 is 0.5.

   Say: Write the number sentence to estimate the product in your Math Notebook. Estimate: $1 \times 0.5 = ?$

   Ask: What is the estimated product of those two friendly numbers? $1 \times 0.5 = 0.5$

   Have students write the answer to the number sentence for the estimate.

2. Tell students they will now use models to multiply decimal numbers by decimal numbers.

3. Give students a copy of the printout. Have them write $0.8 \times 0.4 = ?$ above a 10 by 10 grid.

4. Tell students to use diagonal lines to mark 4 columns of the grid to show 0.4. Have them use opposite diagonal lines to mark 8 rows of the grid to show 0.8.

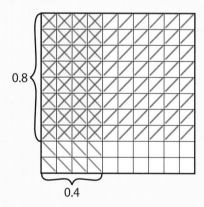

5. Tell students that the Xs formed by both diagonal lines show the product of 0.8×0.4. Have them count the squares with Xs. Each square is equal to 1 hundredth.

   Ask: How many hundredths have Xs? 32 hundredths

   Ask: What is the product of 0.8×0.4? 0.32

   Have students write 0.32 as the exact answer in the number sentence above the grid.

6. Tell students they can also use a step-by-step approach, or an algorithm, to find the product of 0.8×0.4. Have students read the first problem in the Worked Examples on the activity page. Guide them as necessary.

7. Have students compare their estimate of 0.8×0.4 to the exact answer.

   Ask: What was your estimate of 0.8×0.4? 0.5

   Ask: How do you know that your exact answer, 0.32, is reasonable? The exact answer, 0.32, can be rounded to the friendly number 0.5, which is the same as the estimated answer. So the exact answer, 0.32, is reasonable.

8. Tell students they will multiply decimal numbers without a model in the next problem. Have them write $4.08 \times 0.25 = ?$ in their Math Notebook. Tell them to use friendly numbers to estimate the product. For 4.08, they should write the friendly number 4, and 0.25 is already a friendly number. Remind students that $0.25 = \frac{1}{4}$. Have them write "Estimate: $4 \times \frac{1}{4} = ?$" in their Math Notebook.

   Ask: What is $4 \times \frac{1}{4}$? 1

   Have students write 1 as the answer in the estimate number sentence.

9. Tell students they can also use an algorithm to find the product of 4.08×0.25. Have students read the second problem in the Worked Examples on the activity page. Guide them as necessary.

10. Have students compare their estimate of 4×0.25 to the exact answer.

    Ask: What is the product of 4.08×0.25? 1.02

    Have students write 1.02 as the answer in the exact number sentence.

    Ask: How do you know if your answer is reasonable? The exact answer, 1.02, rounded to the nearest whole number, is 1, which is the same as the estimated answer. So the exact answer, 1.02, is reasonable.

    Ask: What about the rounded numbers affects whether the estimate will be reasonable or not? The closer the rounded numbers are to the exact numbers, the more reasonable the estimate will be.

11. Have students complete the activity page problems in their Math Notebook.

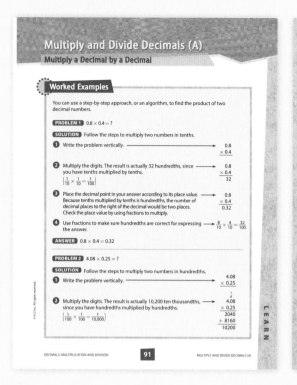

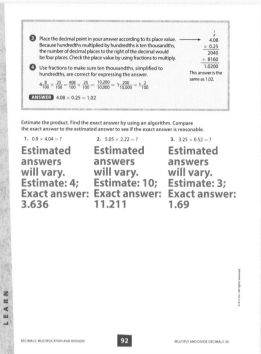

Multiply and Divide Decimals (A)
Multiply a Decimal by a Decimal

Worked Examples

You can use a step-by-step approach, or an algorithm, to find the product of two decimal numbers.

PROBLEM 1 $0.8 \times 0.4 = ?$

SOLUTION Follow the steps to multiply two numbers in tenths.

① Write the problem vertically.
$$\begin{array}{r} 0.8 \\ \times\ 0.4 \\ \hline \end{array}$$

② Multiply the digits. The result is actually 32 hundredths, since you have tenths multiplied by tenths.
$\left(\frac{1}{10} \times \frac{1}{10} = \frac{1}{100}\right)$
$$\begin{array}{r} 0.8 \\ \times\ 0.4 \\ \hline 32 \end{array}$$

③ Place the decimal point in your answer according to its place value. Because tenths multiplied by tenths is hundredths, the number of decimal places to the right of the decimal would be two places. Check the place value by using fractions to multiply.
$$\begin{array}{r} 0.8 \\ \times\ 0.4 \\ \hline 0.32 \end{array}$$

④ Use fractions to make sure hundredths are correct for expressing the answer. $\frac{8}{10} \times \frac{4}{10} = \frac{32}{100}$

ANSWER $0.8 \times 0.4 = 0.32$

PROBLEM 2 $4.08 \times 0.25 = ?$

SOLUTION Follow the steps to multiply two numbers in hundredths.

① Write the problem vertically.
$$\begin{array}{r} 4.08 \\ \times\ 0.25 \\ \hline \end{array}$$

② Multiply the digits. The result is actually 10,200 ten thousandths, since you have hundredths multiplied by hundredths.
$\left(\frac{1}{100} \times \frac{1}{100} = \frac{1}{10,000}\right)$
$$\begin{array}{r} 4.08 \\ \times\ 0.25 \\ \hline 2040 \\ +\ 8160 \\ \hline 10200 \end{array}$$

③ Place the decimal point in your answer according to its place value. Because hundredths multiplied by hundredths is ten thousandths, the number of decimal places to the right of the decimal would be four places. Check the place value by using fractions to multiply.
$$\begin{array}{r} 4.08 \\ \times\ 0.25 \\ \hline 2040 \\ +\ 8160 \\ \hline 1.0200 \end{array}$$
This answer is the same as 1.02.

④ Use fractions to make sure ten thousandths, simplified to hundredths, are correct for expressing the answer.
$4\frac{8}{100} \times \frac{25}{100} = \frac{408}{100} \times \frac{25}{100} = \frac{10,200}{10,000} = 1\frac{200}{10,000} = 1\frac{2}{100}$

ANSWER $4.08 \times 0.25 = 1.02$

Estimate the product. Find the exact answer by using an algorithm. Compare the exact answer to the estimated answer to see if the exact answer is reasonable.

1. $0.9 \times 4.04 = ?$
Estimated answers will vary. Estimate: 4; Exact answer: 3.636

2. $5.05 \times 2.22 = ?$
Estimated answers will vary. Estimate: 10; Exact answer: 11.211

3. $3.25 \times 0.52 = ?$
Estimated answers will vary. Estimate: 3; Exact answer: 1.69

LEARN

LEARN

TRY IT Practice Multiplying Decimals

OFFLINE
15 min

Students will practice estimating products with decimal numbers. View or print the Practice Multiplying Decimals activity page and read the directions with students.

Students should copy the problems from the Activity Book into their Math Notebook as necessary and solve them there.

Objectives

- Solve a multiplication or division problem that involves decimal numbers.

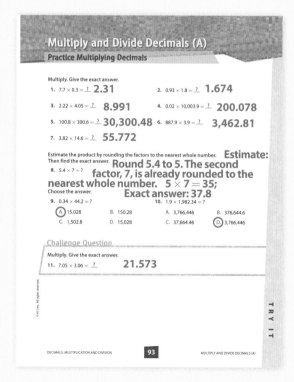

Multiply and Divide Decimals (A)
Practice Multiplying Decimals

Multiply. Give the exact answer.

1. $7.7 \times 0.3 = ?$ **2.31**

2. $0.93 \times 1.8 = ?$ **1.674**

3. $2.22 \times 4.05 = ?$ **8.991**

4. $0.02 \times 10,003.9 = ?$ **200.078**

5. $100.8 \times 300.6 = ?$ **30,300.48**

6. $887.9 \times 3.9 = ?$ **3,462.81**

7. $3.82 \times 14.6 = ?$ **55.772**

Estimate the product by rounding the factors to the nearest whole number. Then find the exact answer.

8. $5.4 \times 7 = ?$ Estimate: Round 5.4 to 5. The second factor, 7, is already rounded to the nearest whole number. $5 \times 7 = 35$; Exact answer: 37.8

Choose the answer.

9. $0.34 \times 44.2 = ?$
(A) 15.028
B. 150.28
C. 1,502.8
D. 15,028

10. $1.9 \times 1,982.34 = ?$
A. 3,766,446
B. 376,644.6
C. 37,664.46
(D.) 3,766.446

Challenge Question

Multiply. Give the exact answer.

11. $7.05 \times 3.06 = ?$ **21.573**

TRY IT

Multiply and Divide Decimals (B)

Lesson Overview

GET READY Divide Whole Numbers	5 minutes	ONLINE
LEARN Divide Whole Numbers and Decimals	25 minutes	OFFLINE
LEARN Divide a Decimal by a Decimal	15 minutes	OFFLINE
TRY IT Practice Dividing Decimals	15 minutes	OFFLINE

▶ Lesson Objectives

Solve a multiplication or division problem that involves decimal numbers.

▶ Prerequisite Skills

Estimate or calculate a product or a quotient in a whole-number problem.

▶ Content Background

Decimal numbers and whole numbers can be dividends and divisors when students are finding quotients. Students will continue to learn to use a step-by-step algorithm to divide decimal numbers by whole numbers, whole numbers by decimal numbers, and decimal numbers by decimal numbers.

When students write and compute with decimal numbers, they often use numbers that are between 0 and 1—for example, 0.1. While it is acceptable to write this number as .1, mathematicians usually write the leading zero, to show that the whole-number value for the decimal number is zero and to avoid confusion about the value of the number.

▶ Advance Preparation

Print three copies of the Hundredths Decimal Squares.

▶ Safety

Make sure students handle the scissors carefully and be sure to store them in a safe place.

Materials to Gather

SUPPLIED

Hundredths Decimal Squares (printout)

Divide Whole Numbers and Decimals activity page

Divide a Decimal by a Decimal activity page

Practice Dividing Decimals activity page

ALSO NEEDED

markers, coloring

scissors, pointed-end safety

GET READY Divide Whole Numbers

ONLINE
5min

Objectives

- Estimate or calculate a product or a quotient in a whole-number problem.

Students will practice estimating and computing quotients of whole numbers. They will use rounding to the nearest ten and friendly numbers to estimate the quotients.

LEARN Divide Whole Numbers and Decimals

Objectives

- Solve a multiplication or division problem that involves decimal numbers.

Students will estimate quotients, use models, and learn a step-by-step approach to divide whole numbers by decimal numbers and decimal numbers by whole numbers. They will compare the exact answers to their estimates to check the reasonableness of their answers.

Gather the Hundredths Decimal Squares printouts, markers, and scissors.

View or print the Divide Whole Numbers and Decimals activity page. Students should copy the problems from the Activity Book into their Math Notebook as necessary and solve them there. Throughout this activity, have students write the problem in their Math Notebook so they can refer to it as they estimate and work with the models.

In some problems in this activity, the decimal number will be the divisor and in other problems, the decimal number will be the dividend. Students will see other problems where the dividend and the divisor are both decimal numbers.

1. Tell students they will use models and a step-by-step process to divide whole numbers by decimal numbers and decimal numbers by whole numbers.

1.8 ÷ 2 = ?

2. Give students a copy of the printout. Tell them they will estimate the quotient of 1.8 ÷ 2 so they can check the reasonableness of their answer when they divide and find the exact answer.

   Ask: How do you estimate 1.8 ÷ 2 rounding both numbers to the nearest whole number? Round 1.8 to 2. The divisor, 2, is already a whole number.

   Say: Write the number sentence to estimate the quotient in your Math Notebook. What is the estimate? Estimate: 2 ÷ 2 = 1

3. Have students follow these steps to model 1.8 ÷ 2 on the printout.

   - Write 1.8 ÷ 2 = ? above two grids.
   - Shade 1.8.

     1.8 ÷ 2 = ?

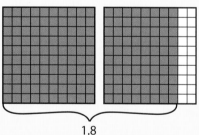

     1.8

   - Cut the model of 1.8 into tenths.

- Divide the tenths into 2 equal groups.

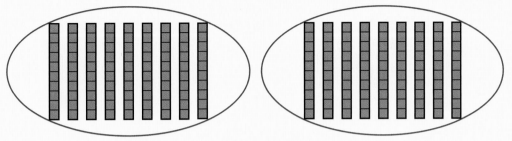

4. Discuss the model with students.

   Ask: How many tenths are in each group? 9 tenths

   Ask: What is 1.8 ÷ 2? 9 tenths

5. Tell students they can also use a step-by-step approach, or an algorithm, to find 1.8 ÷ 2. Have students read the first problem in the Worked Examples on the activity page. Guide them to follow the steps for dividing a decimal number by a whole number.

6. **Ask: How does the model relate to the division?** One whole decimal grid and $\frac{8}{10}$ of another decimal grid represents the number you divide. The dividend, 2, shows that you divide one whole decimal grid and $\frac{8}{10}$ of another grid into 2 equal groups. The quotient is 0.9.

   Have students compare their estimate of 1.8 ÷ 2 to the exact quotient.

   Ask: How do you know that your exact answer, 0.9, is reasonable? The exact answer, 0.9, rounded to the nearest whole number, is 1, which is the same as the estimated answer. So the exact answer, 0.9, is reasonable.

0.21 ÷ 7 = ?

7. Tell students that the next problem is 0.21 ÷ 7. Have them first estimate the quotient.

   Ask: How do you estimate 0.21 ÷ 7 by rounding both numbers to the nearest whole number? 0.21 rounded to the nearest whole number is 0. 7 is already a whole number.

   Say: Write the number sentence to estimate the quotient in your Math Notebook. What is the estimate? Estimate: 0 ÷ 7 = 0

8. Have students follow these steps to model 0.21 ÷ 7 on another printout.

   - Write 0.21 ÷ 7 = ? above one grid.

   - Shade 0.21.

   0.21 ÷ 7 = ?

   0.21 {

- Cut the shaded strips, which are 21 hundredths.

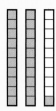

- Divide the 21 hundredths into 7 equal groups with 3 hundredths in each group.

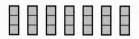

9. Tell students they can also use an algorithm to find the quotient of 0.21 ÷ 7. Have them read the second problem in the Worked Examples on the activity page. Guide them to follow the steps for dividing a decimal number by a whole number.

10. **Ask:** How does the model relate to the division? The dividend, 0.21, represents the number you divide on the decimal grid. The divisor, 7, divides 0.21 into 7 groups. Each square represents $\frac{1}{100}$, and there are 3 squares in each of the 7 equal groups. 0.03 is the quotient.

    Have students compare their exact quotient of 0.21 ÷ 7 = 0.03 to the estimate.

    Ask: Is 0.03 close to 0? Yes

    Say: The exact answer, 0.03, is close to 0, so 0.03 is a reasonable answer.

6 ÷ 1.2 = ?

11. Give students another copy of the printout. Tell them they will divide a whole number by a decimal: 6 ÷ 1.2.

    Ask: How do you estimate 6 ÷ 1.2 by rounding both numbers to the nearest whole number? 6 is already a whole number. 1.2 rounded to the nearest whole number is 1.

    Say: Write the number sentence to estimate the quotient in your Math Notebook. Estimate: 6 ÷ 1 = 6

12. Tell them to follow these steps to model 6 ÷ 1.2 on the printout.

    - Write 6 ÷ 1.2 = ? above the grids.
    - Shade 6 whole grids. The grids represent the dividend.

    6 ÷ 1.2 = ?

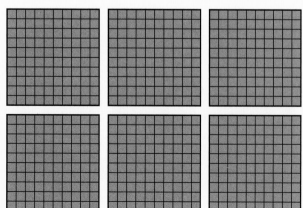

- Cut 1 grid into groups of 2 tenths (20 hundredths) to prepare to show 1.2, the divisor.

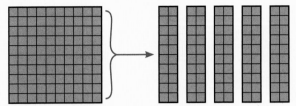

- Divide the 5 whole grids and tenths into groups of 1.2.

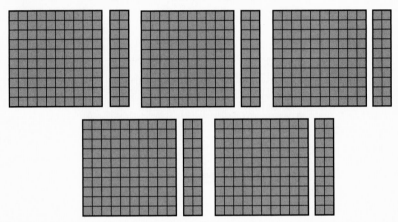

13. Have students read the third problem in the Worked Examples on the activity page. Guide them to follow the steps for dividing a whole number by a decimal number.

14. Discuss the model with students.

    Ask: How many groups of 1.2 are there? 5

    Ask: What is $6 \div 1.2$? 5

    Ask: How does the model relate to the quotient? There are 5 groups of 12 in 60, or there are 5 groups of 1.2 in 6.

15. Have students compare their estimate of $6 \div 1.2$ to the actual quotient.

    Ask: Is 5 close to 6? Yes

    Say: The estimate of the quotient, 6, is close to 5, so 5 is a reasonable answer.

$20 \div 1.25 = ?$

16. Tell students that they won't model the following problem. In the fouth problem in the Worked Examples, have students estimate the quotient.

    Ask: How do you estimate $20 \div 1.25$ by rounding both numbers to the nearest whole number? 20 is already a whole number. 1.25 rounded to the nearest whole number is 1.

    Say: Write the number sentence to estimate the quotient in your Math Notebook. Estimate: $20 \div 1 = 20$

17. Have students read the fouth problem. Guide them to follow the steps for dividing a whole number by a decimal number.

18. Have students compare the estimate of 20 with the exact quotient of 16.

    Ask: How do you know that your exact answer, 16, is reasonable? The exact answer, 16, rounded to the nearest ten is 20, which is the same as the estimated answer. So the exact answer, 16, is reasonable.

19. Have students complete the activity page problems in their Math Notebook.

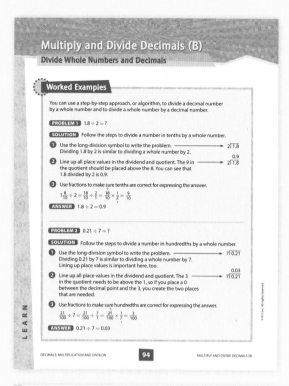

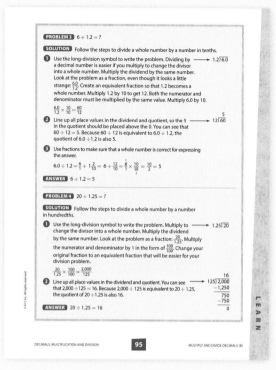

Estimate the quotient. Find the exact answer by using an algorithm.
Compare the exact answer to the estimated answer to see if the exact
answer is reasonable.

1. $0.25 \div 5 = ?$ **Estimated answers will vary.**
    Estimate: 0.06; Exact answer: 0.05

2. $6 \div 1.5 = ?$

Estimated answers will vary.
Estimate: 3; Exact answer: 4

LEARN Divide a Decimal by a Decimal

OFFLINE 15 min

Students will estimate quotients and use a step-by-step approach, or an
algorithm, to divide decimal numbers by decimal numbers.

Objectives

- Solve a multiplication or
  division problem that involves
  decimal numbers.

View or print the Divide a Decimal by a Decimal activity page and read the directions with students. They should copy the problems from the Activity Book into their Math Notebook as necessary and solve them there.

Tips

Have students describe each step they take as they use an algorithm to divide.

1. Tell students they will use an algorithm to find $3.9 \div 1.3$. Have them write $3.9 \div 1.3 = ?$ in their Math Notebook. First they will estimate the quotient.

   Ask: How do you estimate $3.9 \div 1.3$ rounding both numbers to the nearest whole number? Round 3.9 to 4. Round 1.3 to 1.

   Say: Write the number sentence to estimate the quotient in your Math Notebook. Estimate: $4 \div 1 = 4$

2. **Say:** To find the exact answer, make the divisor, 1.3, a whole number to simplify the division. The division problem is the same as this fraction: $\frac{3.9}{1.3}$.

   Have students write $\frac{3.9}{1.3} = ?$ in their Math Notebook.

   Say: To make the denominator a whole number, multiply it by 10. You need to multiply the numerator by the same number, 10. When you multiply $\frac{3.9}{1.3}$ by $\frac{10}{10}$, you are multiplying $\frac{3.9}{1.3}$ by 1, so you aren't changing the value of the numbers in this problem.

   Have students write $\frac{3.9}{1.3} = \frac{3.9}{1.3} \times \frac{10}{10} = ?$ in their Math Notebook.

   Ask: What is $\frac{3.9}{1.3} \times \frac{10}{10}$? $\frac{39}{13}$

   Have students write $\frac{3.9}{1.3} = \frac{3.9}{1.3} \times \frac{10}{10} = \frac{39}{13} = ?$ in their Math Notebook.

   Say: $\frac{39}{13}$ equals $\frac{3.9}{1.3}$.

   Ask: What is $39 \div 13$? 3

   Ask: So what is $3.9 \div 1.3$? 3

   Have students write $\frac{3.9}{1.3} = \frac{3.9}{1.3} \times \frac{10}{10} = \frac{39}{13} = 3$

3. Have students compare their exact answer to $3.9 \div 1.3$ to their estimate.

   Ask: How do you know that your exact answer, 3, is reasonable? The exact answer, 3, is close to the estimate, 4, so 3 is a reasonable answer.

4. Have students estimate the quotient of $13.44 \div 0.12$.

   Ask: How do you estimate $13.44 \div 0.12$ rounding the dividend to the nearest whole number and the divisor to the nearest tenth? Round 13.44 to 13. Round 0.12 to 0.1.

   Say: Write the number sentence to estimate the quotient in your Math Notebook. Estimate: $13 \div 0.1 = 130$

5. Read the problem in the Worked Examples on the activity page with students. Guide them to follow the steps for dividing a decimal number by a decimal number.

6. Have students compare the exact answer to $13.44 \div 0.12$ to their estimate. The exact answer, 112, rounded to the nearest ten, is 110, which is close to the estimated answer. So the exact answer, 112, is reasonable.

7. Have students complete the activity page problems in their Math Notebook using a step-by-step approach. Remind them to estimate the quotients first, either by rounding the dividend and divisor or by using friendly numbers, and to use the estimates to check the reasonableness of the exact answers.

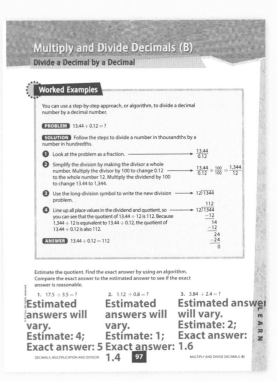

TRY IT Practice Dividing Decimals

OFFLINE 15 min

Objectives

- Solve a multiplication or division problem that involves decimal numbers.

Students will practice using a step-by-step approach to divide decimal numbers. View or print the Practice Dividing Decimals activity page and read the directions with students.

Students should copy the problems from the Activity Book into their Math Notebook as necessary and solve them there.

Tips

Remind students that they can change a division problem to a fraction to make it simpler to find the answer. By multiplying the numerator and the denominator by a fraction that is equivalent to 1, they can change the divisor to a whole number.

Multiply and Divide Decimals (B)
Practice Dividing Decimals

Estimate the quotient by using friendly numbers.
Then find the exact answer.

1. $14.7 \div 7 = ?$
   See below.

Divide. Give the exact answer.

2. $5.84 \div 0.8 = \underline{?}$
   7.3
3. $7.2 \div 0.9 = \underline{?}$
   8
4. $4.48 \div 3.2 = \underline{?}$
   1.4
5. $99.88 \div 0.01 = \underline{?}$
   9,988
6. $998.91 \div 0.22 = \underline{?}$
   4,540.5
7. $4,556.29 \div 99.7 = \underline{?}$
   45.7
8. $0.17 \div 0.02 = \underline{?}$
   8.5
9. $89,997 \div 0.5 = \underline{?}$
   179,994

Choose the answer.

10. $8,997.3 \div 999.7 = ?$

   A. 9,000   B. 900   C. 90   (D.) 9

Challenge Question

Use the order of operations to find the answer.

11. $(1.2 \times 1.8) \div 0.6 = \underline{?}$ **3.6**

TRY IT

Additional Answers

1. **Estimate:** Use 14 as a friendly number for the dividend, 14.7. Keep 7 as the divisor, since it is already a friendly number. $14 \div 7 = 2$
   Exact answer: 2.1

Multiply and Divide Decimals (C)

Lesson Overview

LEARN Decimal Quotients	15 minutes	OFFLINE
LEARN Divide and Check	15 minutes	ONLINE
TRY IT Practice Multiplying and Dividing	20 minutes	OFFLINE
CHECKPOINT	10 minutes	ONLINE

▶ Lesson Objectives

- Solve a multiplication or division problem that involves decimal numbers.
- Verify that the calculated result of a problem involving multiplication or division of decimal numbers is reasonable.

▶ Prerequisite Skills

Estimate or calculate a product or a quotient in a whole-number problem.

▶ Content Background

Decimal numbers and whole numbers can be factors in multiplication problems, and they can be dividends and divisors in division problems. Students will learn to use a step-by-step algorithm to divide a whole number by a greater whole number, resulting in a decimal quotient.

Students build number-sense skills when they verify the reasonableness of answers. One way to determine whether an exact answer is reasonable is to estimate the answer before finding the exact answer and solving the problem. Students can compare the estimate to the exact answer to determine whether the answer is reasonable.

When students write and compute with decimal numbers, they often use numbers that are between 0 and 1—for example, 0.1. While it is acceptable to write this number as .1, mathematicians usually write the leading zero, to show that the whole-number value for the decimal number is zero and to avoid confusion about the value of the number.

▶ Advance Preparation

Print the Hundredths Decimal Squares.

▶ Safety

Make sure students handle the scissors carefully and be sure to store them in a safe place.

Materials to Gather

SUPPLIED

Hundredths Decimal Squares (printout)
Decimal Quotients activity page
Practice Multiplying and Dividing activity page

ALSO NEEDED

markers, coloring
scissors, pointed-end safety

LEARN Decimal Quotients

OFFLINE 15 min

Objectives

- Solve a multiplication or division problem that involves decimal numbers.

Students will divide a whole number by a greater whole number, resulting in a decimal quotient. They will use a model and then a step-by-step approach.

Gather the Hundredths Decimal Squares printout, markers, and scissors.

View or print the Decimal Quotients activity page and read the directions with students. They should copy the problems from the Activity Book into their Math Notebook as necessary and solve them there.

1. Tell students they will use a model and then a step-by-step approach to divide whole numbers that have a decimal quotient. Give students the printout.

2. Tell students they will model 3 ÷ 10. Have them follow these steps to model 3 ÷ 10.

   • Shade 3 whole grids.

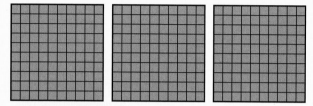

   • Cut each shaded grid into tenths.

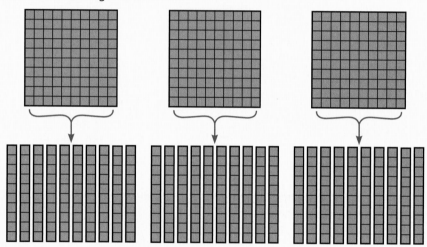

   • Divide the tenths into 10 equal groups.

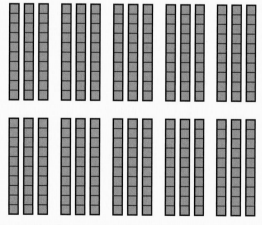

3. Discuss the final model with students.

   Ask: How many tenths of an entire grid are in each group? 3 tenths

   Ask: What is 3 ÷ 10? 3 tenths

   Ask: How does the model relate to the division? Three whole decimal grids represent the number you divide. Three tenths in each of 10 equal groups represents the quotient.

4. Tell students they can also use a step-by-step approach, or an algorithm, to divide 3 by 10.

5. Have students read the first problem in the Worked Examples on the activity page. Explain that if students don't know how many zeros to add to the dividend, they can add one zero at a time until the division comes out evenly (or shows a pattern). Have students write 0.3 or $\frac{3}{10}$ as the answer to the problem in their Math Notebook.

6. Have students read the second problem in the Worked Examples. Guide them to follow the steps for dividing a whole number by a greater whole number, resulting in a decimal quotient in the tenths place.

7. Have students read the third problem in the Worked Examples. Guide them to follow the steps for dividing a whole number by a greater whole number, resulting in a decimal quotient in the hundredths place.

8. Have them complete the activity page problems in their Math Notbook, using a step-by-step approach.

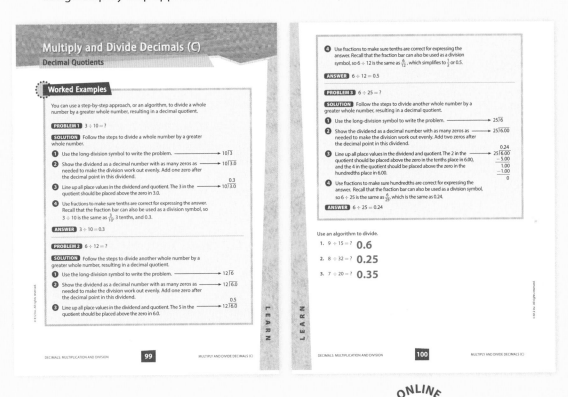

99

100

LEARN Divide and Check

ONLINE **15min**

Students will divide decimals and verify the reasonableness of the answers. They will see how to compare the exact answer to the estimate to decide if it is reasonable. They will also use multiplication to check their division.

Objectives

- Solve a multiplication or division problem that involves decimal numbers.
- Verify that the calculated result of a problem involving multiplication or division of decimal numbers is reasonable.

TRY IT Practice Multiplying and Dividing

Students will practice multiplying and dividing decimal numbers. View or print the Practice Multiplying and Dividing activity page and read the directions with students.

Students should copy the problems from the Activity Book into their Math Notebook as necessary and solve them there.

Tips Have students choose two problems and explain how they found the answers. Ask students to also explain how they know the exact answers are reasonable compared to the estimated answers.

Objectives

- Solve a multiplication or division problem that involves decimal numbers.
- Verify that the calculated result of a problem involving multiplication or division of decimal numbers is reasonable.

Additional Answers

4. The exact quotient, 1.76, rounded to the nearest whole number is 2, which is the same as the estimated answer. So the exact answer, 1.76, is reasonable.

5. Answers will vary. **Estimate:** 30, rounding to the nearest whole number; **Exact:** 32.58
   The exact answer, 32.58, rounded to the nearest ten is 30, which is the same as the estimated answer. So the exact answer is reasonable.

6. Answers will vary. **Estimate:** 0.06, using friendly numbers 0.1 and 0.6; **Exact:** 0.084
   The exact answer, 0.084, and the estimated answer, 0.06, can both be rounded to the friendly number 0.075. So the exact answer is reasonable.

7. Answers will vary. **Estimate:** 0.6, using friendly numbers 15 and 25; **Exact:** 0.56
   The exact answer, 0.56, rounded to the nearest tenth is 0.6, which is the same as the estimated answer. So the exact answer is reasonable.

8. Answers will vary. **Estimate:** 1.25, using friendly numbers 7.5 and 6; **Exact:** 1.2
   The exact answer, 1.2, can be rounded to the friendly number 1.25, which is the same as the estimated answer. So the exact answer is reasonable.

CHECKPOINT

Students will complete an online Checkpoint. If necessary, read the directions, problems, and answer choices to students and help them with keyboard or mouse operations.

Objectives

- Solve a multiplication or division problem that involves decimal numbers.
- Verify that the calculated result of a problem involving multiplication or division of decimal numbers is reasonable.

Compute Decimal Story Problems (A)

GET READY Multiply Decimals	5 minutes	ONLINE
LEARN Multiply Decimals in Story Problems	20 minutes	ONLINE
LEARN Bicycle Race Decimal Story Problems	20 minutes	OFFLINE
TRY IT Multiply Decimals to Solve Problems	15 minutes	ONLINE

▶ Lesson Objectives

Solve a story problem that involves multiplication or division of decimal numbers.

▶ Prerequisite Skills

Solve a multiplication or division problem that involves decimal numbers.

▶ Content Background

Students will calculate the answers to multiplication story problems involving decimal numbers and whole numbers.

When students write and compute with decimal numbers, they often use numbers that are between 0 and 1—for example, 0.1. While it is acceptable to write this number as .1, mathematicians usually write the leading zero, to show that the whole-number value for the decimal number is zero and to avoid confusion about the value of the number.

Materials to Gather

SUPPLIED

Bicycle Race Decimal Story Problems activity page

ONLINE 5 min

GET READY Multiply Decimals

Students will multiply decimal numbers and whole numbers to find products.

Objectives

- Solve a multiplication or division problem that involves decimal numbers.

ONLINE 20 min

LEARN Multiply Decimals in Story Problems

In this activity, students will multiply decimal numbers and whole numbers to solve story problems about bicycle races.

Objectives

- Solve a story problem that involves multiplication or division of decimal numbers.

LEARN Bicycle Race Decimal Story Problems

Objectives

- Solve a story problem that involves multiplication or division of decimal numbers.

Students will set up and then solve multiplication problems with decimal numbers and whole numbers as factors.

View or print the Bicycle Race Decimal Story Problems activity page and read the directions with students. They should copy the problems from the Activity Book into their Math Notebook as necessary and solve them there.

1. Have students read the problems in the Worked Examples.

2. Tell students that they will find exact products.

3. Note that some problems require students to multiply decimal numbers by whole numbers, and other problems require students to multiply decimal numbers by decimal numbers.

4. Make sure students understand where the place the decimal when they multiply a decimal number by a decimal number.

5. **Ask:** In Problem 2 of the problem set, what are the two factors? 134.4 and 0.62

   Ask: What decimal place will the answer be in? thousandths

   Ask: How do you know it will be in the thousandths place? Since 10 times 100 is 1,000, tenths multiplied by hundredths will give an answer in the thousandths.

   Have students use a step-by-step process to solve.

$$
\begin{array}{r}
\overset{2\,2\,2}{134.4} \\
\times\ 0.62 \\
\hline
2688 \\
+\ 80640 \\
\hline
83.328
\end{array}
$$

6. Have students solve Problem 1 and Problems 3–10 on their own.

Tips

Encourage students to estimate the product before they find the exact answer. The estimate will help them determine whether their exact answer is reasonable.

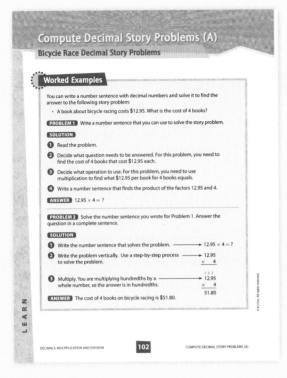

Additional Answers

1. $23.76 \times 3 = 71.28$
   The relay is 71.28 kilometers long.

2. $134.4 \times 0.62 = 83.328$
   So 134.4 kilometers is equivalent to 83.328 miles.

5. $24 \times 3.6 = 86.4$
   A cyclist will bike 86.4 kilometers in 3.6 hours.

6. $17.8 \times 11 = 195.8$
   The combined weight of 11 bicycles is 195.8 pounds.

7. $45.85 \times 8 = 366.8$
   Cyclists ride 366.8 kilometers during the 8 days of the Tour of the Valley trip.

8. $0.62 \times 19.6 = 12.152$
   A time trial that is 19.6 kilometers long is equivalent to 12.152 miles.

9. $16.30 \times 6 = 97.80$
   The 6 T-shirts will cost $97.80.

10. $28.3 \times 5.7 = 161.31$
    The rider will ride 161.31 kilometers in 5.7 hours.

TRY IT Multiply Decimals to Solve Problems

ONLINE
15 min

Students will complete an online Try It. If necessary, read the directions, problems, and answer choices to students and help them with keyboard or mouse operations.

Objectives

- Solve a story problem that involves multiplication or division of decimal numbers.

Compute Decimal Story Problems (B)

Lesson Overview

GET READY Divide Decimals	5 minutes	ONLINE
LEARN Divide Decimals in Story Problems	20 minutes	ONLINE
LEARN Picnic Decimal Story Problems	20 minutes	OFFLINE
TRY IT Divide Decimals to Solve Story Problems	15 minutes	ONLINE

▶ **Lesson Objectives**

Solve a story problem that involves multiplication or division of decimal numbers.

▶ **Prerequisite Skills**

Solve a multiplication or division problem that involves decimal numbers.

▶ **Content Background**

Students will calculate the answers to division story problems involving decimal numbers and whole numbers.

When students write and compute with decimal numbers, they often use numbers that are between 0 and 1—for example, 0.1. While it is acceptable to write this number as .1, mathematicians usually write the leading zero, to show that the whole-number value for the decimal number is zero and to avoid confusion about the value of the number.

Materials to Gather

SUPPLIED

Picnic Decimal Story Problems activity page

GET READY Divide Decimals

ONLINE **5**min

Students will divide decimal numbers and whole numbers to find quotients.

Tips Allow students to use multiplication as another way to verify the reasonableness of their answers.

Objectives

- Solve a multiplication or division problem that involves decimal numbers.

LEARN Divide Decimals in Story Problems

ONLINE **20**min

Students will divide decimal numbers by decimal numbers and decimal numbers by whole numbers to solve story problems about a picnic.

Objectives

- Solve a story problem that involves multiplication or division of decimal numbers.

LEARN Picnic Decimal Story Problems

- Solve a story problem that involves multiplication or division of decimal numbers.

Students will set up and then solve division problems in which decimal numbers are divided by whole numbers and decimal numbers.

View or print the Picnic Decimal Story Problems activity page and read the directions with students. They should copy the problems from the Activity Book into their Math Notebook as necessary and solve them there.

1. Have students read the problems in the Worked Examples.

2. Tell students that they will find exact quotients.

3. Note that some problems require students to divide decimal numbers by whole numbers, and other problems require students to divide decimal numbers by decimal numbers.

4. In Problem 2 of the problem set, remind students that when they divide a decimal number by another decimal number, the divisor needs to be changed to a whole number.

5. Guide students to multiply both the dividend and the divisor by the same number. Remind them that they are actually multiplying a fraction (the dividend over the divisor) by a fraction that is the equivalent of 1.

6. **Ask:** What will you multiply 36.5 by to make it into a whole number? 10

   Ask: What will you then multiply 54.75 by? 10

   Ask: What will the division problem be after you multiply the divisor and dividend by 10? 547.5 divided by 365 or $\frac{547.5}{365}$

   Have students use a step-by-step process to solve.

$$36.5\overline{)54.75} = \begin{array}{r} 1.5 \\ 365\overline{)547.5} \\ -\ 365.0 \\ \hline 182.5 \\ -\ 182.5 \\ \hline 0 \end{array}$$

7. Have students solve Problem 1 and Problems 3–10 on their own.

Tips

Encourage students to estimate the quotient before they find the exact quotient. The estimate will help them verify the reasonableness of their exact answer.

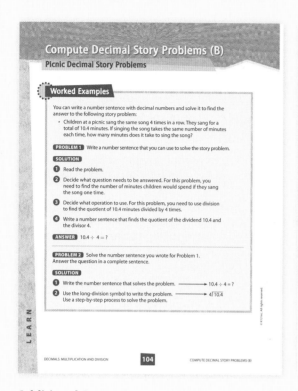

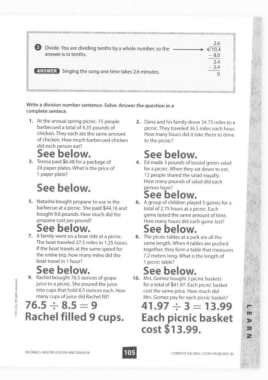

Additional Answers

1. $4.35 \div 15 = 0.29$; Each person ate 0.29 pounds of chicken.

2. $54.75 \div 36.5 = 1.5$; It took 1.5 hours to drive to the picnic.

3. $6.48 \div 24 = 0.27$; Each plate costs $0.27.

4. $3 \div 12 = 0.25$; Each person had 0.25 pound of salad.

5. $44.16 \div 9.6 = 4.6$; The propane cost $4.60 per pound.

6. $2.75 \div 5 = 0.55$; Each game lasted 0.55 of an hour.

7. $27.5 \div 1.25 = 22$; The boat traveled 22 miles in 1 hour.

8. $7.2 \div 4 = 1.8$; Each table is 1.8 meters long.

TRY IT Divide Decimals to Solve Story Problems

ONLINE 15 min

Students will complete an online Try It. If necessary, read the directions, problems, and answer choices to students and help them with keyboard or mouse operations.

Objectives

- Solve a story problem that involves multiplication or division of decimal numbers.

Compute Decimal Story Problems (C)

Lesson Overview

LEARN Hidden Picture Story Problems	15 minutes	ONLINE
LEARN Camping Trip Story Problems	15 minutes	ONLINE
LEARN More Camping Trip Story Problems	15 minutes	OFFLINE
TRY IT Multiply and Divide Decimals	5 minutes	ONLINE
CHECKPOINT	10 minutes	ONLINE

▶ Lesson Objectives

Solve a story problem that involves multiplication or division of decimal numbers.

▶ Prerequisite Skills

Solve a multiplication or division problem that involves decimal numbers.

▶ Content Background

Students will calculate the answers to multiplication and division story problems involving decimal numbers and whole numbers.

When students write and compute with decimal numbers, they often use numbers that are between 0 and 1—for example, 0.1. While it is acceptable to write this number as .1, mathematicians usually write the leading zero, to show that the whole-number value for the decimal number is zero and to avoid confusion about the value of the number.

Materials to Gather

SUPPLIED

More Camping Trip Story Problems activity page

LEARN Hidden Picture Story Problems

ONLINE **15min**

Students will solve story problems involving multiplication and division of decimal numbers to unveil a hidden picture.

Objectives

- Solve a story problem that involves multiplication or division of decimal numbers.

LEARN Camping Trip Story Problems

ONLINE **15min**

Students will multiply and divide using decimal numbers. They will solve story problems about activities people do on camping trips.

Objectives

- Solve a story problem that involves multiplication or division of decimal numbers.

LEARN More Camping Trip Story Problems

Objectives

- Solve a story problem that involves multiplication or division of decimal numbers.

Students will set up and then solve multiplication problems and division problems involving decimal numbers and whole numbers.

  View or print the More Camping Trip Story Problems activity page and read the directions with students. They should copy the problems from the Activity Book into their Math Notebook as necessary and solve them there.

1. Have students read the Worked Examples.

2. Tell students they will find the exact products and quotients.

3. Note that some problems require students to multiply and divide decimal numbers by whole numbers, and other problems require students to multiply and divide decimal numbers by decimal numbers.

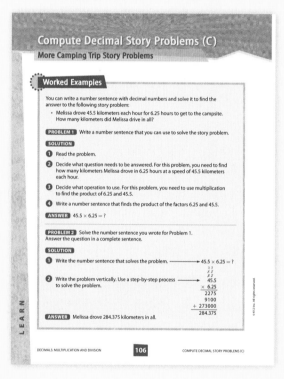

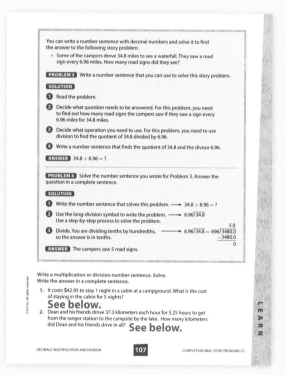

Additional Answers

1. $42.95 \times 5 = 214.75$; It costs $214.75 to stay 5 nights in the cabin.

2. $37.3 \times 5.25 = 195.825$; Dean and his friends drove 195.825 kilometers in all.

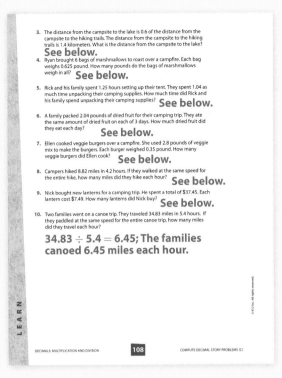

Additional Answers

3. $0.6 \times 1.4 = 0.84$; The distance from the campsite to the lake is 0.84 kilometer.

4. $6 \times 0.625 = 3.75$; The 6 bags of marshmallows weigh 3.75 pounds in all.

5. $1.25 \times 1.04 = 1.3$; Rick and his family spent 1.3 hours unpacking their camping supplies.

6. $2.04 \div 3 = 0.68$; The family ate 0.68 pound of dried fruit each day.

7. $2.8 \div 0.35 = 8$; Ellen cooked 8 veggie burgers.

8. $8.82 \div 4.2 = 2.1$; The campers hiked 2.1 miles each hour.

9. $37.45 \div 7.49 = 5$; Nick bought 5 lanterns.

TRY IT Multiply and Divide Decimals

ONLINE **5**min

Students will complete an online Try It. If necessary, read the directions, problems, and answer choices to students and help them with keyboard or mouse operations.

Objectives

- Solve a story problem that involves multiplication or division of decimal numbers.

CHECKPOINT

ONLINE **10**min

Students will complete an online Checkpoint. If necessary, read the directions, problems, and answer choices to students and help them with keyboard or mouse operations.

Objectives

- Solve a story problem that involves multiplication or division of decimal numbers.

Core Focus
Decimal Numbers

Lesson Overview

GET READY Round Decimal Numbers	10 minutes	ONLINE
LEARN Compare Decimals and Solve Problems	20 minutes	ONLINE
TRY IT Numbers with Decimals	15 minutes	OFFLINE
CHECKPOINT	15 minutes	ONLINE

▶ Lesson Objectives

- Use place value to round decimals to any place.
- Estimate the product or quotient of a computation problem involving decimal numbers.
- Read, write, compare, and order decimals to thousandths.

Materials to Gather

SUPPLIED

Numbers with Decimals activity page

▶ Content Background

Students will continue to work with place value to gain a much greater understanding of decimal numbers. Students should find that reading, writing, comparing, and rounding decimal numbers is easier to understand once they understand place value. In this lesson, students will review these important ideas that lead to better estimation and computation skills they can use in daily life.

GET READY Round Decimal Numbers

ONLINE 10 min

Students will use online flash cards to review the rounding of decimal numbers.

Objectives

- Use place value to round decimals to any place.

LEARN Compare Decimals and Solve Problems

ONLINE 20 min

Students will compare decimals and complete a multistep problem involving rounding, comparing, and estimating products and quotients with decimal numbers.

Objectives

- Use place value to round decimals to any place.
- Estimate the product or quotient of a computation problem involving decimal numbers.
- Read, write, compare, and order decimals to thousandths.

TRY IT Numbers with Decimals

Objectives

- Use place value to round decimals to any place.

- Estimate the product or quotient of a computation problem involving decimal numbers.

- Read, write, compare, and order decimals to thousandths.

Students will practice skills they have learned using place value and problem solving with decimal numbers. View or print the Numbers with Decimals activity page. Students should copy the problems into their Math Notebook and solve them there.

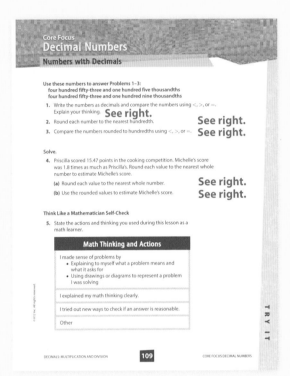

Additional Answers

1. $453.105 < 453.109$ or $453.109 > 453.105$
   Possible explanation: The only difference between the values of the numbers is the digit in the thousandths place, so the comparison is between 5 thousandths and 9 thousandths. Because 5 thousandths is less than 9 thousandths (or 9 thousandths is greater than 5 thousandths), $453.105 < 453.109$ (or $453.109 > 453.105$).

2. 453.105 rounded to the nearest hundredth is 453.11 and 453.109 rounded to the nearest hundredth is 453.11.

3. $453.11 = 453.11$

4. **(a)** 15.47 rounded to the nearest whole number is 15 and 1.8 rounded to the nearest whole number is 2.

   (b) Since $15 \times 2 = 30$, Michelle's score is about 30.

CHECKPOINT

Objectives

- Use place value to round decimals to any place.

- Estimate the product or quotient of a computation problem involving decimal numbers.

- Read, write, compare, and order decimals to thousandths.

Students will complete an online Checkpoint. If necessary, read the directions, problems, and answer choices to students and help them with keyboard or mouse operations.

Unit Review

Lesson Overview

UNIT REVIEW Look Back	10 minutes	**ONLINE**
UNIT REVIEW Checkpoint Practice	50 minutes	**ONLINE**
⏩ **UNIT REVIEW** Prepare for the Checkpoint		

▶ Unit Objectives

- Multiply or divide by a multiple or power of 10.
- Write decimals in expanded form.
- Compare decimal numbers.
- Estimate the product or quotient of a computation problem involving decimal numbers.
- Use place value to round decimals to any place.
- Solve a multiplication or division problem that involves decimal numbers.
- Verify that the calculated result of a problem involving multiplication or division of decimal numbers is reasonable.
- Solve a story problem that involves multiplication or division of decimal numbers.
- Read, write, compare, and order decimals to thousandths.

Materials to Gather

There are no materials to gather for this lesson.

▶ Advance Preparation

In this lesson, students will have an opportunity to review previous activities in the Decimals: Multiplication and Division unit. Look at the suggested activities in Unit Review: Prepare for the Checkpoint online and gather any needed materials.

UNIT REVIEW Look Back
ONLINE 10min

Students will review key concepts from the unit to prepare for the Unit Checkpoint.

Objectives

- Review unit objectives.

UNIT REVIEW Checkpoint Practice
ONLINE 50min

Students will complete an online Checkpoint Practice to prepare for the Unit Checkpoint. If necessary, read the directions, problems, and answer choices to students. Have students answer the problems on their own. Review any missed problems with students.

Objectives

- Review unit objectives.

⏩ UNIT REVIEW Prepare for the Checkpoint

What you do next depends on how students performed in the previous activity, Unit Review: Checkpoint Practice. If students had difficulty with any of the problems, complete the appropriate review activity listed in the table online.

Unit Checkpoint

| **UNIT CHECKPOINT** Online | 60 minutes | **ONLINE** |

▶ ## Unit Objectives

This lesson assesses the following objectives:

- Multiply or divide by a multiple or power of 10.
- Write decimals in expanded form.
- Compare decimal numbers.
- Estimate the product or quotient of a computation problem involving decimal numbers.
- Use place value to round decimals to any place.
- Solve a multiplication or division problem that involves decimal numbers.
- Verify that the calculated result of a problem involving multiplication or division of decimal numbers is reasonable.
- Solve a story problem that involves multiplication or division of decimal numbers.
- Read, write, compare, and order decimals to thousandths.

Materials to Gather

There are no materials to gather for this lesson.

ONLINE 60min

UNIT CHECKPOINT Online

Objectives

- Assess unit objectives.

Students will complete the Unit Checkpoint online. If necessary, read the directions, problems, and answer choices to students and help them with keyboard or mouse operations.

Extended Problems: Real-World Application

USE WHAT YOU KNOW Offline | 60 minutes | **OFFLINE**

▶ Lesson Objectives

This lesson assesses the following objectives:

- Multiply or divide by a multiple or power of 10.
- Compare decimal numbers.
- Estimate the product or quotient of a computation problem involving decimal numbers.
- Use place value to round decimals to any place.
- Solve a story problem that requires finding rectangular area.
- Solve simple put-together problems using information from a bar graph.
- Organize or display data using tables, bar graphs, line graphs, or pictographs.
- Solve a story problem that involves multiplication or division of decimal numbers.
- Solve a story problem involving addition or subtraction of decimal numbers.
- Apply mathematical knowledge and skills to evaluate and analyze real-world situations.

Materials to Gather

SUPPLIED

Extended Problems: Real-World Application (printout)

OFFLINE 60 min

USE WHAT YOU KNOW Offline

Open the Extended Problems: Real-World Application. Read the directions, problems, and answer choices to students, if necessary.

The teacher will grade this assignment.

- Students should save the graded assignment to their computer. In the filename, they should replace "studentname" with their last name followed by their first initial.
- Students should complete the assignment on their own.
- Students should submit the completed assignment according to the teacher's instructions.

Objectives

- Apply mathematical knowledge and skills to evaluate and analyze real-world situations.

Semester Review

Lesson Overview

SEMESTER REVIEW Look Back	30 minutes	**ONLINE**
SEMESTER REVIEW Checkpoint Practice	30 minutes	**ONLINE**
⏩ **SEMESTER REVIEW** Prepare for the Checkpoint		

▶ Semester Objectives

This lesson reviews the following objectives:

- Round whole numbers in a story problem.
- Estimate or calculate a sum or a difference in a whole-number problem.
- Estimate or calculate a sum or a difference in a whole-number story problem.
- Represent and compute a power by using repeated multiplication.
- Solve a problem that involves powers.
- Recognize that in a multidigit number, a digit in one place represents 10 times as much as it represents in the place to its right and $\frac{1}{10}$ of what it represents in the place to its left.
- Solve with proficiency for quotients of up to a four-digit dividend by a two-digit divisor using strategies.
- Fluently multiply multidigit whole numbers using the standard algorithm.
- Solve multistep problems using multiple operations.
- Define and sketch different types of triangles and identify their attributes.
- Know how to define and sketch different quadrilaterals.
- Identify, measure, and draw angles with appropriate math tools.
- Identify and draw perpendicular or parallel lines with appropriate math tools.
- Identify that the sum of the interior angles of any triangle is 180° and solve related problems.
- Identify that the sum of the interior angles of any quadrilateral is 360° and solve related problems.
- Understand that attributes that apply to a category of two-dimensional figures also apply to all subcategories of that category.
- Classify two-dimensional figures in a hierarchy based on their properties.
- Interpret multiplication as scaling.
- Represent division of a unit fraction by a whole number such as $\frac{1}{3} \div 7$ using objects and pictorial models, including area models.
- Divide whole numbers by unit fractions and unit fractions by whole numbers.
- Use models and equations to multiply a whole number or a fraction by a fraction.
- Compare the size of a product to the size of one factor on the basis of the size of the other factor, without multiplying.

Materials to Gather

There are no materials to gather for this lesson.

- Solve real-world problems involving multiplication of fractions and mixed numbers.
- Solve a simple problem involving addition or subtraction of fractions.
- Compare decimal numbers.
- Order three or more decimal numbers.
- Round a decimal number to any place through hundredths.
- Read, write, compare, and order decimals to thousandths.
- Add or subtract decimals to hundredths, using models or drawings and strategies based on place value.
- Estimate the sum or difference in a problem involving decimal numbers.
- Solve a story problem involving addition or subtraction of decimal numbers.
- Write decimals in expanded form.
- Solve a multiplication or division problem that involves decimal numbers.
- Multiply or divide by a multiple or power of 10.
- Estimate the product or quotient of a computation problem involving decimal numbers.
- Verify that the calculated result of a problem involving multiplication or division of decimal numbers is reasonable.
- Use place value to round decimals to any place.
- Solve a story problem that involves multiplication or division of decimal numbers.

▶ Advance Preparation

In this lesson, students will have an opportunity to review previous activities from the semester. Look at the suggested activities in Semester Review: Prepare for the Checkpoint online and be prepared to gather any needed materials.

ONLINE
30min

SEMESTER REVIEW Look Back

Objectives

- Review semester objectives.

As students prepare to complete the semester, they should refresh their knowledge of the math they have learned thus far. You may notice that some of the objectives in the Semester Review are not necessarily included in the Semester Checkpoint. Some of these concepts are particularly important to review in order to be successful with the upcoming topics students will encounter, and others contribute to a greater understanding of the concepts that are being assessed. Therefore, a complete review of the objectives in this lesson is recommended.

To review, students will play a Super Genius game. If students answer a problem incorrectly, the correct answer will display. Be sure to help students understand why the answer is correct before they move on to the next problem. If they miss several problems, have students play the game again.

Objectives

- Review semester objectives.

Students will complete an online Checkpoint Practice to prepare for the Semester Checkpoint. If necessary, read the directions, problems, and answer choices to students. Have students answer the problems on their own. Review any missed problems with students.

⮞ SEMESTER REVIEW Prepare for the Checkpoint

What you do next depends on how students performed in the previous activity, Semester Review: Checkpoint Practice. If students had difficulty with any of the problems, complete the appropriate review activity listed in the Unit Review tables online.

Because there are many concepts to review, consider using the Your Choice day to continue preparing for the Semester Checkpoint.

Semester Checkpoint 1

Lesson Overview

SEMESTER CHECKPOINT Online   60 minutes | **ONLINE**

▶ Semester Objectives

This lesson assesses the following objectives:

- Round whole numbers in a story problem.
- Estimate or calculate a sum or a difference in a whole-number problem.
- Estimate or calculate a sum or a difference in a whole-number story problem.
- Represent and compute a power by using repeated multiplication.
- Solve a problem that involves powers.
- Recognize that in a multidigit number, a digit in one place represents 10 times as much as it represents in the place to its right and $\frac{1}{10}$ of what it represents in the place to its left.
- Solve with proficiency for quotients of up to a four-digit dividend by a two-digit divisor using strategies.
- Fluently multiply multidigit whole numbers using the standard algorithm.
- Solve multistep problems using multiple operations.
- Define and sketch different types of triangles and identify their attributes.
- Know how to define and sketch different quadrilaterals.
- Identify, measure, and draw angles with appropriate math tools.
- Identify and draw perpendicular or parallel lines with appropriate math tools.
- Identify that the sum of the interior angles of any triangle is 180º and solve related problems.
- Identify that the sum of the interior angles of any quadrilateral is 360º and solve related problems.
- Understand that attributes that apply to a category of two-dimensional figures also apply to all subcategories of that category.
- Classify two-dimensional figures in a hierarchy based on their properties.
- Interpret multiplication as scaling.
- Represent division of a unit fraction by a whole number such as $\frac{1}{3} \div 7$ using objects and pictorial models, including area models.
- Divide whole numbers by unit fractions and unit fractions by whole numbers.
- Use models and equations to multiply a whole number or a fraction by a fraction.
- Compare the size of a product to the size of one factor on the basis of the size of the other factor, without multiplying.
- Solve real-world problems involving multiplication of fractions and mixed numbers.
- Solve a simple problem involving addition or subtraction of fractions.
- Compare decimal numbers.

Materials to Gather

There are no materials to gather for this lesson.

- Order three or more decimal numbers.
- Round a decimal number to any place through hundredths.
- Read, write, compare, and order decimals to thousandths.
- Add or subtract decimals to hundredths, using models or drawings and strategies based on place value.
- Estimate the sum or difference in a problem involving decimal numbers.
- Solve a story problem involving addition or subtraction of decimal numbers.
- Write decimals in expanded form.
- Solve a multiplication or division problem that involves decimal numbers.
- Multiply or divide by a multiple or power of 10.
- Estimate the product or quotient of a computation problem involving decimal numbers.
- Verify that the calculated result of a problem involving multiplication or division of decimal numbers is reasonable.
- Use place value to round decimals to any place.
- Solve a story problem that involves multiplication or division of decimal numbers.

ONLINE

60min

SEMESTER CHECKPOINT Online

Objectives

Students will complete this part of the Semester Checkpoint online. If necessary, read the directions, problems, and answer choices to students and help them with keyboard or mouse operations.

- Assess semester objectives.

Semester Checkpoint 2

SEMESTER CHECKPOINT Offline   60 minutes   **OFFLINE**

▶ Semester Objectives

This lesson assesses the following objectives:

- Know how to define and sketch different quadrilaterals.

- Represent division of a unit fraction by a whole number such as $\frac{1}{3} \div 7$ using objects and pictorial models, including area models.

- Read, write, compare, and order decimals to thousandths.

Materials to Gather

Semester Checkpoint 2 (printout)
Semester Checkpoint 2 Answer Key
(printout)

SEMESTER CHECKPOINT Offline   OFFLINE 60min

Objectives

- Assess semester objectives.

This part of the Semester Checkpoint and its answer key are located in the Resources section for this unit in the Online Book Menu of *Math+ Yellow Lesson Guide*. Give students the Semester Checkpoint 2. Have students complete the Semester Checkpoint 2 on their own. Use the answer key to score the Semester Checkpoint 2, and then enter the results online.

Algebra

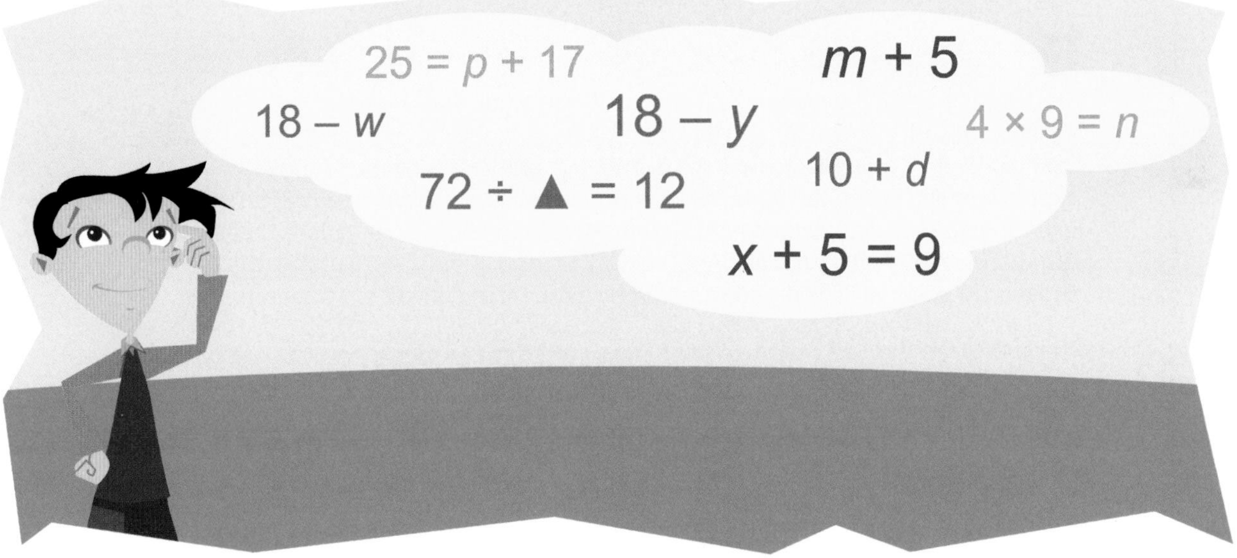

$25 = p + 17$

$m + 5$

$18 - w$

$18 - y$

$4 \times 9 = n$

$72 \div \blacktriangle = 12$

$10 + d$

$x + 5 = 9$

- Use a letter to represent an unknown value in an expression or an equation.
- Use the order of operations to simplify expressions with mixed operations.
- Simplify expressions with grouping symbols.
- Find a mathematical expression that corresponds to a given word phrase.
- Interpret a numerical expression without evaluating the expression.
- Evaluate a simple algebraic expression in one variable by using substitution.
- Identify or use an expression or an equation to answer questions about a problem.
- Evaluate numerical expressions using order of operations (expressions include with parentheses and powers, whole numbers only).

▶ Big Ideas

- A variable is a symbol, usually a letter, that is used to stand for a number or a set of numbers.
- The distributive property illustrates how to multiply a specific multiplier by a series of numbers being added or subtracted.
- An expression represents a value that can be a number, a variable, or a group of numbers, variables, and operation symbols. Some examples of expressions are $10 - 4 + 1$, $3 + x$, $5y + 2$, b, and 5.

▶ Unit Introduction

Students will begin the Algebra unit with an introduction to using letters to represent variables in both expressions and equations. To extend their investigation of variables, they will explore examples of how the distributive property is correctly applied in expressions and equations. Students will use substitution to evaluate an expression with one variable. The unit culminates with identifying expressions or equations that answer questions about a story problem. Another way to think about a story problem is as a situation. Students will work with story problems in many activities in this unit.

▶ Keywords

distributive property	expression	substitution
equation	order of operations	term
evaluate	solve	variable

Understand Variables in Algebra (A)

GET READY Build Expressions and Equations	5 minutes	ONLINE
LEARN Variables	15 minutes	ONLINE
LEARN Find the Value of Expressions	15 minutes	OFFLINE
LEARN Variables in Situations: Add, Subtract	15 minutes	ONLINE
TRY IT Variables in Expressions and Equations	10 minutes	ONLINE

▶ Lesson Objectives

Use a letter to represent an unknown value in an expression or an equation.

▶ Prerequisite Skills

Use symbols to stand for variables in simple expressions or equations.

▶ Content Background

Students will learn the meaning of a variable and use it to represent an unknown value in an expression or an equation. They will also relate expressions and equations to different situations.

- An *expression* is a part of a number sentence and can have numbers, operation symbols (such as $+$, $-$, $\cdot$, or $\div$), and variables. An expression does *not* have a relational symbol, such as $<$, $>$, or $=$, in it. Some examples of expressions are $m + 7$, $12 - 2w$, $11 \cdot 6$, and $100 \div 4$.

- An *equation* is a number sentence that shows that two quantities are equal. Equations can include numbers, variables, and operation symbols (such as $+$, $-$, $\cdot$, or $\div$). Some examples of equations are $2r - 3 = 9$ and $16 = 2 + 4$.

- A *variable* is a symbol that stands for a quantity. For example, in the equation $2 + m = 5$, m stands for the number that makes the equation true. So in $2 + m = 5$, $m = 3$, since $2 + 3 = 5$. Sometimes the variable stands for many possible quantities. One reason the symbols are called *variables* is that the amount they represent can vary. For example, in the expression $52 - p$, you can replace p with any number and find the value of the expression. You may often see x and y used as variables in expressions and equations, but any letter can be used as a variable.

When students multiply in expressions and equations in this lesson, they will not always see the $\times$ symbol. They might see the dot that represents multiplication: $\cdot$. Students might also see implied multiplication, where no multiplication symbol is used. For example, they will see $3n$ instead of $3 \cdot n$.

Materials to Gather

SUPPLIED

There are no materials to gather for this lesson.

▶ Common Errors and Misconceptions

- Students might have a difficult time understanding that a letter can represent varying values or that different letters can represent the same value. They commonly interpret a letter as representing a specific number. For example, students might think that $7w + 22 = 109$ and $7n + 22 = 109$ have different answers because they don't understand that w and n represent the same number.

- Students might not understand that arithmetic and algebra treat the placement of symbols differently. For example, $8y$ means $8 \cdot y$ while 54 means $50 + 4$. So when solving for x in $2x = 24$, students often think that $x = 4$.

▶ Advance Preparation

In the Math Notebook, create the charts shown.

z	$z + 4$	Value of the expression
1		
2		
3		
4		

x	$5 - x$	Value of the expression
1		
2		
3		
4		

GET READY Build Expressions and Equations

ONLINE 5min

Students will read a description of an expression or an equation. They will then use numbers and symbols to build the expression or equation.

Objectives

- Use symbols to stand for variables in simple expressions or equations.

LEARN Variables

ONLINE 15min

Students will learn what a variable is and how it is used in expressions and equations. They will also practice reading expressions and equations with variables.

Objectives

- Use a letter to represent an unknown value in an expression or an equation.

LEARN Find the Value of Expressions

Objectives

- Use a letter to represent an unknown value in an expression or an equation.

Students will complete charts to write expressions and find values for each expression.

Gather the two charts you created in the Math Notebook.

1. Tell students that when they write expressions and equations that have addition, there can be more than one way to write them because the addends can switch places and still represent the same expression or equation.

   Ask: In subtraction expressions and equations, why can't you switch around the numbers and variables as you can in addition expressions and equations? Addition has the commutative property, which means the order of the addends can be changed and the sum will remain the same. Subtraction doesn't have the commutative property.

2. Give students the addition chart.

   Say: The chart shows values for the variable z. It also has the expression $z + 4$. Read the expression as "an unknown number, z, combined with 4." You will fill in the chart to write four values for the variable z and find the value of four expressions for those values of z.

3. Read the column headings and the values of z on the chart.

   Say: Find out what values you can get for the expression $z + 4$. You will write the values for the expression in the third column, Value of the expression.

4. Have students look at the first row. Tell them that in this row, z has a value of 1. That means they can rewrite the expression $z + 4$ as $1 + 4$.

   Say: Add $1 + 4$. For z equal to 1, the value of the expression $z + 4$ is 5.

   On the chart, have students write $1 + 4$ in the second column, $z + 4$. Have them write 5 in the third column, Value of the expression.

5. Have students fill in the other rows of the chart as they did with the first row. The completed chart is shown.

z	$z + 4$	Value of the expression
1	$1 + 4$	5
2	$2 + 4$	6
3	$3 + 4$	7
4	$4 + 4$	8

6. Have students read aloud and explain each row in the chart. They should say the variable, the expression with the value of the variable, and the value of the expression. For example, students would read the first row as, "For the variable z with the value of 1, the value of the expression $z + 4$ equals $1 + 4$, which equals 5."

7. Give students the subtraction chart and have them complete it, using their experience from the addition chart. Repeat Step 6 with this chart. The completed chart is shown.

x	5 − x	Value of the expression
1	5 − 1	4
2	5 − 2	3
3	5 − 3	2
4	5 − 4	1

LEARN Variables in Situations: Add, Subtract

Students will hear a discussion between two characters about how to write expressions and equations to match story problems. Then they will match expressions and equations to story problems that involve addition and subtraction.

Objectives

- Use a letter to represent an unknown value in an expression or an equation.

TRY IT Variables in Expressions and Equations

Students will complete an online Try It. If necessary, read the directions, problems, and answer choices to students and help them with keyboard or mouse operations.

Objectives

- Use a letter to represent an unknown value in an expression or an equation.

Tips

It may be helpful for students to read the expressions and equations aloud to help them match the expressions and equations with story problems.

Understand Variables in Algebra (B)

Lesson Overview

LEARN Other Ways to Show Multiplication	20 minutes	ONLINE
LEARN Variables in Situations: Multiply, Divide	15 minutes	ONLINE
TRY IT Find Expressions and Equations	10 minutes	ONLINE
CHECKPOINT	10 minutes	ONLINE

▶ Lesson Objectives

Use a letter to represent an unknown value in an expression or an equation.

▶ Content Background

Students will continue to learn the meaning of a variable and use it to represent an unknown value in an expression or an equation. They will also relate expressions and equations to different situations.

- An *expression* is a part of a number sentence and can have numbers, operation symbols (such as $+$, $-$, $\cdot$, or $\div$), and variables. An expression does **not** have a relational symbol, such as $<$, $>$, or $=$, in it. Some examples of expressions are $m + 7$, $12 - 2w$, $11 \cdot 6$, and $100 \div 4$.

- An *equation* is a number sentence that shows that two quantities are equal. Equations can include numbers, variables, and operation symbols (such as $+$, $-$, $\cdot$, or $\div$). Some examples of equations are $2r - 3 = 9$ and $16 = 12 + 4$.

- A *variable* is a symbol that stands for a quantity. For example, in the equation $2 + m = 5$, m stands for the number that makes the equation true. So in $2 + m = 5$, $m = 3$, since $2 + 3 = 5$. Sometimes the variable stands for many possible quantities. One reason the symbols are called *variables* is that the amount they represent can vary. For example, in the expression $52 - p$, you can replace p with any number and find the value of the expression. You may often see x and y used as variables in expressions and equations, but any letter can be used as a variable.

When students multiply in expressions and equations in this lesson, they will not always see the $\times$ symbol. They might see the dot that represents multiplication: $\cdot$. Students might also see implied multiplication, where no multiplication symbol is used. For example, they will see $3n$ instead of $3 \cdot n$.

▶ Common Errors and Misconceptions

- Students might have a difficult time understanding that a letter can represent varying values or that different letters can represent the same value. They commonly interpret a letter as representing a specific number. For example, students might think that $7w + 22 = 109$ and $7n + 22 = 109$ have different answers because they don't understand that w and n represent the same number.

- Students might not understand that arithmetic and algebra treat the placement of symbols differently. For example, $8y$ means $8 \cdot y$ while 54 means $50 + 4$. So when solving for x in $2x = 24$, students often think that $x = 4$.

Materials to Gather

SUPPLIED

There are no materials to gather for this lesson.

LEARN Other Ways to Show Multiplication

ONLINE 20min

Students will learn different ways to represent multiplication expressions and equations with numbers and variables.

Objectives

- Use a letter to represent an unknown value in an expression or an equation.

LEARN Variables in Situations: Multiply, Divide

ONLINE 15min

Students will hear a discussion between two characters about how to write multiplication and division expressions and equations to match situations. Then they will match expressions and equations to situations.

Objectives

- Use a letter to represent an unknown value in an expression or an equation.

TRY IT Find Expressions and Equations

ONLINE 10min

Students will complete an online Try It. If necessary, read the directions, problems, and answer choices to students and help them with keyboard or mouse operations.

Objectives

- Use a letter to represent an unknown value in an expression or an equation.

CHECKPOINT

ONLINE 10min

Students will complete an online Checkpoint. If necessary, read the directions, problems, and answer choices to students and help them with keyboard or mouse operations.

Objectives

- Use a letter to represent an unknown value in an expression or an equation.

Evaluate Numerical Expressions

Lesson Overview		
LEARN The Order of Operations	20 minutes	ONLINE
LEARN Brackets and Exponents	5 minutes	ONLINE
LEARN More Grouping Symbols	15 minutes	OFFLINE
TRY IT Evaluate Expressions with Numbers	10 minutes	ONLINE
CHECKPOINT	10 minutes	ONLINE

▶ Lesson Objectives

- Use the order of operations to simplify expressions with mixed operations.
- Simplify expressions with grouping symbols.

▶ Content Background

Students will use the order of operations to evaluate expressions with numbers. They will begin with expressions that use the four basic operations and use parentheses as the only grouping symbols. The problems will progress to include powers of 10. Students will then be introduced to nested grouping symbols, including brackets and braces, in addition to parentheses.

The order of operations is a set of rules that states the order in which students need to perform computation problems that are written horizontally and include more than one operation. If students don't follow the correct order, they will not calculate the answer correctly. The order of operations is used to find the value of the expression or equation, or to evaluate the expression or equation. The order of operations follows a step-by-step priority:

1. If there are parentheses, complete the computations inside the parentheses. If there are multiple grouping symbols, parentheses may be inside brackets, which may be inside braces. Students should work within the innermost grouping symbol and work their way outward. If two or more computations are within any grouping symbols, the following order is also used there.

2. Simplify exponents.

3. Multiply or divide from left to right, starting with the operation that comes first (either division or multiplication).

4. Subtract or add from left to right, starting with the operation that comes first (either addition or subtraction).

Mastering the order of operations, particularly with nested grouping symbols, will greatly benefit students as they move into the formal study of algebra.

Materials to Gather

SUPPLIED
More Grouping Symbols activity page

LEARN The Order of Operations

Students will learn the order of operations with the four basic operations and with parentheses as the only type of grouping symbol.

Objectives
- Use the order of operations to simplify expressions with mixed operations.

LEARN Brackets and Exponents

Students will extend their work with the order of operations to include exponents in the form of powers of 10 and the use of brackets enclosing parentheses.

Objectives
- Simplify expressions with grouping symbols.

LEARN More Grouping Symbols

Students will work with the order of operations using powers of 10 and three sets of grouping symbols. View or print the More Grouping Symbols activity page and read the directions with students.

Students should copy the problems from the Activity Book into their Math Notebook as necessary and solve them there. Assist students with the Worked Examples and instructions as needed.

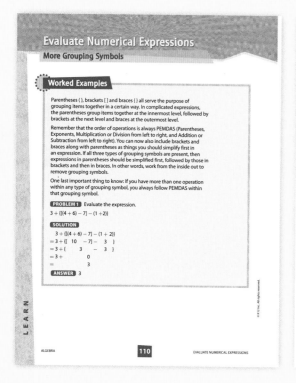

Evaluate Numerical Expressions
More Grouping Symbols

Worked Examples

Parentheses ( ), brackets [ ] and braces { } all serve the purpose of grouping items together in a certain way. In complicated expressions, the parentheses group items together at the innermost level, followed by brackets at the next level and braces at the outermost level.

Remember that the order of operations is always PEMDAS (Parentheses, Exponents, Multiplication or Division from left to right, and Addition or Subtraction from left to right). You can now also include brackets and braces along with parentheses as things you should simplify first in an expression. If all three types of grouping symbols are present, then expressions in parentheses should be simplified first, followed by those in brackets and then in braces. In other words, work from the inside out to remove grouping symbols.

One last important thing to know: If you have more than one operation within any type of grouping symbol, you always follow PEMDAS within that grouping symbol.

PROBLEM 1 Evaluate the expression.

$3 + \{[(4 + 6) - 7] - (1 + 2)\}$

SOLUTION

$$3 + \{[(4 + 6) - 7] - (1 + 2)\}$$
$$= 3 + \{[\ 10\ - 7] - \ 3\ \}$$
$$= 3 + \{\quad 3\quad - \quad 3\ \}$$
$$= 3 + \quad\quad 0$$
$$= \quad\quad 3$$

ANSWER 3

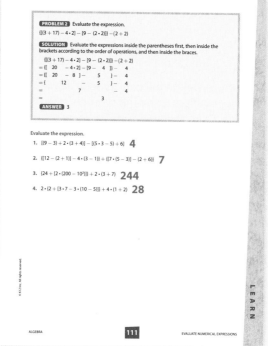

PROBLEM 2 Evaluate the expression.

$\{[(3 + 17) - 4 \cdot 2] - [9 - (2 \cdot 2)]\} - (2 + 2)$

SOLUTION Evaluate the expressions inside the parentheses first, then inside the brackets according to the order of operations, and then inside the braces.

$$\{[(3 + 17) - 4 \cdot 2] - [9 - (2 \cdot 2)]\} - (2 + 2)$$
$$= \{[\ 20\ - 4 \cdot 2] - [9 - \ 4\ ]\} - \ 4$$
$$= \{[\ 20\ - \ 8\ ] - \ 5\ \} - \ 4$$
$$= \{\quad 12\quad - \quad 5\ \} - \ 4$$
$$= \quad\quad 7\quad\quad - \ 4$$
$$= \quad\quad\quad 3$$

ANSWER 3

Evaluate the expression.

1. $[(9 - 3) + 2 \cdot (3 + 4)] - [(5 \cdot 3 - 5) + 6]$ **4**

2. $\{[12 - (2 + 1)] - 4 \cdot (3 - 1)\} + [7 \cdot (5 - 3)] - (2 + 6)\}$ **7**

3. $\{24 + [2 \cdot (200 - 10^2)] + 2 \cdot (3 + 7)$ **244**

4. $2 \cdot \{2 + [3 \cdot 7 - 3 \cdot (10 - 5)]\} + 4 \cdot (1 + 2)$ **28**

ALGEBRA   **110**   EVALUATE NUMERICAL EXPRESSIONS

ALGEBRA   **111**   EVALUATE NUMERICAL EXPRESSIONS

TRY IT Evaluate Expressions with Numbers

ONLINE 10 min

Students will complete an online Try It. If necessary, read the directions, problems, and answer choices to students and help them with keyboard or mouse operations.

Objectives

- Use the order of operations to simplify expressions with mixed operations.
- Simplify expressions with grouping symbols.

CHECKPOINT

ONLINE 10 min

Students will complete an online Checkpoint. If necessary, read the directions, problems, and answer choices to students and help them with keyboard or mouse operations.

Objectives

- Use the order of operations to simplify expressions with mixed operations.
- Simplify expressions with grouping symbols.

Create and Interpret Numerical Expressions

GET READY Match Words and Symbols	5 minutes	ONLINE
LEARN Create Numerical Expressions from Words	25 minutes	ONLINE
LEARN Interpret Numerical Expressions	10 minutes	ONLINE
TRY IT Create and Interpret Expressions	10 minutes	OFFLINE
CHECKPOINT	10 minutes	OFFLINE

▶ Lesson Objectives

- Find a mathematical expression that corresponds to a given word phrase.
- Interpret a numerical expression without evaluating the expression.

▶ Prerequisite Skills

- Use models and math symbols to represent addition.
- Use models and math symbols to represent subtraction.
- Recognize that the $\times$ sign refers to multiplication.
- Recognize that the $\div$ sign refers to division.

▶ Content Background

Students will translate word expressions into numerical expressions using mathematical symbols, including grouping symbols. Vocabulary is important when determining which operation to use and in which order to place numbers. Emphasize the keywords throughout the lesson.

Students will continue to use the order of operations. The order of operations is a set of rules that states the order in which students need to perform computation problems that are written horizontally and include more than one operation. If students don't follow the correct order, they will not calculate the answer correctly. The order of operations is used to find the value of the expression or equation, or to evaluate the expression or equation. The order of operations follows a step-by-step priority:

1. If there are parentheses, complete the computations inside the parentheses. If there are multiple grouping symbols, parentheses may be inside brackets, which may be inside braces. Students should work within the innermost grouping symbol and work their way outward. If two or more computations are within any grouping symbols, the following order is also used there.

2. Simplify exponents.

Materials to Gather

SUPPLIED

Create and Interpret Expressions
   activity page

Checkpoint (printout)

Checkpoint Answer Key (printout)

3. Multiply or divide from left to right, starting with the operation that comes first (either division or multiplication).

4. Subtract or add from left to right, starting with the operation that comes first (either addition or subtraction).

Mastering the order of operations, particularly with nested grouping symbols, will greatly benefit students as they move into the formal study of algebra.

ONLINE 5 min

GET READY Match Words and Symbols

Students will match mathematical words and symbols.

Objectives

- Use models and math symbols to represent addition.
- Use models and math symbols to represent subtraction.
- Recognize that the × sign refers to multiplication.
- Recognize that the ÷ sign refers to division.

ONLINE 25 min

LEARN Create Numerical Expressions from Words

Students will create numerical expressions from word phrases. The expressions may include one operation or two operations.

Objectives

- Find a mathematical expression that corresponds to a given word phrase.

ONLINE 10 min

LEARN Interpret Numerical Expressions

Students will explain the relationships among the numbers and symbols in a numerical expression. They will be encouraged to create practical scenarios that could be represented by the expresssions.

Objectives

- Interpret a numerical expression without evaluating the expression.

TRY IT Create and Interpret Expressions

Objectives

Students will practice creating and interpreting numerical expressions. View or print the Create and Interpret Expressions activity page. Students should copy the problems into their Math Notebook and solve them there.

- Find a mathematical expression that corresponds to a given word phrase.
- Interpret a numerical expression without evaluating the expression.

Create and Interpret Numerical Expressions
Create and Interpret Expressions

Translate the word phrase into a numerical expression.

1. the quotient of 6 divided by 12
$6 \div 12$
2. 15 less than 30
$30 - 15$
3. the difference between 7 and 2
$7 - 2$
4. twice the sum of 6 and 4
$2 \cdot (6 + 4)$ or $2 \cdot (4 + 6)$
5. 15 less than the product of 8 and 3
See right.
6. triple the quotient of 12 divided by 4
See right.

For the expression, describe the relationship among the numbers and symbols in two different ways.

7. $(12 - 6) \div 2$ **See right.**
8. $4 \cdot (13 + 7)$ **See right.**

Additional Answers

5. $(8 \cdot 3) - 15$ or $8 \cdot 3 - 15$ or $(3 \cdot 8) - 15$ or $3 \cdot 8 - 15$
6. $3 \cdot (12 \div 4)$ or $(12 \div 4) \cdot 3$
7. **Possible answers:**
The difference between 12 and 6 is being split into 2 groups.
The difference between 12 and 6 is being cut in half.
The expression has a value that is one-half the value of $12 - 6$.
Practical scenario: Sal took $6 from the $12 he had and gave an equal amount to each of his 2 children.

8. **Possible answers:**
The sum of 13 and 7 is being quadrupled.
The expression has a value that is 4 times the value of $13 + 7$.
Practical scenario: Joy saw 13 cars and 7 vans in the parking lot and determined the total number of tires on all the vehicles.

CHECKPOINT

Objectives

The Checkpoint and its answer key are located in the Resources section for this unit in the Online Book Menu of *Math+ Yellow Lesson Guide*. Give students the Checkpoint. Have students complete the Checkpoint on their own. Use the answer key to score the Checkpoint, and then enter the results online.

- Find a mathematical expression that corresponds to a given word phrase.
- Interpret a numerical expression without evaluating the expression.

One Variable in Algebraic Expressions

Lesson Overview

GET READY Order of Operations in Expressions	10 minutes	ONLINE
LEARN Use Substitution in Expressions	15 minutes	OFFLINE
LEARN Distributive Property Substitution	15 minutes	ONLINE
TRY IT Practice with Variable Expressions	10 minutes	ONLINE
CHECKPOINT	10 minutes	ONLINE

▶ Lesson Objectives

Evaluate a simple algebraic expression in one variable by using substitution.

▶ Prerequisite Skills

Use parentheses and the order of operations to write or evaluate an expression.

▶ Content Background

Students will learn to evaluate simple algebraic expressions with one variable using substitution. They will evaluate one-, two-, and three-step expressions. They will also use the distributive property to evaluate expressions with one variable.

A *variable* is a symbol that stands for a quantity. For example, in the equation $2 + m = 5$, m stands for the number that makes the equation true. So in $2 + m = 5$, $m = 3$, since $2 + 3 = 5$. Sometimes the variable stands for many possible quantities. One reason the symbols are called *variables* is that the amount they represent can vary. For example, in the expression $52 - p$, you can replace p with any number and find the value of the expression. The letters x and y are often used as variables in expressions and equations, but any letter can be used as a variable.

▶ Common Errors and Misconceptions

- Students might have a difficult time understanding that a letter can represent varying values or that different letters can represent the same value. They commonly interpret a letter as representing a specific number. For example, students might think that $7w + 22 = 109$ and $7n + 22 = 109$ have different answers because they don't understand that w and n represent the same number.

- Students might not understand variables partly because there are limited examples of variables in the elementary grades. For example, they see equations such as $52 = 5$ tens $\square$ ones in which the unknown has a specific value. They also see boxes and letters that represent a specific unknown such as $7 + \square = 10$ or $7 + a = 10$. Students rarely see cases where letters represent general unknown values or patterns.

- Students might see equations such as $5 + a = 12$ as merely abstract symbols with little or no connection to everyday situations.

- Students might not understand that letters in algebraic expressions and equations represent different values.

Materials to Gather

SUPPLIED

Use Substitution in Expressions
   activity page

ONE VARIABLE IN ALGEBRAIC EXPRESSIONS **295**

GET READY Order of Operations in Expressions

Students will follow the order of operations, including parentheses, to evaluate expressions.

- Use parentheses and the order of operations to write or evaluate an expression.

LEARN Use Substitution in Expressions

Objectives

Students will learn how to use substitution to evaluate a simple algebraic expression with one variable. Some of the expressions they will evaluate will have more than one operation, giving them practice with using the order of operations. View or print the Use Substitution in Expressions activity page and read the directions with students.

- Evaluate a simple algebraic expression in one variable by using substitution.

Students should copy the problems from the Activity Book into their Math Notebook as necessary and solve them there.

Tips

1. Read Problem 1 of the Worked Examples with students. Explain that to find the value of an expression that has a variable, students can replace the variable with any number. This process is known as evaluating using substitution. The value of the expression will depend on the number that replaces the variable.

   Ask: What operation was used to evaluate the expression in Problem 1? multiplication

   Ask: How would you know to use 2 to multiply by 19? The directions said to substitute 2 for the variable m, so that's how I would know to multiply 19 by 2.

If students have trouble understanding how to substitute a value for the variable, have them practice substituting different values in Problem 1 of the Worked Examples.

2. Read Problem 2 of the Worked Examples with students.

   Ask: Why was 7 multiplied by 2 before 8 was added? The order of operations requires that multiplication be calculated before addition.

3. Read Problem 3 of the Worked Examples with students. Note that this problem has two operations. The expression in parentheses is calculated first. Operations within parentheses are calculated first in the order of operations.

4. Read Problem 4 of the Worked Examples with students. Note that this problem has three operations. Make sure students read and understand how to use the correct order of operations to calculate the addition first, then the multiplication, and then the division.

   Say: These problems all have one variable each. As you study mathematics more, you may evaluate expressions and equations that have more than one variable.

5. Have students complete the problems in the problem set.

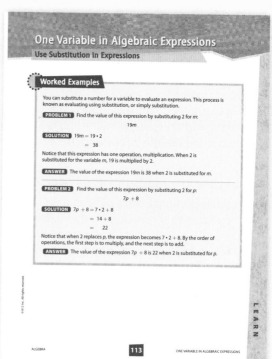

One Variable in Algebraic Expressions
Use Substitution in Expressions

Worked Examples

You can substitute a number for a variable to evaluate an expression. This process is known as evaluating using substitution, or simply substitution.

PROBLEM 1 Find the value of this expression by substituting 2 for m:

$$19m$$

SOLUTION $19m = 19 \cdot 2$
$$= 38$$

Notice that this expression has one operation, multiplication. When 2 is substituted for the variable m, 19 is multiplied by 2.

ANSWER The value of the expression $19m$ is 38 when 2 is substituted for m.

PROBLEM 2 Find the value of this expression by substituting 2 for p:
$$7p + 8$$

SOLUTION $7p + 8 = 7 \cdot 2 + 8$
$$= 14 + 8$$
$$= 22$$

Notice that when 2 replaces p, the expression becomes $7 \cdot 2 + 8$. By the order of operations, the first step is to multiply, and the next step is to add.

ANSWER The value of the expression $7p + 8$ is 22 when 2 is substituted for p.

ALGEBRA   **113**   ONE VARIABLE IN ALGEBRAIC EXPRESSIONS

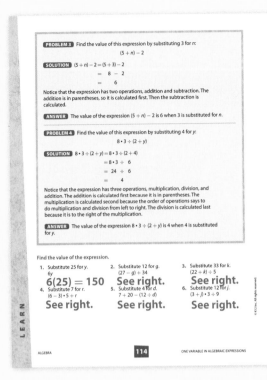

Additional Answers

2. $(27 - 12) + 34 = 15 + 34$
$\qquad\qquad\qquad\quad = \quad 49$

3. $(22 + 33) \div 5 = 55 \div 5$
$\qquad\qquad\qquad\quad = \quad 11$

4. $(6 - 3) \cdot 5 + 7 = 3 \cdot 5 + 7$
$\qquad\qquad\qquad\quad = 15 + 7$
$\qquad\qquad\qquad\quad = \quad 22$

5. $7 + 20 - (12 \div 4) = 7 + 20 - 3$
$\qquad\qquad\qquad\qquad = \quad 27 - 3$
$\qquad\qquad\qquad\qquad = \qquad 24$

6. $(3 + 12) \cdot 3 \div 9 = 15 \cdot 3 \div 9$
$\qquad\qquad\qquad\quad = \quad 45 \div 9$
$\qquad\qquad\qquad\quad = \qquad 5$

LEARN Distributive Property Substitution

ONLINE 15 min

Students will see worked examples and then use substitution with one variable to evaluate algebraic expressions. They will use the distributive property and order of operations to find the value of expressions.

Objectives

- Evaluate a simple algebraic expression in one variable by using substitution.

TRY IT Practice with Variable Expressions

ONLINE 10 min

Students will complete an online Try It. If necessary, read the directions, problems, and answer choices to students and help them with keyboard or mouse operations.

Objectives

- Evaluate a simple algebraic expression in one variable by using substitution.

CHECKPOINT

ONLINE 10 min

Students will complete an online Checkpoint. If necessary, read the directions, problems, and answer choices to students and help them with keyboard or mouse operations.

Objectives

- Evaluate a simple algebraic expression in one variable by using substitution.

Expression and Equation Problems (A)

Lesson Overview

GET READY Evaluate Expressions	10 minutes	ONLINE
LEARN Expressions and Story Problems	10 minutes	OFFLINE
LEARN Match Expressions and Story Problems	20 minutes	OFFLINE
TRY IT Practice with Expressions	20 minutes	OFFLINE

▶ Lesson Objectives

Identify or use an expression or an equation to answer questions about a problem.

▶ Prerequisite Skills

Evaluate a simple algebraic expression in one variable by using substitution.

▶ Content Background

Students will learn to connect expressions to story problems.

▶ Common Errors and Misconceptions

- Students might not understand variables partly because there are limited examples of variables in the elementary grades. For example, they see equations such as $52 = 5$ tens $\square$ ones in which the unknown has a specific value. They also see boxes and letters that represent a specific unknown such as $7 + \square = 10$ or $7 + a = 10$. Students rarely see cases where letters represent general unknown values or patterns.

- Students might not understand that letters in algebraic expressions and equations represent different values.

- Students might see equations such as $5 + a = 12$ as merely abstract symbols with little or no connection to everyday situations.

Materials to Gather

SUPPLIED

Expressions and Story Problems activity page

Match Expressions and Story Problems activity page

Practice with Expressions activity page

ONLINE
10min

GET READY Evaluate Expressions

Students will use substitution to evaluate expressions that have one variable.

Objectives

- Evaluate a simple algebraic expression in one variable by using substitution.

LEARN Expressions and Story Problems

OFFLINE
10 min

Students will write expressions that represent story problems. Students may use letters for variables that are different from the letters shown in answers in the story problems. View or print the Expressions and Story Problems activity page and read the directions with students.

Students should copy the problems from the Activity Book into their Math Notebook as necessary and solve them there.

1. Read the Worked Example with students.

   Ask: Instead of the answer, 3*c*, what addition expression could have been used? $c + c + c$

   Ask: What expression would have been the answer if Anna's mom bought only 2 bags of cheese? The expression would have been 2*c*.

   Say: At this point, you know an expression that helps you answer a question about a problem. The expression is 3 • *c*, which you can also write as 3*c*. As you continue to study mathematics, you'll take further steps to find the value of an expression like this or others in this activity.

2. Have students read Problem 1 in the problem set.

   Ask: What do you know? I know Percy earned $16 mowing lawns.

   Ask: What don't you know? I don't know how much Percy will spend at the county fair.

   Ask: Pick a letter for a variable. What expression stands for how much money Percy will have left after he goes to the county fair? Answers will vary, depending on the variable students pick. **Example:** $16 - m$

3. Have students complete the rest of the problems.

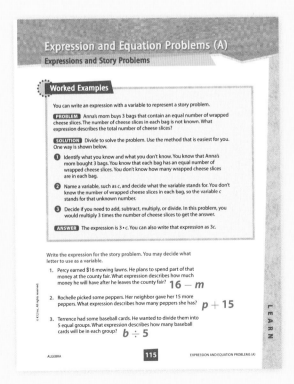

LEARN Match Expressions and Story Problems

- Identify or use an expression or an equation to answer questions about a problem.

Students will match expressions to story problems and story problems to expressions. They also will change an expression to match a changed story problem. View or print the Match Expressions and Story Problems activity page and read the directions with students.

Students should copy the problems from the Activity Book into their Math Notebook as necessary and solve them there.

1. Read Problem 1 in the first Worked Examples box with students.

2. Explain to students that an important step in understanding the relationship between a story problem and an expression is figuring out what information the story problem includes and doesn't include.

3. Have students complete Problems 1–3 in the problem set.

4. Point out that students won't solve the story problems now. Instead, they will learn how to write expressions. As they continue to study mathematics, they will learn how to solve story problems by writing and evaluating expressions.

5. Read all problems in the second Worked Examples box with students.

   Ask: In Problem 3 of the Worked Examples, why did the expression change to $b - 9$? The story problem changed. Bill sold 2 more baseball cards.

   Ask: In Problem 4 of the Worked Examples, how do you know to add 13? Caron bought 4 milk boxes and 9 milk boxes, so the expression needs to represent $4 + 9$.

6. Have students complete Problems 4–6 in the problem set. Encourage them to look at the Worked Examples if they need help with the problems.

Expression and Equation Problems (A)
Match Expressions and Story Problems

Worked Examples

You can show how an expression matches the details in the following story problem:
- Kim reads all the books her favorite author writes. On Wednesday, she checked out the author's newest book from the library and read 38 pages. On Thursday, she read more pages of the book. How many pages did Kim read in 2 days?

PROBLEM 1 What does the expression $38 + p$ mean in relation to the story problem?

SOLUTION

1. Figure out what p stands for in the expression. It represents the unknown number of pages Kim read on Thursday. You do not know what that number is yet.

2. Figure out what $38 + p$ means. It means 38 pages plus an unknown number of pages.

3. Use the expression in an explanation of how it relates to the story problem.

ANSWER The expression $38 + p$ represents the number of pages Kim read on Wednesday and Thursday.

Explain what the variable and numbers in the given expression mean. Then explain how the given expression is related to the story problem.

1. $5c \div 3$
   Larry washed cars for $5 each. He donated the money he earned equally to 3 groups that help students go to college. How much money did Larry donate to each group? **See right.**

2. $b - 2$
   Inez is hiking on a park trail that is measured in miles. She has hiked 2 miles so far. How many miles does Inez have to hike until she completes the entire trail? **See right.**

3. $12b$
   David removed all the books from 12 shelves. Each shelf had the same number of books on it. How many books did David remove from shelves? **See right.**

ALGEBRA | 116 | EXPRESSION AND EQUATION PROBLEMS (A)

Additional Answers

1. The 5 stands for the $5 that Larry received for each car he washed. The c represents the unknown number of cars Larry washed. The 3 stands for the 3 groups he donated money to. The expression $5c \div 3$ represents the amount of money Larry donated to each of the 3 groups.

2. The b represents the unknown length of the trail in miles. The 2 stands for the 2 miles of the trail Inez has hiked so far. The expression $b - 2$ represents the number of remaining miles Inez will hike.

3. The 12 stands for the number of bookshelves. The b represents the unknown number of books on each shelf. The expression $12b$ represents the number of books David removed from the shelves.

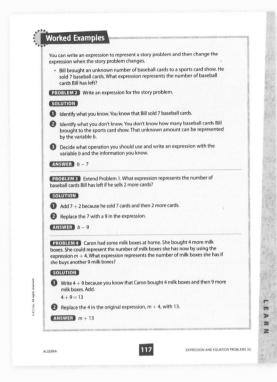

Additional Answers

4. I know that Adam has 5 baskets. I don't know how many onions he has. The variable n can stand for the onions Adam has. An expression that represents the story problem is $n \div 5$.

TRY IT Practice with Expressions

OFFLINE **20**min

Objectives

Students will choose expressions that represent story problems. View or print the Practice with Expressions activity page and read the directions with students.

Students should copy the problems from the Activity Book into their Math Notebook as necessary and solve them there.

- Identify or use an expression or an equation to answer questions about a problem.

Expression and Equation Problems (A)

Practice with Expressions

Choose the answer.

1. Becky made beaded necklaces. She put 8 beads on each necklace. She could use the expression 8 • n to represent the number of beads she used to make n necklaces.

   Which expression represents the number of beads Becky could use if she put 4 more beads on each necklace?

   A. 12 • 4
   B. 8 • 4
   C. 4 • n
   D. 12 • n

2. Randy bought several postcards when he was on vacation. He mailed 5 of the postcards to his friends. He could use the expression p − 5 to represent the number of postcards he has left.

   Which expression represents the number of postcards Randy has left if he sends 3 more postcards to friends?

   A. p − 3
   B. p − 8
   C. 5 − 3
   D. 8 − 5

3. Jennifer can do 6 fewer sit-ups than Michelle can. Jennifer described the number of sit-ups she can do using the expression m − 6.

   One day Jennifer was tired and did 2 fewer sit-ups than usual. Which expression represents the number of sit-ups Jennifer did that day?

   A. 6 − 2
   B. m − 4
   C. m − 6
   D. m − 8

4. Beth bought 2 packages of coloring markers. She could use the expression 2m to represent the total number of coloring markers she bought.

   Which expression represents the total number of coloring markers Beth would have if she bought 5 more packages of coloring markers?

   A. 2 × 7
   B. 2 × 5
   C. 7m
   D. 5m

5. Pedro rented some movies on Saturday. He returned 1 movie on Monday. He could use the expression m − 1 to represent the number of movies he has left.

   Which expression represents the number of movies Pedro has left if he returns 2 more movies?

   A. m − 2
   B. m − 3
   C. 3 − 2
   D. 2 − 1

6. Jeffrey had some apples at home. He bought 6 more apples. He could represent the number of apples that he now has by using the expression a + 6.

   Which expression represents the number of apples Jeffrey has if he buys another 8 apples?

   A. a + 6
   B. a + 14
   C. 6 + 8
   D. 6 + 14

7. Megan worked 10 hours overtime in one month. She could use the expression t + 10 to represent the total time she worked.

   Which expression represents the total number of hours Megan worked if she had worked an additional 12 hours overtime?

   A. t + 2
   B. t + 10
   C. 2 + 12
   D. t + 22

8. Peter has 4 fewer trophies than Jack. Peter can represent the number of trophies he has with the expression t − 4.

   Peter won another 2 trophies. Which expression represents the number of trophies Peter has now?

   A. t − 2
   B. t − 4
   C. t − 6
   D. t − 10

9. Carla had several jigsaw puzzles. She bought 6 more jigsaw puzzles. She could use the expression p + 6 to represent the number of jigsaw puzzles she has now.

   Which expression represents the number of jigsaw puzzles Carla has if she buys 4 more jigsaw puzzles?

   A. 10 + 4
   B. p + 4
   C. 6 + 4
   D. p + 10

10. Anna had some peaches at home. She bought 5 more peaches. She could represent the number of peaches that she now has by using the expression p + 5.

    Which expression represents the number of peaches Anna has if she buys another 3 peaches?

    A. p + 3
    B. p + 5
    C. p + 8
    D. 3 + 5

11. Jason bought a number of packages of buns. There are 8 buns in each package. He could use the expression 8b to represent the number of buns he bought.

    Which expression would represent the number of buns Jason bought if the store had put an additional 2 buns into each package?

    A. 10 × 8
    B. 2b
    C. 2 × 8
    D. 10b

12. Edgar has a pack of stickers to share with his 4 friends. He could represent the number of stickers each friend would get using the expression s ÷ 4.

    Edgar is thinking of sharing his stickers with 1 additional friend. Which expression would represent the number of stickers each person would get now?

    A. s ÷ 1
    B. s ÷ 3
    C. s ÷ 5
    D. 4 + 1

13. Paul paid $5 per ticket for a number of tickets to the baseball game on Wednesday. He could represent the total he spent on baseball tickets by using the expression 5t.

    On Saturday, Paul bought the same number of tickets. However, the price of these tickets was $2 more per ticket. Which expression represents the amount Paul paid for tickets on Saturday?

    A. 5 × 2
    B. 2t
    C. 7t
    D. 10t

14. Eddie has a set of football cards he wants to put in an album. He is planning on putting 9 cards on each page. He could represent the number of pages he would need by using the expression b ÷ 9.

    Eddie is thinking of putting 5 fewer cards on each page. Which expression would represent the number of pages he would need?

    A. b ÷ 4
    B. b ÷ 5
    C. b ÷ 14
    D. b ÷ 45

TRY IT

Expression and Equation Problems (B)

Lesson Overview

GET READY Solve Equations	10 minutes	ONLINE
LEARN Equations and Story Problems	10 minutes	OFFLINE
LEARN Match Equations and Story Problems	20 minutes	OFFLINE
TRY IT Practice with Equations	20 minutes	OFFLINE

▶ Lesson Objectives

Identify or use an expression or an equation to answer questions about a problem.

▶ Prerequisite Skills

Solve for one variable in a two-variable equation when the value of the other variable is given.

▶ Content Background

Students will continue to learn to connect equations to story problems.

▶ Common Errors and Misconceptions

- Students might not understand variables partly because there are limited examples of variables in the elementary grades. For example, they see equations such as $52 = 5$ tens $\square$ ones in which the unknown has a specific value. They also see boxes and letters that represent a specific unknown such as $7 + \square = 10$ or $7 + a = 10$. Students rarely see cases where letters represent general unknown values or patterns.
- Students might not understand that letters in algebraic expressions and equations represent different values.
- Students might see equations such as $5 + a = 12$ as merely abstract symbols with little or no connection to everyday situations.

Materials to Gather

SUPPLIED

Equations and Story Problems activity page

Match Equations and Story Problems activity page

Practice with Equations activity page

ONLINE

10 min

GET READY Solve Equations

Students will find the solution to two-variable equations when given the value of one variable.

Tips Remind students that when they solve equations, they want the values on the left and right sides to be equal.

Objectives

- Solve for one variable in a two-variable equation when the value of the other variable is given.

OFFLINE

10 min

- Identify or use an expression or an equation to answer questions about a problem.

Students will write equations that represent story problems. They will not solve the equations at this stage in their study of mathematics. Instead they will read story problems and write equations that use a variable to represent the unknown fact. Students may use letters for variables that are different from the letters shown in answers in the story problems. View or print the Equations and Story Problems activity page and read the directions with students.

Students should copy the problems from the Activity Book into their Math Notebook as necessary and solve them there.

1. Read the Worked Example with students.

   Ask: If the painter needs 2.5 gallons to paint 1 room, what expression with numbers stands for the number of gallons the painter needs for 2 rooms? $2.5 \cdot 2$ or $2 \cdot 2.5$

   Ask: What does the variable p stand for? It stands for the unknown number of gallons of paint the painter needs to complete the entire job.

   Ask: What does $2.5 \cdot 6 = p$ mean in relation to the story problem? It means that 2.5 gallons of paint times 6 rooms equals an unknown number of gallons of paint.

   Say: At this point, you know an equation that helps answer a question in a story problem. As you continue to study mathematics, you'll take further steps to solve an equation for the value of a variable.

2. Have students read Problem 1 in the problem set.

   Ask: What do you know and what don't you know? I know that Meredith used 54 seashells to decorate 6 picture frames, and she put an equal number of seashells on each picture frame. I don't know the number of seashells Meredith put on each picture frame.

   Ask: Choose a letter for a variable. What equation represents the number of seashells Meredith put on each picture frame? $54 \div n = 6$

3. Make sure students understand that equations have equals symbols. Expressions have numbers, variables, and operation signs, but they don't have equals symbols.

4. Have students complete Problem 2. Have them refer to Worked Examples for help if needed.

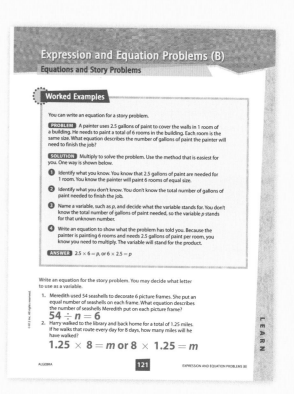

Expression and Equation Problems (B)
Equations and Story Problems

Worked Examples

You can write an equation for a story problem.

PROBLEM A painter uses 2.5 gallons of paint to cover the walls in 1 room of a building. He needs to paint a total of 6 rooms in the building. Each room is the same size. What equation describes the number of gallons of paint the painter will need to finish the job?

SOLUTION Multiply to solve the problem. Use the method that is easiest for you. One way is shown below.

❶ Identify what you know. You know that 2.5 gallons of paint are needed for 1 room. You know the painter will paint 6 rooms of equal size.

❷ Identify what you don't know. You don't know the total number of gallons of paint needed to finish the job.

❸ Name a variable, such as p, and decide what the variable stands for. You don't know the total number of gallons of paint needed, so the variable p stands for that unknown number.

❹ Write an equation to show what the problem has told you. Because the painter is painting 6 rooms and needs 2.5 gallons of paint per room, you know you need to multiply. The variable will stand for the product.

ANSWER $2.5 \times 6 = p$, or $6 \times 2.5 = p$

Write an equation for the story problem. You may decide what letter to use as a variable.

1. Meredith used 54 seashells to decorate 6 picture frames. She put an equal number of seashells on each frame. What equation describes the number of seashells Meredith put on each picture frame?
$54 \div n = 6$

2. Harry walked to the library and back home for a total of 1.25 miles. If he walks that route every day for 8 days, how many miles will he have walked?
$1.25 \times 8 = m$ or $8 \times 1.25 = m$

ALGEBRA **121** EXPRESSION AND EQUATION PROBLEMS (B)

L E A R N

LEARN Match Equations and Story Problems

Objectives

- Identify or use an expression or an equation to answer questions about a problem.

Students will match equations to story problems and story problems to equations. They will also write an equation to match a changed story problem. View or print the Math Equations and Story Problems activity page and read the directions with students.

Students should copy the problems from their Activity Book into their Math Notebook as necessary and solve them there.

1. Tell students that they will show how an equation can match the details in a story problem. Another way to describe story problems is situations.

2. Read Problem 1 in the first Worked Examples box with students.

3. Explain that it is important to carefully read a problem and decide what information is known and unknown. Those steps will help students understand the relationship between the story problem and the equation that represents the problem.

4. Point out that students won't solve the problems now; they will do that as they continue to study mathematics. Don't discourage students who want to solve the equation and find the number of wolves that are not at the pond that day. Rather, focus their attention on connecting the equation to the details of the story problem.

5. Have students complete Problems 1 and 2 in the problem set.

6. Read all problems in the second Worked Examples box with students.

   Ask: In Problem 3 of the Worked Examples, why is the expression $6 + 8$ multiplied by 3? The problem was extended to have Raul plant 3 rows of flowers.

   Ask: In Problem 4 of the Worked Examples , why is the expression $9 + 6$ divided by 3? The problem was extended to have Sherman divide the items into 3 equal groups.

7. Have students complete Problems 3–5 in the problem set. Encourage them to look at the Worked Examples if they need help with the problems.

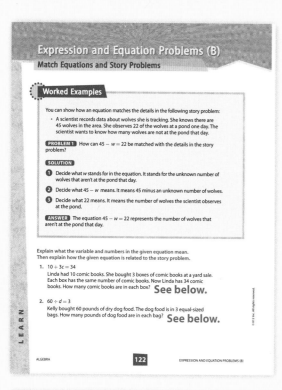

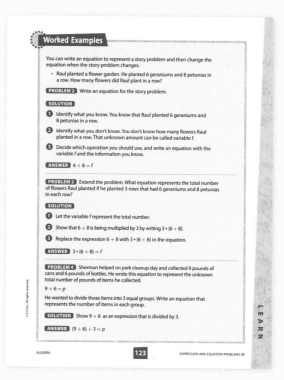

Additional Answers

1. The 10 stands for the number of comic books Linda started with. The 3 stands for the 3 boxes she bought. Each box has the same number of comic books in it. The c represents the unknown number of comic books in each box. The 34 stands for the total number of comic books she has. The equation $10 + 3c = 34$ represents one way to find the number of comic books in each box.

2. The 60 stands for the total pounds of dry dog food. The d represents the unknown number of pounds of dog food in each bag. The 3 stands for the number of bags of dog food. The equation $60 \div d = 3$ represents one way to find the amount of food in each bag.

3. I know how many poems Aisha wrote in the summer. She wrote the same number of poems in 4 seasons. I don't know how many poems she will have written altogether. Let a represent the unknown number of poems Aisha will write: $12 \cdot 4 = a$.

TRY IT Practice with Equations

Students will choose equations that match story problems and choose situations that match equations. View or print the Practice with Equations activity page and read the directions with students.

Students should copy the problems from the Activity Book into their Math Notebook as necessary and solve them there.

Expression and Equation Problems (B)
Practice with Equations

Choose the answer.

1. Tara did 3 hours of math practice and 4 hours of social studies reading in 1 week. She wrote the following equation to represent the total number of hours, h, of practice and reading she did: $h = 3 + 4$.

   Tara expects to have 3 hours of math practice and 4 hours of social studies reading each week for the next 5 weeks. Now let the variable h represent the total number of hours of homework Tara will have. Which equation represents the total number of hours of work she will have in the next 5 weeks?

   A. $h = 3 + 4$ B. $h = 3 \times 4 \times 5$
   C. $h = 3 + 4 + 5$ D. $h = 5 \cdot (3 + 4)$

2. Tess made 6 corn muffins and 12 bran muffins. She wrote the following equation to represent the total number of muffins, m, she made: $m = 6 + 12$.

   Tess stores an equal number of the total number of muffins she made in each of 3 small containers. Now let the variable m stand for the number of muffins in each container. Which equation represents the number of muffins in each container?

   A. $m = 6 + 12 \div 3$ B. $m = 6 + 12 - 3$
   C. $m = (6 + 12) \div 3$ D. $m = (6 + 12) \times 3$

3. Nathan always reads 2 more books than he is required to read in a month. He could show the total number of books he reads in a month with the expression $b + 2$, where b represents the number of books he is required to read.

   Which expression represents the total number of books Nathan read in a month if he read an additional 5 books more than required that month?

   A. $b + 2$ B. $2 + 5$
   C. $b + 7$ D. $2 + 3$

4. Maria planned to read 9 fiction and 12 history books each month. She could show the total number of books she planned to read each month with the equation $b = 9 + 12$, where b represents the number of books Maria planned to read.

   Now let the variable b represent the total number of books Maria planned to read in 5 months. Which equation would represent the number of books Maria would read in 5 months?

   A. $b = 5 + (9 + 12)$ B. $b = 5 \cdot (9 + 12)$
   C. $b = 9 + 12 \cdot 5$ D. $b = 5 \cdot 9 + 12$

5. Ben had 15 stamps in his stamp collection. He sold 6 stamps. Ben wrote the following equation to represent the number of stamps he has left: $15 - 6 = t$. The variable t represents the total number of stamps Ben has left.

   Ben bought 7 more stamps. Now let the variable t stand for the total number of stamps Ben has now. Which equation represents the number of stamps Ben has now?

   A. $15 + 7 = t$ B. $15 - 6 + 7 = t$
   C. $15 + 6 - 7 = t$ D. $15 \div 6 = t$

6. Pang weeded gardens for 2 hours on Friday. He wants to weed gardens for a total of 5 hours on Friday and Saturday. He wrote the following equation to describe the total number of hours he wants to weed gardens on Friday and Saturday: $2 + h = 5$.

   The variable h represents the number of hours Pang will weed gardens on Saturday. Which situation does this equation describe?

   A. Pang weeded gardens for 2 hours on Friday. He wasn't sure how many hours he would weed gardens on Saturday. He wants to weed gardens for a total of 5 hours on Friday and Saturday.

   B. Pang weeded gardens for 2 hours on Friday. He weeded gardens for 5 hours on Saturday. He wasn't sure how many hours he would weed gardens on both Friday and Saturday.

   C. Pang wasn't sure how many hours he would weed gardens on Friday. He wasn't sure how many hours he would weed gardens on Saturday. He wants to weed gardens for a total of 5 hours on Friday and Saturday.

   D. Pang wasn't sure how many hours he would weed gardens on Friday. He weeded gardens for 5 hours on Saturday. He wants to weed gardens for a total of 5 hours on Friday and Saturday.

7. A farmer wants to plant a total of 80 stalks of corn. He plants 8 cornstalks in each row. He wrote the following equation to describe the number of rows of cornstalks he will plant: $80 = 8r$.

   The variable r represents the number of rows the farmer wants to plant. Which situation does this equation describe?

   A. A farmer wants to plant a total of 80 stalks of corn. He isn't sure how many rows of cornstalks he will plant. He isn't sure how many cornstalks he will plant in each row.

   B. A farmer wants to plant a total of 80 stalks of corn. He plants 72 rows of cornstalks. He isn't sure how many cornstalks he will plant in each row.

   C. A farmer wants to plant a total of 80 stalks of corn. He plants 8 cornstalks in each row. He isn't sure how many rows of cornstalks he will plant.

   D. A farmer wants to plant a total of 80 stalks of corn. He plants 8 cornstalks in each row. He will plant 8 rows of cornstalks.

8. April read 5 newspaper articles and 3 magazine articles every week. She wrote the following equation to represent the number of articles she read in a week: $r = 3 + 5$. The variable r represents the total number of articles April reads every week.

   Now let the variable r represent the total number of articles April reads in 6 weeks. Which equation would represent the total number of articles April would read in 6 weeks?

   A. $r = 6 + (3 + 5)$ B. $r = 3 + (6 \cdot 5)$ C. $r = (6 \cdot 3) + 5$ D. $r = 6 \cdot (3 + 5)$

9. Claudia bought some apples. She gave away 16 of them. She could represent the total number of apples she has left with the expression $a - 16$, where the variable a represents the total number of apples Claudia first bought.

   Claudia then gave away another 5 apples. Which expression represents the number of apples that Claudia has now?

   A. $16 - 5$ B. $a - 5$ C. $a - 16$ D. $a - 21$

10. Benny spends \$3 a day on bus fare. He can represent the total amount he spends riding the bus with the expression $3b$, where b represents the number of days Benny rides the bus.

    The bus company is thinking of increasing the fares by \$1 a day. Which expression would represent the amount Benny would spend at the new rate?

    A. $4b$ B. $12b$ C. 4×3 D. 1×3

11. Zoe sends letters to her pen pal by mail. She spends 42¢ on a stamp and 55¢ on an envelope. She wrote this equation to represent the total cost for sending a letter to her pen pal: $c = 42 + 55$. The variable c represents the total cost for sending a letter.

    Zoe writes to her pen pal 8 times a year. Now let the variable c represent the total cost of sending her pen pals letters. Which equation would represent the total cost of sending her pen pal letters for a year?

    A. $c = 8 + (42 - 55)$ B. $c = 42 + (8 \cdot 55)$
    C. $c = 8 \cdot (42 + 55)$ D. $c = (8 \cdot 42) + 55$

12. Veronica had some cherries to give to 3 friends. She could represent the total number of cherries each friend would get with the expression $g \div 3$, where the variable g represents the total number of cherries Veronica has.

    Veronica is thinking about giving cherries to 2 additional friends. Which expression represents the number of cherries each friend would now get?

    A. $g \div 1$ B. $g \div 2$ C. $g \div 5$ D. $g \div 6$

13. Ms. Tania is planning the seating arrangements for her concert. She is dividing the seats equally into 6 rows. She could represent the total number of seats in each row with the expression $s \div 6$, where the variable s represents the total number of seats.

    Ms. Tania is thinking about dividing all of the seats into 2 fewer rows than the original plan. Which expression would represent the number of seats in each row now?

    A. $s \div 4$ B. $s \div 8$ C. $s \div 12$ D. $s \div 36$

14. John is planning the seating arrangements for the music show. He is dividing the total number of seats equally into 8 rows. He could represent the total number of seats in each row with the expression $t \div 8$, where the variable t represents the total number of seats.

    John is thinking of dividing the seats into 2 more rows than the original plan. Which expression represents the total number of seats in each row now?

    A. $t \div 6$ B. $t \div 10$ C. $t \div 16$ D. $8 \div 2$

Expression and Equation Problems (C)

Lesson Overview

LEARN Examples of Story Problems	15 minutes	ONLINE
LEARN Write Story Problems	25 minutes	OFFLINE
TRY IT Practice with Story Problems	10 minutes	ONLINE
CHECKPOINT	10 minutes	ONLINE

▶ Lesson Objectives

Identify or use an expression or an equation to answer questions about a problem.

▶ Content Background

Students will learn to write story problems about expressions and equations.

▶ Common Errors and Misconceptions

- Students might not understand variables partly because there are limited examples of variables in the elementary grades. For example, they see equations such as $52 = 5$ tens $\square$ ones in which the unknown has a specific value. They also see boxes and letters that represent a specific unknown such as $7 + \square = 10$ or $7 + a = 10$. Students rarely see cases where letters represent general unknown values or patterns.

- Students might not understand that letters in algebraic expressions and equations represent different values.

- Students might see equations such as $5 + a = 12$ as merely abstract symbols with little or no connection to everyday situations.

Materials to Gather

SUPPLIED

Write Story Problems activity page

ONLINE
15min

LEARN Examples of Story Problems

Students will see examples of expressions and equations that can be used to answer questions about a story problem. Then they will see an example of a changed story problem and the equation that answers it. Students will also match story problems to equations and expressions.

Objectives

- Identify or use an expression or an equation to answer questions about a problem.

LEARN Write Story Problems

Students will be given expressions and equations and will write story problems about them. They also will write changed expressions and equations for story problems that have changes. View or print the Write Story Problems activity page and read the directions with students.

 Students should copy the problems from the Activity Book into their Math Notebook as necessary and solve them there.

1. Read the problems in the first Worked Examples box with students.

2. Have students complete Problems 1–6 in the problem set. Answers will vary. The given answers are examples.

3. Read the problems in the second Worked Examples box with students.

4. Have students complete Problems 7–9 in the problem set. Encourage students to use the Worked Examples for reference if needed.

5. As time permits, have students write their own story problem and an expression or equation that represents it.

Objectives

- Identify or use an expression or an equation to answer questions about a problem.

Tips

Have students illustrate their favorite problem and its matching expression or equation in their Math Notebook.

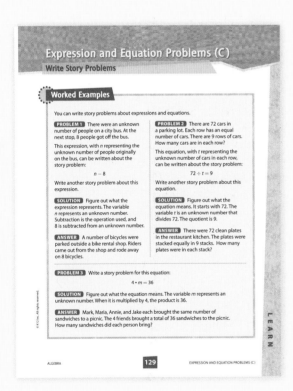

Expression and Equation Problems (C)
Write Story Problems

Worked Examples

You can write story problems about expressions and equations.

PROBLEM 1 There were an unknown number of people on a city bus. At the next stop, 8 people got off the bus.

This expression, with n representing the unknown number of people originally on the bus, can be written about the story problem:

$$n - 8$$

Write another story problem about this expression.

SOLUTION Figure out what the expression represents. The variable n represents an unknown number. Subtraction is the operation used, and 8 is subtracted from an unknown number.

ANSWER A number of bicycles were parked outside a bike rental shop. Riders came out from the shop and rode away on 8 bicycles.

PROBLEM 2 There are 72 cars in a parking lot. Each row has an equal number of cars. There are 9 rows of cars. How many cars are in each row?

This equation, with t representing the unknown number of cars in each row, can be written about the story problem:

$$72 \div t = 9$$

Write another story problem about this equation.

SOLUTION Figure out what the equation means. It starts with 72. The variable t is an unknown number that divides 72. The quotient is 9.

ANSWER There were 72 clean plates in the restaurant kitchen. The plates were stacked equally in 9 stacks. How many plates were in each stack?

PROBLEM 3 Write a story problem for this equation:

$$4 \cdot m = 36$$

SOLUTION Figure out what the equation means. The variable m represents an unknown number. When it is multiplied by 4, the product is 36.

ANSWER Mark, Maria, Annie, and Jake each brought the same number of sandwiches to a picnic. The 4 friends brought a total of 36 sandwiches to the picnic. How many sandwiches did each person bring?

ALGEBRA   129   EXPRESSION AND EQUATION PROBLEMS (C)

LEARN

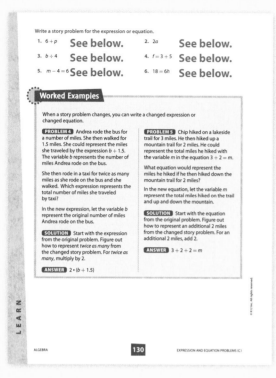

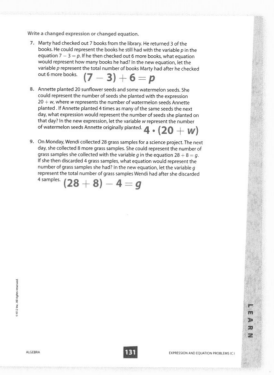

Additional Answers

1. **Example:** There were 6 people in line at the movie theater. More people got in line.

2. **Example:** The distance around the track is 2 miles. Gary walked around the track multiple times.

3. **Example:** Cass made muffins. She shared the muffins she made equally among 4 friends.

4. **Example:** One afternoon, Ron sent 3 e-mails to his friends and 5 e-mails to his family. How many e-mails did he send in all?

5. **Example:** Ling knitted scarves to sell at the fair. She sold 4 scarves and has 6 scarves left. How many scarves did Ling knit to sell at the fair?

6. **Example:** A clerk at a store unpacked 18 snow globes from boxes. Each box contained 6 snow globes. How many boxes of snow globes did the clerk unpack?

TRY IT Practice with Story Problems

ONLINE **10** min

Students will complete an online Try It. If necessary, read the directions, problems, and answer choices to students and help them with keyboard or mouse operations.

Objectives

- Identify or use an expression or an equation to answer questions about a problem.

CHECKPOINT

ONLINE **10** min

Students will complete an online Checkpoint. If necessary, read the directions, problems, and answer choices to students and help them with keyboard or mouse operations.

Objectives

- Identify or use an expression or an equation to answer questions about a problem.

Core Focus
Numerical Expressions

Lesson Overview

LEARN More Order of Operations	25 minutes	ONLINE
LEARN Writing and Evaluating Expressions	15 minutes	ONLINE
TRY IT Work with Numerical Expressions	10 minutes	OFFLINE
CHECKPOINT	10 minutes	OFFLINE

▶ Lesson Objectives

- Simplify expressions with grouping symbols.
- Find a mathematical expression that corresponds to a given word phrase.
- Evaluate numerical expressions using order of operations (expressions include with parentheses and powers, whole numbers only).

▶ Content Background

Students have worked with numerical expressions by using the order of operations with grouping symbols and by translating word expressions into mathematical expressions. In this lesson, students will extend their knowledge of these topics by working with expressions involving fractions and decimals and evaluating translated numerical expressions. If necessary, review operations of fractions and decimals with students.

Materials to Gather

SUPPLIED

Work with Numerical Expressions activity page

Checkpoint (printout)

Checkpoint Answer Key (printout)

LEARN More Order of Operations

ONLINE **25**min

Students will insert grouping symbols into expressions to create a given result. Some expressions will involve fraction or decimal operations.

Objectives

- Simplify expressions with grouping symbols.

LEARN Writing and Evaluating Expressions

ONLINE **15**min

Students will translate word expressions involving fractions and decimals into math expressions. They will then use the order of operations to evaluate the expressions to form equations.

Objectives

- Find a mathematical expression that corresponds to a given word phrase.
- Evaluate numerical expressions using order of operations (expressions include with parentheses and powers, whole numbers only).

TRY IT Work with Numerical Expressions

Objectives

Students will practice simplifying expressions and creating expressions using the order of operations and also translate word phrases into math expressions, which they will then evaluate.

View or print the Work with Numerical Expressions activity page. Students should copy the problems into their Math Notebook and solve them there.

- Simplify expressions with grouping symbols.

- Find a mathematical expression that corresponds to a given word phrase.

- Evaluate numerical expressions using order of operations (expressions include with parentheses and powers, whole numbers only).

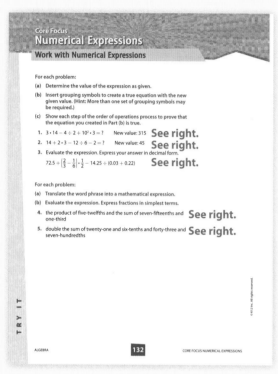

Additional Answers

1. **(a)** 340

   (b) $3 \cdot (14 - 4) \div 2 + 10^2 \cdot 3 = 315$

   (c) $3 \cdot (14 - 4) \div 2 + 10^2 \cdot 3$
   $= 3 \cdot \quad 10 \quad \div 2 + 10^2 \cdot 3$
   $= 3 \cdot \quad 10 \quad \div 2 + 100 \cdot 3$
   $= 3 \cdot \quad\quad 5 \quad + 100 \cdot 3$
   $= 3 \cdot \quad\quad 5 \quad + \quad 300$
   $= \quad\quad 15 \quad\quad + \quad 300$
   $= \quad\quad\quad 315$

2. **(a)** 16

   (b) $(14 + 2) \cdot 3 - 12 \div (6 - 2) = 45$

   (c) $(14 + 2) \cdot 3 - 12 \div (6 - 2)$
   $= \quad 16 \quad \cdot 3 - 12 \div (6 - 2)$
   $= \quad 16 \quad \cdot 3 - 12 \div \quad 4$
   $= \quad\quad 48 \quad - 12 \div \quad 4$
   $= \quad\quad 48 \quad - \quad\quad 3$
   $= \quad\quad\quad 45$

3. 15.75

   $72.5 + \left(\dfrac{2}{3} - \dfrac{1}{6}\right) \cdot \dfrac{1}{2} - 14.25 \div (0.03 + 0.22)$

   $72.5 + \quad \dfrac{1}{2} \quad \cdot \dfrac{1}{2} - 14.25 \div (0.03 + 0.22)$

   $72.5 + \quad \dfrac{1}{2} \quad \cdot \dfrac{1}{2} - 14.25 \div \quad 0.25$

   $72.5 + \quad\quad \dfrac{1}{4} \quad - 14.25 \div \quad 0.25$

   $72.5 + \quad\quad \dfrac{1}{4} \quad - \quad\quad 57$

   $72.5 + \quad 0.25 \quad - \quad\quad 57$

   $72.75 \quad\quad\quad - \quad\quad 57$

   $\quad\quad\quad\quad 15.75$

4. **(a)** $\dfrac{5}{12} \cdot \left(\dfrac{7}{15} + \dfrac{1}{3}\right)$

   (b) $\dfrac{1}{3}$

5. **(a)** $2 \cdot (21.6 + 43.07)$

   (b) 129.34

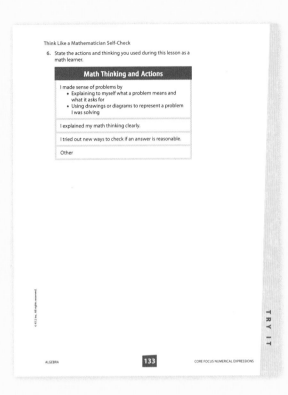

OFFLINE

10 min

CHECKPOINT

The Checkpoint and its answer key are located in the Resources section for this unit in the Online Book Menu of *Math+ Yellow Lesson Guide*. Open the Checkpoint. Record students' responses on the Learning Coach Recording Sheet. Use the answer key to score the Checkpoint, and then enter the results online.

Objectives

- Simplify expressions with grouping symbols.

- Find a mathematical expression that corresponds to a given word phrase.

- Evaluate numerical expressions using order of operations (expressions include with parentheses and powers, whole numbers only).

Unit Review

Lesson Overview

UNIT REVIEW Look Back	10 minutes	**ONLINE**
UNIT REVIEW Checkpoint Practice	50 minutes	**ONLINE**
⊳ UNIT REVIEW Prepare for the Checkpoint		

▶ Unit Objectives

- Use a letter to represent an unknown value in an expression or an equation.
- Use the order of operations to simplify expressions with mixed operations.
- Simplify expressions with grouping symbols.
- Find a mathematical expression that corresponds to a given word phrase.
- Interpret a numerical expression without evaluating the expression.
- Evaluate a simple algebraic expression in one variable by using substitution.
- Identify or use an expression or an equation to answer questions about a problem.
- Evaluate numerical expressions using order of operations (expressions include with parentheses and powers, whole numbers only).

Materials to Gather

There are no materials to gather for this lesson.

▶ Advance Preparation

In this lesson, students will have an opportunity to review previous activities in the Algebra unit. Look at the suggested activities in Unit Review: Prepare for the Checkpoint online and gather any needed materials.

UNIT REVIEW Look Back

ONLINE
10min

Students will review key concepts from the unit to prepare for the Unit Checkpoint.

Objectives

- Review unit objectives.

- Review unit objectives.

Students will complete an online Checkpoint Practice to prepare for the Unit Checkpoint. If necessary, read the directions, problems, and answer choices to students. Have students answer the problems on their own. Review any missed problems with students.

⊡ UNIT REVIEW Prepare for the Checkpoint

What you do next depends on how students performed in the previous activity, Unit Review: Checkpoint Practice. If students had difficulty with any of the problems, complete the appropriate review activity listed in the table online.

Unit Checkpoint

UNIT CHECKPOINT Online	60 minutes	**ONLINE**

▶ ## Unit Objectives

- Use a letter to represent an unknown value in an expression or an equation.
- Use the order of operations to simplify expressions with mixed operations.
- Simplify expressions with grouping symbols.
- Find a mathematical expression that corresponds to a given word phrase.
- Interpret a numerical expression without evaluating the expression.
- Evaluate a simple algebraic expression in one variable by using substitution.
- Identify or use an expression or an equation to answer questions about a problem.
- Evaluate numerical expressions using order of operations (expressions include with parentheses and powers, whole numbers only).

Materials to Gather

There are no materials to gather for this lesson.

UNIT CHECKPOINT Online

ONLINE 60min

Students will complete the Unit Checkpoint online. If necessary, read the directions, problems, and answer choices to students and help them with keyboard or mouse operations.

Objectives

- Assess unit objectives.

Extended Problems: Real-World Application

Lesson Overview

USE WHAT YOU KNOW Offline
60 minutes | OFFLINE

▶ Lesson Objectives

- Solve a story problem that involves multiplication or division of decimal numbers.
- Use a letter to represent an unknown value in an expression or an equation.
- Multiply or divide by a multiple or power of 10.
- Interpret a numerical expression without evaluating the expression.
- Use the order of operations to simplify expressions with mixed operations.
- Use a variable to represent an unknown number in an equation.
- Extend a linear pattern, such as stating what number comes next in a series.
- Apply mathematical knowledge and skills to evaluate and analyze real-world situations.

Materials to Gather

SUPPLIED

Extended Problems: Real-World Application (printout)

Extended Problems: Real-World Application Answer Key (printout)

USE WHAT YOU KNOW Offline

The Extended Problems: Real-World Application and its answer key are located in the Resources section for this unit in the Online Book Menu of *Math+ Yellow Lesson Guide*. Give students the Extended Problems: Real-World Application. Read the directions, problems, and answer choices to students, if necessary.

You will grade this assignment.

- Students should complete the assignment on their own.
- Students should submit the completed assignment to you.

Objectives

- Apply mathematical knowledge and skills to evaluate and analyze real-world situations.

Coordinate Planes

- Identify the parts of a coordinate graph, including *x*-axis, *y*-axis, *x*-coordinate, *y*-coordinate, ordered pair, and origin.
- Locate and plot points in Quadrant I of the coordinate plane.
- Solve word problems involving graphs of points on a coordinate plane.
- Graph or write an equation to solve a problem that involves a linear function.

- Use the situation presented in a problem to describe the meaning of each coordinate of an ordered pair displayed on a graph.
- Given a rule such as "Add 3," generate and graph ordered pairs on a coordinate plane.
- Graph to compare the corresponding terms of two patterns.

▶ Big Ideas

Any point in a coordinate plane can be described by an ordered pair of coordinates.

▶ Unit Introduction

In this unit, students will explore the component parts of all four quadrants of the coordinate plane, but they will only work with points within the first quadrant. They will relate ordered pairs and their locations in the plane to problem situations. They will continue their investigation of coordinate planes by graphing as well as writing equations to solve a story problem. Students will work with linear functions, which are equations whose graphs are straight lines in the coordinate plane.

In this unit's lessons, students will sometimes see that the axes on the coordinate plane show only even numbers. It is sometimes necessary to skip labels of numbers on the coordinate plane to make it easier to read the numbers on each axis. The origin is still located at (0, 0), and odd-numbered coordinates can still be plotted and labeled.

▶ Keywords

axis (plural: axes)	line	quadrants
coordinate	linear function	quantity
coordinate plane	ordered pair	variable
equation	origin	*x*-axis
function table	output	*x*-coordinate
graph	perimeter	*y*-axis
input	point on a coordinate plane	*y*-coordinate

The Coordinate Plane

Lesson Overview

LEARN Parts of the Coordinate Plane	15 minutes	ONLINE
LEARN Points, Lines, and Distances	15 minutes	ONLINE
TRY IT Coordinate Plane Practice	15 minutes	OFFLINE
CHECKPOINT	15 minutes	OFFLINE

▶ Lesson Objectives

- Identify the parts of a coordinate graph, including *x*-axis, *y*-axis, *x*-coordinate, *y*-coordinate, ordered pair, and origin.
- Locate and plot points in Quadrant I of the coordinate plane.
- Solve word problems involving graphs of points on a coordinate plane.

▶ Content Background

Students will learn to identify important components of the coordinate plane. They will also identify and graph ordered pairs in the first quadrant of a coordinate plane.

A *coordinate* is a position along a number line or within the *coordinate plane*, the coordinate grid formed by two number lines, called *axes*. The *x*-axis is the horizontal number line, and the *y*-axis is the vertical number line. The two axes are perpendicular. Other names for the coordinate plane are *coordinate grid* and *Cartesian plane*.

The point where the *x*- and *y*-axes meet is called the *origin*. When labeling points on the coordinate plane, you label the origin with the ordered pair (0, 0).

One way to describe the coordinate plane is to talk about each of the four sections, or *quadrants*. The sections are usually labeled using roman numerals. Starting in the upper-right section and moving counterclockwise, the sections are called Quadrant I, Quadrant II, Quadrant III, and Quadrant IV.

A pair of numbers, shown inside parentheses with a comma separating the numbers, is one way to describe the position of a point on a plane. This pair of numbers is known as an *ordered pair*. On the coordinate plane, the way to label all points is to write the horizontal distance from the origin, moving along the *x*-axis, as the first coordinate, and the vertical distance, moving parallel to the *y*-axis, as the second coordinate. Examples of ordered pairs are (x, y) and $(^+2, ^+3)$. In the latter example, the ordered pair $(^+2, ^+3)$ is 2 steps to the right from the origin, then 3 steps above that point. Coordinates in an ordered pair can be both positive, both negative, or one positive and one negative, but in this lesson, students will only work with the origin and positive coordinates.

▶ Advance Preparation

Print one copy of the Coordinate Graphs. On the second graph, have students label the *x*-axis with an *x* at the end of the horizontal arrow and the *y*-axis with a *y* at the end of the vertical arrow. Each axis should be numbered along the grid lines from 1 to 10. Having students complete this work will reinforce their understanding of the coordinate plane.

Materials to Gather

SUPPLIED

Coordinate Graphs (printout)
Coordinate Plane Practice activity page
Checkpoint (printout)
Checkpoint Answer Key (printout)

LEARN Parts of the Coordinate Plane

Students will review parts of a coordinate plane and learn about quadrants. They will also learn how to label and find coordinates of ordered pairs.

Tips If students have difficulty remembering where the quadrants are in the coordinate plane, have students draw x- and y-axes on a piece of paper to form a coordinate plane. Have them label the axes x and y but not number the units on the axes. Guide students to correctly label the quadrants.

Objectives

- Identify the parts of a coordinate graph, including x-axis, y-axis, x-coordinate, y-coordinate, ordered pair, and origin.

LEARN Points, Lines, and Distances

Students will locate and graph ordered pairs in the first quadrant of a coordinate plane. They will also learn to locate a vertex of a shape when given information about the other vertices of the shape and apply the distance formula for vertical and horizontal distances on the plane. Although students can count spaces along a vertical or horizontal line to determine distance, they will be required to use the distance formula to prepare them for future work with distance formulas.

Objectives

- Locate and plot points in Quadrant I of the coordinate plane.
- Solve word problems involving graphs of points on a coordinate plane.

TRY IT Coordinate Plane Practice

Students will practice the coordinate-plane skills they have learned throughout the lesson. Gather a copy of the Coordinate Graphs printout for students to use for Problems 7–10. View or print the Coordinate Plane Practice activity page.

Students should copy the problems into their Math Notebook as necessary and solve them there.

Tips If students have difficulty remembering the distance formula, remind them that for vertical distances $d = |y_2 - y_1|$ and for horizontal distances $d = |x_2 - x_1|$.

Objectives

- Identify the parts of a coordinate graph, including x-axis, y-axis, x-coordinate, y-coordinate, ordered pair, and origin.
- Locate and plot points in Quadrant I of the coordinate plane.
- Solve word problems involving graphs of points on a coordinate plane.

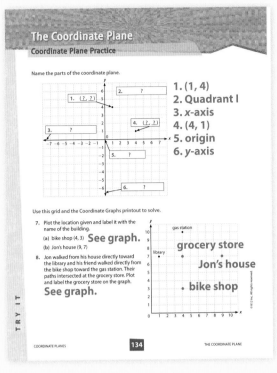

Additional Answers

9. from Jon's house to the grocery store:

$$d = |x_2 - x_1|$$
$$d = |4 - 9|$$
$$d = |-5|$$
$$d = 5$$

from the grocery store to the bike shop:

$$d = |y_2 - y_1|$$
$$d = |3 - 7|$$
$$d = |-4|$$
$$d = 4$$

Jon rode 5 blocks then 4 blocks for a total of 9 blocks.

CHECKPOINT

The Checkpoint and its answer key are located in the Resources section for this unit in the Online Book Menu of *Math+ Yellow Lesson Guide*. Give students the Checkpoint. Have students complete the Checkpoint on their own. Use the answer key to score the Checkpoint, and then enter the results online.

Objectives

- Identify the parts of a coordinate graph, including *x*-axis, *y*-axis, *x*-coordinate, *y*-coordinate, ordered pair, and origin.

- Locate and plot points in Quadrant I of the coordinate plane.

- Solve word problems involving graphs of points on a coordinate plane.

Ordered Pairs

▶ **Lesson Objectives**

Use the situation presented in a problem to describe the meaning of each coordinate of an ordered pair displayed on a graph.

▶ **Prerequisite Skills**

Locate and plot points in Quadrant I of the coordinate plane.

▶ **Content Background**

Students will explore the relationship of story problems to their graphs. Often students plot points related to story problems without understanding the meaning of the points and the significance of their locations on the coordinate plane. For example, suppose they plot points to show the cost of multiple DVDs. In this case, points in the second, third, and fourth quadrants make no sense, since a negative number of DVDs or negative cost is impossible. Understanding the meaning of coordinates can be a difficult idea for students to grasp in their early experiences with story problems and graphs on the coordinate plane, so this lesson concentrates on problems with data graphed in Quadrant I only. Because students focus on positive values of x and y, there are no positive signs in front of the coordinates.

This lesson introduces students to two types of data on the graphs. Although they will not learn these terms, the two types of data are called *discrete data* and *continuous data*. With discrete data, only the coordinates plotted make sense in the problem. For example, plotting points to show the cost of multiple DVDs is discrete data, since points in between the data points are irrelevant. Fractions of DVDs are not for sale, so a point showing the cost of $1\frac{1}{2}$ DVDs would make no sense. So with discrete data, points remain separate. They are not connected with a line. With continuous data, however, even the points along the line between the plotted points make sense to consider in the problem. For example, plotting points that show how much gas is used over several miles of driving is continuous data. Fractions of a mile and fractions of a gallon of gas exist, so connecting plotted points with a line in this case does make sense. In some problems, students will see an arrow on the end of the line. The arrow means that the data for this situation could continue beyond the points that are plotted.

Although the terms *positive correlation* and *negative correlation* (also known as *direct* and *inverse relationships*) are not part of this lesson, it is important for students to notice these relationships on their graphs. A positive correlation, or

Materials to Gather

SUPPLIED

Quadrant I Coordinate Grid (printout) – 2

Interpret Coordinates on a Graph activity page

Practice to Understand Coordinates activity page

direct relationship, is one where the *y*-coordinates increase as the *x*-coordinates increase, so the path of the points moves up to the right on the graph. A negative correlation, or inverse relationship, is one where the *y*-coordinates decrease as the *x*-coordinates increase, so the path of the points moves down to the right on the graph.

A *coordinate* is a position along a number line or within the coordinate plane.

An *ordered pair* is a pair of numbers, shown inside parentheses, with a comma separating the numbers. It is one way to describe the position of a point on a plane. On the coordinate plane, all points can be labeled by writing the horizontal distance from the origin, moving along the *x*-axis, as the first coordinate, and the vertical distance, moving parallel to the *y*-axis, as the second coordinate, such as (x, y) or $(^+2, ^+3)$. For example, the ordered pair $(^+2, ^+3)$ is 2 steps to the right of the origin, then 3 steps above that point. Even though this lesson concentrates on problems with data graphed in Quadrant I only, coordinates in an ordered pair can be positive and negative, depending on the quadrant in which they are located.

▶ Advance Preparation

Print two copies of the Quadrant I Coordinate Grid.

ONLINE 15 min

LEARN Increase (*x*, *y*) Coordinates

Students will graph and describe the meaning of ordered pairs on the coordinate plane. They will work with story problems from everyday situations. The data that students will see in the problems have a positive correlation.

Objectives

- Use the situation presented in a problem to describe the meaning of each coordinate of an ordered pair displayed on a graph.

Tips

If students have difficulty understanding why sometimes the data in a problem can be graphed so a line can connect the points, have them think of another example like the bike-riding problem, where the data between graphed points make sense in the context of the problem. Then have students think of another example like the zoo problem, where the data between the graphed points do not make sense in the context of the problem.

ONLINE 10 min

LEARN Coordinates Increase or Decrease

Students will graph and describe the meaning of ordered pairs on the coordinate plane. They will work with a story problem from an everyday situation. The data that students will see in the problem have a negative correlation.

Objectives

- Use the situation presented in a problem to describe the meaning of each coordinate of an ordered pair displayed on a graph.

OFFLINE 10min

Students will graph and describe the meaning of ordered pairs on the coordinate plane. Gather the Quadrant I Coordinate Grid printout. View or print the Interpret Coordinates on a Graph activity page and read the directions with students.

Students should copy the problems from the Activity Book into their Math Notebook as necessary and solve them there.

- Use the situation presented in a problem to describe the meaning of each coordinate of an ordered pair displayed on a graph.

1. Read the problem in the Worked Examples box with students. Make sure they understand the graph and how the graph was interpreted.

2. Have students read Problem 1. Have them plot the points on the Quadrant I Coordinate Grid. Check that they plotted the points correctly.

3. Have students complete Problems 2–11. Check that they answered the problems correctly. If they have trouble, go over the Worked Example again and then have them look at the problems again.

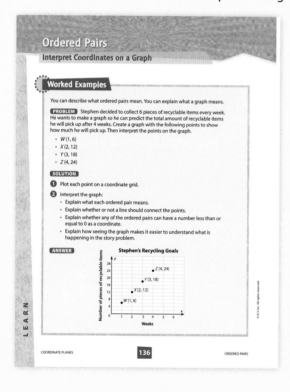

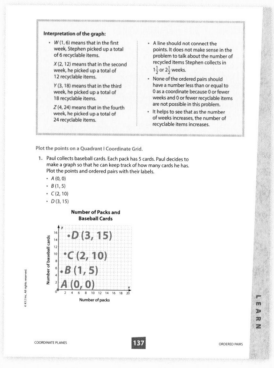

Refer to the story problem and the points, ordered pairs, and labels you plotted in Problem 1 to answer the following questions.

2. What does the ordered pair (0, 0) mean? **See below.**

3. What does the ordered pair (1, 5) mean? **See below.**

4. What does the ordered pair (2, 10) mean? **See below.**

5. What does the ordered pair (3, 15) mean? **See below.**

6. Can there be a negative number of baseball card packs? **See below.**

7. Can there be a negative number of baseball cards? **See below.**

8. What happens to the number of baseball cards as the number of packs increase? **See below.**

9. What happens to the graph as the number of packs increases and the number of cards increases? **See below.**

10. Does it make sense to connect the points in the graph with a line? Why? **See below.**

11. How does seeing the graph make it easier to understand what is happening in the situation?
It helps to see that as the number of packs of cards increases, the number of baseball cards increases.

COORDINATE PLANES   **138**   ORDERED PAIRS

Additional Answers

2. Paul has 0 packs and 0 baseball cards.

3. Paul has 1 pack with 5 baseball cards.

4. Paul has 2 packs with 10 baseball cards.

5. Paul has 3 packs with 15 baseball cards.

6. No, there are 0 or more packs of baseball cards. Fewer than 0 packs is not possible in this problem.

7. No, there are 0 or more baseball cards. Fewer than 0 baseball cards is not possible in this problem.

8. The number of baseball cards increases as the number of packs increases.

9. The ordered pairs move up and to the right of the origin.

10. No, in this problem, there are only whole packs of baseball cards.

TRY IT   Practice to Understand Coordinates

OFFLINE **15** min

Students will plot points on a coordinate grid. They will describe what the coordinates on a graph of an everyday situation mean. And they'll answer questions based on graphs. Gather the Quadrant I Coordinate Grid printout. View or print the Practice to Understand Coordinates activity page and read the directions with students.

Students should copy the problems from the Activity Book into their Math Notebook as necessary and solve them there.

Objectives

- Use the situation presented in a problem to describe the meaning of each coordinate of an ordered pair displayed on a graph.

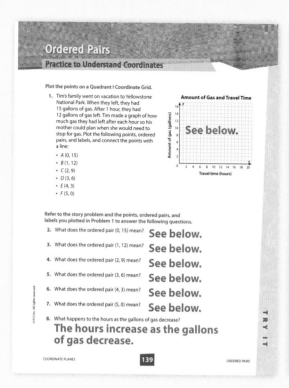

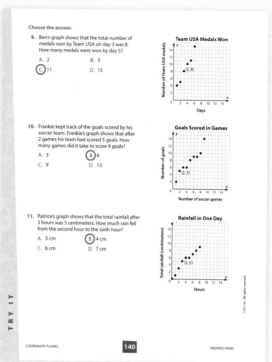

Additional Answers

1.

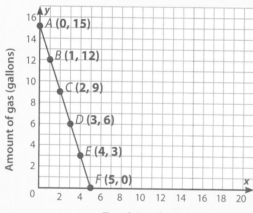

Amount of Gas and Travel Time

2. Tim's family travels for 0 hours and has 15 gallons of gas left.

3. Tim's family travels for 1 hour and has 12 gallons of gas left.

4. Tim's family travels for 2 hours and has 9 gallons of gas left.

5. Tim's family travels for 3 hours and has 6 gallons of gas left.

6. Tim's family travels for 4 hours and has 3 gallons of gas left.

7. Tim's family travels for 5 hours and has 0 gallons of gas left.

CHECKPOINT

ONLINE
10min

Students will complete an online Checkpoint. If necessary, read the directions, problems, and answer choices to students and help them with keyboard or mouse operations.

Objectives

- Use the situation presented in a problem to describe the meaning of each coordinate of an ordered pair displayed on a graph.

Graph or Write an Equation (A)

Lesson Overview

LEARN Inputs and Outputs of Function Tables	15 minutes	ONLINE
LEARN Equations and Function Tables	20 minutes	OFFLINE
LEARN Find Equations for Function Tables	15 minutes	OFFLINE
TRY IT Practice Completing Function Tables	10 minutes	ONLINE

▶ Lesson Objectives

Graph or write an equation to solve a problem that involves a linear function.

▶ Prerequisite Skills

- Use an equation to represent a relationship between quantities.
- Use the situation presented in a problem to describe the meaning of each coordinate of an ordered pair displayed on a graph.
- Plot a linear relationship in the first quadrant of a coordinate plane.

▶ Content Background

Students will complete the *x*- and *y*-values of a function table and learn to write an equation based on a linear function.

An *equation* is a number sentence that shows that two quantities are equal. Equations can include numbers, variables, and operation signs (such as $+, -, \cdot,$ or $\div$). Some examples of equations are $2r - 3 = 9$ and $16 = 12 + 4$.

A *linear function* is a relationship between two quantities in which one variable depends on another. One reason this type of function is called linear is that the graph of the equation has points that fall on a straight line. Most often, linear equations are written in the form of $y = mx + b$, where *x* and *y* are the two quantities. In that linear equation, the variable *m* stands for any number that is multiplied by *x*. When you multiply *m* by *x*, you have a linear function. The variable *b* stands for any number that is added to the expression *mx*. The equation $y = mx + b$ is a linear function. It's also the case that *b* can be a negative number, so that $y = mx - b$ is also a linear function.

Materials to Gather

SUPPLIED

Equations and Function Tables activity page

Find Equations for Function Tables activity page

ALSO NEEDED

ruler, dual-scale

LEARN Inputs and Outputs of Function Tables

ONLINE **15** min

Students will learn about input-output tables. They will apply a rule to an input to get an output. They also will find missing values in input-output tables. They will learn that input-output tables can also be called function tables.

Objectives

- Graph or write an equation to solve a problem that involves a linear function.

LEARN Equations and Function Tables

Objectives

- Graph or write an equation to solve a problem that involves a linear function.

Students will learn that a function table lists input and output values for a function, which is an equation. A function table uses one variable to represent input and another variable to represent output. Students will find missing values for variables in function tables. Gather a ruler. View or print the Equations and Function Tables activity page and read the directions with students.

Students should copy the problems from the Activity Book into their Math Notebook as necessary and solve them there. Have them use a ruler to help them draw the function tables in their Math Notebook.

1. Read the Problem and Solution in the Worked Examples box with students.

2. Make sure students understand the function table.

   Ask: How would you read the rows in this incomplete function table? Read a few rows. **Sample answer:** In the third row, the value of x is 7 and the value of y isn't known. Next row: The value of x isn't known and the value of y is 13. Next row: The value of x is 9 and the value of y is 14.

3. Point to the rule at the top of the function table. Explain that instead of writing a rule with words such as "add 5" or "subtract 1," the rule of a function table is written as an equation. Remind students that while the tables in this activity use x and y, other letters can also be used as variables.

4. Read the Answer in the Worked Examples box with students. Make sure they understand how the table was completed.

5. Have students look at Problem 1 in the problem set. Point to the first row of function values. Tell students that the value for x is 3 and they should substitute 3 in the equation for x.

   Ask: What will you write as the first value for y in the function table? 6

   Have students continue to substitute the values of x into the equation to fill in the missing values for y.

6. Have students complete Problem 2 on their own. If they have difficulty, first encourage them to look at the Worked Example and follow the process shown.

7. Have students look at the function table in Problem 3. Tell them that some of the values for x and y are missing.

   Say: In the fourth row of function values in the function table, both values are missing. Look for a pattern in the values for x to find the missing value. The three numbers before the missing value are 10, 11, and 12 and the number after the missing value is 14.

   Ask: What is the missing value for x? 13

   Have students complete the remaining rows on the function table.

8. Have students complete Problem 4 on their own. If they have difficulty, have them review the steps they took to complete the function table in Problem 3.

9. Discuss with students that in these examples, the x-values have always been numbers that are in counting order. Tell them that as they continue to study mathematics, x-values may not always be in counting order. In fact, x-values may be in a random order or may include other types of numbers, such as negative numbers. To find missing x-values, think about the equation and the y-value. Then work backward.

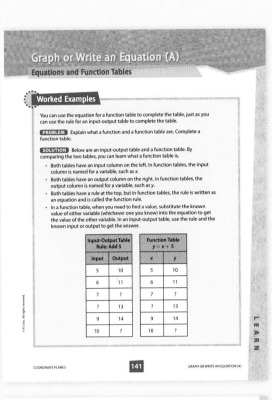

Equations and Function Tables

Worked Examples

You can use the equation for a function table to complete the table, just as you can use the rule for an input-output table to complete the table.

PROBLEM Explain what a function and a function table are. Complete a function table.

SOLUTION Below are an input-output table and a function table. By comparing the two tables, you can learn what a function table is.

- Both tables have an input column on the left. In function tables, the input column is named for a variable, such as x.
- Both tables have an output column on the right. In function tables, the output column is named for a variable, such as y.
- Both tables have a rule at the top, but in function tables, the rule is written as an equation and is called the function rule.
- In a function table, when you need to find a value, substitute the known value of either variable (whichever one you know) into the equation to get the value of the other variable. In an input-output table, use the rule and the known input or output to get the answer.

Input-Output Table
Rule: Add 5

Input	Output
5	10
6	11
7	?
?	13
9	14
10	?

Function Table
$y = x + 5$

x	y
5	10
6	11
7	?
?	13
9	14
10	?

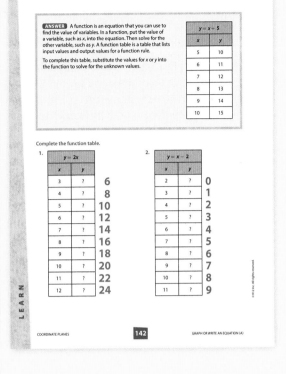

ANSWER A function is an equation that you can use to find the value of variables. In a function, put the value of a variable, such as x, into the equation. Then solve for the other variable, such as y. A function table is a table that lists input values and output values for a function rule.

To complete this table, substitute the values for x or y into the function to solve for the unknown values.

$y = x + 5$

x	y
5	10
6	11
7	12
8	13
9	14
10	15

Complete the function table.

1. $y = 2x$

x	y	
3	?	6
4	?	8
5	?	10
6	?	12
7	?	14
8	?	16
9	?	18
10	?	20
11	?	22
12	?	24

2. $y = x - 2$

x	y	
2	?	0
3	?	1
4	?	2
5	?	3
6	?	4
7	?	5
8	?	6
9	?	7
10	?	8
11	?	9

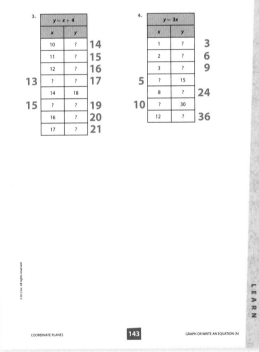

3. $y = x + 4$

	x	y	
	10	?	14
	11	?	15
	12	?	16
13	?	?	17
	14	18	
15	?	?	19
	16	?	20
	17	?	21

4. $y = 3x$

	x	y	
	1	?	3
	2	?	6
	3	?	9
5	?	15	
	8	?	24
10	?	30	
	12	?	36

LEARN Find Equations for Function Tables

OFFLINE
15 min

Objectives

- Graph or write an equation to solve a problem that involves a linear function.

Tips

Allow students to use paper and pencil to write values from the function table and possible equations for Problem 3, using a guess-and-test problem-solving strategy to find the equation that matches the values.

Students will use the values for variables in a function table to find the equation that matches all the values. Gather a ruler. View or print the Find Equations for Function Tables activity page and read the directions with students.

Students should copy the problems from the Activity Book into their Math Notebook as necessary and solve them there. Have them use the ruler to help them copy the function tables into their Math Notebook. They will need to use function tables in their Math Notebook to work out the answers to the problems in the problem set.

1. Read Problem 1 of the Worked Examples with students.

   Ask: Why did you substitute the values for x and y in the two equations?
   I wanted to find out if the equations were true for the x- and y-values in the two function tables.

   Ask: What happened when 2 was substituted for x and 6 for y in the two equations? For those values, one equation, $y = 3x$, was true. The other equation, $y = x + 2$, was not true.

2. Explain that students always need to check each row of values in the function table with the equation that they believe is correct. They need to be sure that the equation works for all pairs of x- and y-values.

3. Read Problem 2 of the Worked Examples with students.

   Ask: Why did the Solution try out the equation $y = x + 1$? The numbers for x and y showed a pattern of each y-value being 1 greater than its matching x-value.

4. Summarize the strategy used in the Worked Examples problems.

   Say: If you are asked to write an equation for a function table with given x- and y-values, look at all the numbers to find a pattern and to find what operation you might need to use in the equation. Check all the values in the function table to see if they all work in the equation you are trying.

5. Have students complete Problems 1–3 in the problem set. Note that for all the problems in this set, the equation that matches a function table needs only one operation, such as add a number or multiply by a number. If students have difficulty, first encourage them to look at the Worked Examples and follow the process shown. Help them as needed.

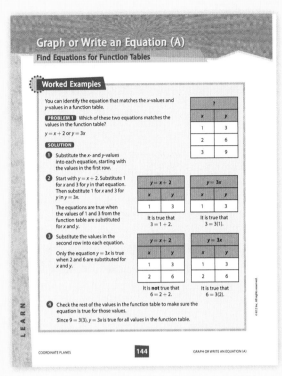

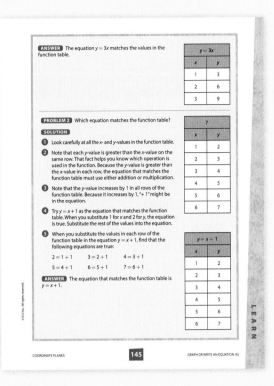

Graph or Write an Equation (A)
Find Equations for Function Tables

Worked Examples

You can identify the equation that matches the *x*-values and *y*-values in a function table.

PROBLEM 1 Which of these two equations matches the values in the function table?

$y = x + 2$ or $y = 3x$

SOLUTION

① Substitute the *x*- and *y*-values into each equation, starting with the values in the first row.

② Start with $y = x + 2$. Substitute 1 for *x* and 3 for *y* in that equation. Then substitute 1 for *x* and 3 for *y* in $y = 3x$.

The equations are true when the values of 1 and 3 from the function table are substituted for *x* and *y*.

It is true that $3 = 1 + 2$.

It is true that $3 = 3(1)$.

③ Substitute the values in the second row into each equation.

Only the equation $y = 3x$ is true when 2 and 6 are substituted for *x* and *y*.

It is **not** true that $6 = 2 + 2$.

It is true that $6 = 3(2)$.

④ Check the rest of the values in the function table to make sure the equation is true for those values.

Since $9 = 3(3)$, $y = 3x$ is true for all values in the function table.

?	
x	**y**
1	3
2	6
3	9

$y = x + 2$	
x	**y**
1	3

$y = 3x$	
x	**y**
1	3

$y = x + 2$	
x	**y**
1	3
2	6

$y = 3x$	
x	**y**
1	3
2	6

ANSWER The equation $y = 3x$ matches the values in the function table.

$y = 3x$	
x	**y**
1	3
2	6
3	9

PROBLEM 2 Which equation matches the function table?

SOLUTION

① Look carefully at all the *x*- and *y*-values in the function table.

② Note that each *y*-value is greater than the *x*-value on the same row. That fact helps you know which operation is used in the function. Because the *y*-value is greater than the *x*-value in each row, the equation that matches the function table must use either addition or multiplication.

③ Note that the *y*-value increases by 1 in all rows of the function table. Because it increases by 1, "+ 1" might be in the equation.

④ Try $y = x + 1$ as the equation that matches the function table. When you substitute 1 for *x* and 2 for *y*, the equation is true. Substitute the rest of the values into the equation.

⑤ When you substitute the values in each row of the function table in the equation $y = x + 1$, find that the following equations are true:

$2 = 1 + 1$ $3 = 2 + 1$ $4 = 3 + 1$
$5 = 4 + 1$ $6 = 5 + 1$ $7 = 6 + 1$

ANSWER The equation that matches the function table is $y = x + 1$.

?	
x	**y**
1	2
2	3
3	4
4	5
5	6
6	7

$y = x + 1$	
x	**y**
1	2
2	3
3	4
4	5
5	6
6	7

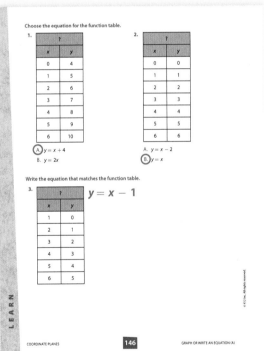

Choose the equation for the function table.

1.

?	
x	**y**
0	4
1	5
2	6
3	7
4	8
5	9
6	10

Ⓐ $y = x + 4$
B. $y = 2x$

2.

?	
x	**y**
0	0
1	1
2	2
3	3
4	4
5	5
6	6

A. $y = x - 2$
Ⓑ $y = x$

Write the equation that matches the function table.

3.

?	
x	**y**
1	0
2	1
3	2
4	3
5	4
6	5

$y = x - 1$

TRY IT Practice Completing Function Tables

ONLINE 10min

Students will complete an online Try It. If necessary, read the directions, problems, and answer choices to students and help them with keyboard or mouse operations.

Objectives

- Graph or write an equation to solve a problem that involves a linear function.

Graph or Write an Equation (B)

LEARN Complete a Function Table and Graph	15 minutes	ONLINE
LEARN Graph Linear Functions	10 minutes	ONLINE
LEARN Find an Equation Used to Make a Graph	20 minutes	OFFLINE
TRY IT Practice Function Tables and Graphs	15 minutes	OFFLINE

▶ Lesson Objectives

Graph or write an equation to solve a problem that involves a linear function.

▶ Prerequisite Skills

- Use an equation to represent a relationship between quantities.
- Use the situation presented in a problem to describe the meaning of each coordinate of an ordered pair displayed on a graph.
- Plot a linear relationship in the first quadrant of a coordinate plane.

▶ Content Background

Students will learn to graph a set of points from a function table that has an equation and data for x- and y-values.

An *equation* is a number sentence that shows that two quantities are equal. Equations can include numbers, variables, and operation signs (such as $+$, $-$, $\cdot$, or $\div$). Some examples of equations are $2r - 3 = 9$ and $16 = 12 + 4$.

A *linear function* is a relationship between two quantities in which one variable depends on another. One reason this type of function is called linear is that the graph of the equation has points that fall on a straight line. Most often linear equations are written in the form of $y = mx + b$, where x and y are the two quantities. In that linear equation, the variable m stands for any number that is multiplied by x. When you multiply m by x, you have a linear function. The variable b stands for any number that is added to the expression mx. The equation $y = mx + b$ is a linear function. It's also the case that b can be a negative number, so that $y = mx - b$ is also a linear function.

▶ Advance Preparation

Print two copies of Graphing Equations.

Materials to Gather

SUPPLIED

Graphing Equations (printout) – 2

Find an Equation Used to Make a Graph activity page

Practice Function Tables and Graphs activity page

LEARN Complete a Function Table and Graph

ONLINE 15 min

Objectives

- Graph or write an equation to solve a problem that involves a linear function.

Students will complete a function table and plot the values from the table on a graph. The function table values, graph, and equation represent a linear function.

Tips Tell students that an infinite number of points can be plotted for any linear function.

LEARN Graph Linear Functions

ONLINE 10 min

Objectives

- Graph or write an equation to solve a problem that involves a linear function.

Students will use the Coordinate Grid Learning Tool to graph a linear function.

DIRECTIONS FOR USING THE COORDINATE GRID LEARNING TOOL

1. Explain to students that they will be graphing a type of equation called a linear function.

   Say: A linear function is a relationship between two quantities. The two quantities will be the x- and y-values in a function table with y dependent on x.

2. Tell students to select Stage 2: $^-$15 to $^+$15 and click Next.

3. Then have students select Linear Equations and click Next. Have them read the Help text.

4. Explain that the function table shows an equation and x- and y-values. Have students read the equation and the x- and y-values before they graph the points.

5. To graph the linear function, have students plot a point on the coordinate plane for each pair of x- and y-values in the function table.

6. Have students graph the remaining functions in the problem set.

LEARN Find an Equation Used to Make a Graph

OFFLINE 20 min

Objectives

- Graph or write an equation to solve a problem that involves a linear function.

Students will look at the graph of a linear function and use the information in it to write the equation that was used to create the graph. Gather two copies of the Graphing Equations printout. View or print the Find an Equation Used to Make a Graph activity page and read the directions with students.

Students will solve the problems in this activity on the Graphing Equations printouts. They also may copy the problems from the Activity Book into their Math Notebook.

1. Read all the text, the graph, and the tables in Worked Examples with students.

   Ask: How was the function table completed? It was completed by entering each x-value and y-value in the ordered pairs on the graph into the function table.

2. Tell students that they can enter *x*- and *y*-values into the function table out of sequential order. The equation would still be correct and, if the graph were created again with this table, it would still look the same. When the values appear in sequential order, plotting points is easier. But as long as the values in the function table are correct with the equation, it does not matter if the values are in sequential order.

3. Remind students that when they find an equation that works with some of the variables in a function table, they need to substitute the remaining *x*- and *y*-values in the function table. They need to check that the equation is correct for all *x*- and *y*-values in the table.

4. Discuss with students that in these examples, the *x*-values have always been positive numbers that are in counting order. Tell students that as they continue to study graphing and other topics in mathematics, *x*-values may not always be in counting order. In fact, the *x*-values may be in a random order or may include other types of numbers, such as negative numbers.

5. Before they begin, discuss the problem set with students.

   Ask: The Worked Examples box shows a graph and function table for an addition equation. What other operations could be used in equations for graphed lines? subtraction, multiplication, or division

   Say: Even if the problem had an operation other than addition, you would still follow the same process by taking the information from the graph to write the equation that was used to create the graph.

6. Have students complete both problems in the problem set.

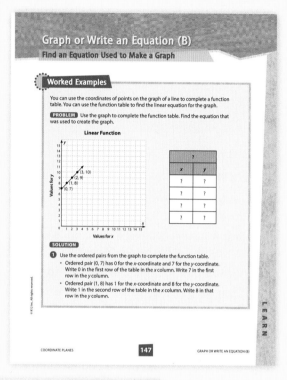

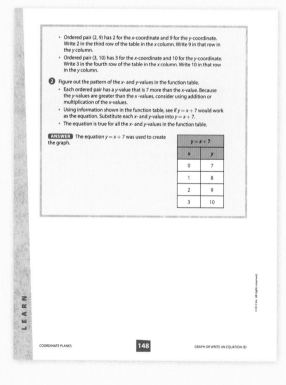

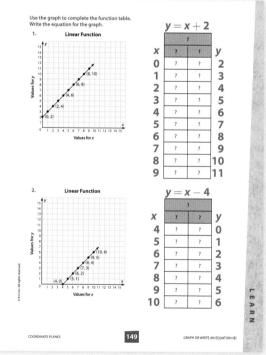

TRY IT Practice Function Tables and Graphs

Objectives

Students will practice finding the graph that matches an equation and writing the equation that matches a graph. View or print the Practice Function Tables and Graphs activity page and read the directions with students.

Students should copy the problems from the Activity Book into their Math Notebook as necessary and solve them there.

- Graph or write an equation to solve a problem that involves a linear function.

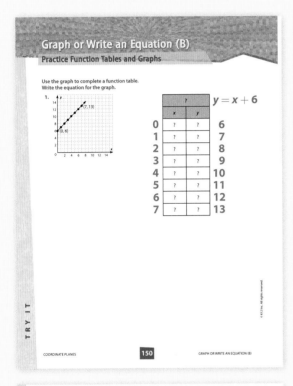

Graph or Write an Equation (B)
Practice Function Tables and Graphs

Use the graph to complete a function table.
Write the equation for the graph.

1.

?		$y = x + 6$
x	**y**	
0	?	?	6
1	?	?	7
2	?	?	8
3	?	?	9
4	?	?	10
5	?	?	11
6	?	?	12
7	?	?	13

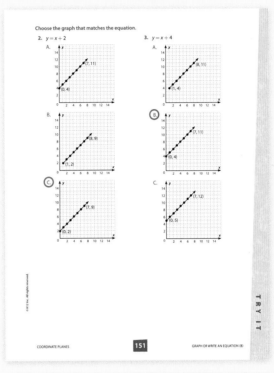

Choose the graph that matches the equation.

2. $y = x + 2$ 3. $y = x + 4$

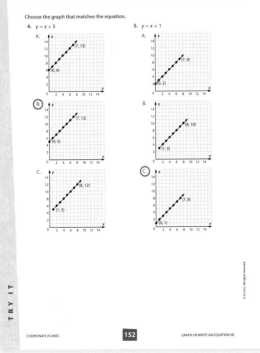

Choose the graph that matches the equation.

4. $y = x + 5$ 5. $y = x + 1$

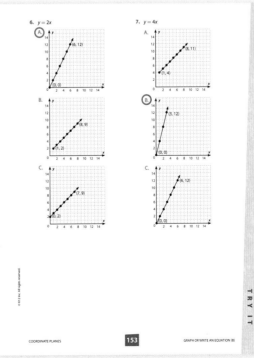

6. $y = 2x$ 7. $y = 4x$

GRAPH OR WRITE AN EQUATION (B)   337

Choose the equation that could have been used to create the graph.

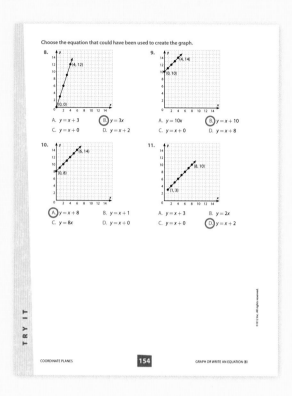

8.

A. $y = x + 3$ B. $y = 3x$
C. $y = x + 0$ D. $y = x + 2$

9.

A. $y = 10x$ B. $y = x + 10$
C. $y = x + 0$ D. $y = x + 8$

10.

A. $y = x + 8$ B. $y = x + 1$
C. $y = 8x$ D. $y = x + 0$

11.

A. $y = x + 3$ B. $y = 2x$
C. $y = x + 0$ D. $y = x + 2$

Graph or Write an Equation (C)

Lesson Overview

LEARN Graph Equations for Story Problems	15 minutes	ONLINE
LEARN Graph Circumference Equations	20 minutes	ONLINE
LEARN Graph Equations About Animals	15 minutes	OFFLINE
TRY IT Practice with Graphs of Equations	10 minutes	OFFLINE

▶ Lesson Objectives

Graph or write an equation to solve a problem that involves a linear function.

▶ Prerequisite Skills

- Use an equation to represent a relationship between quantities.
- Use the situation presented in a problem to describe the meaning of each coordinate of an ordered pair displayed on a graph.
- Plot a linear relationship in the first quadrant of a coordinate plane.

▶ Content Background

Students will continue to complete the x- and y-values of a function table and learn to write an equation based on a linear function.

An *equation* is a number sentence that shows that two quantities are equal. Equations can include numbers, variables, and operation signs (such as $+$, $-$, $\cdot$, or $\div$). Some examples of equations are $2r - 3 = 9$ and $16 = 12 + 4$.

A *linear function* is a relationship between two quantities in which one variable depends on another. One reason this type of function is called linear is that the graph of the equation has points that fall on a straight line. Most often, linear equations are written in the form of $y = mx + b$, where x and y are the two quantities. In that linear equation, the variable m stands for any number that is multiplied by x. When you multiply m by x, you have a linear function. The variable b stands for any number that is added to the expression mx. The equation $y = mx + b$ is a linear function. It's also the case that b can be a negative number, so that $y = mx - b$ is also a linear function.

▶ Advance Preparation

Print one copy of Graphing Equations.

Materials to Gather

SUPPLIED

Graphing Equations (printout)

Graph Equations About Animals activity page

Practice with Graphs of Equations activity page

LEARN Graph Equations for Story Problems

ONLINE 15min

Students will create a function table, write an equation, and graph data for a linear function that represents a story problem. They will work with data about the rate of speed that shorebirds fly.

Objectives

- Graph or write an equation to solve a problem that involves a linear function.

LEARN Graph Circumference Equations

ONLINE 20min

Students will create a function table, write an equation, and graph data for a linear function that represents a story problem. They will work with data about the circumference of circles with different diameter lengths.

Objectives

- Graph or write an equation to solve a problem that involves a linear function.

LEARN Graph Equations About Animals

OFFLINE 15min

Students will create a function table, write an equation, and graph data for a linear function representing a story problem about animals. Gather the Graphing Equations printout. View or print the Graph Equations About Animals activity page and read the directions with students.

Objectives

- Graph or write an equation to solve a problem that involves a linear function.

1. Have students read the Worked Example.

   Say: The value of variable r depends on variable m in this problem because to find the number of meters the tortoise walked, represented by r, you multiply the minutes, represented by m, by 5. Also remember that other letters could have been used for the variables. When you find an equation to solve a story problem, you can choose the variables you want to use.

2. Ask students to explain the graph in the answer. Their explanation should include the axes, the graphed points, and the equation used to determine the points. **Sample answer:** The m-axis is labeled "Time (minutes)" because it shows each minute the tortoise walked. The r-axis is labeled "Distance walked (meters)" because it shows the number of meters the tortoise walked. The point (1, 5) means that the tortoise walked 1 minute and went 5 meters. The point (2, 10) means it walked 2 minutes and went 10 meters, the point (3, 15) means it walked 3 minutes and went 15 meters, and so on. The equation in the function table, $r = 5m$, was used to find the ordered pairs. The problem asked about 2, 3, 4, and 5 minutes. Those numbers were substituted for the variable m in the equation.

3. Discuss with students how they could use the graph to figure out how many meters the tortoise would walk in $2\frac{1}{2}$ minutes. On the m-axis, locate $2\frac{1}{2}$ halfway between 2 and 3. Then move up to the graphed line. On the graphed line, the r-axis shows that you are at $12\frac{1}{2}$ meters. The tortoise would walk $12\frac{1}{2}$ meters in $2\frac{1}{2}$ minutes.

4. Point out to students that they are using a different interval on the r-axis than they are using on the m-axis but that the data can still be accurately graphed.

5. Have students complete Problem 1 in the problem set. Give them the Graphing Equations printout and have them create a function table and plot the data on the graph. Have students refer to the Worked Examples for assistance and help them as needed.

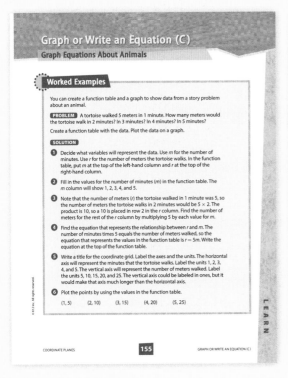

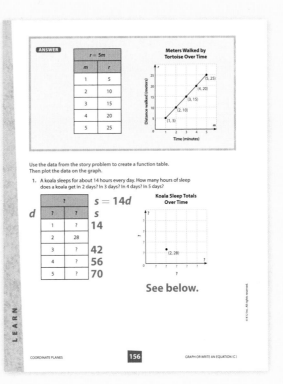

Additional Answers

1.

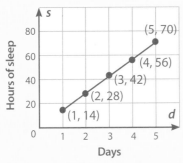

Koala Sleep Totals Over Time

days = 1 and hours of sleep = 14
days = 2 and hours of sleep = 28
days = 3 and hours of sleep = 42
days = 4 and hours of sleep = 56
days = 5 and hours of sleep = 70

OFFLINE
10min

Objectives

Students will choose the graph or equation that matches the given story problem. View or print the Practice with Graphs of Equations activity page and read the directions with students.

Students should copy the problems from the Activity Book into their Math Notebook as necessary and solve them there.

- Graph or write an equation to solve a problem that involves a linear function.

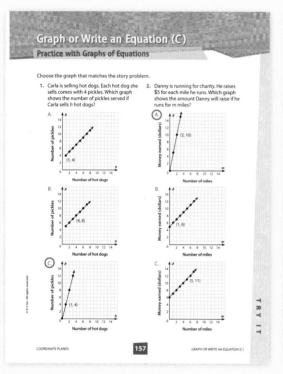

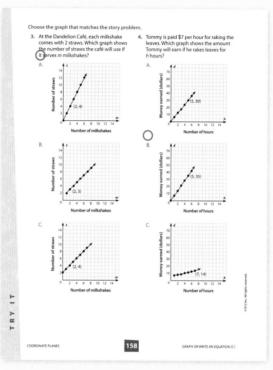

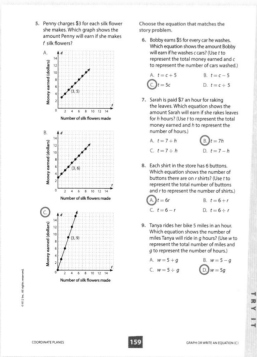

Graph or Write an Equation (D)

▶ Lesson Objectives

Graph or write an equation to solve a problem that involves a linear function.

▶ Prerequisite Skills

- Use an equation to represent a relationship between quantities.
- Use the situation presented in a problem to describe the meaning of each coordinate of an ordered pair displayed on a graph.
- Plot a linear relationship in the first quadrant of a coordinate plane.

▶ Content Background

Students will continue to complete the *x*- and *y*-values of a function table and learn to write an equation based on a linear function.

An *equation* is a number sentence that shows that two quantities are equal. Equations can include numbers, variables, and operation signs (such as $+$, $-$, $\cdot$, or $\div$). Some examples of equations are $2r - 3 = 9$ and $16 = 12 + 4$.

A *linear function* is a relationship between two quantities in which one variable depends on another. One reason this type of function is called linear is that the graph of the equation has points that fall on a straight line. Most often, linear equations are written in the form of $y = mx + b$, where *x* and *y* are the two quantities. In that linear equation, the variable *m* stands for any number that is multiplied by *x*. When you multiply *m* by *x*, you have a linear function. The variable *b* stands for any number that is added to the expression *mx*. The equation $y = mx + b$ is a linear function. It's also the case that *b* can be a negative number, so that $y = mx - b$ is also a linear function.

▶ Advance Preparation

Print one copy of Graphing Equations.

Materials to Gather

SUPPLIED

Graphing Equations (printout)

Graph Equations About Purchases activity page

Graph Two-Step Equations activity page

LEARN Graph Equations About a DVD Club

Objectives

- Graph or write an equation to solve a problem that involves a linear function.

Students will create a function table, write a two-step equation, and graph data for a linear function that represents a story problem. They will work with data about the costs of renting DVDs.

Tips | Allow some students to use the variables *x* and *y* in the function table, equation, and graph, if they wish. Tell them they can choose any variables they want to represent unknown values in a story problem, but they should decide which variables to use as they begin to solve the problem and use those same variables as they complete all the steps to solve the problem.

LEARN Graph Equations About Plants

Objectives

- Graph or write an equation to solve a problem that involves a linear function.

Students will create a function table, write a two-step equation, and graph data for a linear function that represents a story problem. They will work with data about the growth of bamboo plants.

LEARN Graph Equations About Purchases

Objectives

- Graph or write an equation to solve a problem that involves a linear function.

Students will create a function table, write a two-step equation, and graph data from a story problem. Gather the Graphing Equations printout. View or print the Graph Equations About Purchases activity page and read the directions with students.

1. Read the Worked Example with students.

   Ask: How would you know by reading the problem that you would use multiplication and addition in the equation? **Sample answer:** The problem says "4 bags of vegetables for $2.50 each," which means I need to multiply 4 by 2.5. It says Daniella bought 1 loaf of bread for $2.00. That means I need to add 2 to the product of 4 times 2.5.

2. Tell students that because multiplication and addition are used, there are two steps needed to solve this equation. The function table shows solutions after both steps have been completed.

3. Have students read Problem 1 about the lemonade stand. Give them the Graphing Equations printout.

4. Have students choose variables they will use. They should choose variables for the number of jumbo cups sold and the amount of the profit. They should put the variables at the top of the columns in the function table, with the jumbo cups variable on the left and the profit variable on the right.

   Note: The remaining steps in this activity will refer to *j* for the left-hand column and *p* for the right-hand column.

   Ask: Which variable depends on the other variable. Why? The variable *p* depends on *j* because the amount of profit depends on the number of jumbo cups of lemonade sold.

5. Work with students as they develop the equation. Ask them which two operations the equation will have. It will have multiplication to find the amount of money Ralph earns selling jumbo cups of lemonade and subtraction to find the profit after the $9 cost of setting up the lemonade stand.

   After students come up with the equation, have them write it at the top of the function table: $p = 1.50j - 9$.

6. Have students use the equation and function table to find the profit after selling 7, 8, 9, 10, and 11 jumbo cups of lemonade.

   Ask: How much profit did Ralph make when he sold 11 jumbo cups of lemonade? $7.50

7. Discuss with students what they think the profit will be when Ralph sells 14 jumbo cups of lemonade. Have them use the equation and function table to check their prediction. $12

8. Have students complete the function table on the Graphing Equations printout by putting j-values in each row they haven't yet completed and solving for p-values.

9. Have students use the ordered pairs to plot points on the coordinate grid. Tell them that the broken line between 0 and 7 on the j-axis indicates that data are not shown for 1 through 6 cups. They should show the same broken line on the graph they are making.

   Say: In other activities, the x-axis has been labeled with an x. The axes are labeled for the variables in this problem. The horizontal axis is labeled with a j, rather than an x. The vertical axis is labeled with a p, rather than a y.

   - Have students label the j-axis from 0 to 16 with an interval of 1 and the p-axis from 0 to 20 with an interval of 2.
   - Remind students that because the numbers on the p-axis are in intervals of 2, the points they plot on the graph will fall between the p-values.

10. Ask students if it would make sense to draw a line through the points they graphed. Lead students to conclude that it wouldn't make sense to talk about the data between the points they graphed. In this problem, Ralph is unlikely to sell a part of a jumbo cup of lemonade and charge only part of $1.50 for the drink.

11. After they complete the problem, ask students the following questions about the data in the function table and the graph:

    Ask: How many jumbo cups of lemonade does Ralph need to sell to make at least $10 in profit? 13

    Ask: Why is there no profit until Ralph sells 7 jumbo cups of lemonade? The cost of supplies is $9. Until Ralph earns more than $9 selling lemonade, he will not make any profit. There is no profit after Ralph sells 1 through 5 jumbo cups of lemonade. After Ralph sells 6 jumbo cups of lemonade, he has earned $9.00. There is still no profit. After Ralph sells 7 cups, he has earned $10.50. The profit at this point is $1.50.

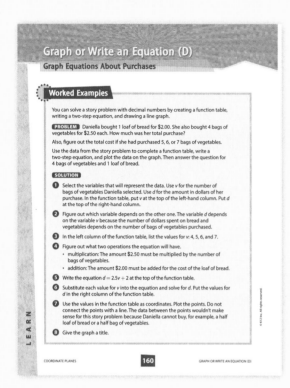

Graph or Write an Equation (D)

Graph Equations About Purchases

Worked Examples

You can solve a story problem with decimal numbers by creating a function table, writing a two-step equation, and drawing a line graph.

PROBLEM Daniella bought 1 loaf of bread for $2.00. She also bought 4 bags of vegetables for $2.50 each. How much was her total purchase?

Also, figure out the total cost if she had purchased 5, 6, or 7 bags of vegetables.

Use the data from the story problem to complete a function table, write a two-step equation, and plot the data on the graph. Then answer the question for 4 bags of vegetables and 1 loaf of bread.

SOLUTION

1. Select the variables that will represent the data. Use v for the number of bags of vegetables Daniella selected. Use d for the amount in dollars of her purchase. In the function table, put v at the top of the left-hand column. Put d at the top of the right-hand column.

2. Figure out which variable depends on the other one. The variable d depends on the variable v because the number of dollars spent on bread and vegetables depends on the number of bags of vegetables purchased.

3. In the left column of the function table, list the values for v: 4, 5, 6, and 7.

4. Figure out what two operations the equation will have.
   - multiplication: The amount $2.50 must be multiplied by the number of bags of vegetables.
   - addition: The amount $2.00 must be added for the cost of the loaf of bread.

5. Write the equation $d = 2.5v + 2$ at the top of the function table.

6. Substitute each value for v into the equation and solve for d. Put the values for d in the right column of the function table.

7. Use the values in the function table as coordinates. Plot the points. Do not connect the points with a line. The data between the points wouldn't make sense for this story problem because Daniella cannot buy, for example, a half loaf of bread or a half bag of vegetables.

8. Give the graph a title.

COORDINATE PLANES 160 GRAPH OR WRITE AN EQUATION (D)

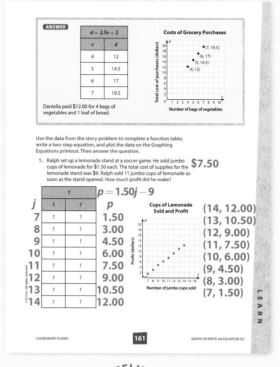

ANSWER

$d = 2.5v + 2$

v	d
4	12
5	14.5
6	17
7	19.5

Daniella paid $12.00 for 4 bags of vegetables and 1 loaf of bread.

Costs of Grocery Purchases

Use the data from the story problem to complete a function table, write a two-step equation, and plot the data on the Graphing Equations printout. Then answer the question.

1. Ralph set up a lemonade stand at a soccer game. He sold jumbo cups of lemonade for $1.50 each. The total cost of supplies for the lemonade stand was $9. Ralph sold 11 jumbo cups of lemonade as soon as the stand opened. How much profit did he make?

$7.50

$p = 1.50j - 9$

j	?	?	p
7	?	?	1.50
8	?	?	3.00
9	?	?	4.50
10	?	?	6.00
11	?	?	7.50
12	?	?	9.00
13	?	?	10.50
14	?	?	12.00

Cups of Lemonade Sold and Profit

(14, 12.00)
(13, 10.50)
(12, 9.00)
(11, 7.50)
(10, 6.00)
(9, 4.50)
(8, 3.00)
(7, 1.50)

COORDINATE PLANES 161 GRAPH OR WRITE AN EQUATION (D)

OFFLINE
10 min

TRY IT Graph Two-Step Equations

Objectives

Students will choose the graph or equation that matches the given story problem that is solved with a two-step equation. View or print the Graph Two-Step Equations activity page and read the directions with students.

Students should copy the problems from the Activity Book into their Math Notebook as necessary and solve them there.

- Graph or write an equation to solve a problem that involves a linear function.

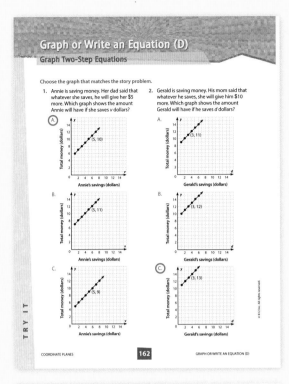

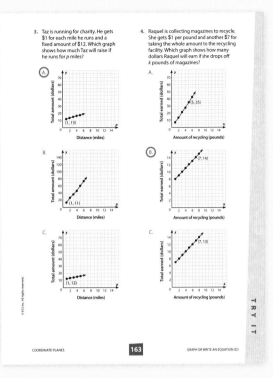

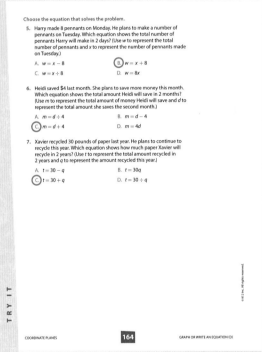

Graph or Write an Equation (D)
Graph Two-Step Equations

Choose the graph that matches the story problem.

1. Annie is saving money. Her dad said that whatever she saves, he will give her $5 more. Which graph shows the amount Annie will have if she saves v dollars?

2. Gerald is saving money. His mom said that whatever he saves, she will give him $10 more. Which graph shows the amount Gerald will have if he saves d dollars?

3. Taz is running for charity. He gets $1 for each mile he runs and a fixed amount of $12. Which graph shows how much Taz will raise if he runs for p miles?

4. Raquel is collecting magazines to recycle. She gets $1 per pound and another $7 for taking the whole amount to the recycling facility. Which graph shows how many dollars Raquel will earn if she drops off k pounds of magazines?

COORDINATE PLANES 162 GRAPH OR WRITE AN EQUATION (D)

COORDINATE PLANES 163 GRAPH OR WRITE AN EQUATION (D)

Choose the equation that solves the problem.

5. Harry made 8 pennants on Monday. He plans to make a number of pennants on Tuesday. Which equation shows the total number of pennants Harry will make in 2 days? (Use w to represent the total number of pennants and x to represent the number of pennants made on Tuesday.)

   A. $w = x - 8$ B. $w = x + 8$

   C. $w = x \div 8$ D. $w = 8x$

6. Heidi saved $4 last month. She plans to save more money this month. Which equation shows the total amount Heidi will save in 2 months? (Use m to represent the total amount of money Heidi will save and d to represent the total amount she saves the second month.)

   A. $m = d \div 4$ B. $m = d - 4$

   C. $m = d + 4$ D. $m = 4d$

7. Xavier recycled 30 pounds of paper last year. He plans to continue to recycle this year. Which equation shows how much paper Xavier will recycle in 2 years? (Use t to represent the total amount recycled in 2 years and q to represent the amount recycled this year.)

   A. $t = 30 - q$ B. $t = 30q$

   C. $t = 30 + q$ D. $t = 30 \div q$

COORDINATE PLANES 164 GRAPH OR WRITE AN EQUATION (D)

ONLINE
10 min

CHECKPOINT

Objectives

Students will complete an online Checkpoint. If necessary, read the directions, problems, and answer choices to students and help them with keyboard or mouse operations.

- Graph or write an equation to solve a problem that involves a linear function.

Core Focus
Numerical Patterns

Lesson Overview

GET READY Plot Straight Lines	15 minutes	ONLINE
LEARN Graph and Compare	25 minutes	OFFLINE
TRY IT Number Patterns	10 minutes	OFFLINE
CHECKPOINT	10 minutes	OFFLINE

▶ Lesson Objectives

- Given a rule such as "Add 3," generate and graph ordered pairs on a coordinate plane.
- Graph to compare the corresponding terms of two patterns.

▶ Prerequisite Skills

Plot a linear relationship in the first quadrant of a coordinate plane.

▶ Advance Preparation

Print three copies of the First-Quadrant Grids.

Materials to Gather

SUPPLIED

Graph and Compare activity page
Number Patterns activity page
First-Quadrant Grids (printout) – 3
Checkpoint (printout)
Checkpoint Answer Key (printout)

GET READY Plot Straight Lines
ONLINE 15min

Students will learn how to use an input-output table to write ordered pairs.

Objectives

- Plot a linear relationship in the first quadrant of a coordinate plane.

LEARN Graph and Compare
OFFLINE 25min

Students will use function tables to generate ordered pairs for rules. Then they will graph both sets of ordered pairs on the same coordinate plane to compare the patterns.

Gather two copies of the First-Quadrant printout. View or print the Graph and Compare activity page. Students should copy the problems into their Math Notebook and create the tables there.

1. Read the Worked Examples Problem with students. To check for understanding, have students recap the directions for the problem in their own words.

2. Read the first step of the Worked Examples Answer with students. Have them explain how the missing input and output values in each table were generated.

Objectives

- Given a rule such as "Add 3," generate and graph ordered pairs on a coordinate plane.
- Graph to compare the corresponding terms of two patterns.

Ask: In the table of "Add 6," the output value for 1 is 7, but in the table of "Add 2," the output value for 1 is 3. Why are the output values different? Each table has a different rule. In the first table, 6 is added to the input value of 1: $1 + 6 = 7$. In the second table, 2 is added to the input value of 1: $1 + 2 = 3$.

Ask: What other numbers could have been used for the missing input values? Any real number could be an input value. **Possible answers:** 2, 2.5, $3\frac{3}{4}$

Say: All real numbers—even fractions and decimal numbers—could be inputs. When you solve the problems, however, choose input values between 0 and 14 so that you'll be able to graph them easily.

3. Read the second step with students and confirm that they understand how to create ordered pairs from the function tables.

   Ask: In the ordered pair (0, 6), which number is the input value? Which number is the output value? The number 0 is the input value, and 6 is the output value.

4. Read the third step with students. Have them identify the ray that matches with each of the function tables. Show students that the points on each ray correspond with the inputs and outputs in the function tables.

5. Read the fourth step with students. Then have them compare the graphs using their own words. Encourage them to add their own observations about what the graphs reveal about the patterns "Add 6" and "Add 2." To help students see that the output values in the graph of "Add 6" are all 4 greater than the output values in the graph of "Add 2," have them lightly draw a vertical line segment between the two points graphed from the same input value.

6. Have students solve Problems 1–3. Students should use the First-Quadrant Grids printouts to create their graphs. Encourage multiple means of comparison of the two patterns, as shown in the fourth step of the Worked Examples Answer. For Problem 3, students will supply all input values. Remind them that the inputs need to be the same in each table.

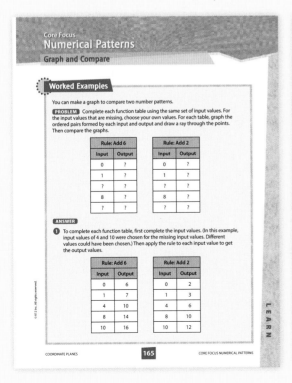

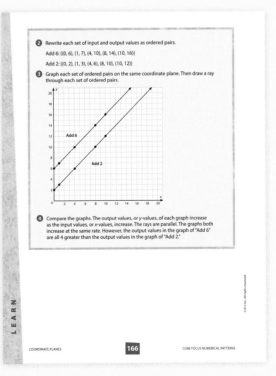

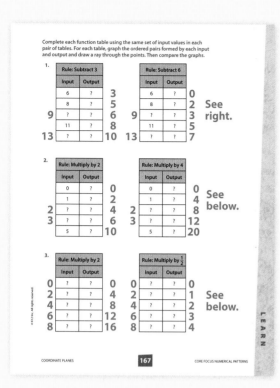

Additional Answers

1. The input and output values in the third and fifth rows will vary. Possible values are shown.

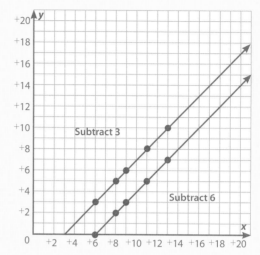

The output values of each graph increase as the input values increase. The rays are parallel. The graphs both increase at the same rate. However, the output values in the graph of "Subtract 3" are all 3 greater than the output values in the graph of "Subtract 6." Put differently, the output values in the graph of "Subtract 6" are all 3 less than the output values in the graph of "Subtract 3."

2. The input and output values in the third and fourth rows will vary. Possible values are shown.

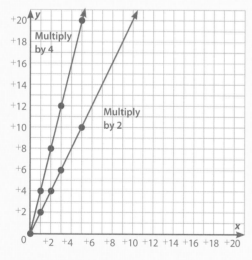

The output values of each graph increase as the input values increase. The graph of "Multiply by 4," however, increases at a much faster rate. The rays are not parallel. Each output value in the graph of "Multiply by 4" is double the corresponding output value in the graph of "Multiply by 2." Put differently, each output value in the graph of "Multiply by 2" is half the corresponding output value in the graph of "Multiply by 4."

3. The input and output values will vary but input values in each table must be the same. Possible values are shown.

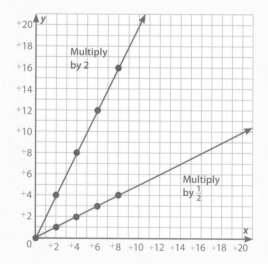

The output values of each graph increase as the input values increase. The graph of "Multiply by 2," however, increases at a much faster rate. The rays are not parallel. Each output value in the graph of "Multiply by 2" is 4 times the corresponding output value in the graph of "Multiply by $\frac{1}{2}$." Put differently, each output value in the graph of "Multiply by $\frac{1}{2}$" is one-fourth the corresponding output value in the graph of "Multiply by 2."

TRY IT Number Patterns

Objectives

Students will practice completing function tables and graphing the results. They will also compare the graphs. Gather the First-Quadrant printout. View or print the Number Patterns activity page. Students should copy the problems into their Math Notebook and solve them there. Students may use the First-Quadrant Grids printout to make their graphs.

- Given a rule such as "Add 3," generate and graph ordered pairs on a coordinate plane.
- Graph to compare the corresponding terms of two patterns.

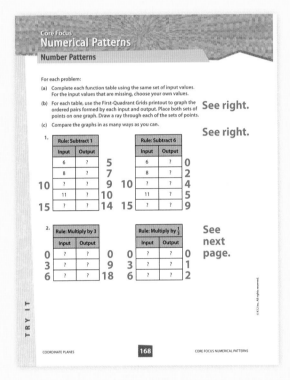

Additional Answers

1. (a) The input and output values in the third and fifth rows will vary. Possible values are shown.

(b)

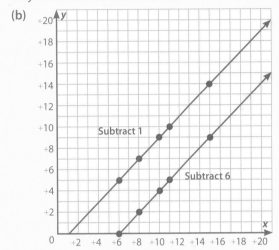

(c) The output values of each graph increase as the input values increase.

The rays are parallel.

The graphs both increase at the same rate.

The output values in the graph of "Subtract 1" are all 5 greater than the output values in the graph of "Subtract 6." Put differently, the output values in the graph of "Subtract 6" are all 5 less than the output values in the graph of "Subtract 1."

Additional Answers

2. (a) The input and output values will vary but input values in each table must be the same and output values must follow the given rule. Possible values are shown.

(b)

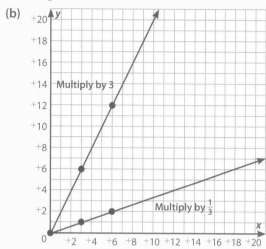

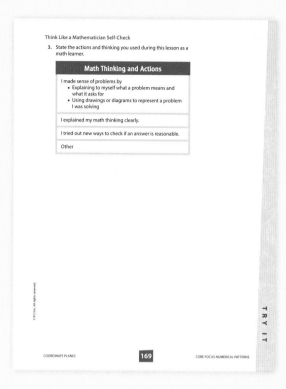

Think Like a Mathematician Self-Check

3. State the actions and thinking you used during this lesson as a math learner.

Math Thinking and Actions
I made sense of problems by • Explaining to myself what a problem means and what it asks for • Using drawings or diagrams to represent a problem I was solving
I explained my math thinking clearly.
I tried out new ways to check if an answer is reasonable.
Other

(c) The output values of each graph increase as the input values increase. The graph of "Multiply by 3" increases at a much faster rate than the graph of "Multiply by $\frac{1}{3}$."

The rays are not parallel.

Each output value in the graph of "Multiply by 3" is 6 times the corresponding output value in the graph of "Multiply by $\frac{1}{3}$." Put differently, each output value in the graph of "Multiply by $\frac{1}{3}$" is one-sixth the corresponding output value in the graph of "Multiply by 3."

OFFLINE

10 min

CHECKPOINT

Objectives

The Checkpoint and its answer key are located in the Resources section for this unit in the Online Book Menu of *Math+ Yellow Lesson Guide*. Give students the Checkpoint. Have students complete the Checkpoint on their own. Use the answer key to score the Checkpoint, and then enter the results online.

- Given a rule such as "Add 3," generate and graph ordered pairs on a coordinate plane.
- Graph to compare the corresponding terms of two patterns.

Unit Review

Lesson Overview

UNIT REVIEW Look Back	10 minutes	**ONLINE**
UNIT REVIEW Checkpoint Practice	50 minutes	**ONLINE**
⏩ **UNIT REVIEW** Prepare for the Checkpoint		

▶ Unit Objectives

- Identify the parts of a coordinate graph, including *x*-axis, *y*-axis, *x*-coordinate, *y*-coordinate, ordered pair, and origin.
- Locate and plot points in Quadrant I of the coordinate plane.
- Solve word problems involving graphs of points on a coordinate plane.
- Use the situation presented in a problem to describe the meaning of each coordinate of an ordered pair displayed on a graph.
- Graph or write an equation to solve a problem that involves a linear function.
- Given a rule such as "Add 3," generate and graph ordered pairs on a coordinate plane.
- Graph to compare the corresponding terms of two patterns.

Materials to Gather

There are no materials to gather for this lesson.

▶ Advance Preparation

In this lesson, students will have an opportunity to review previous activities in the Coordinate Planes unit. Look at the suggested activities in Unit Review: Prepare for the Checkpoint online and gather any needed materials.

UNIT REVIEW Look Back

ONLINE **10**min

Objectives

- Review unit objectives.

Students will review key concepts from the unit to prepare for the Unit Checkpoint.

UNIT REVIEW Checkpoint Practice

ONLINE **50**min

Objectives

- Review unit objectives.

Students will complete an online Checkpoint Practice to prepare for the Unit Checkpoint. If necessary, read the directions, problems, and answer choices to students. Have students answer the problems on their own. Review any missed problems with students.

⏩ UNIT REVIEW Prepare for the Checkpoint

What you do next depends on how students performed in the previous activity, Unit Review: Checkpoint Practice. If students had difficulty with any of the problems, complete the appropriate review activity listed in the table online.

Unit Checkpoint

UNIT CHECKPOINT   60 minutes   ONLINE

▶ Unit Objectives

- Identify the parts of a coordinate graph, including x-axis, y-axis, x-coordinate, y-coordinate, ordered pair, and origin.
- Locate and plot points in Quadrant I of the coordinate plane.
- Solve word problems involving graphs of points on a coordinate plane.
- Use the situation presented in a problem to describe the meaning of each coordinate of an ordered pair displayed on a graph.
- Graph or write an equation to solve a problem that involves a linear function.
- Given a rule such as "Add 3," generate and graph ordered pairs on a coordinate plane.
- Graph to compare the corresponding terms of two patterns.

Materials to Gather

There are no materials to gather for this lesson.

ONLINE
60min

UNIT CHECKPOINT

Objectives

- Assess unit objectives.

Students will complete the Unit Checkpoint online. If necessary, read the directions, problems, and answer choices to students and help them with keyboard or mouse operations.

Extended Problems: Real-World Application

USE WHAT YOU KNOW   60 minutes   OFFLINE

▶ Lesson Objectives

- Use the situation presented in a problem to describe the meaning of each coordinate of an ordered pair displayed on a graph.
- Graph or write an equation to solve a problem that involves a linear function.
- Determine which operations are appropriate to use to solve a multistep story problem.
- Solve multistep story problems using multiple operations.
- Use a variable to represent an unknown number in an equation.
- Interpret a numerical expression without evaluating the expression.
- Apply mathematical knowledge and skills to evaluate and analyze real-world situations.

Materials to Gather

SUPPLIED

Extended Problems: Real-World Application (printout)

OFFLINE
60min

USE WHAT YOU KNOW

Open the Extended Problems: Real-World Application. Read the directions, problems, and answer choices to students, if necessary.

The teacher will grade this assignment.

- Students should save the graded assignment to their computer. In the filename, they should replace "studentname" with their last name followed by their first initial.
- Students should complete the assignment on their own.
- Students should submit the completed assignment according to the teacher's instructions.

Objectives

- Apply mathematical knowledge and skills to evaluate and analyze real-world situations.

Perimeter, Area, and Volume

▶ Unit Objectives

- Determine the perimeter of a plane figure and use appropriate units.
- Construct a cube or a rectangular box from a two-dimensional pattern and determine the surface area.
- Use squares to approximate the area of an irregular shape.
- Estimate or determine the number of cubes required to fill a solid figure.
- Explain and determine the volume of a solid figure and use appropriate units.
- Differentiate among appropriate units to measure perimeter, area, and volume.
- Use the fact that volume is additive to solve problems.

▶ Big Ideas

- The perimeter of any polygon is the sum of the lengths of its sides.
- Area is a measure of how much material is needed to cover a plane figure.
- Volume is a measure of the amount of space a solid figure occupies.
- Measurement is the process of repeatedly using a unit over a quantity to determine how much you have.

▶ Unit Introduction

The focus of this unit is exploring perimeter and area of two-dimensional shapes and surface area and volume of three-dimensional figures. Students first will find perimeter of regular and irregular plane figures. They will use their prior knowledge of finding the area of a square or rectangle as a reference for finding the area of a parallelogram or triangle. They will see how the formulas for finding the areas of parallelograms and triangles are developed, or derived. After exploring area of two-dimensional objects, students will construct a three-dimensional figure using a pattern and find the surface area of that figure. They will extend their understanding of finding the area of regular shapes to use a square to find the approximate area of an irregular two-dimensional shape. Once students have a foundation in area and surface area, they will explain the meaning of the volume of solid figures and compute the volume. To conclude the unit, students will compare and contrast the different units used to measure perimeter, area, and volume to better understand linear, square, and cubic measurements with respect to dimensions.

▶ Keywords

area	height	square unit
attributes	irregular shape	surface area
base of a figure	linear unit	two-dimensional pattern
cubic unit	net	unit
edge	perimeter	volume
formula	right prism	

Find the Perimeter of Plane Figures

▶ Lesson Objectives

Determine the perimeter of a plane figure and use appropriate units.

▶ Prerequisite Skills

- Define and demonstrate understanding of the perimeter of any polygon.
- Use a formula to find the perimeter of a rectangle or a square.

▶ Content Background

Students will find the perimeter of plane figures and use appropriate units of measure.

Perimeter is the distance around a geometric figure or an everyday object. Perimeter is a linear measurement since it measures length, so the units used to measure perimeter have an understood exponent of 1. That is, the units for perimeter measures are written without the exponent. For example, you might see perimeter measured in centimeters (cm), meters (m), kilometers (km), inches (in.), feet (ft), yards (yd), or miles (mi).

▶ Advance Preparation

For the Get Ready: Rectangle and Square Perimeters activity, print one copy of the Rectangle and Square Perimeters printout.

    For the Learn: Rectangles with the Same Perimeter activity,

- Print one copy of the Centimeter Grid Paper.
- Gather string such as yarn, kite string, or lightweight cord. Measure 36 centimeters (see Hints), form a loop with that length, and tie a knot to make a loop of 36 centimeters in circumference.

    Hints: Use string or cord that will stretch very little and that has been kept on a roll or in a ball so it will lie flat on paper. When you measure 36 centimeters, add a few centimeters to allow for the knot. Leave a short length of yarn beyond the loop and the knot. On the Centimeter Grid Paper, form and hold the loop in a 9 cm by 9 cm shape to make sure the loop will measure the perimeter of a 36-centimeter rectangle. Cut the loop from the roll of string.

    For the Learn: Perimeter of Everyday Objects activity, use a ruler and a pencil to draw a 3-inch square on drawing paper and cut it out.

Materials to Gather

SUPPLIED

Rectangle and Square Perimeters (printout)

Centimeter Grid Paper (printout)

Perimeter of Plane Figures activity page

ALSO NEEDED

string

ruler, dual-scale

paper, 8.5 in. by 11 in.

index card, 3 in. by 5 in.

paper, drawing

scissors, adult

► **Safety**

Make sure students do not place the loop of string around their necks.

GET READY Rectangle and Square Perimeters

Students will use the correct formula to find the perimeter of a rectangle and a square.

Gather the Rectangle and Square Perimeters printout.

1. Point to the rectangle at the top of the page. Ask students to describe how to measure the perimeter of a rectangle. Add the measurements of the 4 sides.

2. Have students add the side measurements to find the perimeter. $8 + 5 + 8 + 5 = 26$; The perimeter is 26 cm.

3. Ask students if the measurement is in linear or square units. linear

4. Tell students to use the formula $P = 2l + 2w$ to calculate the perimeter of the rectangle. $P = 2l + 2w$; $P = 2(8) + 2(5)$; $P = 16 + 10$; $P = 26$; The perimeter is 26 cm.

   Have students compare the results of the two methods of finding the perimeter. Guide them to see that both ways led them to find the correct perimeter. Tell them that they may find that using a perimeter formula will be quicker when they need to find the perimeter of a figure with many sides.

5. Repeat Steps 1 and 2 to find the perimeter of the square. $6 + 6 + 6 + 6 = 24$; The perimeter is 24 cm.

6. Repeat Steps 3 and 4 using the formula $P = 4s$ to find the perimeter of the square. $P = 4s$; $P = 4(6)$; $P = 24$; The perimeter is 24 cm.

Objectives

- Define and demonstrate understanding of the perimeter of any polygon.
- Use a formula to find the perimeter of a rectangle or a square.

LEARN Rectangles with the Same Perimeter

Students will use a loop of string to form rectangles with different lengths and widths on grid paper to show that many different rectangles can have the same perimeter.

Gather the Centimeter Grid Paper and the loop of string you made.

1. Tell students that they are going to make different rectangles with perimeters of 36 centimeters and record the rectangles' measurements in a table.

2. Have students make a table in their Math Notebook with 6 rows and 4 columns. The top row is for the column headings. Have them write the column headings as follows: "Shape name," "Length of 1 side," "Width of 1 side," and "Perimeter."

Objectives

- Determine the perimeter of a plane figure and use appropriate units.

Tips

If students have difficulty with the string moving before they find the perimeter of the rectangle, help them use a pencil to trace along the string. They can then remove the string to find the perimeter of the rectangle.

3. Under "Shape name" for each row, have them write "rectangle." Under "Perimeter" for each row, have them write "36 cm."

Rectangles with Perimeter of 36 cm			
Shape name	Length of 1 side	Width of 1 side	Perimeter
rectangle			36 cm
rectangle			36 cm
rectangle			36 cm
rectangle			36 cm
rectangle			36 cm

4. Show students how to lay the loop of string on the grid paper so that it forms a rectangle with a length of 12 centimeters and a width of 6 centimeters. Show them how to use their thumbs to hold the bottom 2 corners in place and their fingers to hold the top 2 corners in place.

5. Have students count the outer edges of the squares (the perimeter) on the grid paper to check that the rectangle has a perimeter of 36 centimeters. You may need to help them count as they hold the string, or you can hold the string while they count the squares. Note that as they count in the corners, they are not counting number of squares but number of outer edges of squares that make up the perimeter. So each square in a corner has 2 edges that are counted.

6. Guide students to complete their table for that row. The row of the table should have this information: rectangle, 12 cm, 6 cm, 36 cm.

7. Tell students that they can find many more rectangles with a perimeter of 36 centimeters. Help them make at least four more rectangles. Remind them to record their findings in their table. They may add more rows to the table if needed.

8. Guide students to include one rectangle that has dimensions of 9 centimeters per side.

9. Have students use the information they recorded in their table to answer the following questions:

    Ask: Describe the dimensions of two of the different rectangles. How were the rectangles alike? How were they different? **Sample answer:** One rectangle had a length of 14 centimeters and a width of 4 centimeters, so the length was greater than the width. The other rectangle had a length of 7 centimeters and a width of 11 centimeters, so the width was greater than the length.

    Ask: If you were to make another rectangle with the same dimensions as one of the rectangles you made, but oriented differently on the paper, would the perimeter still be the same? Why? The way a shape is oriented does not change its dimensions, so the perimeter would still be the same.

    Ask: What special kind of rectangle did you make that had a perimeter of 36 centimeters? What were its dimensions? One rectangle was a square. Each side was 9 centimeters long.

LEARN Perimeter of Plane Figures

- Determine the perimeter of a plane figure and use appropriate units.

Students will use two methods to find perimeter. They will find the perimeter of regular and irregular plane figures. View or print the Perimeter of Plane Figures activity page and read the directions with students.

Students should copy the problems from the Activity Book into their Math Notebook as necessary and solve them there.

Extend the activity by having students write and solve a word problem about measuring and finding the perimeter of an everyday object or in an everyday setting.

1. Tell students that they will find the perimeter of plane figures in these two ways: adding the measures of the sides and using a formula.

2. Tell students that both methods are reasonable ways to find the perimeter of a plane figure. Using the formula may simplify the process, but adding the side lengths might be easier for some figures.

3. Read the Worked Examples box with students.

   Say: The tick marks on the octagon mean that all 8 sides have the same length. When tick marks on a plane figure match each other, then the sides marked by those ticks have the same length.

   Say: Because all sides are the same length, you were able to solve this problem with the formula $P = 8s$.

4. Have students focus on the equations in Solution 1 and Solution 2.

   Ask: What operation was used in Solution 1 and what was the answer? addition; 16

   Ask: What operation was used in Solution 2 and what was the answer? multiplication; 16

5. Have students look at Problem 1 in the problem set.

   Ask: What formula can you use to find the perimeter of the hexagon? Use the variables P and s and tell what the variables mean. The formula for finding the perimeter of a hexagon is $P = 6s$, where the variable s stands for the length of a side of the hexagon. The variable P stands for the perimeter.

6. Have students solve the problem. They should substitute 12 for s in the perimeter formula to find a perimeter of 72 cm. Be sure students write the formulas, steps they used, and answers in their Math Notebook.

7. Repeat Steps 5 and 6 for Problem 2.

8. Tell students that they can write a formula to find the perimeter of any plane figure. Explain that a formula can even be written for irregular shapes like the ones in Problems 3 and 4.

   Say: In Problem 3, the sides of the pentagon are not all the same length. The base has one length. The vertical sides have a different length from the base. The slanted sides have a different length from the base and the vertical sides. The vertical sides are marked with a single tick mark to show that their lengths are the same. The slanted sides are marked with double tick marks to show that their lengths are the same but are a different length from the vertical sides.

9. Guide students to see that a formula can be written to find the perimeter of the pentagon. Have them substitute the measurements into the formula and solve.

10. Have students read Problem 4.

    Ask: How many different lengths do you see for the sides of this shape? five different lengths

    Guide students to use five different variables for the lengths as they write the formula. Have them substitute values for the variables and solve the problem.

11. Have students look at Problem 5 in the problem set.

    Ask: What formula can you use to find the perimeter of the square? Use the variables P and s and tell what the variables mean. The formula for finding the perimeter of a square is $P = 4s$, where the variable s stands for the length of a side of the square. The variable P stands for the perimeter.

12. Have students solve the problem. They should substitute 9.4 for s in the perimeter formula to find a perimeter of 37.6 cm. Be sure students write the formulas, steps they used, and answers in their Math Notebook.

13. Repeat Steps 11 and 12 for Problem 6. Students will find the perimeter of a rectangle using the formula $P = 2a + 2b$.

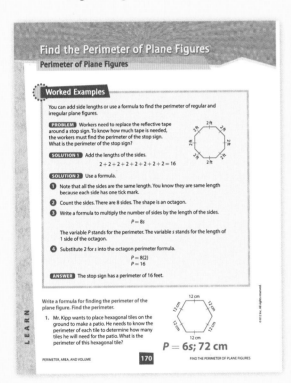

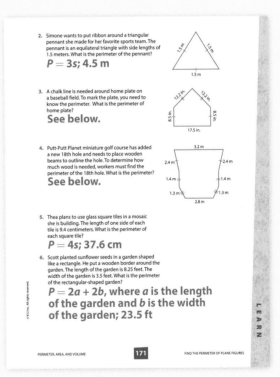

Additional Answers

3. $P = a + 2b + 2c$, where a is the length of the base, b is the length of the vertical sides, and c is the length of the slanted sides; 58.9 in.

4. $P = a + 2b + 2c + 2d + e$, where a is the length of the top of the figure; b, c, and d are the lengths of the pairs of equal sides of the figure; and e is the length of the base of the figure; 16.2 m

LEARN Perimeter of Everyday Objects

- Determine the perimeter of a plane figure and use appropriate units.

Students will measure and find the perimeter of three everyday objects.
  Gather the ruler, index card, sheet of paper, and 3-inch square of paper. Don't tell students the measurements of any of the objects.

1. Tell students that they are going to measure and find the perimeter of an index card, a sheet of paper, and the square you cut out. Explain to students that they will record their findings in a table.

2. Have students make a table in their Math Notebook with 4 rows and 4 columns. The top row is for the column headings. Have them write the column headings as follows: "Object name," "Length of 1 side," "Width of 1 side," and "Perimeter." Under "Object name" for each row, have them write the name of each of the three objects.

Measures and Perimeters of Objects			
Object name	Length of 1 side	Width of 1 side	Perimeter
index card			
sheet of paper			
square			

3. Give students the index card. Have them use the ruler to measure its length and record the measurement in inches on their table. Remind students to include the unit of measure. 5 in.

   Have students measure the width and record the measurement on their table. 3 in.

4. Have students add all 4 side measurements to find the perimeter of the index card. 16 in.

   Ask: What shape is the index card? rectangle

   Ask: What is the formula for finding the perimeter of a rectangle?
   $P = 2l + 2w$

5. Have students find the perimeter of the index card again, this time using the formula. Talk about whether students found the same perimeter each time.

6. Have students place the index card to the side and pick up the square.

7. Have students use the ruler to measure the length and width of the square of paper and record the measurements in inches on their table. Length of 1 side is 3 in.; width of 1 side is 3 in.

   Have students add all 4 side measurements to find the perimeter of the square. 12 in.

   Ask: What is the formula for finding the perimeter of a square? $P = 4s$

8. Have students use the formula to find the perimeter of the square. Discuss whether students found the same perimeter each time.

9. Have students place the square to the side and pick up the full sheet of paper.

10. Have students use the ruler to measure the sheet of paper and record the measurements on their table. Length of 1 side is 11 in.; width of 1 side is 8.5 in.

Have students add the measurements together to find the perimeter of the sheet of paper. 39 in.

11. Tell students to substitute the measurements into the rectangle perimeter formula $P = 2l + 2w$ and solve.

Ask: Why does the formula for finding a rectangle's perimeter work, such as when you used it to find the perimeter of the index card and the sheet of paper? The formula $P = 2l + 2w$ works because the perimeter is the total distance around the rectangle. Since there are 2 sides that are l units long and 2 sides that are w units long, I add the lengths of the sides to find the perimeter of the rectangle.

ONLINE
10min

TRY IT Practice Finding Perimeter

Students will complete an online Try It. If necessary, read the directions, problems, and answer choices to students and help them with keyboard or mouse operations.

Objectives

- Determine the perimeter of a plane figure and use appropriate units.

ONLINE
10min

CHECKPOINT

Students will complete an online Checkpoint. If necessary, read the directions, problems, and answer choices to students and help them with keyboard or mouse operations.

Objectives

- Determine the perimeter of a plane figure and use appropriate units.

Nets, Solids, and Surface Area

▶ Lesson Objectives

Construct a cube or a rectangular box from a two-dimensional pattern and determine the surface area.

▶ Prerequisite Skills

Identify or draw a two-dimensional view of a three-dimensional object.

▶ Content Background

Students will learn how to construct a cube and a rectangular prism from a net and how to find the surface area of a cube and a rectangular prism.

Surface area is the sum of the areas of all the faces, bases, and curved surfaces of a solid figure. Surface area is not the same as volume, which measures the space inside a solid figure. One way to find the surface area of a solid figure is to make a two-dimensional pattern called a net, calculate the area of each surface of the figure, and then find the sum of the areas. For example, to find the surface area of a cube, first find the area of one of the 6 faces, and then multiply that area by 6 because a cube has 6 congruent faces. Surface area is a square-unit measurement because it is a measure of the length times the width of each face of a solid figure. The units that measure surface area have an exponent of 2. For example, the units for the surface area of a solid figure might be square meters (m^2), square inches (in^2), square miles (mi^2), or square centimeters (cm^2).

A *net* is a two-dimensional pattern that folds to make a three-dimensional solid.

These illustrations are a two-dimensional net and the three-dimensional result for a rectangular prism.

Materials to Gather

SUPPLIED

Net for Cube (printout)

Net for Rectangular Prism (printout)

Centimeter Grid Paper (printout)

Solve Surface Area Problems activity page

Find Surface Area activity page

ALSO NEEDED

household objects that are the shape of cubes and rectangular prisms (such as cereal boxes, tissue boxes, books, pads of sticky notes)

scissors, pointed-end safety

tape, clear

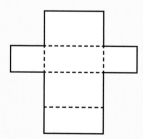

Net for a rectangular prism

The result of folding a net for a rectangular prism

These illustrations are the two-dimensional net and the three-dimensional result for a cube.

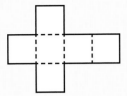

Net for a cube

The result of folding a net for a cube

▶ Common Errors and Misconceptions

- Students might think of all measurements as length. For example, they might perceive area as a distance—something that they can measure with a ruler. Consequently, they often measure the perimeter (the path around the figure).
- Students might believe that it doesn't matter if units are all identical. They may believe that if they can fill a region (such as a box) with units of measure (such as beans), it doesn't matter if some of the units of measure (beans) are of a different size. They will simply count the number of objects contained within the region (box).
- Students might believe that although the units of measure should be identical, it doesn't matter if the units do not completely cover a region.

▶ Advance Preparation

Print two copies each of the Net for Cube printout, Net for Rectangular Prism printout, and Centimeter Grid Paper.

Gather household objects shaped like cubes or rectangular prisms, such as cereal boxes and tissue boxes.

▶ Safety

Make sure students handle the scissors carefully and be sure to store them in a safe place.

| GET READY Views of Solid Objects | OFFLINE 5min | Objectives |

Students will view various household objects shaped like cubes or rectangular prisms from different perspectives to draw the top, bottom, front, and side views. Each view of the three-dimensional object will show a two-dimensional shape.

Gather two copies of the Centimeter Grid Paper and the household objects that are cubes and rectangular prisms.

Objectives

- Identify or draw a two-dimensional view of a three-dimensional object.

1. Have students choose one household object and identify it as the shape of a cube or a rectangular prism. Then have them identify the top, bottom, side, and front views of the object.

2. Tell students to draw and label each view on Centimeter Grid Paper. For example, if the object is a rectangular prism, they might draw a large rectangle for the front view and a small rectangle for the side view.

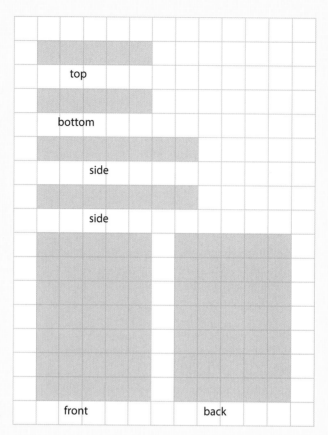

3. Have students use the object to describe what they drew for each view.

4. Repeat Steps 1–3 with the second copy of the grid paper for another household object.

LEARN Nets and Solid Figures

Objectives

Students will make a cube and a rectangular prism from nets.
  Gather the Net for Cube and Net for Rectangular Prism printouts, scissors, and tape.

- Construct a cube or a rectangular box from a two-dimensional pattern and determine the surface area.

1. Place the Net for Cube printout, scissors, and tape in front of students. Tell students the net is a pattern for making a cube.

2. Discuss the Net for Cube printout with students.

    Ask: What is the shape of each two-dimensional figure in the net? square

    Ask: What is the shape of each face of a cube? square

    Ask: How many squares are in the net? 6

    Ask: How many faces does a cube have? 6

3. Give students the Net for Rectangular Prism printout. Tell students the net is a pattern for making a rectangular prism.

4. Discuss the Net for Rectangular Prism printout with students.

Ask: What is the shape of each two-dimensional figure in the net? rectangle

Ask: What is the shape of each face of a rectangular prism? rectangle

Ask: How many rectangles are in the net? 6

Ask: How many faces does a rectangular prism have? 6

Ask: Are all the faces on a rectangular prism congruent? No

5. Have students cut out the net for the cube and the net for the rectangular prism on the solid lines. Then have students fold each net on the fold lines and tape each net together to make a cube and a rectangular prism.

LEARN Nets and Surface Area

OFFLINE
10 min

Students will use nets to find the surface area of a cube and a rectangular prism. Students will calculate surface area in their Math Notebook.

Gather the Net for Cube and Net for Rectangular Prism printouts.

1. Tell students they can use nets to find the surface area of a cube and a rectangular prism. Explain to students that the surface area of a solid figure is the sum of the areas of all the faces, bases, and curved surfaces of a solid figure.

   • To find the surface area of a cube, first find the area of one of the 6 faces, and then multiply that area by 6 because a cube has 6 congruent faces.

   • To find the surface area of a rectangular prism, find the area of each of the 6 faces, and then find the sum of the areas.

2. Place the Net for Cube printout in front of students. Have students find the area of one face of the cube by counting the square units. 16 square units

   Ask: How many square faces does a cube have? 6

   Ask: Are all the faces congruent? Yes

3. Remind students that surface area is a square-unit measurement because it is a measure of the length times the width of each face of a solid figure. The units that measure surface area have an exponent of 2.

   Explain to students that since the 6 faces are congruent, they can multiply the area of one face, 16 square units, by 6, to find the surface area of the entire cube.

   Have students find the surface area of the cube. 96 square units or 96 units^2

4. Now place the Net for Rectangular Prism printout in front of students.

   Ask: How many faces does a rectangular prism have? 6

   Ask: Are all the faces congruent? No

   Lead students to understand that because all the faces are not congruent, they cannot find the area of one face and multiply that area by 6 to find the surface area of a rectangular prism, as they did when they found the surface area of a cube.

5. Have students count square units to find the area of each face of the rectangular prism and add the areas together to find the surface area. $28 + 12 + 21 + 12 + 28 + 21 = 122$; The surface area is 122 units^2.

Objectives

• Construct a cube or a rectangular box from a two-dimensional pattern and determine the surface area.

Tips

Suggest to students that they write the number of square units on each face of the net and mark off each face when they find its area in Step 5. It will prevent them from skipping or duplicating the area of any faces.

6. Guide students to discover a quicker way to find the surface area of the rectangular prism.

   Ask: How many different sizes of faces are there? 3 sizes

   Say: Multiply the area of each size by 2, and then add the products.

7. Tell students they can also use the distributive property to find the surface area of the rectangular prism. Write the following equation in the Math Notebook and discuss how the distributive property is applied:

   2(area of face 1 + area of face 2 + area of face 3) = 2(area of face 1) + 2(area of face 2) + 2(area of face 3) = surface area

   Guide students to fill in the values in the equation to find the surface area as follows:

   2(28 + 21 + 12) = 2(28) + 2(21) + 2(12) = 56 + 42 + 24 = 122

   Have students solve both sides of the equation to show that the surface area is still 122 square units or 122 units^2.

LEARN Solve Surface Area Problems

OFFLINE 10 min

Students will find the surface area of rectangular prisms and cubes to solve problems. Have students turn to the Solve Surface Area Problems activity page in their Activity Book and read the directions with them.

   Students should copy the problems from the Activity Book into their Math Notebook as necessary and solve them there.

1. Read Problem 1 of the Worked Examples with students. Tell students that some rectangular prisms have only 2 different rectangular faces because 4 of the faces are congruent. Faces that are congruent have the same shape and size. Point out on the net the 2 different sizes of rectangular faces.

2. Point out to students that they will use both multiplication and addition in the equation to find surface area. The first equation shows addition of the area of each face. The following equations work through the math until the answer is reached.

3. Read Problem 2 of the Worked Examples with students. Tell them that some rectangular prisms have 3 different rectangular faces. Point out on the net the 3 different sizes of rectangular faces and the 3 pairs of faces that are the same—that is, are congruent.

4. Again point out to students that both multiplication and addition should be used in the equation to find surface area.

   Say: To find surface area, multiply the number of faces by the area of a face. Do the same for each different face. Then add the products.

5. Have students complete Problems 1 and 2 in the problem set.

6. Read Problem 3 of the Worked Examples with students. In this problem, students find the surface area of a cube. They do not use a net to help them write the equation.

   Ask: How many congruent faces does a cube have? 6

Objectives

- Construct a cube or a rectangular box from a two-dimensional pattern and determine the surface area.

Tips

Encourage students to find the surface area of rectangular prisms two ways: add the areas of the 6 faces, and apply the distributive property.

7. Have students complete Problems 3 and 4 in the problem set. Have them refer to the Worked Example as needed.

8. Have students complete Problems 5 and 6 in which they solve story problems about surface area. When they write the equations, have them refer to the Worked Examples boxes for help as needed.

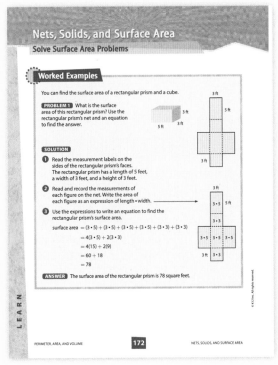

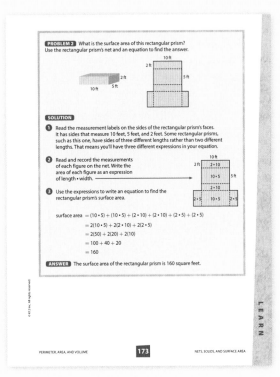

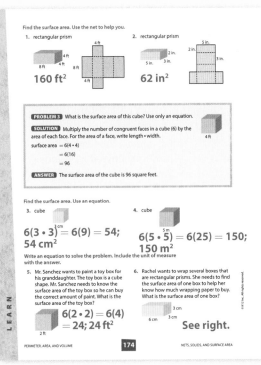

Additional Answers

6. $4(6 \cdot 3) + 2(3 \cdot 3) = 4(18) + 2(9) = 90; 90 \text{ cm}^2$

TRY IT Find Surface Area

Objectives

Students will practice finding the surface area of cubes and rectangular prisms. View or print the Find Surface Area activity page and read the directions with students.

Students should copy the problems from the Activity Book into their Math Notebook as necessary and solve them there.

- Construct a cube or a rectangular box from a two-dimensional pattern and determine the surface area.

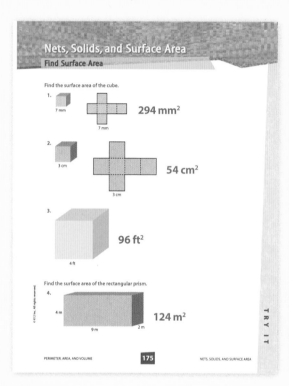

Nets, Solids, and Surface Area
Find Surface Area

Find the surface area of the cube.

1. 7 mm   **294 mm²**

2. 3 cm   **54 cm²**

3. 4 ft   **96 ft²**

Find the surface area of the rectangular prism.

4. 4 m 9 m 2 m   **124 m²**

PERIMETER, AREA, AND VOLUME   175   NETS, SOLIDS, AND SURFACE AREA

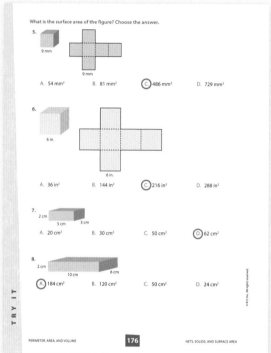

What is the surface area of the figure? Choose the answer.

5. 9 mm 9 mm
   A. 54 mm²   B. 81 mm²   Ⓒ 486 mm²   D. 729 mm²

6. 6 in. 6 in.
   A. 36 in²   B. 144 in²   Ⓒ 216 in²   D. 288 in²

7. 2 cm 5 cm 3 cm
   A. 20 cm²   B. 30 cm²   C. 50 cm²   Ⓓ 62 cm²

8. 2 cm 10 cm 6 cm
   Ⓐ 184 cm²   B. 120 cm²   C. 50 cm²   D. 24 cm²

PERIMETER, AREA, AND VOLUME   176   NETS, SOLIDS, AND SURFACE AREA

CHECKPOINT

Objectives

Students will complete an online Checkpoint. If necessary, read the directions, problems, and answer choices to students and help them with keyboard or mouse operations.

- Construct a cube or a rectangular box from a two-dimensional pattern and determine the surface area.

Area of Irregular Shapes

Lesson Overview

GET READY Area of Rectangles	10 minutes	**OFFLINE**
LEARN Whole Squares and Partial Squares	10 minutes	**ONLINE**
LEARN Solve Area Problems	20 minutes	**OFFLINE**
TRY IT Area and Irregular Shapes	15 minutes	**OFFLINE**
CHECKPOINT	5 minutes	**ONLINE**

▶ Lesson Objectives

Use squares to approximate the area of an irregular shape.

▶ Prerequisite Skills

- Define and demonstrate understanding of the area of any plane figure.
- Find the area of a rectangular shape and use the appropriate unit.

▶ Content Background

Students will learn to approximate the area of irregular shapes in square units.

Area is the measure of the region inside a two-dimensional figure or the surface of a three-dimensional figure. Since it measures length and width, area is a square measurement. Area is measured by finding the number of square units within a region. The units used to measure area have an exponent of 2. For example, you might see area measured in square meters (m^2), square inches (in^2), square miles (mi^2), or square centimeters (cm^2).

▶ Common Errors and Misconceptions

- Students might think of all measurements as length. For example, they might perceive area as a distance—something that they can measure with a ruler. Consequently, they often measure the perimeter (the path around the figure).
- Students might believe that it doesn't matter if units are all identical. They may believe that if they can fill a region (such as a box) with units of measure (such as beans), it doesn't matter if some of the units of measure (beans) are of a different size. They will simply count the number of objects contained within the region (box).
- Students might believe that although the units of measure should be identical, it doesn't matter if they do not completely cover a region.

▶ Advance Preparation

Print one copy of the Centimeter Grid Paper.

Materials to Gather

SUPPLIED

Centimeter Grid Paper (printout)

Solve Area Problems activity page

Area and Irregular Shapes activity page

GET READY Area of Rectangles

Students will draw rectangles, label the dimensions, and use the area formula to find the area of each rectangle.

Gather the Centimeter Grid Paper.

1. Remind students that a formula is a standard equation used to compute values, such as area, perimeter, or volume.

   Say: Write the formula for finding the area of a rectangle, $A = bh$, at the top of the grid paper.

   Say: Explain what the variables in the formula mean. *A stands for area, which is equal to the measure of the base (b) times the measure of the height (h).*

2. Have students use a scale of 1 foot per square centimeter to draw a rectangle on the grid paper with a base of 12 and height of 8. Have them label the base "12 ft" and the height "8 ft."

3. Have students use the formula to find the area of the rectangle.

   $A = bh$

   $A = 12 \cdot 8$

   $A = 96$

   The area of the rectangle is 96 square feet.

   Ask: Why is the area measured in square feet, rather than in linear feet that aren't squared? *Since area measures length and width, area is a square measurement.*

4. Have students check their calculation by counting the centimeter squares inside the rectangle. Remind students that each square on the grid paper has a scale of 1 foot per centimeter.

5. Repeat Steps 2–4 for a rectangle that has a base of 6 meters and a height of 14 meters using a scale of 1 meter per centimeter.

   $A = bh$

   $A = 6 \cdot 14$

   $A = 84$

   The area of the rectangle is 84 square meters.

LEARN Whole Squares and Partial Squares

Students will count whole squares and partial squares on a grid to find the approximate area of an irregular shape.

Objectives

- Define and demonstrate understanding of the area of any plane figure.
- Find the area of a rectangular shape and use the appropriate unit.

Objectives

- Use squares to approximate the area of an irregular shape.

LEARN Solve Area Problems

Students will solve story problems by estimating the area of irregular shapes. View or print the Solve Area Problems activity page and read the directions with students.

Students should copy the problems from the Activity Book into their Math Notebook as necessary and solve them there.

1. Read the Worked Examples box with students. Help them count the 5 whole squares and the 11 partial squares on the grid.

2. Help them estimate as they mentally combine the partial squares to form about 4 whole squares.

3. Remind students that area is a square measure, so they need to write their answers to area problems with square-unit measures, such as square miles.

4. Tell students that answers to questions about the area of irregular shapes can vary. The estimated area can range from the number of whole squares without any partial squares counted to the number of all squares covered and partially covered by the irregular shape. In this activity, the acceptable answers include those ranges.

5. Help students systematically record their work to help eliminate simple tracking or counting errors. One method is to have students draw a grid and mark "P" for a partial square and "W" for a whole square as they look at the irregular shape they are measuring. Then they can count the whole squares, estimate the area of partial squares, and add them together.

6. Have students complete Problem 1 in the problem set. They should discover that there are no whole squares covered by the shape of the rug. They will mentally combine the partial squares to reach their answer.

7. Have students complete Problem 2 in the problem set.

8. When students reach Problem 3, have them pay close attention to the fact that each square on the grid represents more than 1 square unit. Each square represents 4 square feet. Tell them they will need to multiply to find the approximate area.

   Ask: This problem uses squares that equal 4 square feet each. After you count the squares in the area, what will you do to get the estimate?
   Multiply the number of estimated squares by 4.

   Have students complete Problem 3.

9. Make sure students see that Problem 4 uses squares that represent 10,000 square miles.

   Ask: After you count the squares in the area, what will you do to get the estimate? Multiply the number of estimated squares by 10,000.

10. After students solve Problem 4, challenge them to use a different way to estimate the area of Nevada.

    - Have students divide the Nevada shape into a rectangle and a triangle, use formulas to estimate the area of each shape, and then add the areas.
      The formula for finding the area of a rectangle is $A = bh$.

      The formula for finding the area of a triangle is $A = \frac{bh}{2}$.

    - Remind students that each square on the grid represents 10,000 square miles.

    - Have students compare their answer to the answer they got when they used the whole and partial squares method. See the following illustration and solution equations.

Objectives

- Use squares to approximate the area of an irregular shape.

Tips

The formula for the area of a rectangle is $A = bh$. The formula for the area of a triangle is $A = \frac{bh}{2}$. Extend the activity by investigating the actual area of the state of Nevada.

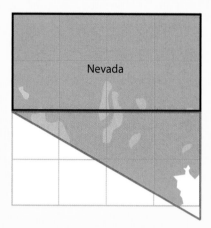

Nevada

Find the area of the rectangle.

$A = bh$

$A = 4 \cdot 2$

$A = 8$

Find the area of the triangle.

$A = \dfrac{bh}{2}$

$A = \dfrac{4 \cdot 2}{2}$

$A = 4$

$10,000(8 + 4) = 10,000(12) = 120,000$

The approximate area of the shape, calculated by adding the area of the rectangle and the triangle, is 120,000 mi².

11. Discuss that the answer reached by using formulas and the answer reached by counting squares are both estimates of the exact area.

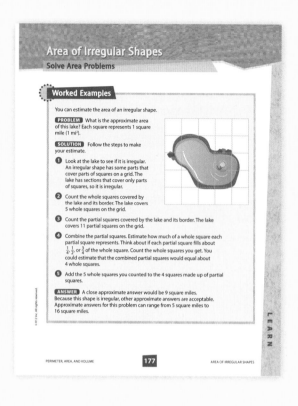

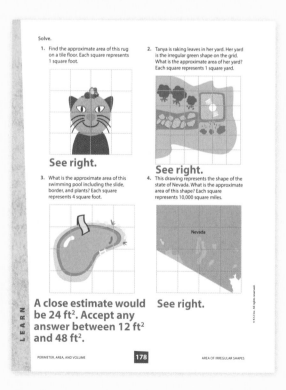

Additional Answers

1. A close estimate would be 6 ft². Accept any answer between 6 ft² and 10 ft².

2. A close estimate would be 26 yd². Accept any answer between 18 yd² and 36 yd².

4. A close estimate would be 120,000 mi². Accept any answer between 100,000 mi² and 140,000 mi².

TRY IT Area and Irregular Shapes

Students will practice finding the approximate area of irregular shapes. View or print the Area and Irregular Shapes activity page and read the directions with students.

Students should copy the problems from the Activity Book into their Math Notebook as necessary and solve them there.

Objectives

- Use squares to approximate the area of an irregular shape.

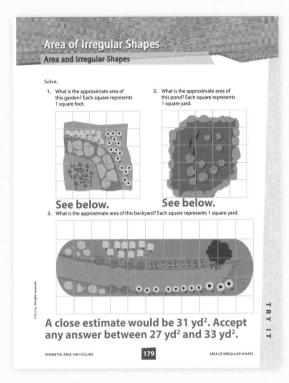

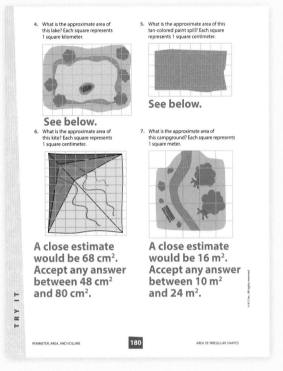

Additional Answers

1. A close estimate would be 17 ft². Accept any answer between 9 ft² and 25 ft².

4. A close estimate would be 27 km² for the blue areas representing the lake. Accept any answer between 23 km² and 35 km².

2. A close estimate would be 18 yd². Accept any answer between 11 yd² and 25 yd².

5. A close estimate would be 26 cm². Accept any answer between 18 cm² and 40 cm².

CHECKPOINT

Students will complete an online Checkpoint. If necessary, read the directions, problems, and answer choices to students and help them with keyboard or mouse operations.

Objectives

- Use squares to approximate the area of an irregular shape.

How Many Cubes Does It Take?

Lesson Overview		
LEARN Use Blocks to Model Volume	20 minutes	OFFLINE
LEARN Strategies to Find Volume	15 minutes	ONLINE
TRY IT Measure Volume	15 minutes	OFFLINE
CHECKPOINT	10 minutes	ONLINE

▶ Lesson Objectives

Estimate or determine the number of cubes required to fill a solid figure.

▶ Content Background

Students will learn about the volume of rectangular solids by finding how many cubes are needed to fill a solid figure.

Volume is measured in cubic units (cubic centimeters, cubic inches, or just cubic units when the cubes are not a standard measure). Students will not use a rule or formula to find the volume of objects, but will be encouraged to count cubes or find their own strategy to determine volume.

Students may recognize that when finding the volume of rectangular solids, they can find the number of cubes on the bottom layer and then repeatedly add that amount for each layer. They will learn that they can use multiplication instead of repeated addition.

Students will explore solids in which not every cube is visible and will use their knowledge of three-dimensional shapes to figure out how many cubes will fill the solid. They will label volume with cubic centimeters or cubic units. Students will also learn to write the standard notation of cubic units as u^3. At this level, students will not be taught why this notation is used but will understand it as a shortcut to writing cubic units.

▶ Common Errors and Misconceptions

- Students might think of all measurements as length. For example, they might perceive area as a distance—something that they can measure with a ruler. Consequently, they often measure the perimeter (the path around the figure).

- Students might believe that it doesn't matter if units are all identical. They may believe that if they can fill a region (such as a box) with units of measure (such as beans), it doesn't matter if some of the units of measure (beans) are of a different size. They will simply count the number of objects contained within the region (box).

Materials to Gather

SUPPLIED

Measure Volume activity page

ALSO NEEDED

household items – small cubes, such as sugar cubes or bouillon cubes

tape, clear – $\frac{3}{4}$ in. wide

▶ Advance Preparation

Use small cubes and tape to make three 3-by-3 arrangements of cubes that stay together. Place a piece of tape down with the sticky side up and place a cube in the center of the tape. Make sure that the tape is wide enough to place cubes on either side of the first cube so that all three will stick to the tape even though they're each held by just a small amount of tape. Lay down a new piece of tape right next to the first one and make another line of three cubes. Repeat this step so that you have a 3-by-3 arrangement of cubes. Trim any tape that extends beyond the edge of the cubes. Make two more sets and then stack the three sets into a 3-by-3-by-3 cube.

 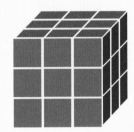

LEARN Use Blocks to Model Volume

OFFLINE
20 min

Objectives

- Estimate or determine the number of cubes required to fill a solid figure.

Students will learn how to find the volume of an object by finding how many cubes it takes to fill an object. They will model volume with base-10 blocks.
Gather the small cubes and the 3-by-3-by-3 cube you made.

1. Tell students they have learned that perimeter, or the distance around the outside of an object, is measured in centimeters (cm), inches (in.), or other units of length (u). They have also learned that the area of a rectangular shape is measured in square units (u²).

2. Tell students they will explore how many cubes it takes to fill rectangular prisms. Show students the 3-by-3-by-3 cube that you made. Have students estimate how many small cubes make up the larger cube. Try to get students to estimate without calculating. If they hesitate, ask if they think the number is greater than 10 or greater than 20.

3. Have students separate the three layers and count each layer to figure out how many small cubes make up the larger cube. Since each layer has 9 cubes, there are 27, or 3 × 9, cubes in the three layers.

4. Have students put the layers back together to make the larger cube.

5. Explain to students that they have measured the volume of water by using cups and gallons, and milliliters and liters. When they measure the volume of solid figures, they measure the volume in cubic units. Show students a small cube and explain that it has a volume of 1 cubic unit. Show students the 3-by-3-by-3 cube and explain that it has a volume of 27 cubic units because it takes 27 one-unit cubes to fill the larger cube. Model how to write the volume in three ways: 27 cubic units; 27 cubic u; 27 u³. Explain to students that they use a small 3 to indicate cubic units.

6. Take one layer off the cube.

   Ask: How many cubes make up this shape? 18

   Explain that the volume of the shape is 18 cubic units. Have students say the volume to be sure they are expressing the units correctly.

7. Put the three layers side by side into one long, flat prism that is 3 by 9 by 1.

    Ask: What is the volume of this prism? 27 u³

    Have students make a tower with the three layers that is 3 by 3 by 3.

    Ask: What is the volume of this tower? 27 u³

8. Explain to students that units can be any size, as long as they identify what units they are using. For example, they can make shapes with small blocks that are cubes, sugar cubes, or bouillon cubes. Since cubes are not a standard measure, they will call it 1 cubic unit, or 1 unit³, or simply 1 u³.

LEARN Strategies to Find Volume

ONLINE
15 min

Objectives

Students will use different strategies to estimate and determine the number of cubes needed to fill a rectangular solid.

- Estimate or determine the number of cubes required to fill a solid figure.

DIRECTIONS FOR USING THE VOLUME LAB LEARNING TOOL

1. Select Explore.

    Say: Look at the single cube. This is 1 cubic centimeter. Abbreviate it by writing cm³. (Point to the 1 cm³.) You have seen that volume is the number of cubes that fill a space. You will use this tool to make rectangular prisms and see the volume. The volume of this cube is 1 cubic centimeter.

2. Use the sliders to make a prism that has length 4, width 5, and height 1.

    Ask: How many cubes make up this prism? 20

    Ask: What multiplication problem is shown by this shape? 4 × 5 or 5 × 4

    Ask: If you added a second layer, how many cubes would there be? 40

    Have the students move the slider for height to 2.

    Ask: If you keep adding layers, how many more cubes will you add with each layer? 20

    Have students change the height to 3, then 4, and then 5. Have them count by 20s with each layer to state the volume. Continue to 10, where the volume will be 200.

    Have students check Expand to see all the layers.

    Uncheck Expand to have the layers go back to a solid prism.

3. Have students make prisms of their choice and explain how to find the volume. Encourage them to look for shortcuts. For example, if a prism has dimensions of 3, 4, and 5, students could look at the top layer and say the each layer has 12 cubes and there are five layers, so the volume is 5 × 12 = 60 cubic centimeters. But they might also notice that the front layer has 20 cubes and there are three layers going toward the back, so the volume is 3 × 20 = 60 cubic centimeters. Either way you get the same answer, but the calculation is easier the second way.

4. When students confidently understand volume, select Menu and choose Find the Volume to try some challenge problems.

TRY IT Measure Volume

Students will practice finding the volume of objects. View or print the Measure Volume activity page and read the directions with students.

Students should copy the problems from the Activity Book into their Math Notebook as necessary and solve them there.

- Estimate or determine the number of cubes required to fill a solid figure.

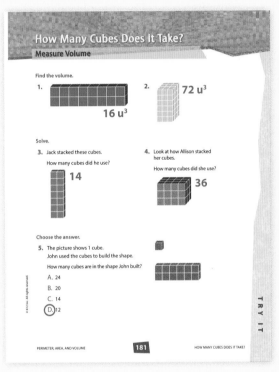

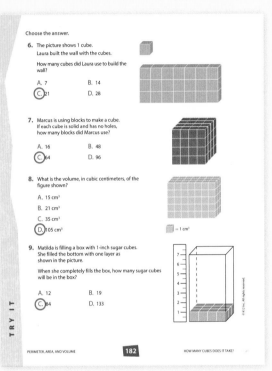

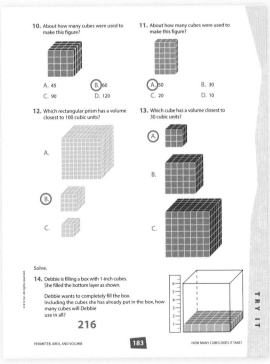

Objectives

- Estimate or determine the number of cubes required to fill a solid figure.

Students will complete an online Checkpoint. If necessary, read the directions, questions, and answer choices to students and help them with keyboard or mouse operations.

Volume of Solid Figures (A)

GET READY Estimate Cubes in a Solid Figure	10 minutes	OFFLINE
LEARN Build in Three Dimensions for Volume	15 minutes	OFFLINE
LEARN Different Shapes with the Same Volume	15 minutes	ONLINE
LEARN Choose Reasonable Units for Volume	10 minutes	ONLINE
TRY IT Practice Volume of Solid Figures	10 minutes	OFFLINE

▶ Lesson Objectives

Explain and determine the volume of a solid figure and use appropriate units.

▶ Prerequisite Skills

Estimate or determine the number of cubes required to fill a solid figure.

▶ Content Background

Students will learn how to find the volume of three-dimensional objects by counting cubes that fit inside an object. They will explore that the same volume measurement can represent different shapes and sizes. They will also learn how to decide which unit of measurement is reasonable to measure the volume of an object.

Volume is the measure of the number of cubic units that a space occupies. Volume is a cubic-unit measurement (since it measures the three dimensions of length, width, and height), so the units used to measure volume have an exponent of 3. For example, you might see volume measured in cubic meters (m^3), cubic inches (in^3), cubic miles (mi^3), or cubic centimeters (cm^3).

▶ Common Errors and Misconceptions

Students might think that volume is a two-dimensional concept since they have worked with representations of three-dimensional figures on a two-dimensional textbook page.

▶ Advance Preparation

Gather two rectangular boxes of different sizes and some small cubes, such as sugar cubes or toy blocks. Gather enough cubes to fill the boxes. Try filling each box with the cubes, and then remove the cubes so students don't see how many cubes the boxes will hold. Students will measure the boxes separately by putting cubes into them. They will use small cubes in two activities in this lesson.

Materials to Gather

SUPPLIED

Practice Volume of Solid Figures activity page

ALSO NEEDED

household objects – 27 small cubes of the same size (such as sugar cubes or toy blocks); 2 small rectangular boxes of different sizes (such as a gelatin box, rice box, cereal box, or reusable plastic container)

ruler, dual-scale

GET READY Estimate Cubes in a Solid Figure

Objectives

- Estimate or determine the number of cubes required to fill a solid figure.

Students will estimate how many cubes fill different small boxes. Then they will find out if their estimate was close to the exact answer. They will write measurements of volume in cubic units (units³).

Gather the small cubes, ruler, and two small rectangular boxes of different sizes.

1. Tell students that they are going to estimate the number of cubes that will fit in each box. Have them write a description of one of the small boxes in their Math Notebook and predict the number of cubes that will fill it. Have them use units³ as the unit of measurement for each cube and for the volume of cubes that fill the box. An example would be "gelatin box, estimated volume: 12 units³."

2. Tell students to use the cubes to fill the box. Explain that they may not get an exact "tight fit" of their cubes in the box, but they should come as close as they can. Have them count the number of cubes they put in the box.

3. Have students compare their prediction to the actual number of cubes they were able to put in the box. They should write the actual number of cubes in units cubed in their notebook under their prediction. An example would be "gelatin box, actual number of cubes: 15 units³."

4. Have students discuss whether their estimate was close to the actual number of cubes they used to fill the box. Point out that the true volume of the box is the number of cubes that will fit in the box exactly, with no gaps. Sometimes that means that the number of cubic units will be fractional.

5. Have students determine whether there were any gaps or additional spaces not filled when they placed the cubes in the box. If so, the number of cubes they used is not the actual volume, and the actual volume may be fractional.

6. Repeat Steps 1–5 with the box that is a different size.

LEARN Build in Three Dimensions for Volume

Objectives

- Explain and determine the volume of a solid figure and use appropriate units.

Students will learn about the volume of a rectangular prism by counting units as they build prisms. They will also multiply measurements.

Gather 27 small cubes.

1. Ask students what the dimensions of one cube are. 1 unit by 1 unit by 1 unit

   - Have students make a layer of cubes that is 2 by 3.
   - Make sure their layer looks like the diagram to the right. It is 2 cubes across (or long), 3 cubes wide (or down), and 1 cube high. Another way to think of it is 2 units by 3 units by 1 unit.
   - Explain to students that this first layer has a volume of 6 cubic units because the layer is 2 units long, 3 units wide, and 1 unit high.
   - Have students count the cubes in the layer to confirm that 6 cubic units is the volume.
   - Tell them they can count cubes to calculate the volume, or the measure of the number of cubic units a space occupies.
   - Tell students that the length of the first layer is 2 units and the width is 3 units.

Tips

Note that dimensions of solids, such as 2 by 3 by 5, are sometimes written as $2 \times 3 \times 5$.

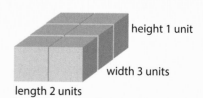

height 1 unit

width 3 units

length 2 units

- Remind students that the area of a rectangle is $A = lw$. The area of this rectangle is $2 \cdot 3 = 6$.
- Explain to students that because this is the first layer, 6 cubic units is the volume and 6 square units is the area. Point out that the units of measure for the volume are cubic units and the units of measure for the area are square units.

2. Have students add another 2-by-3 layer on top of the first layer.

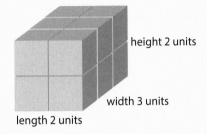

height 2 units

width 3 units

length 2 units

   - Tell students that adding this layer doubles the volume of the solid figure.
   - Explain to students that they can count the cubes in the second layer just like they counted the cubes in the first layer.
   - Have students count the second layer's cubes.
   - Ask students what the volume of the second layer is. 6 units³

   Ask: If you know that the volume of the second layer is 6 cubic units and you know that the volume of the first layer was also 6 cubic units, then what is the volume of the two layers together? 2 units long times 3 units wide times 2 layers, which is $(2 \cdot 3) \cdot 2 = 12$. (2 · 3 is in parentheses to indicate the volume of the first layer.) The volume of the two layers of the solid is 12 units³.

3. Have students add another 2-by-3 layer on top of the second layer.

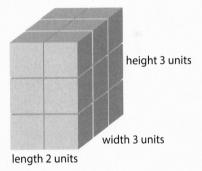

height 3 units

width 3 units

length 2 units

   - Explain to students that they can count the cubes in the third layer just like they counted the cubes in the first and second layers.
   - Have them count the third layer's cubes.
   - Ask students what the volume of the third layer is. 6 units³

   Ask: If you know that the volume of the third layer is 6 cubic units, the volume of the second layer is 6 cubic units, and the volume of the first layer was also 6 cubic units, then what is the volume of all three layers together? 2 units long times 3 units wide times 3 layers, which is $(2 \cdot 3) \cdot 3 = 18$. (2 · 3 is in parentheses to indicate the volume of the first layer.) The volume of the three layers of the rectangular solid is 18 units³.

4. Tell students they will now use the cubes to build another three-dimensional rectangular prism. This time, they will build a special case of the rectangular prism, a cube.

   Ask: If you are building a special-case rectangular prism, a cube, what do you know about the number of cubes in the first layer? There must be the same number of cubes in the length and the width.

5. Tell students they are going to build a special-case rectangular prism, a cube, that is 3 cubes long and 3 cubes wide.

   Ask: If you are building a cube with a bottom layer that is 3 cubes long and 3 cubes wide, what do you know about the number of layers that will be in the cube? There will be 3 layers, because a cube has the same dimension for the height—in this case, 3 cubes—as for the length and width.

6. Have students make a layer of cubes that is 3 by 3.

   - Ask students to count the cubes in the layer to find the volume. 9 units³
   - Tell students that the length of the first layer is 3, the width is 3, and the height is 1.
   - Remind students that the area of a square is $A = lw$. The area of this square is $3 \cdot 3 = 9$.
   - Explain to students that because this is the first layer, 9 cubic units is the volume and 9 square units is the area. Remind students that the units of measure for the volume are cubic units and the units of measure for the area are square units.

7. Have students add another 3-by-3 layer on top of the cubes in the first layer.

- Tell them that they've doubled the volume of the solid figure.
- Ask students to count the cubes in the second layer just like they counted the cubes in the first layer.
- Ask students what the volume of the second layer is. 9 units³

Ask: If you know that the volume of the second layer is 9 cubic units and the volume of the first layer was also 9 cubic units, then what is the volume of the two layers together? 3 units long times 3 units wide times 2 layers, which is (3 • 3) • 2 = 18. (3 • 3 is in parentheses to indicate the volume of the first layer.) The volume of the two layers is 18 units³.

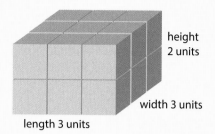

height
2 units

width 3 units

length 3 units

8. Have students add another 3-by-3 layer on top of the second layer.

- Explain to students that they can count the cubes in the third layer just like they counted the cubes in the first and second layers.
- Have them count the cubes in the third layer.
- Ask students what the volume of the third layer is. 9 units³

Ask: If you know that the volume of the third layer is 9 cubic units, the volume of the second layer is 9 cubic units, and the volume of the first layer was also 9 cubic units, then what is the volume of all three layers together? 3 units long times 3 units wide times 3 layers, which is (3 • 3) • 3 = 27. (3 • 3 is in parentheses to indicate the volume of the first layer.) The volume of the three layers that form the cube is 27 units³.

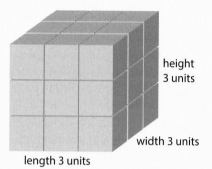

height
3 units

width 3 units

length 3 units

9. Ask: Why would the process you just used work for finding the volume of any rectangular prism, including a cube? A rectangular prism is built with layers that all have the same length and width, so I can repeat the process of finding the volume of each layer and adding the layers' volumes to find the total volume for the prism.

Tips | If students have difficulty understanding how to find volume this way, have them repeat the activity, making rectangular prisms that have layers with different lengths and widths.

LEARN Different Shapes with the Same Volume

 ONLINE 15min

Objectives

- Explain and determine the volume of a solid figure and use appropriate units.

Students will explore different rectangular prisms that have the same volume. Then they will use the Volume Lab Learning Tool to make different rectangular prisms with the same volume.

DIRECTIONS FOR USING THE VOLUME LAB LEARNING TOOL

1. Select Explore.

Say: Not all rectangular prisms have two or more layers. Move the sliders to make a rectangular prism that has one layer, is 10 centimeters long, and has a volume of 30 cubic centimeters. The number of layers of a rectangular prism is the same thing as the measurement of height.

Ask: What is the width of the rectangular prism? 3 cm

Ask: How many cubes are in the rectangular prism? 30

2. Have students move the sliders to make a rectangular prism with the same number of cubes but with multiple layers. Their rectangular prism should be 2 by 3 by 5 (or any combination of those numbers). Tell students to keep reading the changing volume on the learning tool to help them. The volume should be 30 cubic centimeters when they've finished building their rectangular prism.

3. Tell students they'll now make rectangular prisms with another volume. Have them make a rectangular prism with 1 layer and a volume of 8 cubic centimeters. The rectangular prism may be 1 by 8 by 1 (or any combination of those numbers) or 2 by 4 by 1 (or any combination of those numbers).

4. Have students move sliders to make another rectangular prism with a volume of 8 cubic centimeters but with two layers. Students should make a $2 \times 2 \times 2$ rectangular prism.

   Ask: Can a rectangular prism with a volume of 8 cubic centimeters be a cube and why? Yes, if a rectangular prism has equal length, width, and height, it is a cube. A rectangular prism with a length, width, and height of 2 cm has a volume of 8 cm³ and is a cube.

5. Tell students they'll now make rectangular prisms with another volume. Have them make two different rectangular prisms with a volume of 24 cubic centimeters. Possible dimensions (or combinations within these dimensions) for their two solids include the following:

   - 1 by 24 by 1
   - 2 by 12 by 1
   - 3 by 8 by 1
   - 4 by 6 by 1
   - 2 by 3 by 4
   - 2 by 6 by 2

LEARN Choose Reasonable Units for Volume

ONLINE 10min

Students will choose reasonable units for measuring the volume of various everyday objects shaped like rectangular prisms. Before starting the activity,

Say: You can use cubes to build rectangular prisms and find the volume of three-dimensional common objects. Those cubes are often described as having a volume of 1 cubic unit.

Ask: What are some common units of measurement that might be used to measure volume? Answers will vary but may include cubic meters, cubic centimeters, cubic inches, cubic feet, and cubic yards.

Objectives

- Explain and determine the volume of a solid figure and use appropriate units.

TRY IT Practice Volume of Solid Figures

OFFLINE 10min

Students will count the cubes in each layer to find the volume of rectangular prisms. View or print the Practice Volume of Solid Figures activity page and read the directions with students.

Students should copy the problems from the Activity Book into their Math Notebook as necessary and solve them there.

Objectives

- Explain and determine the volume of a solid figure and use appropriate units.

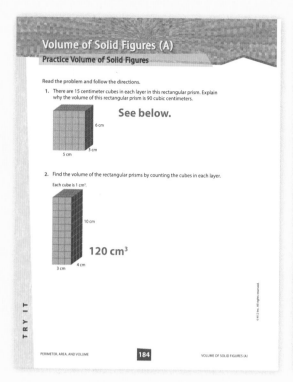

Volume of Solid Figures (A)

Practice Volume of Solid Figures

Read the problem and follow the directions.

1. There are 15 centimeter cubes in each layer in this rectangular prism. Explain why the volume of this rectangular prism is 90 cubic centimeters.

See below.

6 cm

5 cm   3 cm

2. Find the volume of the rectangular prisms by counting the cubes in each layer.

Each cube is 1 cm³.

10 cm

120 cm³

3 cm   4 cm

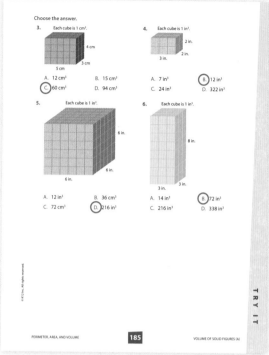

Choose the answer.

3. Each cube is 1 cm³.

4 cm

5 cm   3 cm

A. 12 cm³   B. 15 cm³
C. 60 cm³   D. 94 cm³

4. Each cube is 1 in³.

2 in.
2 in.
3 in.

A. 7 in³   B. 12 in³
C. 24 in³   D. 322 in³

5. Each cube is 1 in³.

6 in.

6 in.

6 in.

A. 12 in³   B. 36 cm³
C. 72 cm³   D. 216 in³

6. Each cube is 1 in³.

8 in.

3 in.   3 in.

A. 14 in³   B. 72 in³
C. 216 in³   D. 338 in³

Additional Answers

1. **Example:** Volume means how many cubes the rectangular prism will hold. The top layer has 15 centimeter cubes, and there are six layers, so there would be 15 by 6 centimeter cubes, or 90 centimeter cubes, in the rectangular prism. The rectangular prism's volume is 90 cm³.

Volume of Solid Figures (B)

Lesson Overview

LEARN Derive the Formula for Volume	20 minutes	ONLINE
LEARN Use the Volume Formula	20 minutes	OFFLINE
TRY IT Practice the Formula for Volume	10 minutes	OFFLINE
CHECKPOINT	10 minutes	ONLINE

▶ **Lesson Objectives**

Explain and determine the volume of a solid figure and use appropriate units.

▶ **Content Background**

Students will derive the formula and practice using the formula to find the volume of rectangular prisms. A cube is a special case of a rectangular prism.

Volume is the measure of the number of cubic units that a space occupies. Volume is a cubic-unit measurement (since it measures the three dimensions of length, width, and height), so the units used to measure volume have an exponent of 3. For example, you might see volume measured in cubic meters (m^3), cubic inches (in^3), cubic miles (mi^3), or cubic centimeters (cm^3).

Students will also see the connection between volume (packing a container with unit cubes) and capacity (filling a container with liquid). They will learn that 1 cubic centimeter is equivalent to 1 milliliter. This conversion is particularly helpful in the sciences.

▶ **Common Errors and Misconceptions**

Students might think that volume is a two-dimensional concept since they have worked with representations of three-dimensional figures on a two-dimensional textbook page.

Materials to Gather

SUPPLIED

Use the Volume Formula activity page

Practice the Formula for Volume activity page

LEARN Derive the Formula for Volume

ONLINE
20min

Students will see how volume measures the cubic units that a space occupies and will derive the formula for calculating the volume of a rectangular prism.

Objectives

- Explain and determine the volume of a solid figure and use appropriate units.

LEARN Use the Volume Formula

OFFLINE
20min

Objectives

- Explain and determine the volume of a solid figure and use appropriate units.

Students will solve problems by using the formula $V = lwh$, or $V = Bh$, for finding the volume of a rectangular prism. They will also find missing measurements when the volume is given. View or print the Use the Volume Formula activity page and read the directions with students.

Students should copy the problems from the Activity Book into their Math Notebook as necessary and solve them there.

1. Read Problem 1 of the Worked Examples with students. Remind them that volume is a cubic measurement, so their answers will be in cubic units.

2. Read Problem 2 of the Worked Examples with students.

   Ask: What is the inverse of multiplication by 280? division by 280

3. Remind students that dividing 280 by 280 equals 1, so the right side of the equation for that step will end up with $1 \cdot h$, or just h.

4. Have students solve the problems in the problem set. Make sure they write the formula, correctly substitute the values, and write the volume in a cubic measurement.

5. If students have difficulty, first encourage them to look at the Worked Examples and follow the process shown. If they still have difficulty, help them apply the process shown in the Worked Examples.

Tips

If students have difficulty understanding how to substitute measurements for variables in the formula for volume, have them write the variable and corresponding measurement. For example, in Problem 1 in the problem set, students would write $l = 7$ inches, $w = 9$ inches, and $h = 4$ inches.

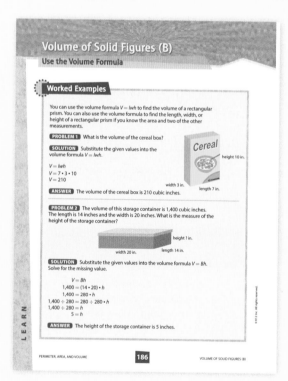

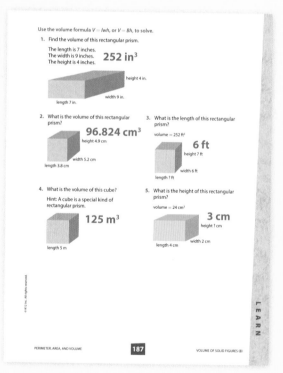

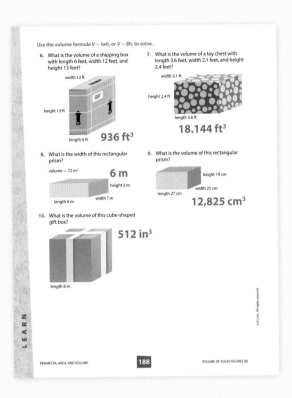

TRY IT Practice the Formula for Volume

OFFLINE
10min

Objectives

Students will use the formula $V = lwh$, or $V = Bh$, to find the volume of rectangular prisms. They will also use the formula to find the width of a rectangular prism given its length and height. View or print the Practice the Formula for Volume activity page and read the directions with students.

Students should copy the problems from the Activity Book into their Math Notebook as necessary and solve them there.

- Explain and determine the volume of a solid figure and use appropriate units.

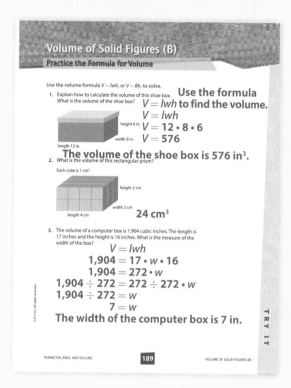

Volume of Solid Figures (B)
Practice the Formula for Volume

Use the volume formula $V = lwh$, or $V = Bh$, to solve.

1. Explain how to calculate the volume of this shoe box. What is the volume of the shoe box?

   height 6 in.
   width 8 in.
   length 12 in.

   Use the formula $V = lwh$ to find the volume.
   $V = lwh$
   $V = 12 \cdot 8 \cdot 6$
   $V = 576$
   The volume of the shoe box is 576 in³.

2. What is the volume of this rectangular prism?

   Each cube is 1 cm³.

   height 2 cm
   width 3 cm
   length 4 cm

   24 cm³

3. The volume of a computer box is 1,904 cubic inches. The length is 17 inches and the height is 16 inches. What is the measure of the width of the box?

   $V = lwh$
   $1{,}904 = 17 \cdot w \cdot 16$
   $1{,}904 = 272 \cdot w$
   $1{,}904 \div 272 = 272 \div 272 \cdot w$
   $1{,}904 \div 272 = w$
   $7 = w$
   The width of the computer box is 7 in.

TRY IT

PERIMETER, AREA, AND VOLUME   189   VOLUME OF SOLID FIGURES (B)

CHECKPOINT

ONLINE
10 min

Objectives

Students will complete an online Checkpoint. If necessary, read the directions, problems, and answer choices to students and help them with keyboard or mouse operations.

- Explain and determine the volume of a solid figure and use appropriate units.

Units of Perimeter, Area, and Volume

Lesson Overview

LEARN Units for Perimeter	5 minutes	OFFLINE
LEARN Units for Area	15 minutes	OFFLINE
LEARN Units for Volume	10 minutes	ONLINE
LEARN Differentiate Among Appropriate Units	10 minutes	ONLINE
TRY IT Practice with Appropriate Units	10 minutes	ONLINE
CHECKPOINT	10 minutes	ONLINE

▶ Lesson Objectives

Differentiate among appropriate units to measure perimeter, area, and volume.

▶ Prerequisite Skills

- Determine the perimeter of a plane figure and use appropriate units.
- Derive and use the formula for the area of a parallelogram and use appropriate units.
- Derive and use the formula for the area of a triangle and use appropriate units.
- Explain and determine the volume of a solid figure and use appropriate units.

▶ Content Background

Students will learn to differentiate among appropriate units to measure perimeter, area, and volume in the context of architecture.

Perimeter is the distance around a geometric shape or figure, or an everyday object. Perimeter is a linear measurement (since it measures length), so the units used to measure perimeter have an understood exponent of 1. That is, the units for perimeter measures are written without the exponent. For example, you might see perimeter measured in centimeters (cm), meters (m), kilometers (km), inches (in.), feet (ft), yards (yd), or miles (mi).

Area is the measure of the region inside a two-dimensional figure or the surface of a three-dimensional figure. Area is a square-unit measurement (since it measures length and width), so the units used to measure area have an exponent of 2. For example, you might see area measured in square meters (m^2), square inches (in^2), square miles (mi^2), or square centimeters (cm^2).

Volume is the measure of the number of cubic units that a space occupies. Volume is a cubic-unit measurement (since it measures the three dimensions of length, width, and height), so the units used to measure volume have an exponent of 3. For example, you might see volume measured in cubic meters (m^3), cubic inches (in^3), cubic miles (mi^3), or cubic centimeters (cm^3).

Materials to Gather

SUPPLIED
Centimeter Grid Paper (printout)
Net for Rectangular Prism (printout)

▶ Common Errors and Misconceptions

- Students might think of all measurements as length. For example, they might perceive area as a distance—something that they can measure with a ruler. Consequently, they often measure the perimeter (the path around the figure).

- Students might believe that it doesn't matter if units are all identical. They may believe that if they can fill a region (such as a box) with units of measure (such as beans), it doesn't matter if some of the units of measure (beans) are of a different size. They will simply count the number of objects contained within the region (box).

- Students might believe that although the units of measure should be identical, it doesn't matter if they do not completely cover a region.

▶ Advance Preparation

Print four copies of the Centimeter Grid Paper.

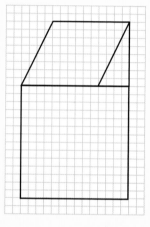

- For the Learn: Units for Perimeter activity, draw a 14-by-14 square on one copy of the Centimeter Grid Paper. The square will represent the floor plan of a building. Students will use a second printout to design their own floor plan.

- For the Learn: Units for Area activity, use one copy of the Centimeter Grid Paper to draw the following figures: a square, a parallelogram, and a triangle (see the sample figure at right). The square represents a house, and the parallelogram and triangle represent the house's front yard. Students will use a second printout to design the house's backyard.

Print one copy of the Net for Rectangular Prism printout.

LEARN Units for Perimeter

OFFLINE
5min

Objectives

- Differentiate among appropriate units to measure perimeter, area, and volume.

Students will discuss the perimeter of a building. They will decide the appropriate unit for measuring perimeter.

Gather the Centimeter Grid Paper on which you drew a 14-by-14 square, plus a second copy of the grid paper.

1. Tell students they will apply geometry and measurement concepts to architecture. Explain that one of the first steps in designing a building is to create a floor plan. A floor plan shows the dimensions of the building as if viewed from above the building.

2. Show students the square you drew on Centimeter Grid Paper. Tell students that the square is the floor plan of a building.

   Say: A builder wants to install drainage pipes around the perimeter of the building. Water will then drain away from the building. The builder wants to know the perimeter of the building.

   Ask: What unit of measurement would you use to describe the perimeter of the building and why? Answers will vary. Answers may include meters, feet, or yards. Answers about why the unit was chosen will vary but should include that the unit chosen is a type of unit used for measuring length. Students may also say that inches, centimeters, and certain other units are too small to use for measuring the building's perimeter, while miles and kilometers are too large to use for measuring the building's perimeter.

3. Have students draw a floor plan of a building on another sheet of grid paper. They can decide what type of building it is, such as an office building, a community center, or a museum.

- Tell students the building can be a square, a rectangle, or a parallelogram, or a shape with edges that vary, such as a large square connected to a small square.

- Have them label the dimensions, including the unit of measure, such as feet or meters.

- Have students find the perimeter of the building and write it, using an appropriate unit of measure. Answers will vary. Make sure students have chosen a linear unit in the perimeter measurement.

OFFLINE
15 min

LEARN Units for Area

Objectives

- Differentiate among appropriate units to measure perimeter, area, and volume.

Students will identify appropriate units to measure area of a parallelogram, area of a triangle, and surface area of a rectangular prism and cube in the context of a house plan.

Gather the Centimeter Grid Paper on which you drew the square, triangle, and parallelogram. Also gather a second copy of the grid paper and the Net for Rectangular Prism printout.

1. Show students the figures you drew on Centimeter Grid Paper. Tell students that a design for a house frequently includes a plan for the yard.

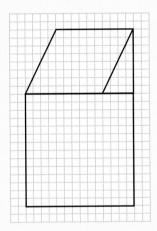

Tips

These are the formulas for area for different plane figures:

square: $A = bh$

rectangle: $A = bh$

parallelogram: $A = bh$

triangle: $A = \frac{bh}{2}$

2. Discuss the plan for the yard.

Say: The square represents a house and the parallelogram and triangle represent the front yard. If the homeowners want to plant grass in the front yard, they need to find the area of the parallelogram and triangle to determine how much grass seed to buy.

Ask: What type of unit—linear, squared, or cubed—would you use to describe the area of the parallelogram and why? Square units, because area is a measure of two dimensions, base and height. Area is the number of square units that cover a shape.

Ask: What type of unit would you use to describe the area of the triangle and why? Square units, because area is a measure of two dimensions, base and height. Area is the number of square units that cover a shape.

3. Have students draw and label the dimensions (including the unit of measure, such as feet or meters) of the backyard of a house on another sheet of grid paper.

   - Tell students the backyard can be a square, rectangle, parallelogram, or triangle.

   - Have students find the area of the yard and use an appropriate unit to record the area. Have them write the formula and substitute the value of each dimension in the formula to find the area. An example of finding the area of a triangle with base 12 meters and height 10 meters is shown.

   $A = \frac{bh}{2}$

   $A = \frac{12 \cdot 10}{2}$

   $A = \frac{120}{2}$

   $A = 60$

   The area of the triangle is 60 square meters.

4. Tell students they can also use surface area to solve problems about other rectangular prisms.

   Say: Surface area is the sum of the areas of all the faces, bases, and curved surfaces of a solid figure. These are two examples of problems you could solve by finding surface area:

   - If you want to cover the outside of a box with wrapping paper, the surface area of the outside of the box determines the amount of paper you need.

   - If you want to paint the inside of the box, the surface area of the inside of the box determines the amount of paint you need.

5. Give students the Net for Rectangular Prism printout. Tell them that the net represents the living room of a house.

   Say: Suppose the homeowners want to cover the floor with carpeting, the walls with wallpaper, and the ceiling with paint. Use the printout to label the walls, floor, and ceiling of the net.

6. Discuss the net and the labeled parts of the living room.

   Ask: What unit of measurement would you use to find the area of the ceiling if each unit in the net is 1 foot? Square feet, or ft², because area is a square measure of two dimensions: base and height.

   Ask: What unit of measurement would you use to find the area of the floor and the walls if each unit in the net is 1 foot? Would it be the same unit of measurement as the area of the ceiling? Why? Square feet, or ft², because area is a square measure of two dimensions: base and height. Each square in the net represents 1 foot, so I would use a square measure for the area of the floor and walls, just like the area of the ceiling.

7. Use the net to discuss surface area.

   Ask: How would you calculate the surface area of all the surfaces in the room that would be covered with carpeting, paint, or wallpaper? Add the areas of the surfaces of the rectangular prism together.

   Ask: If each square in the net represents 1 foot, what unit of measurement would you use for the surface area and why? Square feet, or ft², because surface area is a square-unit measurement. It measures the length times the width of each face of a solid figure.

LEARN Units for Volume

Objectives

- Differentiate among appropriate units to measure perimeter, area, and volume.

Students will identify appropriate units to measure the volume of rectangular prisms and cubes in the context of different types of buildings.

Tips Allow students to sketch each building and label the dimensions (including the unit of measure, such as feet or meters) before finding the volume.

LEARN Differentiate Among Appropriate Units

Objectives

- Differentiate among appropriate units to measure perimeter, area, and volume.

Students will differentiate among appropriate units to measure perimeter, area, surface area, and volume of two notable buildings in New York City.

TRY IT Practice with Appropriate Units

Objectives

- Differentiate among appropriate units to measure perimeter, area, and volume.

Students will complete an online Try It. If necessary, read the directions, problems, and answer choices to students and help them with keyboard or mouse operations.

CHECKPOINT

Objectives

- Differentiate among appropriate units to measure perimeter, area, and volume.

Students will complete an online Checkpoint. If necessary, read the directions, problems, and answer choices to students and help them with keyboard or mouse operations.

Core Focus
Volumes of Rectangular Prisms

LEARN Volume from a Net	15 minutes	ONLINE
LEARN Combined Rectangular Prism Volume	15 minutes	ONLINE
TRY IT Rectangular Prism Volume	15 minutes	ONLINE
CHECKPOINT	10 minutes	ONLINE

▶ Lesson Objectives

- Explain and determine the volume of a solid figure and use appropriate units.
- Use the fact that volume is additive to solve problems.

▶ Content Background

Students will expand their understanding of volume to find the volume of a rectangular prism from a net and to look at the same prism from several perspectives. They will also explore the volume of figures made up of more than one rectangular prism.

Materials to Gather

Threre are no materials to gather for this lesson.

LEARN Volume from a Net

ONLINE
15 min

Students will use a net to determine the dimensions of a rectangular prism and then calculate the volume using a formula. They will see that the same prism can be oriented several ways, interchanging the dimensions, but still have the same volume.

Objectives

- Explain and determine the volume of a solid figure and use appropriate units.
- Use the fact that volume is additive to solve problems.

Tips

Use a cereal box or other rectangular prism to help students more easily visualize the prisms.

LEARN Combined Rectangular Prism Volume

ONLINE 15min

Students will decompose figures made up of more than one prism to determine the volume of the individual prisms. They will then combine the volumes to determine the volume of the entire figure.

Objectives

- Explain and determine the volume of a solid figure and use appropriate units.
- Use the fact that volume is additive to solve problems.

TRY IT Rectangular Prism Volume

ONLINE 15min

Students will complete an online Try It. If necessary, read the directions, problems, and answer choices to students and help them with keyboard or mouse operations.

Objectives

- Explain and determine the volume of a solid figure and use appropriate units.
- Use the fact that volume is additive to solve problems.

CHECKPOINT

ONLINE 10min

Students will complete an online Checkpoint. If necessary, read the directions, problems, and answer choices to students and help them with keyboard or mouse operations.

Objectives

- Explain and determine the volume of a solid figure and use appropriate units.
- Use the fact that volume is additive to solve problems.

Unit Review

Lesson Overview

UNIT REVIEW Look Back	10 minutes	**ONLINE**
UNIT REVIEW Checkpoint Practice	50 minutes	**ONLINE**
▶ **UNIT REVIEW** Prepare for the Checkpoint		

▶ Unit Objectives

- Determine the perimeter of a plane figure and use appropriate units.
- Construct a cube or a rectangular box from a two-dimensional pattern and determine the surface area.
- Use squares to approximate the area of an irregular shape.
- Estimate or determine the number of cubes required to fill a solid figure.
- Explain and determine the volume of a solid figure and use appropriate units.
- Differentiate among appropriate units to measure perimeter, area, and volume.
- Use the fact that volume is additive to solve problems.

▶ Advance Preparation

In this lesson, students will have an opportunity to review previous activities in the Perimeter, Area, and Volume unit. Look at the suggested activities in Unit Review: Prepare for the Checkpoint online and gather any needed materials.

Materials to Gather

There are no materials to gather for this lesson.

UNIT REVIEW Look Back   ONLINE 10 min

Students will review key concepts from the unit to prepare for the Unit Checkpoint.

Objectives

- Review unit objectives.

UNIT REVIEW Checkpoint Practice   ONLINE 50 min

Students will complete an online Checkpoint Practice to prepare for the Unit Checkpoint. If necessary, read the directions, problems, and answer choices to students. Have students answer the problems on their own. Review any missed problems with students.

Objectives

- Review unit objectives.

▶ UNIT REVIEW Prepare for the Checkpoint

What you do next depends on how students performed in the previous activity, Unit Review: Checkpoint Practice. If students had difficulty with any of the problems, complete the appropriate review activity listed in the table online.

Unit Checkpoint

UNIT CHECKPOINT   60 minutes | ONLINE

▶ Unit Objectives

- Determine the perimeter of a plane figure and use appropriate units.
- Construct a cube or a rectangular box from a two-dimensional pattern and determine the surface area.
- Use squares to approximate the area of an irregular shape.
- Estimate or determine the number of cubes required to fill a solid figure.
- Explain and determine the volume of a solid figure and use appropriate units.
- Differentiate among appropriate units to measure perimeter, area, and volume.
- Use the fact that volume is additive to solve problems.

Materials to Gather

There are no materials to gather for this lesson.

UNIT CHECKPOINT

ONLINE
60min

Students will complete the Unit Checkpoint online. If necessary, read the directions, problems, and answer choices to students and help them with keyboard or mouse operations.

Objectives

- Assess unit objectives.

Extended Problems: Reasoning

GRADED ASSIGNMENT   60 minutes   OFFLINE

▶ Lesson Objectives

- Estimate or determine the number of cubes required to fill a solid figure.
- Explain and determine the volume of a solid figure and use appropriate units.
- Use the fact that volume is additive to solve problems.
- Determine the perimeter of a plane figure and use appropriate units.
- Analyze complex problems using mathematical knowledge and skills.

Materials to Gather

SUPPLIED

Extended Problems: Reasoning

OFFLINE
60 min

GRADED ASSIGNMENT

Objectives

Open the Extended Problems: Reasoning. Read the directions, problems, and answer choices to students, if necessary.

You will grade this assignment.

- Students should complete the assignment on their own.
- Students should submit the completed assignment to you.
- Enter the results online.

- Analyze complex problems using mathematical knowledge and skills.

Math Reasoning: Methods and Strategies

Pólya's Problem-
Solving Plan

Step 1: Understand
the problem.
Step 2: Devise
a plan.
Step 3: Carry out
the plan.
Step 4: Look back.

▶ Unit Objectives

- Prioritize and sequence the information in a story problem that involves multiplication or division of decimal numbers.

- Determine when and how to break a multistep whole-number story problem or money problem into simpler parts.

- Use a variety of methods, such as words, numbers, symbols, charts, graphs, tables, diagrams, and models, to explain mathematical reasoning in nonroutine or complex problems.

- Identify and generalize methods for solving problems that are similar to each other.

- Apply strategies and results from simple story problems involving fractions to more complex problems.

- Graph or write an equation to solve a problem that involves a linear function.

- Estimate or calculate a product or quotient in a whole-number story problem.

- Solve for one variable in a two-variable equation when the value of the other variable is given.

▶ Unit Introduction

In this unit, students will develop ways to solve story problems. They will list by priority and will sequence the information in the problem. They will determine when and how to break a multistep problem into simpler parts. They will use methods such as words, numbers, graphs, tables, and models to explain their problem-solving reasoning with complex problem situations.

Students will identify and generalize the methods they use to solve problems so they can apply these procedures to problems that are similar to one another. They will also apply the strategies and results used to answer simple problems to solve more complex problems. As they study problem solving in this unit, students will work with whole numbers, fractions, multiplication and division of decimal numbers, and money amounts.

▶ Keywords

conjecture
reasoning

representation
sequence information

solution
strategy

Steps to Solve Story Problems (A)

▶ Lesson Objectives

Prioritize and sequence the information in a story problem that involves multiplication or division of decimal numbers.

▶ Prerequisite Skills

Analyze a story problem by identifying the question, recognizing relevant information, sequencing and prioritizing information, and developing a solution strategy.

▶ Content Background

Students will determine and sequence steps to find solutions to story problems that involve multiplication or division of decimal numbers.

Solving a story problem is a strategic process that is not always straightforward. The following problem-solving method was developed by George Pólya and is an effective way to solve a variety of story problems: (1) understand the problem; (2) devise a plan; (3) carry out the plan; and (4) look back.

The first step of this process, "understand the problem," often interferes with students' ability to follow a problem to its solution. The secret to success is in the ability to carefully read the problem, reword the problem, analyze the question, and figure out relationships among the given pieces of information. Only then can students recognize an effective strategy for solving the problem.

Students should also realize that there are often different ways to solve a problem and different strategies that will work. By using many different strategies, they learn to be flexible in their problem solving and learn that some strategies are more efficient than others.

Materials to Gather

There are no materials to gather for this lesson.

GET READY Explain Steps to Solve a Problem

Students will walk through the steps to solve a problem involving decimal numbers and find the solution.

Tips Have students solve the problem a different way to show them that they can arrive at the same solution in more than one way.

Objectives

- Analyze a story problem by identifying the question, recognizing relevant information, sequencing and prioritizing information, and developing a solution strategy.

LEARN Sequence Steps to Solve Problems

Students will sequence the steps to solve a multistep problem involving finding the cost of purchases.

Tips Ask students what would happen if they reversed the order of solving the first two smaller problems, finding the cost of the strawberries before finding the cost of the apples. Have them discuss whether or not the order of solving these two smaller problems makes a difference in finding the solution to the original problem.

Objectives

- Prioritize and sequence the information in a story problem that involves multiplication or division of decimal numbers.

LEARN Correct Order to Solve Story Problems

Students will determine the steps needed to solve multistep problems involving multiplication of decimal numbers, including money amounts.

Objectives

- Prioritize and sequence the information in a story problem that involves multiplication or division of decimal numbers.

LEARN Order Steps to Solve Story Problems

Students will determine the steps needed to solve multistep problems involving division of decimal numbers, including money amounts.

Objectives

- Prioritize and sequence the information in a story problem that involves multiplication or division of decimal numbers.

TRY IT Determine Steps to Solve Problems

Students will complete an online Try It. If necessary, read the directions, problems, and answer choices to students and help them with keyboard or mouse operations.

Objectives

- Prioritize and sequence the information in a story problem that involves multiplication or division of decimal numbers.

Steps to Solve Story Problems (B)

▶ Lesson Objectives

Prioritize and sequence the information in a story problem that involves multiplication or division of decimal numbers.

▶ Prerequisite Skills

Analyze a story problem by identifying the question, recognizing relevant information, sequencing and prioritizing information, and developing a solution strategy.

▶ Content Background

Students will continue to determine and sequence steps to find solutions to story problems that involve multiplication or division of decimal numbers.

Solving a story problem is a strategic process that is not always straightforward. The following problem-solving plan was developed by George Pólya and is an effective way to solve a variety of story problems: (1) understand the problem; (2) devise a plan; (3) carry out the plan; and (4) look back.

▶ Advance Preparation

Print the Problem-Solving Plan.

Materials to Gather

SUPPLIED
Problem-Solving Plan (printout)
Analyze Problems and Make Steps
   activity page

GET READY Relevant and Irrelevant Numbers

ONLINE
10 min

Objectives

Students will determine what information is needed to solve a problem and what information is irrelevant.

- Analyze a story problem by identifying the question, recognizing relevant information, sequencing and prioritizing information, and developing a solution strategy.

LEARN Analyze Problems and Make Steps

Objectives

- Prioritize and sequence the information in a story problem that involves multiplication or division of decimal numbers.

Tips

Have students rewrite their plan reversing the first three steps to show that the order of those steps do not matter in finding the solution.

Students will see how Pólya's 4-step problem-solving plan can be used to solve a story problem. They will make sure they understand the problem and will put steps in a correct order for solving it. Gather the Problem-Solving Plan. View or print the Analyze Problems and Make Steps activity page and read the directions with students.

Students should copy the problems from the Activity Book into their Math Notebook as necessary and solve them there.

1. Give students the Problem-Solving Plan. Read the information about George Pólya with students. Read the four numbered steps on the printout with students.

2. Tell students that the first step, "understand the problem," is critical to solving a problem correctly.

3. Read the Worked Examples box with students through the section called "understand the problem." Point out the questions in that section on the printout.

4. Read the rest of the Worked Examples box with students. Explain that there is more than one way to solve most problems.

   Ask: Why doesn't the order of the first three steps matter? I can figure the costs of items in any order because the costs will be added together when I take the fourth step to find the answer.

   Ask: Why does the order of the last step matter? I can't add the costs of the supplies without knowing each item's cost.

   Ask: How do you know if this path was the right one for solving this problem? **Example:** In the last section, "look back," the questions and answers supported the answer that I found for the story problem. The question in the story problem has been answered. The answer makes sense when compared with an estimate.

5. Have students complete the problems in the problem set. Have them refer to the Problem-Solving Plan and the Worked Example as needed.

6. After students finish Problem 3, ask the following question:

   Ask: What information in the problem wasn't needed for solving it? Don has 7 neighbors. A neighbor has 3 dogs. Another neighbor has 4 cars.

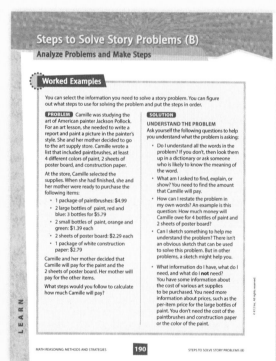

Steps to Solve Story Problems (B)
Analyze Problems and Make Steps

Worked Examples

You can select the information you need to solve a story problem. You can figure out what steps to use for solving the problem and put the steps in order.

PROBLEM Camille was studying the art of American painter Jackson Pollock. For an art lesson, she needed to write a report and paint a picture in the painter's style. She and her mother decided to go to the art supply store. Camille wrote a list that included paintbrushes, at least 4 different colors of paint, 2 sheets of poster board, and construction paper.

At the store, Camille selected the supplies. When she had finished, she and her mother were ready to purchase the following items:

- 1 package of paintbrushes: $4.99
- 2 large bottles of paint, red and blue: 3 bottles for $5.79
- 2 small bottles of paint, orange and green: $1.39 each
- 2 sheets of poster board: $2.29 each
- 1 package of white construction paper: $2.79

Camille and her mother decided that Camille will pay for the paint and the 2 sheets of poster board. Her mother will pay for the other items.

What steps would you follow to calculate how much Camille will pay?

SOLUTION

UNDERSTAND THE PROBLEM
Ask yourself the following questions to help you understand what the problem is asking:

- Do I understand all the words in the problem? If you don't, then look them up in a dictionary or ask someone who is likely to know the meaning of the word.
- What am I asked to find, explain, or show? You need to find the amount that Camille will pay.
- How can I restate the problem in my own words? An example is this question: How much money will Camille owe for 4 bottles of paint and 2 sheets of poster board?
- Can I sketch something to help me understand the problem? There isn't an obvious sketch that can be used to solve this problem. But in other problems, a sketch might help you.
- What information do I have, what do I need, and what do I **not** need? You have some information about the cost of various art supplies to be purchased. You need more information about prices, such as the per-item price for the large bottles of paint. You don't need the cost of the paintbrushes and construction paper or the color of the paint.

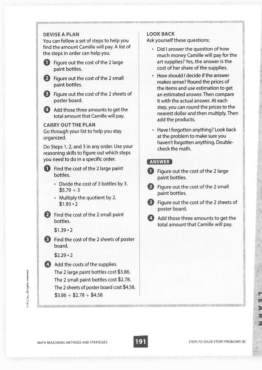

DEVISE A PLAN

You can follow a set of steps to help you find the amount Camille will pay. A list of the steps in order can help you.

① Figure out the cost of the 2 large paint bottles.

② Figure out the cost of the 2 small paint bottles.

③ Figure out the cost of the 2 sheets of poster board.

④ Add those three amounts to get the total amount that Camille will pay.

CARRY OUT THE PLAN

Go through your list to help you stay organized.

Do Steps 1, 2, and 3 in any order. Use your reasoning skills to figure out which steps you need to do in a specific order.

① Find the cost of the 2 large paint bottles.
- Divide the cost of 3 bottles by 3.
  $5.79 ÷ 3
- Multiply the quotient by 2.
  $1.93 • 2

② Find the cost of the 2 small paint bottles.
$1.39 • 2

③ Find the cost of the 2 sheets of poster board.
$2.29 • 2

④ Add the costs of the supplies.
The 2 large paint bottles cost $3.86.
The 2 small paint bottles cost $2.78.
The 2 sheets of poster board cost $4.58.
$3.86 + $2.78 + $4.58

LOOK BACK

Ask yourself these questions:

- Did I answer the question of how much money Camille will pay for the art supplies? Yes, the answer is the cost of her share of the supplies.

- How should I decide if the answer makes sense? Round the prices of the items and use estimation to get an estimated answer. Then compare it with the actual answer. At each step, you can round the prices to the nearest dollar and then multiply. Then add the products.

- Have I forgotten anything? Look back at the problem to make sure you haven't forgotten anything. Double-check the math.

ANSWER

① Figure out the cost of the 2 large paint bottles.

② Figure out the cost of the 2 small paint bottles.

③ Figure out the cost of the 2 sheets of poster board.

④ Add those three amounts to get the total amount that Camille will pay.

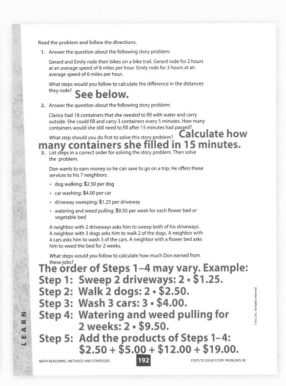

Read the problem and follow the directions.

1. Answer the question about the following story problem:

Gerard and Emily rode their bikes on a bike trail. Gerard rode for 2 hours at an average speed of 8 miles per hour. Emily rode for 3 hours at an average speed of 6 miles per hour.

What steps would you follow to calculate the difference in the distances they rode? **See below.**

2. Answer the question about the following story problem:

Clarice had 18 containers that she needed to fill with water and carry outside. She could fill and carry 3 containers every 5 minutes. How many containers would she still need to fill after 15 minutes had passed?

What step should you do first to solve this story problem? **Calculate how many containers she filled in 15 minutes.**

3. List steps in a correct order for solving the story problem. Then solve the problem.

Don wants to earn money so he can save to go on a trip. He offers these services to his 7 neighbors:
- dog walking: $2.50 per dog
- car washing: $4.00 per car
- driveway sweeping: $1.25 per driveway
- watering and weed pulling: $9.50 per week for each flower bed or vegetable bed

A neighbor with 2 driveways asks him to sweep both of his driveways. A neighbor with 3 dogs asks him to walk 2 of the dogs. A neighbor with 4 cars asks him to wash 3 of the cars. A neighbor with a flower bed asks him to weed the bed for 2 weeks.

What steps would you follow to calculate how much Don earned from these jobs?
The order of Steps 1–4 may vary. Example:
Step 1: Sweep 2 driveways: 2 • $1.25.
Step 2: Walk 2 dogs: 2 • $2.50.
Step 3: Wash 3 cars: 3 • $4.00.
Step 4: Watering and weed pulling for 2 weeks: 2 • $9.50.
Step 5: Add the products of Steps 1–4: $2.50 + $5.00 + $12.00 + $19.00.

Additional Answers

1. **Step 1:** Multiply 2 by 8.
   Step 2: Multiply 3 by 6.
   Step 3: Subtract the lesser product from the greater product.

LEARN Make a Plan to Solve Story Problems

ONLINE 10 min

Students will determine the steps needed to solve multistep problems involving multiplication or division of decimal amounts, including money.

Objectives

- Prioritize and sequence the information in a story problem that involves multiplication or division of decimal numbers.

TRY IT Steps for Multistep Problems

ONLINE 10 min

Students will complete an online Try It. If necessary, read the directions, problems, and answer choices to students and help them with keyboard or mouse operations.

Objectives

- Prioritize and sequence the information in a story problem that involves multiplication or division of decimal numbers.

CHECKPOINT

ONLINE 10 min

Students will complete an online Checkpoint. If necessary, read the directions, problems, and answer choices to students and help them with keyboard or mouse operations.

Objectives

- Prioritize and sequence the information in a story problem that involves multiplication or division of decimal numbers.

Break Down Multistep Problems

Lesson Overview

LEARN Simpler Parts	15 minutes	**OFFLINE**
LEARN Who Owes Whom?	10 minutes	**ONLINE**
TRY IT Find the Simpler Parts of a Problem	10 minutes	**ONLINE**
CHECKPOINT	10 minutes	**ONLINE**

▶ Lesson Objectives

Determine when and how to break a multistep whole-number story problem or money problem into simpler parts.

▶ Content Background

Students will determine and sequence steps to find solutions to story problems that involve multiplication or division of decimal numbers.

Solving a story problem is a strategic process that is not always straightforward. The following problem-solving method was developed by George Pólya and is an effective way to solve a variety of story problems: (1) understand the problem; (2) devise a plan; (3) carry out the plan; and (4) look back.

The first step of this process, "understand the problem," often interferes with students' ability to follow a problem to its solution. The secret to success is in the ability to carefully read the problem, reword the problem, analyze the question, and figure out relationships among the given pieces of information. Only then can students recognize an effective strategy for solving the problem.

Students should also realize that there are often different ways to solve a problem and different strategies that will work. By using many different strategies, they learn to be flexible in their problem solving and learn that some strategies are more efficient than others.

▶ Advance Preparation

Print the Problem-Solving Plan.

Materials to Gather

SUPPLIED

Problem-Solving Plan (printout)

Simpler Parts activity page

LEARN Simpler Parts

OFFLINE
15min

Objectives

- Determine when and how to break a multistep whole-number story problem or money problem into simpler parts.

Students will determine when and how to break a multistep whole-number story problem or decimal money problem into simpler parts. Gather the Problem-Solving Plan. View or print the Simpler Parts activity page and read the directions with students.

Students should copy the problems from the Activity Book into their Math Notebook as necessary and solve them there.

1. Give students the Problem-Solving Plan. Review the first step, "understand the problem," by having students read the questions aloud.

2. Explain that this activity focuses on determining how and when breaking a problem into simpler parts will help solve the problem.

3. Read the Worked Examples box with students.

   Ask: What is another way of restating the problem? Answers will vary.

   Example: How much money does Eduardo have left after spending $\frac{3}{4}$ on a baseball glove and then later spending $\frac{1}{3}$ of the money he had left on a baseball book?

   Ask: Can any of the steps in the plan for solving this problem be done in any other order? No, this problem has a certain order for the steps because of the information given in the problem and because of the question that is asked.

4. Have students answer Problem 1 in the problem set.

   Ask: How would you break the problem into simpler parts? Find the total number of people who attended the first 4 performances. Add that amount to the number of people who attended the last performance.

5. Have students read Problem 2.

   Ask: How would you break the problem into simpler parts? Find the number of coins in each jar. Then find the number of coins in each jar that are not gold coins.

6. Have students answer Problem 3.

   Ask: Why didn't this problem need to be broken into simpler parts? There is only one part and one calculation in the problem: multiply $3.45 by 8 to find the cost of 8 packages of stickers.

7. Have students answer Problem 4.

   Ask: If you divide first and then subtract, will you solve the simpler problems in the correct order? Explain your reasoning. No, the answer would be incorrect unless the subtraction is done first to find the number of cans that both Nancy and Elaine collected.

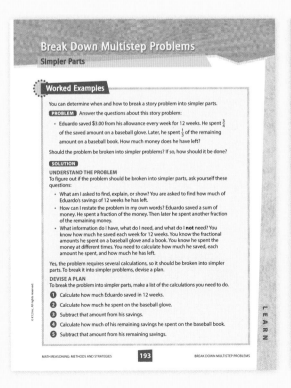

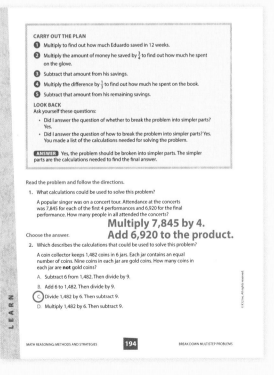

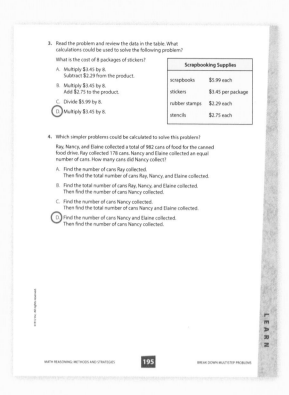

LEARN Who Owes Whom?

ONLINE 10 min

Objectives

Students will determine when and how to break a multistep money problem into simpler parts.

- Determine when and how to break a multistep whole-number story problem or money problem into simpler parts.

Tips   If students have difficulty identifying simpler problems in a story problem, have them copy the story problem in their Math Notebook and highlight the simpler problems in different colors.

TRY IT Find the Simpler Parts of a Problem

ONLINE 10 min

Objectives

Students will complete an online Try It. If necessary, read the directions, problems, and answer choices to students and help them with keyboard or mouse operations.

- Determine when and how to break a multistep whole-number story problem or money problem into simpler parts.

CHECKPOINT

ONLINE 10 min

Objectives

Students will complete an online Checkpoint. If necessary, read the directions, problems, and answer choices to students and help them with keyboard or mouse operations.

- Determine when and how to break a multistep whole-number story problem or money problem into simpler parts.

Mathematical Reasoning Methods (A)

Lesson Overview

GET READY Use Several Strategies for Problems	10 minutes	**ONLINE**
LEARN Solve Simple to Complex Problems	30 minutes	**ONLINE**
TRY IT Choose the Best Strategy	20 minutes	**OFFLINE**

▶ Lesson Objectives

Use a variety of methods, such as words, numbers, symbols, charts, graphs, tables, diagrams, and models, to explain mathematical reasoning in nonroutine or complex problems.

▶ Prerequisite Skills

Explain mathematical reasoning in a story problem by using multiple representations.

▶ Content Background

Students will learn to use different strategies to solve story problems. They will use diagrams, tables, and equations to help them find the answers to complex story problems.

In this lesson, students will solve nonroutine or complex problems. Routine problems involve using the four operations (addition, subtraction, multiplication, and division) without other strategies. *Nonroutine* and complex problems engage students in using a variety of strategies, such as using guess and test, using simpler numbers, drawing a diagram, and making a table, to find a solution.

Solving nonroutine problems often involves "trying this, then trying that" to come upon a solution. Many problems in everyday life are nonroutine and complex, so this type of problem solving provides a solid foundation for students as they mature and face complex problems of their own.

While working with students, include the problem-solving principles of George Pólya. Call attention to each principle as students work. Remind them that nonroutine or complex math problems are not necessarily more difficult, just more interesting and satisfying to solve. The steps of the problem-solving plan are as follows: (1) understand the problem; (2) devise a plan; (3) carry out the plan; and (4) look back.

When students devise a plan to solve problems, they can find many possible strategies in the 4-step problem-solving plan. Two of the strategies are "Translate into a number sentence" and "Apply a rule or definition." This lesson combines these two ideas and names the strategy "Write an equation."

Materials to Gather

SUPPLIED

Problem-Solving Plan (printout)

Choose the Best Strategy activity page

Students should test their strategies on many problems to see if their strategy always works, and ask an adult to check to see if their strategy makes sense mathematically. Once strategies are proven to work, the next goal is for students to decide which strategies are most efficient for them. A strategy that is efficient for one student may not be for another. Problem solving is not only a key to success in math but also in every area of life. To become good problem solvers, students need to have a variety of strategies at their disposal to be able to choose the strategy that applies to the problem. In that way, they build on their prior experiences with problems and develop strategies that work for many similar problems.

When explaining reasoning, students should do the following:

- Explain and justify why they did what they did.
- Know when to use certain properties of arithmetic, applying concepts to an unfamiliar problem.
- Invent procedures that work well with a new problem, such as easier ways to add greater numbers or long lists of numbers.

▶ Advance Preparation

Print the Problem-Solving Plan.

GET READY Use Several Strategies for Problems

ONLINE
10min

Students will use the draw-a-diagram and write-an-equation strategies to solve a story problem.

Objectives

- Explain mathematical reasoning in a story problem by using multiple representations.

LEARN Solve Simple to Complex Problems

ONLINE
30min

Students will solve a nonroutine problem about painting the surface area, or the faces, of different-sized cube models. They will find a solution to a simpler problem, and then build upon that solution to solve more complex problems. Students will use the strategies of using objects to model the problem and finding patterns in a table of data.

Objectives

- Use a variety of methods, such as words, numbers, symbols, charts, graphs, tables, diagrams, and models, to explain mathematical reasoning in nonroutine or complex problems.

TRY IT Choose the Best Strategy

OFFLINE
20min

Students will choose the problem-solving strategy and explanation that correctly show how to solve each story problem. Gather the Problem-Solving Plan and have students refer to it as needed. View or print the Choose the Best Strategy activity page and read the directions with students.

Students should copy the problems from the Activity Book into their Math Notebook as necessary and solve them there.

Objectives

- Use a variety of methods, such as words, numbers, symbols, charts, graphs, tables, diagrams, and models, to explain mathematical reasoning in nonroutine or complex problems.

Mathematical Reasoning Methods (A)
Choose the Best Strategy

Choose the problem-solving strategy and explanation that correctly show how to solve the problem.

1. Daniella made 1 triangle with 3 toothpicks. She discovered she could make 2 triangles if she used 5 toothpicks. If she used 7 toothpicks, she could make 3 triangles. How many toothpicks would Daniella need to make 7 triangles?

   A. **Write an equation.**
   $(1 \cdot 3) + (2 \cdot 5) + (3 \cdot 7) = ?$
   Calculate the number of toothpicks needed to make each triangle and add them all up.

   B. **Guess and test.**
   Guess 17 toothpicks for 7 triangles. Test your guess by drawing the toothpick triangles. If you couldn't draw 7 triangles, revise your guess. Test your guess again. Keep trying.

   C. **Draw a diagram.**
   Draw a diagram of 3 triangles using 7 lines to represent toothpicks. Keep adding lines until you have 7 triangles. Count the number of lines.

2. The perimeter of 1 face of a cube is 28 cm. What is the surface area of the cube?

   A. **Write equations.**
   Calculate the length of 1 edge of the cube. Let n represent the length.
   $28 = 4n$
   The length of 1 edge of the cube is 7 cm.
   Calculate the area of 1 face. $A = 7 \cdot 7$
   Calculate the surface area of the cube. $S = 49 \cdot 6$

   B. **Guess and test.**
   Guess that the surface area of 1 face is 60 cm². Calculate that the area of 1 face is 10 cm². Calculate that the perimeter of 1 face is 40 cm. That guess didn't work, so make another guess. Guess that the surface area of 1 face is 42 cm². Calculate that the area of 1 face is 7 cm². So the perimeter of 1 face is 28 cm.

   C. **Work backward.**
   The perimeter of 1 face is 28 cm. So the length of 1 face is 14 cm. The area of 1 face would be $14 \cdot 14$. Then multiply that answer by 6 to calculate the surface area.

---

3. Kent is planting rows of seeds in the community garden. He plants 5 seeds in his first row, 11 seeds in his second row, and 17 seeds in his third row. If Kent uses the same pattern, how many seeds will he plant in his 7th row?

   A. **Write an equation.**
   $(1 \cdot 5) + (2 \cdot 11) + (3 \cdot 17) = ?$
   Calculate the number of seeds needed in each row and add them together.

   B. **Draw a diagram.**
   Draw 1 seed next to 5 seeds, then 2 seeds next to 11 seeds, and 3 seeds next to 17 seeds. Keep drawing and count all the seeds.

   C. **Make a table.**
   Write the seed-row numbers 1, 2, 3, 4, 5, 6, 7 as column names at the top of the table. In the first row of the table, write 5 in column 1, 11 in column 2, and 17 in column 3. Look for the pattern. Fill in the rest of the table using the same pattern.

4. Denzel can paint 12 tiles in an hour. How many tiles can Denzel paint in $4\frac{1}{2}$ hours?

   A. **Make a table.**
   Look for a pattern in your table.

Hours	1	2	3	4	5	6
Tiles	4.5	4.5	4.5	4.5	4.5	4.5

   B. **Write an equation.**
   Let n equal the number of tiles Denzel can paint in $4\frac{1}{2}$ hours.
   $n = 12 \cdot 4\frac{1}{2} = 12 \cdot \frac{9}{2} = \frac{108}{2} = 54$
   Denzel can paint 54 tiles in $4\frac{1}{2}$ hours.

   C. **Use simpler numbers.**
   Suppose that Denzel could paint only 10 tiles per hour. Calculate how many tiles he could paint in 4 hours: $10 \cdot 4 = 40$. So in 4 hours, he can paint 40 tiles. Now that you have figured out how to solve the problem, go back and solve it using fractions.

Choose the problem-solving strategy and explanation that correctly show how to solve the problem.

5. Maddie bought 3 more pounds of flour than Kath. Together Kath and Maddie bought 13 pounds of flour. How many pounds of flour did Kath buy?

   A. **Guess and test.**
   Guess that Kath bought 2 pounds of flour. This means that Maddie would have bought 5 pounds, because $2 + 3 = 5$. Add $2 + 5$. If the sum doesn't equal 13, revise your guess to be that Kath bought 3 pounds of flour. Figure out how many pounds of flour Maddie bought. Is this sum equal to 13? If not, revise your guess, and test your answer again.

   B. **Draw a diagram.**
   Draw 13 circles to represent the 13 pounds of flour. Divide the circles into two equal groups. Then multiply one group by 3.

   C. **Write an equation.**
   Let m represent the number pounds of flour Kath bought.
   $(3 \cdot m) + 2 = 13$

6. Derek earned some money over the summer. He charged $7 to wash a car and $4 to walk a dog. He washed 12 cars and walked 6 dogs in August. How much money did Derek make in August?

   A. **Work backward.**
   Derek washed 12 cars, so count backward from 12 to 7 to figure out how much money he made washing cars. He walked 6 dogs, so count back from 6 to 4 to see how much money he made walking dogs. Add the two amounts together.

   B. **Write equations.**
   Multiply the number of cars washed by the amount charged per car.
   $12 \cdot 7 = 84$
   Then multiply the number of dogs walked by the amount charged per dog. $6 \cdot 4 = 24$
   Add the two products together to find the total amount earned.

   C. **Draw a picture.**
   Draw 12 cars and 6 dogs. Count the cars and dogs.

---

7. The animal park has 63 butterflies in a special environment for butterflies. There are 28 red butterflies, 19 white butterflies, and the rest are yellow. How many butterflies are yellow?

   A. **Write an equation.**
   $63 - 28 - 19 = ?$

   B. **Guess and test.**
   Guess that there are 20 yellow butterflies. Add 20 to the number of red and white butterflies. Is your answer 28? If not, revise your guess, and test your answer again.

   C. **Draw a diagram.**
   Draw 19 dots. Then figure out how many dots you need to get to 28 butterflies in all.

8. Charlotte was selling pies at a bake sale. She sold 13 pies before lunch and another 5 after lunch. At the end of the day, Charlotte had 8 pies left. How many pies did Charlotte start the day with?

   A. **Write an equation.**
   $8 + 5 - 13 = ?$

   B. **Draw a picture.**
   Draw 8 circles. Add 5 circles and then add 13 circles.

   C. **Guess and test.**
   Guess that Charlotte started with 20 pies. Subtract 8. Is your answer 13? If not, revise your guess, and test your answer again.

Mathematical Reasoning Methods (B)

Lesson Overview

LEARN Strategies for Nonroutine Problems		15 minutes	OFFLINE
LEARN More Strategies for Nonroutine Problems		20 minutes	OFFLINE
TRY IT Practice Solving Nonroutine Problems		15 minutes	OFFLINE
CHECKPOINT		10 minutes	ONLINE

▶ Lesson Objectives

Use a variety of methods, such as words, numbers, symbols, charts, graphs, tables, diagrams, and models, to explain mathematical reasoning in nonroutine or complex problems.

▶ Prerequisite Skills

Explain mathematical reasoning in a story problem by using multiple representations.

▶ Content Background

Students will continue to use different strategies to solve complex story problems.

In this lesson, students will solve nonroutine or complex problems. Routine problems involve using the four operations (addition, subtraction, multiplication, and division) without other strategies. *Nonroutine* and complex problems engage students in using a variety of strategies, such as using guess and test, using simpler numbers, drawing a diagram, and making a table, to find a solution.

Solving nonroutine problems often involves "trying this, then trying that" to come upon a solution. Many problems in everyday life are nonroutine and complex, so this type of problem solving provides a solid foundation for students as they mature and face complex problems of their own.

▶ Advance Preparation

Print the Problem-Solving Plan, Books for the New Library, and Dimensions of the Playing Field printouts.

Materials to Gather

SUPPLIED

Problem-Solving Plan (printout)

Books for the New Library (printout)

Dimensions of the Playing Field (printout)

Practice Solving Nonroutine Problems activity page

LEARN Strategies for Nonroutine Problems

OFFLINE **15 min**

Students will solve nonroutine problems. They will explore the strategies of making a table and looking for patterns. Note that this activity deals with consecutive odd numbers. Carl Friedrich Gauss, a mathematician born in 1777, devised an equation when he was a young student to find the sum of consecutive numbers. This activity is a related problem of finding sums of consecutive odd numbers.

Gather the Problem-Solving Plan and Books for the New Library printouts.

Objectives

- Use a variety of methods, such as words, numbers, symbols, charts, graphs, tables, diagrams, and models, to explain mathematical reasoning in nonroutine or complex problems.

1. Give students the Problem-Solving Plan. Tell them they will solve a nonroutine problem.

   Say: A nonroutine problem is a complex problem. In nonroutine problems, you might use several operations and a variety of strategies.

   Read the Problem-Solving Plan with students to review the four steps and the strategies.

2. Give students the Books for the New Library printout. Read the following story problem to them. Ask them to make notes about the problem in their Math Notebook.

   A new library is opening soon. People are bringing books to donate to the library.

   - The first person donates 1 book.
   - The second person donates 3 books.
   - The third person donates 5 books.
   - Every person who comes continues to donate 2 more books than the previous person did.
   - How many books will the library have if 20 people follow that pattern?

3. Review questions in the first step, "understand the problem."

   Ask: Analyze the problem. What operation will you use to solve it? addition

   Ask: What numbers are important to the problem? 1, 3, 5; the 2 books more than the previous person donated

4. Review some questions students can use to help them devise a plan.

   Ask: Would a diagram, table, chart, or graph help me with this problem? A table would help me keep track of the information.

   Ask: Is there a pattern to the data? Each person gives 2 more books than the previous person does.

5. Tell students that they'll start solving the problem by completing the two left columns of the Books for the New Library table.

   Have them number the top five rows 1–5 in the "Person's number in order of arrival" column.

   Have them complete the "Person's number of books donated" column for the top 5 rows.

   Have them move on to the "Expressions to calculate the running total" column. Explain that a running total is a total that changes as new information is given or calculated.

   Say: To fill the rows in that column, write an expression showing addition of the number of books that have been donated at that point. For example, the first row will have a 1. The second row will have (1 + 3). The third row will have (1 + 3 + 5).

   Have students complete the table for Person 4 and Person 5.

6. Remind students that every new person donates 2 more books than the previous person did.

   Ask: How many books did the fourth person donate? 7 books

   Ask: How many books did the fifth person donate? 9 books

   Ask: Can you solve the problem about how many books the library will have if 20 people follow that pattern at this point? Why or why not? No, I can't answer the problem yet. I need to fill in more data in the table.

   Have students complete the "Running total" column by adding the numbers in the expression on each row.

7. Have students fill in rows 6 and 7. Answers for the first 7 rows are shown.

Books for the New Library			
Person's number in order of arrival	Person's number of books donated	Expressions to calculate the running total	Running total
1	1	1	1
2	3	$(1 + 3)$	4
3	5	$(1 + 3 + 5)$	9
4	7	$(1 + 3 + 5 + 7)$	16
5	9	$(1 + 3 + 5 + 7 + 9)$	25
6	11	$(1 + 3 + 5 + 7 + 9 + 11)$	36
7	13	$(1 + 3 + 5 + 7 + 9 + 11 + 13)$	49

8. Tell students that it would take much time to fill out the table for 20 people. Tell them that the look-for-a-pattern strategy might help them save time because the information is organized in a table. A pattern is easier to spot in a display such as a table.

Ask: Do you notice any special pattern in the "Running total" column? The numbers are all numbers that are perfect squares.

Ask: What happens when you compare each number in the "Running total" column with its related number in the "Person's number in order of arrival" column? You see that the person's number squared is the running total.

9. Have students predict the number of books donated by Person 8. 64 books

Ask: Check your work by adding $(1 + 3 + 5 + 7 + 9 + 11 + 13 + 15)$. What is the sum? 64

10. Tell students that as they carry out their problem-solving plan, they can ask themselves these questions:

Ask: How can I predict how many books the library will have after a certain number of people arrive and follow the pattern of donating books? Find the square of the number of people.

Ask: Do I still need to use the table for the rest of the data? No

Ask: What was I asked to find in the story problem? If 20 people donated, how many books would the library have?

Ask: What strategies will I need to use to answer this story problem, and what is the answer? Figure out 20^2. The answer is 400.

11. Have students "look back" and in doing so discover something more. Have them look at the "Person's number of books donated" column.

Ask: What do you notice about the numbers in this column? They are consecutive odd numbers.

Ask: How can you find the sum of the first 5 consecutive odd numbers? Compute 5 squared.

Ask: How can you find the sum of the first 1,000 consecutive odd numbers? Compute 1,000 squared.

Ask: Suppose the variable S stands for the sum of consecutive odd numbers. What equation would allow you to find the sum of the first n consecutive odd numbers? $S = n^2$

12. Have students complete the far left and the far right columns in the table for 8, 9, 10, and 20 people, using only the equation $S = n^2$. Answers are shown. Check students' work.

Books for the New Library			
Person's number in order of arrival	Person's number of books donated	Expressions to calculate the running total	Running total
1	1	1	1
2	3	$(1 + 3)$	4
3	5	$(1 + 3 + 5)$	9
4	7	$(1 + 3 + 5 + 7)$	16
5	9	$(1 + 3 + 5 + 7 + 9)$	25
6	11	$(1 + 3 + 5 + 7 + 9 + 11)$	36
7	13	$(1 + 3 + 5 + 7 + 9 + 11 + 13)$	49
8			64
9			81
10			100
20			400

OFFLINE

LEARN More Strategies for Nonroutine Problems 20min

Objectives

Students will solve more nonroutine problems. They will use Pólya's 4-step problem-solving plan: (1) understand the problem; (2) devise a plan; (3) carry out the plan; and (4) look back. In the first problem, the strategies they will use include the following: draw a diagram, apply a formula, and guess and test. In the second problem, they will use the work backward strategy. Gather the Problem-Solving Plan and the Dimensions of the Playing Field printouts.

- Use a variety of methods, such as words, numbers, symbols, charts, graphs, tables, diagrams, and models, to explain mathematical reasoning in nonroutine or complex problems.

1. Read the Problem-Solving Plan with students to review the 4 steps and the strategies.

2. Give students the Dimensions of the Playing Field printout. Read the following story problem to them. Ask them to make notes about the problem in their Math Notebook.

   - The perimeter of a rectangular playing field measures 400 meters.
   - Its length is 3 times its width.
   - Find the length and width of the field.

3. Review questions in the first step, "understand the problem."

   Ask: Analyze the problem. What operations will you use to solve it? multiplication and addition

   Ask: What numbers are important to the problem? The perimeter is 400 meters. The length is 3 times the width.

   Ask: What measurements does the question ask for? the length and width of the playing field

   Ask: What questions can you ask yourself? Answers will vary. **Examples:** Will a picture help me understand the problem? Can I make a table to help me try out some numbers?

4. Have students look at the strategies in the second step of the problem-solving plan, "devise a plan."

   Ask: How would a diagram and a table help you solve the problem? A diagram would help me understand what the field would look like. A table would help me keep track of the information.

   Ask: How would the guess-and-test strategy help you solve the problem? It would help me try different numbers for the length and width.

5. Remind students of the formula for the perimeter of a rectangle: $P = 2l + 2w$

6. Ask students to draw a diagram of the playing field in their Math Notebook.

7. Have students guess that the width is 100 meters.

   Ask: If the width is 100 meters, what is the length? 300 meters, because the problem says the length is 3 times the width

   Say: Substitute 100 for w and 300 for l into the perimeter formula in your Math Notebook. Then calculate the perimeter. $P = 600 + 200 = 800$; The perimeter for the width of 100 meters is 800 meters.

   Ask: What was the given perimeter of the playing field? 400 meters

   Ask: Rate the guess of 100 meters: too low, too high, or correct? too high

   Have students fill in the top row of the table with that guess.

8. Have students follow Step 7 to continue guessing and filling out the table until they reach the correct answer. As they work, have them use the information from their previous guess (too high or too low) to make adjustments for the next guess. Students should ask themselves, "Is my strategy (guess and test) helping me find the answer?" and "Do I still need to use the table for the rest of the data?"

9. Check that students found the correct answer for a perimeter of 400 meters.
   length 150 meters, width 50 meters

   Guesses will vary. Students may use as many rows as they need. Some possible guesses for the problem are shown.

Dimensions of the Playing Field					
Width (w)	Length (l) (must be 3 times the width)	2 × w	2 × l	Perimeter (P)	Rate the Guess (too high, too low, or correct)
100	300	200	600	800	too high
30	90	60	180	240	too low
50	150	100	300	400	correct

10. Have students do the fourth step, "look back," by asking themselves the questions on the Problem-Solving Plan printout.

11. Read the following Guess My Number story problem to students and have them take notes on it in their Math Notebook.

   Peter and Billy played the following game.
   - Start with a secret number between 1 and 10.
   - Multiply the number by 8.
   - Subtract 4.
   - Add 10.
   - Divide by 2.
   - Tell me the number you have at the end and I'll tell you the number you had at the start.

   Peter started with a number. He told Billy that he ended with 31. Billy figured out what number Peter had at the start. What number did Peter have at the start?

12. Tell students to make sure they understand the problem by using the questions in the "understand the problem" step.

13. Tell students to devise a plan.

    Ask: Would a diagram, table, chart, or graph help you with this problem? They probably wouldn't help.

    Tell students that as they continue devising a plan and carrying it out, they should do their calculations in their Math Notebook.

    Ask: What strategy would work for solving this problem? To find the number Peter chose at the start, I will need to work backward from his number of 31 and use inverse operations back through the problem.

14. Tell students that organizing information as they solve problems is very important.

    Say: To solve this problem, use the strategy of working up from the bottom as you go through the Guess My Number rules. Use inverse operations so you can reverse what Peter did for each step. The inverse operation of addition is subtraction. The inverse operation of multiplication is division. The last thing he did was divide by 2 to get 31 at the end. Since multiplication is the inverse of division, begin by multiplying 31 by 2.

    Ask: What does $31 \cdot 2$ equal? 62

    Have students write that calculation in their Math Notebook.

15. Continue going backward through the steps with students as they do the inverse operations. Make sure students do the following:

    - Subtract 10 because Peter added 10. The number is now 52.

    - Add 4 because Peter subtracted 4. The number is now 56.

    - Divide by 8 because Peter multiplied by 8. The number is now 7. Peter started with the number 7.

16. Have students "look back," the fourth step in the problem-solving plan, at how they solved the problem. They should figure out that they can check the secret number of 7 by working forward to get 31.

OFFLINE

TRY IT Practice Solving Nonroutine Problems   15 min   **Objectives**

Students will choose the problem-solving strategy and description that correctly explain how to solve story problems. Gather the Problem-Solving Plan. View or print the Practice Solving Nonroutine Problems activity page and read the directions with students.

Students should copy the problems from the Activity Book into their Math Notebook as necessary and solve them there.

- Use a variety of methods, such as words, numbers, symbols, charts, graphs, tables, diagrams, and models, to explain mathematical reasoning in nonroutine or complex problems.

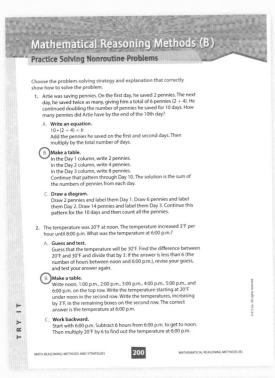
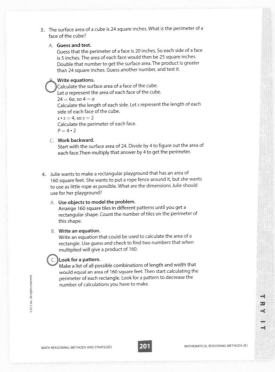

Mathematical Reasoning Methods (B)
Practice Solving Nonroutine Problems

Choose the problem-solving strategy and explanation that correctly show how to solve the problem.

1. Artie was saving pennies. On the first day, he saved 2 pennies. The next day, he saved twice as many, giving him a total of 6 pennies (2 + 4). He continued doubling the number of pennies he saved for 10 days. How many pennies did Artie have by the end of the 10th day?

   A. **Write an equation.**
   $10 \cdot (2 + 4) = b$
   Add the pennies he saved on the first and second days. Then multiply by the total number of days.

   B. **Make a table.**
   In the Day 1 column, write 2 pennies.
   In the Day 2 column, write 4 pennies.
   In the Day 3 column, write 8 pennies.
   Continue that pattern through Day 10. The solution is the sum of the numbers of pennies from each day.

   C. **Draw a diagram.**
   Draw 2 pennies and label them Day 1. Draw 6 pennies and label them Day 2. Draw 14 pennies and label them Day 3. Continue this pattern for the 10 days and then count all the pennies.

2. The temperature was 20°F at noon. The temperature increased 3°F per hour until 8:00 p.m. What was the temperature at 6:00 p.m.?

   A. **Guess and test.**
   Guess that the temperature will be 30°F. Find the difference between 20°F and 30°F and divide that by 3. If the answer is less than 6 (the number of hours between noon and 6:00 p.m.), revise your guess, and test your answer again.

   B. **Make a table.**
   Write noon, 1:00 p.m., 2:00 p.m., 3:00 p.m., 4:00 p.m., 5:00 p.m., and 6:00 p.m. on the top row. Write the temperature starting at 20°F under noon in the second row. Write the temperatures, increasing by 3°F, in the remaining boxes on the second row. The correct answer is the temperature at 6:00 p.m.

   C. **Work backward.**
   Start with 6:00 p.m. Subtract 6 hours from 6:00 p.m. to get to noon. Then multiply 20°F by 6 to find out the temperature at 6:00 p.m.

---

3. The surface area of a cube is 24 square inches. What is the perimeter of a face of the cube?

   A. **Guess and test.**
   Guess that the perimeter of a face is 20 inches, So each side of a face is 5 inches. The area of each face would then be 25 square inches. Double that number to get the surface area. The product is greater than 24 square inches. Guess another number, and test it.

   B. **Write equations.**
   Calculate the surface area of a face of the cube.
   Let a represent the area of each face of the cube.
   $24 = 6a$, so $4 = a$
   Calculate the length of each side. Let s represent the length of each side of each face of the cube.
   $s \cdot s = 4$, so $s = 2$
   Calculate the perimeter of each face.
   $P = 4 \cdot 2$

   C. **Work backward.**
   Start with the surface area of 24. Divide by 4 to figure out the area of each face. Then multiply that answer by 4 to get the perimeter.

4. Julie wants to make a rectangular playground that has an area of 160 square feet. She wants to put a rope fence around it, but she wants to use as little rope as possible. What are the dimensions Julie should use for her playground?

   A. **Use objects to model the problem.**
   Arrange 160 square tiles in different patterns until you get a rectangular shape. Count the number of tiles on the perimeter of this shape.

   B. **Write an equation.**
   Write an equation that could be used to calculate the area of a rectangle. Use guess and check to find two numbers that when multiplied will give a product of 160.

   C. **Look for a pattern.**
   Make a list of all possible combinations of length and width that would equal an area of 160 square feet. Then start calculating the perimeter of each rectangle. Look for a pattern to decrease the number of calculations you have to make.

TRY IT

Choose the series of steps that will result in the correct answer.

5. Timmy bought twice as many plums as apples. He bought 4 more plums than bananas. He bought 6 apples. How many bananas did Timmy buy?

   A. Start with 6. Multiply 6 by 2. Then subtract 4.

   B. Start with 6. Multiply 6 by 2. Then add 4.

   C. Start with 4. Add 4 and 6. Then multiply the sum by 2 and add 4.

6. A number is multiplied by 2. Then 8 is added to the product. The sum is then divided by 5. The answer is 8. What was the original number?

   A. Start with 8. Multiply 8 by 5. Then add 8 and multiply the sum by 2.

   B. Start with 8. Add 8 and 5. Then subtract 8 and multiply the sum by 2.

   C. Start with 8. Multiply 8 by 5. Then subtract 8 and divide the difference by 2.

TRY IT

ONLINE 10 min

CHECKPOINT

Students will complete an online Checkpoint. If necessary, read the directions, problems, and answer choices to students and help them with keyboard or mouse operations.

Objectives

- Use a variety of methods, such as words, numbers, symbols, charts, graphs, tables, diagrams, and models, to explain mathematical reasoning in nonroutine or complex problems.

Choose and Use Strategies (A)

GET READY Simple to Complex	10 minutes	**ONLINE**
LEARN Make-a-Table Strategy	20 minutes	**ONLINE**
LEARN Use Tables to Solve Problems	15 minutes	**OFFLINE**
TRY IT Practice Using Tables	15 minutes	**OFFLINE**

▶ Lesson Objectives

Identify and generalize methods for solving problems that are similar to each other.

▶ Prerequisite Skills

Apply strategies or results from a simpler problem to a similar or more complex problem.

▶ Content Background

Although the context and numbers in story problems vary, good problem solvers realize that they can use certain strategies over and over to solve problems that are similar to each other. That skill relies on students being able to identify similarities between problems. When they learn and are able to use different strategies, they realize that instead of treating every problem they encounter as a new experience, they can apply successful strategies for solving problems that are similar.

As students work on solving problems, they should follow the 4-step problem-solving plan. The following problem-solving method was developed by George Pólya and is an effective way to solve a variety of problems: (1) understand the problem; (2) devise a plan; (3) carry out the plan; and (4) look back. In the "devise a plan" step, students will decide which problem-solving method to use to solve a problem.

When students devise a plan to solve problems, they can find many possible strategies in the 4-step problem-solving plan. Two of the strategies are "Translate into a number sentence" and "Apply a rule or definition." This lesson combines these two ideas and names the strategy "Write an equation."

▶ Advance Preparation

Print the Problem-Solving Plan.

Materials to Gather

SUPPLIED

Problem-Solving Plan (printout)

Use Tables to Solve Problems activity page

Practice Using Tables activity page

GET READY Simple to Complex

ONLINE 10min

Students will apply the write-an-equation strategy to solve a simpler division problem. They will then apply the same strategy to solve a more complex division problem.

LEARN Make-a-Table Strategy

ONLINE 20min

Students will use the make-a-table strategy to solve two similar geometry problems.

LEARN Use Tables to Solve Problems

OFFLINE 15min

Students will make tables to help them find the answers to story problems. Gather the Problem-Solving Plan. View or print the Use Tables to Solve Problems activity page and read the directions with students.

Students should copy the problems from the Activity Book into their Math Notebook as necessary and solve them there.

1. Read the Worked Examples box with students.

   Ask: In the table, when 2 years were added to Nyree's age, what happened to Mia's age? Two years were added to Mia's age.

   Say: If you were making this table, you wouldn't know to make 9 columns after the original column of age 30 and age 6. You would want to sketch a table that had several columns and some space at the end for more columns if you needed them for reaching your answer.

2. Have students complete Problem 1. Make sure they have answered it correctly before they move on to the next problem.

3. Assist students as needed with the remaining problems. If they have difficulty, first encourage them to look at the Worked Example and the Problem-Solving Plan. If they still have difficulty, help them apply the process shown in the Worked Example.

Tips

When students sketch tables for the make-a-table strategy, have them create extra rows and columns in their table. They should leave space on their paper to add rows and columns that are needed to solve the problem.

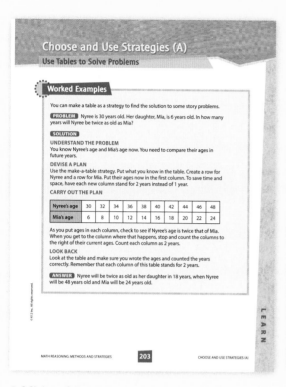

Additional Answers

1.

Time	9:00 p.m.	10:00 p.m.	11:00 p.m.	midnight	1:00 a.m.
Temperature (°F)	28	25	22	19	16

The temperature at 1:00 a.m. was 16°F.

2. $2(\$3.75) + \$2.50 = \$7.50 + \$2.50 = \$10.00$; Cynthia spent $10.00 each day.

Day	1	2	3	4	5	6	7	8	9	10
Total cost	$10	$20	$30	$40	$50	$60	$70	$80	$90	$100

In 10 days, Cynthia spent $100.

3. $2 + 3 = 5$; Ilene uses 5 cups of nuts per batch.

Number of batches	1	2	3	4	5	6	7
Cups of nuts	5	10	15	20	25	30	35

To make 7 batches, Ilene will use 35 cups of nuts.

4.

Number of coaches	3	6	9	12
Number of players	16	32	48	64

There are 64 players going to the tournament.

TRY IT Practice Using Tables

Students will solve problems using the make-a-table strategy. View or print the Practice Using Tables activity page and read the directions with students.

Students should copy the problems from the Activity Book into their Math Notebook as necessary and solve them there.

- Identify and generalize methods for solving problems that are similar to each other.

Choose and Use Strategies (A)
Practice Using Tables

Memory Jogger

MAKE-A-TABLE STRATEGY
Mrs. Fry uses 4 balls of white yarn and 5 balls of blue yarn to knit a blanket. How many balls of yarn does she need to make 5 blankets?

Number of blankets	1	2	3	4	5
Number of balls of yarn	9	18	27	36	45

Mrs. Fry uses 9 balls of yarn to knit a blanket.
To knit 5 blankets, she will use 45 balls of yarn.

Solve by making a table.

1. Peter is 35 years old. His son Nathan is 10 years old. How many years ago was Peter 6 times older than Nathan?
See below.

2. The temperature was 15° at noon. It increased 4°F per hour until 8:00 p.m. What was the temperature at 6:00 p.m.?
See below.

3. Tom bought a daisy and 2 roses for each of his 6 cousins. Daisies cost $1.25 each. Roses cost $2.99 each. How much money did Tom spend?
See next page.

4. Charlie's bread recipe uses 1 cup of whole-wheat flour and 2 cups of white flour for each loaf. How many cups of flour does Charlie need to make 5 loaves of bread? **See next page.**

5. Toby is making a tile mosaic. He puts 3 blue tiles in the first row, 7 blue tiles in the second row, and 11 blue tiles in the third row. If Toby continues using the same pattern, how many blue tiles will he use in the 6th row?
See next page.

6. Karly can make 1 square with 4 toothpicks. She can make 2 squares with 7 toothpicks. She can make 3 squares with 10 toothpicks. Karly continued making squares to the right of the toothpick squares shown.

When Karly had made 9 squares in all, how many toothpicks had she used?
See next page.

MATH REASONING: METHODS AND STRATEGIES **205**   CHOOSE AND USE STRATEGIES (A)

T R Y   I T

Additional Answers

1.

Peter	35	34	33	32	31	30
Nathan	10	9	8	7	6	5

Peter was 6 times older than Nathan 5 years ago.

2.

Time	noon	1:00 p.m.	2:00 p.m.	3:00 p.m.	4:00 p.m.	5:00 p.m.	6:00 p.m.
Temperature (°F)	15	19	23	27	31	35	39

The temperature at 6:00 p.m. was 39°F.

3. $1.25 + (2 \cdot \$2.99) = \$1.25 + \$5.98 = \$7.23$;
Tom spent $7.23 on flowers for each cousin.

Number of cousins	1	2	3	4	5	6
Cost of flowers	$7.23	$14.46	$21.69	$28.92	$36.15	$43.38

Tom spent $43.38 on flowers for his cousins.

4. $1 + 2 = 3$; Charlie needs 3 cups of flour for each loaf.

Number of bread loaves	1	2	3	4	5
Cups of flour	3	6	9	12	15

Charlie needs 15 cups of flour to make 5 loaves of bread.

5.

Rows	1	2	3	4	5	6
Number of blue tiles	3	7	11	15	19	(23)

The number of blue tiles increases by 4 for each row added. Toby will use
23 blue tiles in the 6th row.

6.

Number of squares	1	2	3	4	5	6	7	8	9
Number of toothpicks	4	7	10	13	16	19	22	25	(28)

The number of toothpicks increases by 3 for each new square added. To
make 9 squares, Karly would need 28 toothpicks.

Choose and Use Strategies (B)

LEARN Write-an-Equation Strategy	20 minutes	OFFLINE
LEARN Guess-and-Test Strategy	20 minutes	OFFLINE
TRY IT Use Different Strategies	20 minutes	OFFLINE

▶ Lesson Objectives

Identify and generalize methods for solving problems that are similar to each other.

▶ Prerequisite Skills

Apply strategies or results from a simpler problem to a similar or more complex problem.

▶ Content Background

Although the context and numbers in story problems vary, good problem solver realize that they can use certain strategies over and over to solve problems that are similar to each other. That skill relies on students being able to identify similarities between problems. When they learn and are able to use different strategies, they realize that instead of treating every problem they encounter as a new experience, they can apply successful strategies for solving problems that are similar.

As students work on solving problems, they should follow the 4-step problem-solving plan. The following problem-solving method was developed by George Pólya and is an effective way to solve a variety of problems: (1) understand the problem; (2) devise a plan; (3) carry out the plan; and (4) look back. In the "devise a plan" step, students will decide which problem-solving method to use to solve a problem.

When students devise a plan to solve problems, they can find many possible strategies in the 4-step problem-solving plan. Two of the strategies are "Translate into a number sentence" and "Apply a rule or definition." This lesson combines these two ideas and names the strategy "Write an equation."

▶ Advance Preparation

Print two copies of the Guess-and-Test Table.

Materials to Gather

SUPPLIED

Guess-and-Test Table (printout)

Write-an-Equation Strategy activity page

Guess-and-Test Strategy activity page

Use Different Strategies activity page

LEARN Write-an-Equation Strategy

Students will apply the write-an-equation strategy to find the sum of consecutive even numbers. View or print the Write-an-Equation Strategy activity page and read the directions with students.

Students should copy the problems from the Activity Book into their Math Notebook as necessary and solve them there.

1. Read the Worked Examples box with students.

   Say: The example gives you an equation that was developed by mathematician Carl Friedrich Gauss.

   Ask: What does *S* represent in the equation? the sum of the consecutive even numbers

   Ask: What does *n* represent? the number of consecutive numbers in the group that I'm finding the sum of

2. Have students look again at the third step of the problem-solving plan, "carry out the plan." Note that it begins with looking for a pattern. Tell students that sometimes they will use more than one strategy to solve problems. In this activity, they will use an equation to solve a problem. But they also will use a pattern to figure out what equation to use. Tell them that as they continue to study mathematics, *figuring out an equation* might also be called *deriving an equation*.

3. Have students look at the end of "carry out the plan."

   Ask: Why was 6 substituted for *n* in the equation? There are 6 even numbers from 1 through 12. The *n* in the equation stands for the number of even numbers in the problem.

   Ask: If the problem asked about even numbers through 16, would *n* stand for 16? Why or why not? No, the variable *n* doesn't stand for the greatest number in the problem. It stands for the number of numbers in the problem.

4. Have students solve Problem 1 in the problem set. Make sure they have completed Problem 1 correctly by substituting 8 for *n* before they move on to the next problem.

5. Have students complete the rest of the problems. Encourage them to refer to the Worked Example if they need help in solving the problems. Students may use the shortcut described in the Worked Example to check their answers.

Allow students to use the shortcut in the Worked Example to check the answer they found using the equation. Remind students that when the group of consecutive numbers has an odd number of numbers, there will be one number that does not match in a pair. Students will need to add that individual number to the number pairs.

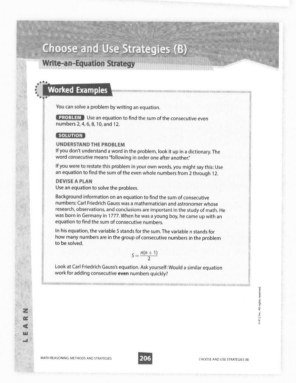

Choose and Use Strategies (B)
Write-an-Equation Strategy

> **Worked Examples**
>
> You can solve a problem by writing an equation.
>
> **PROBLEM** Use an equation to find the sum of the consecutive even numbers 2, 4, 6, 8, 10, and 12.
>
> **SOLUTION**
>
> **UNDERSTAND THE PROBLEM**
> If you don't understand a word in the problem, look it up in a dictionary. The word *consecutive* means "following in order one after another."
>
> If you were to restate this problem in your own words, you might say this: Use an equation to find the sum of the even whole numbers from 2 through 12.
>
> **DEVISE A PLAN**
> Use an equation to solve the problem.
>
> Background information on an equation to find the sum of consecutive numbers: Carl Friedrich Gauss was a mathematician and astronomer whose research, observations, and conclusions are important in the study of math. He was born in Germany in 1777. When he was a young boy, he came up with an equation to find the sum of consecutive numbers.
>
> In his equation, the variable *S* stands for the sum. The variable *n* stands for how many numbers are in the group of consecutive numbers in the problem to be solved.
>
> $$S = \frac{n(n+1)}{2}$$
>
> Look at Carl Friedrich Gauss's equation. Ask yourself: Would a similar equation work for adding consecutive **even** numbers quickly?

L E A R N

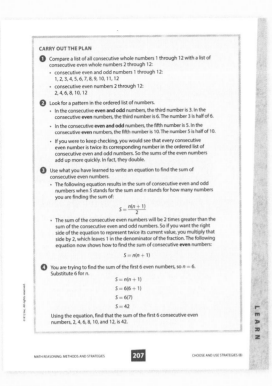

CARRY OUT THE PLAN

❶ Compare a list of all consecutive whole numbers 1 through 12 with a list of consecutive even whole numbers 2 through 12:
- consecutive even and odd numbers 1 through 12:
  1, 2, 3, 4, 5, 6, 7, 8, 9, 10, 11, 12
- consecutive even numbers 2 through 12:
  2, 4, 6, 8, 10, 12

❷ Look for a pattern in the ordered list of numbers.
- In the consecutive **even and odd** numbers, the third number is 3. In the consecutive **even** numbers, the third number is 6. The number 3 is half of 6.
- In the consecutive **even and odd** numbers, the fifth number is 5. In the consecutive **even** numbers, the fifth number is 10. The number 5 is half of 10.
- If you were to keep checking, you would see that every consecutive even number is twice its corresponding number in the ordered list of consecutive even and odd numbers. So the sums of the even numbers add up more quickly. In fact, they double.

❸ Use what you have learned to write an equation to find the sum of consecutive even numbers.
- The following equation results in the sum of consecutive even and odd numbers when S stands for the sum and n stands for how many numbers you are finding the sum of:

$$S = \frac{n(n+1)}{2}$$

- The sum of the consecutive even numbers will be 2 times greater than the sum of the consecutive even and odd numbers. So if you want the right side of the equation to represent twice its current value, you multiply that side by 2, which leaves 1 in the denominator of the fraction. The following equation now shows how to find the sum of consecutive **even** numbers:

$$S = n(n+1)$$

❹ You are trying to find the sum of the first 6 even numbers, so $n = 6$. Substitute 6 for n.

$$S = n(n+1)$$
$$S = 6(6+1)$$
$$S = 6(7)$$
$$S = 42$$

Using the equation, find that the sum of the first 6 consecutive even numbers, 2, 4, 6, 8, 10, and 12, is 42.

MATH REASONING: METHODS AND STRATEGIES · **207** · CHOOSE AND USE STRATEGIES (B)

LEARN

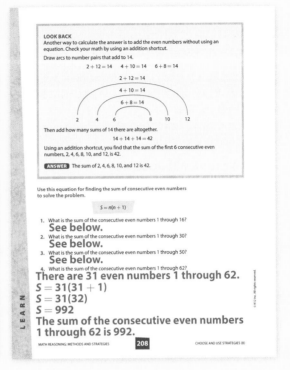

LOOK BACK

Another way to calculate the answer is to add the even numbers without using an equation. Check your math by using an addition shortcut.

Draw arcs to number pairs that add to 14.

$$2 + 12 = 14 \qquad 4 + 10 = 14 \qquad 6 + 8 = 14$$

$$2 + 12 = 14$$
$$4 + 10 = 14$$
$$6 + 8 = 14$$

2   4   6   8   10   12

Then add how many sums of 14 there are altogether.

$$14 + 14 + 14 = 42$$

Using an addition shortcut, you find that the sum of the first 6 consecutive even numbers, 2, 4, 6, 8, 10, and 12, is 42.

ANSWER The sum of 2, 4, 6, 8, 10, and 12 is 42.

Use this equation for finding the sum of consecutive even numbers to solve the problem.

$$S = n(n+1)$$

1. What is the sum of the consecutive even numbers 1 through 16?
   See below.
2. What is the sum of the consecutive even numbers 1 through 30?
   See below.
3. What is the sum of the consecutive even numbers 1 through 50?
   See below.
4. What is the sum of the consecutive even numbers 1 through 62?
   There are 31 even numbers 1 through 62.
   $$S = 31(31 + 1)$$
   $$S = 31(32)$$
   $$S = 992$$
   The sum of the consecutive even numbers 1 through 62 is 992.

MATH REASONING: METHODS AND STRATEGIES · **208** · CHOOSE AND USE STRATEGIES (B)

LEARN

Additional Answers

1. There are 8 even numbers 1 through 16.
   $$S = 8(8 + 1)$$
   $$S = 8(9)$$
   $$S = 72$$
   The sum of the consecutive even numbers 1 through 16 is 72.

3. There are 25 even numbers 1 through 50.
   $$S = 25(25 + 1)$$
   $$S = 25(26)$$
   $$S = 650$$
   The sum of the consecutive even numbers 1 through 50 is 650.

2. There are 15 even numbers 1 through 30.
   $$S = 15(15 + 1)$$
   $$S = 15(16)$$
   $$S = 240$$
   The sum of the consecutive even numbers 1 through 30 is 240.

LEARN Guess-and-Test Strategy

Students will use the guess-and-test strategy to solve problems. Gather the Guess-and-Test Table printouts. View or print the Guess-and-Test Strategy activity page and read the directions with students.

  Students should copy the problems from the Activity Book into their Math Notebook as necessary and solve them there.

1. Read the Worked Examples box with students.

   Ask: Could the guessing have started with the number of comic books Mrs. Jensen owns instead of the number of comic books Sara owns? Yes

   Ask: What would have been the first math operation used if the number being guessed was Mrs. Jensen's number? Explain. division; The guess would have been the guessed number divided by 24.

2. Make sure students understand the table in the solution.

   Say: The table is a way to help you use each guess to get closer to the problem's answer. For example, when you see that a number that you started with is too high, look to see if it is much too high or just a little too high. Use that information to decide what your next guess will be.

   Tell students that with some guesses, they will know that the total will be much too high, so they can decide not to find the total, but instead write "too high" and move to the next guess.

3. Give students a Guess-and-Test Table. Note that the table is like the table in the Worked Example.

4. Have students read Problem 1 in the problem set. Ask them to restate the problem in their own words. **Example:** Joe's father's coin collection has 6 times as many coins as Joe's collection. Their collections together have 49 coins. How many coins does Joe have and how many does his father have?

5. Have students complete Problem 1 by putting guesses in the Guess-and-Test Table until they figure out the answer. They may refer to the Worked Example as needed. Have them write a title at the top of their table, such as Coin Collections.

6. Have students read Problem 2. Ask them to restate the problem in their own words. **Example:** Tom's trip to see his grandmother was 175 times as long as his trip to see his uncle. The two trips together were 2,816 miles.

   Ask: How is Problem 2 like Problem 1? **Example:** Both problems give a total amount. Both problems ask what two combined amounts make the total amount.

7. Give students the other Guess-and-Test Table. Have them complete Problem 2. Remind them to use the results of their guesses to guide them as they make more guesses. Remind them to put a title at the top of their table.

   Ask: How is solving Problem 2 different from solving Problem 1? **Example:** The numbers in Problem 2 were greater numbers than the numbers in Problem 1. It took more guesses to find the correct answer.

Tips

Have students explain their reasoning for their first guess. Students often use estimation to help them make a first guess.

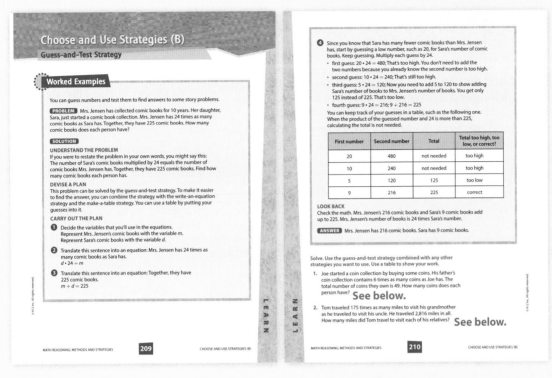

Additional Answers

1. Joe has 7 coins. His father has 42 coins. Guesses will vary. **Example:**

First number	Second number	Total	Total too high, too low, or correct?
9	54	63	too high
5	30	35	too low
6	36	42	too low
7	42	49	correct

2. Tom traveled 16 miles to visit his uncle. He traveled 2,800 miles to visit his grandmother. Guesses will vary. **Example:**

First number	Second number	Total	Total too high, too low, or correct?
20	3,500	not needed	too high
10	1,750	1,760	too low
17	2,975	not needed	too high
16	2,800	2,816	correct

TRY IT Use Different Strategies

Objectives

- Identify and generalize methods for solving problems that are similar to each other.

Students will solve problems using the write-an-equation and guess-and-test strategies. View or print the Use Different Strategies activity page and read the directions with students.

Students should copy the problems from the Activity Book into their Math Notebook as necessary and solve them there. They may use the Guess-and-Test Table to solve Problems 5 and 6.

Additional Answers:

1. ($12 • 6) + ($2 • 3) + $3 = $72 + $6 + $3 = $81
   It would cost $81 to have 6 pizzas and 3 small salads delivered.

2. ($2.25 • 3) + ($6.50 • 2) + ($1.17 • 12) = $6.75 + $13.00 + $14.04 = $33.79
   Kelly spent $33.79.

3. ($4 • 3) + ($10 • 2) + $6 = $12 + $20 + $6 = $38
   Myra's order costs $38 including shipping.

4. There are 20 even numbers 1 through 40.
   Substitute 20 for n in the equation.
   $S = n(n + 1)$
   $S = 20(20 + 1)$
   $S = 20(21)$
   $S = 420$
   The sum of the first 20 consecutive even numbers is 420.

5. Guesses will vary. **Correct guess:**
   $8 + 6 = 14$
   Molly walked 14 miles on Sunday.
   $14 + 8 = 22$
   Jeff walked 8 miles on Sunday.

Choose and Use Strategies (C)

▶ Lesson Objectives

Identify and generalize methods for solving problems that are similar to each other.

▶ Prerequisite Skills

Apply strategies or results from a simpler problem to a similar or more complex problem.

▶ Content Background

Students will learn to use the work-backward strategy and other strategies to solve problems.

Although the context and numbers in story problems vary, good problem solvers realize that they can use certain strategies over and over to solve problems that are similar to each other. That skill relies on students being able to identify similarities between problems. When they learn and are able to use different strategies, they realize that instead of treating every problem they encounter as a new experience, they can apply successful strategies for solving problems that are similar.

As students work on solving problems, they should follow the 4-step problem-solving plan. The following 4-step problem-solving method was developed by George Pólya and is an effective way to solve a variety of problems: (1) understand the problem; (2) devise a plan; (3) carry out the plan; and (4) look back. In the "devise a plan" step, students will decide which problem-solving method to use to solve a problem.

Materials to Gather

SUPPLIED
Practice Using Strategies activity page

LEARN Work Backward to Solve

Objectives

- Identify and generalize methods for solving problems that are similar to each other.

Students will use the strategy of working backward to solve story problems. Tell them that the strategy is useful when they need to find the answer to a problem where the information isn't given in order. Working backward can also help when one piece of information leads them to other information they need to solve the problem.

Tips When students carry out the plan, have them identify which step in the plan each computation represents.

LEARN Use Strategies to Solve Story Problems

Objectives

- Identify and generalize methods for solving problems that are similar to each other.

Students will use two strategies. They will work backward to figure out a starting time based on the ending time. They will substitute simpler numbers to find a perimeter.

TRY IT Practice Using Strategies

Objectives

- Identify and generalize methods for solving problems that are similar to each other.

Students will practice using the various problem-solving strategies to solve problems. View or print the Practice Using Strategies activity page and read the directions with students.

Students should copy the problems from the Activity Book into their Math Notebook as necessary and solve them there.

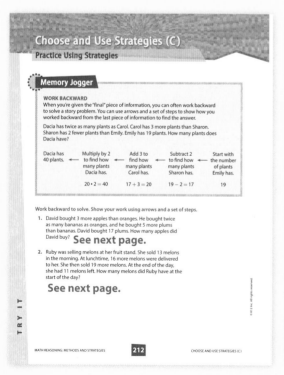

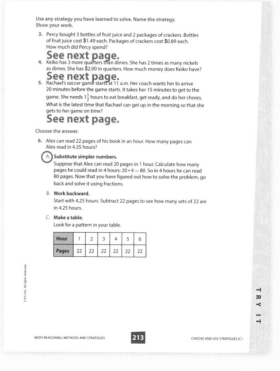

Additional Answers

1. David bought 9 apples. ← Add 3 to the number of oranges to find the number of apples. ← Divide the number of bananas by 2 to find the number of oranges. ← Subtract 5 from the number of plums to find the number of bananas. ← Start with the number of plums.

$6 + 3 = 9$ $12 \div 2 = 6$ $17 - 5 = 12$ 17

2. Ruby started the day with 27 melons. ← Add 13 to find how many melons Ruby had before selling any in the morning. ← Subtract 16 to find how many melons Ruby had before more were delivered. ← Add 19 to find how many melons Ruby had after lunchtime. ← Start with the number of melons Ruby had left at the end of the day.

$14 + 13 = 27$ $30 - 16 = 14$ $19 + 11 = 30$ 11

3. [The cost of 3 bottles of fruit juice] (plus) [the cost of 2 packages of crackers] (equals) [the amount Percy spent.]

$(3 \cdot \$1.49)$ $+$ $(2 \cdot \$0.89)$ $=$?

$\$4.47$ $+$ $\$1.78$ $=$ $\$6.25$

Percy spent $6.25.

4. There are 8 quarters, 5 dimes, and 10 nickels. ← Multiply by 2 to find the number of nickels. ← Subtract 3 to find the number of dimes. ← Divide by $0.25 to find the number of quarters in $2.00. ← Start with $2.00 in quarters.

$5 \cdot 2 = 10$ $8 - 3 = 5$ $\$2.00 \div \$0.25 = 8$ $\$2.00$

[8 quarters] (plus) [5 dimes] (plus) [10 nickels] (equals) [the total amount of money.]

$(8 \cdot \$0.25)$ $+$ $(5 \cdot \$0.10)$ $+$ $(10 \cdot \$0.05)$ $=$?

$\$2.00$ $+$ $\$0.50$ $+$ $\$0.50$ $=$ $\$3.00$

Keiko has $3.00.

5. Rachael must get up by 8:55 a.m. ← Subtract $1\frac{1}{2}$ hours. ← Subtract 15 minutes. ← Subtract 20 minutes. ← Start at 11:00 a.m.

8:55 a.m.   10:25 a.m.   10:40 a.m.   11:00 a.m.

ONLINE
10 min

CHECKPOINT

Objectives

Students will complete an online Checkpoint. If necessary, read the directions, problems, and answer choices to students and help them with keyboard or mouse operations.

- Identify and generalize methods for solving problems that are similar to each other.

Solve Simple to Complex Problems (A)

Lesson Overview

GET READY Mixed Number and Fraction Problems	10 minutes	**ONLINE**
LEARN Solve One-Step Story Problems	20 minutes	**OFFLINE**
LEARN Solve Multistep Story Problems	20 minutes	**OFFLINE**
TRY IT Practice Simple to Complex Problems	10 minutes	**ONLINE**

▶ Lesson Objectives

Apply strategies and results from simple story problems involving fractions to more complex problems.

▶ Prerequisite Skills

- Solve a story problem involving multiplication or division of fractions.
- Solve a simple problem involving addition or subtraction of fractions.

▶ Content Background

Students will use the 4-step problem-solving plan to solve simple to complex story problems.

   Although the context and numbers in story problems vary, good problem solvers realize that they can use certain strategies over and over to solve problems that are similar to each other. A strategy used to solve a simple problem is often the exact strategy needed to solve a more complex problem. When students learn and are able to use different strategies, they realize that instead of treating every problem they encounter as a new experience, they can apply successful strategies for solving problems that are more complex.

   As students work on solving problems, they should follow the 4-step problem-solving plan. The plan, developed by George Pólya, is an effective way to solve a variety of problems: (1) understand the problem; (2) devise a plan; (3) carry out the plan; and (4) look back.

▶ Advance Preparation

Print the Problem-Solving Plan.

GET READY Mixed Number and Fraction Problems

Students will solve multiplication and division story problems with whole numbers, fractions, and mixed numbers.

Objectives

- Solve a story problem involving multiplication or division of fractions.

LEARN Solve One-Step Story Problems

Students will use the problem-solving plan to solve one-step story problems with fractions and mixed numbers. They will solve simpler problems first and then more complex problems. Gather the Problem-Solving Plan. View or print the Solve One-Step Story Problems activity page.

   Students should copy the problems from the Activity Book into their Math Notebook as necessary and solve them there.

Objectives

- Apply strategies and results from simple story problems involving fractions to more complex problems.

1. Give students the Problem-Solving Plan. Briefly review the plan.

2. Tell students that the first Worked Example presents a simple problem and the second Worked Example presents a more complex problem. Tell them that the second Worked Example builds on the type of problem solving in the first Worked Example.

3. Read the first Worked Examples box with students. Tell students that during the "look back" step they should look at the problem and estimate the answer. Then they can compare the estimate with the answer they calculate.

4. Have students solve Problems 1 and 2 in the problem set. Tell them that as they solve the problems they should keep in mind that they will be solving more complex but similar problems next.

5. Read the second Worked Examples box with students.

6. Have students solve Problem 3 using the same methods that they used for Problems 1 and 2. Have them estimate what the answer should be and check to see if their answer is reasonable.

7. Repeat Step 6 for Problem 4.

8. Have students refer to the Worked Examples and the Problem-Solving Plan as needed.

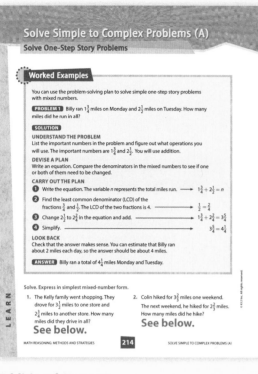

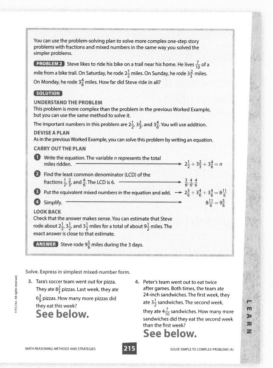

Additional Answers

1. $3\frac{1}{2} + 2\frac{3}{4} = 3\frac{2}{4} + 2\frac{3}{4}$

$\qquad\qquad = 5\frac{5}{4}$

$\qquad\qquad = 6\frac{1}{4}$

The Kelly family drove $6\frac{1}{4}$ miles in all.

2. $3\frac{2}{3} + 2\frac{2}{3} = 5\frac{4}{3}$

$\qquad\qquad\quad = 6\frac{1}{3}$

Colin hiked for $6\frac{1}{3}$ miles.

3. $8\frac{2}{3} - 6\frac{3}{9} = 8\frac{6}{9} - 6\frac{3}{9}$

$\qquad\qquad = 2\frac{3}{9}$

$\qquad\qquad = 2\frac{1}{3}$

Tara's team ate $2\frac{1}{3}$ more pizzas this week than last week.

4. $4\frac{7}{10} - 3\frac{1}{2} = 4\frac{7}{10} - 3\frac{5}{10}$

$\qquad\qquad = 1\frac{2}{10}$

$\qquad\qquad = 1\frac{1}{5}$

Peter's team ate $1\frac{1}{5}$ more sandwiches the second week than they ate the first week.

LEARN Solve Multistep Story Problems

Students will add, subtract, multiply, and divide to solve multistep story problems with fractions and mixed numbers. Gather the Problem-Solving Plan. View or print the Solve Multistep Story Problems activity page and read the directions with students.

Students should copy the problems from the Activity Book into their Math Notebook as necessary and solve them there.

1. Briefly review the Problem-Solving Plan with students.

2. Remind students that they have solved problems in which they have added, subtracted, multiplied, and divided whole numbers, fractions, and mixed numbers.

3. Tell students that the first Worked Example presents a problem that uses two operations but is not very complicated. Tell them that the second Worked Example builds on the type of problem solving in the first Worked Example and is more complex.

4. Read the first Worked Example with students.

5. Have students do Problem 1.

6. Remind students that the next Worked Example will be similar to Problem 1 but is more complex.

   Ask: What strategies did you just use in that problem that might help you solve a more complex problem? I used two equations to solve the problem. First I had to add, and I used common denominators to do that. Then I had to multiply. I simplified my answer.

7. Read the second Worked Example with students.

8. Have students do Problems 2 and 3.

   As they work, have them see if their strategy is helping them find the answer.

   Remind them to ask themselves questions as they complete each step of the problem-solving plan. After they solve a problem, ask them what processes they used that might help them solve more complex problems. Students might say that they used two equations to solve the problem, that they used common denominators to add, and that they simplified their answers.

Tips

If students have difficulty knowing which operations to use in a multistep problem, give them two operations and have them make up multistep story problems.

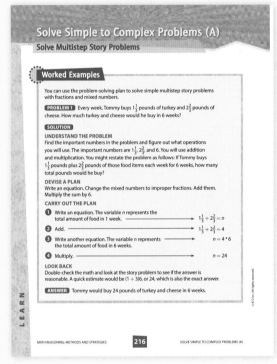

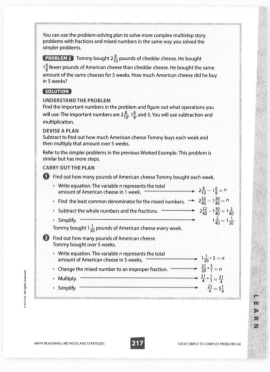

Additional Answers

1.
$$2\frac{2}{4} + 1\frac{1}{3} = 2\frac{6}{12} + 1\frac{4}{12}$$
$$= 3\frac{10}{12}$$
$$= 3\frac{5}{6}$$

Katie buys $3\frac{5}{6}$ pounds of fruit each week.

$$3\frac{5}{6} \cdot 4 = \frac{23}{6} \cdot \frac{4}{1}$$
$$= \frac{23}{3} \cdot \frac{2}{1}$$
$$= \frac{46}{3}$$
$$= 15\frac{1}{3}$$

Katie would buy $15\frac{1}{3}$ pounds of fruit in 4 weeks.

2.
$$5\frac{3}{4} - 1\frac{2}{3} = 5\frac{9}{12} - 1\frac{8}{12}$$
$$= 4\frac{1}{12}$$

Betsy volunteered $4\frac{1}{12}$ hours in February.

$$4\frac{1}{12} + 4\frac{1}{2} = 4\frac{1}{12} + 4\frac{6}{12}$$
$$= 8\frac{7}{12}$$

Betsy volunteered $8\frac{7}{12}$ hours in March.

3.
$$7\frac{1}{5} \div 4 = \frac{36}{5} \div 4$$
$$= \frac{36}{5} \cdot \frac{1}{4}$$
$$= \frac{9}{5} \cdot \frac{1}{1}$$
$$= \frac{9}{5}$$
$$= 1\frac{4}{5}$$

Adam ran $1\frac{4}{5}$ miles the first day.

$$1\frac{4}{5} + 2\frac{3}{8} = 1\frac{32}{40} + 2\frac{15}{40}$$
$$= 3\frac{47}{40}$$
$$= 4\frac{7}{40}$$

Adam ran and walked for $4\frac{7}{40}$ miles the first day.

ONLINE
10 min

TRY IT Practice Simple to Complex Problems

Objectives

Students will complete an online Try It. If necessary, read the directions, problems, and answer choices to students and help them with keyboard or mouse operations

- Apply strategies and results from simple story problems involving fractions to more complex problems.

Solve Simple to Complex Problems (B)

▶ Lesson Objectives

Apply strategies and results from simple story problems involving fractions to more complex problems.

▶ Prerequisite Skills

- Solve a story problem involving multiplication or division of fractions.
- Solve a simple problem involving addition or subtraction of fractions.

▶ Content Background

Students will learn to solve story problems with fractions, mixed numbers, and decimal numbers. They will also move from simpler problems to more complex problems.

Although the context and numbers in story problems vary, good problem solvers realize that they can use certain strategies over and over to solve problems that are similar to each other. A strategy used to solve a simple problem is often the exact strategy needed to solve a more complex problem. When students learn and are able to use different strategies, they realize that instead of treating every problem they encounter as a new experience, they can apply successful strategies for solving problems that are more complex.

As students work on solving problems, they should follow the 4-step problem-solving plan. The following problem-solving plan, developed by George Pólya, is an effective way to solve a variety of problems: (1) understand the problem; (2) devise a plan; (3) carry out the plan; and (4) look back.

▶ Advance Preparation

Print the Problem-Solving Plan.

Materials to Gather

SUPPLIED

Problem-Solving Plan (printout)

Fractions as Decimals in Story Problems activity page

Convert Measurements in Story Problems activity page

GET READY Addition and Subtraction of Fractions

Students will solve simple story problems involving addition or subtraction of fractions and mixed numbers.

- Solve a simple problem involving addition or subtraction of fractions.

LEARN Fractions as Decimals in Story Problems

Students will use the problem-solving plan to solve multistep story problems in which they need to change fractions and mixed numbers to decimal numbers. The problems will become more complex. Gather the Problem-Solving Plan. View or print the Fractions as Decimals in Story Problems activity page and read the directions with students.

Students should copy the problems from the Activity Book into their Math Notebook as necessary and solve them there.

1. Give students the Problem-Solving Plan and tell them to refer to it during the activity.

2. Read the Worked Examples box with students. Tell them that it shows a simple story problem about money.

   Ask: What was the first step in the Worked Examples? I changed $3\frac{1}{5}$ to a decimal number to multiply the amount of ribbon by the cost per meter.

3. Read Problem 1 with students.

   Ask: What operations will you need to use to solve this problem? addition and multiplication

   Make sure students know that they need to change the two mixed numbers to decimal numbers and add them.

   Ask: What plan will you use? I need to change each mixed number to a decimal amount, add the two amounts of ribbon together, and multiply the sum by the price per yard of ribbon.

4. Have students find the product of $7.25 and $1.50. $10.875

   Tell students that money values are shown to the hundredths place with decimal numbers, so they need to round the answer to the nearest cent. Tell them that no matter what value is in the thousandths place, stores usually round dollar amounts up to the next penny.

   Guide students to see that because the amount is $10.875, Jenny paid $10.88.

5. Ask students to estimate what the answer would be. One estimate is approximately $10.50. They should confirm that their answer makes sense.

6. Check students' work after they complete each problem in this activity. Remind them to ask themselves questions as they complete each step of the problem-solving plan. One question they should ask themselves is, "Is my strategy helping me find the answer?"

7. Have students solve Problem 2.

   After students look back at how they solved Problem 2, explain that Problems 3 and 4 will be similar to the first two problems but will be more complex. For example, the problems will contain extra information that students don't need to solve the problems.

Tips

If students have difficulty changing fractions and mixed numbers to decimal numbers, have them make a reference table. Write fractions with denominators of 4, 5, and 8 and have them change them to decimal numbers.

Ask: What strategies did you use in the first two problems that might help you solve a more complex problem? I changed the mixed numbers to decimal numbers before calculating the answer.

8. Have students read Problem 3.

   Ask: Is there any information you don't need to know in the problem? Yes, I don't need to know that Kevin got to the store at 7:00 p.m. or that it took him 15 minutes to check out.

   Have students complete Problem 3.

9. Have students read Problem 4.

   Ask: Is there any information you don't need to know in the problem? Yes, I don't need to know that Amy is using blinds on three windows. I don't need to know the measurements of those three windows.

   Have students complete Problem 4.

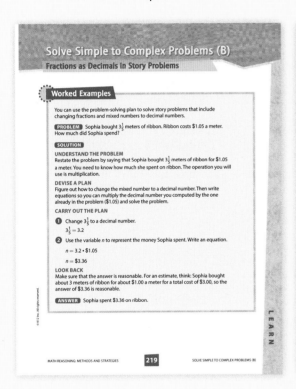

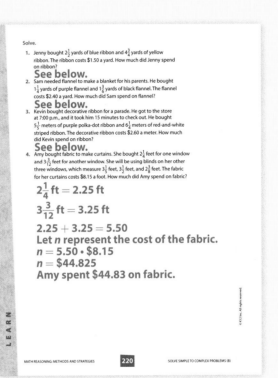

Additional Answers

1. $2\frac{1}{2}$ yd = 2.5 yd

   $4\frac{3}{4}$ yd = 4.75 yd

   2.50 + 4.75 = 7.25

   Let *n* represent the cost of the ribbon.

   n = 7.25 • $1.50

   n = $10.875

   Jenny spent $10.88 on ribbon.

2. $1\frac{1}{4}$ yd = 1.25 yd

   $1\frac{3}{6}$ yd = 1.5 yd

   1.25 + 1.5 = 2.75

   Let *n* represent the cost of the flannel.

   n = 2.75 • $2.40

   n = $6.60

   Sam spent $6.60 on flannel.

3. $5\frac{1}{5}$ m = 5.2 m

   $6\frac{1}{4}$ m = 6.25 m

   5.2 + 6.25 = 11.45

   Let *n* represent the cost of the decorative ribbon.

   n = 11.45 • $2.60

   n = $29.77

   Kevin spent $29.77 on decorative ribbon.

Students will use the problem-solving plan for complex problems in which they need to convert measurements from one unit to another. Gather the Problem-Solving Plan. View or print the Convert Measurements in Story Problems activity page and read the directions with students.

Students should copy the problems from the Activity Book into their Math Notebook as necessary and solve them there.

1. Read the Worked Examples box with students. Give them the Problem-Solving Plan to refer to as they solve the problems.

2. Guide students to understand the conversion of the gallons of water to pounds of water. Tell them that they need to know the weight of 1 gallon of water to convert the measurement, and they will need to know how to convert from one unit of measure to another to solve the problems in this activity.

3. Explain to students that Problem 1 will be similar to the Worked Example but is more complex.

   Ask: What strategies did you use in the Worked Example that might help you solve a more complex problem? I changed the mixed number to a decimal number. Then I multiplied the weight of 1 gallon of water by the decimal value of $3\frac{8}{10}$ to find out the weight of $3\frac{8}{10}$ gallons of water.

4. Have students read Problem 1. Have them ask themselves questions in the "understand the problem" step, including the following:

   Ask: What measurements do I need to convert? gallons of water to pounds of water

   Ask: What operations do I need to use to solve the problem? addition and multiplication

   Ask: Is there extra information in the problem? Yes, the problem tells me that Bella's aunt brought $\frac{1}{4}$ gallon of water.

5. Have students ask themselves questions about the "devise a plan" step, including the following:

   Ask: Would a diagram, table, chart, or graph help me with this problem? No, This problem requires calculation of the data.

   Ask: What equations will I use? I'll change each of the mixed-number values I need for the problem into decimal numbers. Then I'll add the number of gallons of water that Bella and her uncle had. Finally I'll multiply the total gallons of water by 8.35 to find out how much the combined gallons of water weigh.

6. Guide students to carry out their plan. Have them carefully make the calculations. Have them ask themselves, "Is my strategy helping me find the answer?"

7. Remind students that the next step in the 4-step problem-solving plan is to "look back." Have them check their math and make sure they answered the question in the problem.

   Ask: What strategies did you use in this problem that might help you solve other problems? I changed the mixed numbers to decimal numbers. Then I added the data that had the same unit of measurement. Finally, I multiplied the total number of gallons by the weight of 1 gallon of water to find out how many pounds the total gallons of water weighed.

8. Check students' work after they complete each problem in this activity.

9. Have students solve the rest of the problems. Remind them to ask themselves questions as they complete each step of the problem-solving plan.

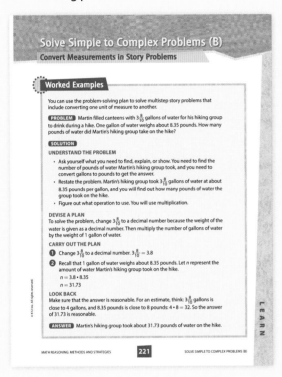

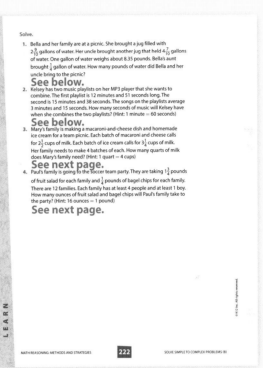

Additional Answers

1. $2\frac{9}{10}$ gallons = 2.9 gallons

   $4\frac{7}{10}$ gallons = 4.7 gallons

   $2.9 + 4.7 = 7.6$

   Let n represent the amount of water Bella and her uncle brought to the picnic.

   $n = 7.6 \cdot 8.35$

   $n = 63.46$

   Bella and her uncle brought about 63.46 pounds of water to the picnic.

2. Add 12 minutes and 15 minutes.

   $12 + 15 = 27$

   Multiply 27 minutes by 60 seconds per minute to find the number of seconds in 27 minutes.

   $27 \cdot 60 = 1,620$

   There are 1,620 seconds in 27 minutes.

   Add 51 seconds and 38 seconds.

   $51 + 38 = 89$

   Add 1,620 seconds and 89 seconds to find the total number of seconds on the combined playlists.

   $1,620 + 89 = 1,709$

   Kelsey will have 1,709 seconds of music when she combines the two playlists.

3. Calculate how many cups of milk are needed for macaroni and cheese.

$2\frac{1}{2} \cdot 4 = 10$

Mary's family needs 10 cups of milk to make macaroni and cheese.

Calculate how many cups of milk are needed for ice cream.

$3\frac{1}{4} \cdot 4 = 13$

Mary's family needs 13 cups of milk to make ice cream.

Calculate how many cups of milk are needed in all.

$10 + 13 = 23$

Mary's family needs 23 cups of milk in all.

Calculate how many quarts are in 23 cups.

$23 \div 4 = 5\frac{3}{4}$

Mary's family needs $5\frac{3}{4}$ quarts of milk.

4. Calculate how many pounds of fruit salad are needed.

$1\frac{3}{4} \cdot 12 = 21$

So 21 pounds of fruit salad are needed.

Calculate how many pounds of bagel chips are needed.

$\frac{1}{4} \cdot 12 = 3$

So 3 pounds of bagel chips are needed.

Calculate how many pounds of fruit salad and bagel chips are needed in all.

$21 + 3 = 24$

So 24 pounds of fruit salad and bagel chips are needed in all.

Calculate how many ounces are in 24 pounds.

$24 \cdot 16 = 384$

Paul's family will take 384 ounces of fruit salad and bagel chips to the party.

TRY IT Practice Story Problems

ONLINE 10 min

Students will complete an online Try It. If necessary, read the directions, problems, and answer choices to students and help them with keyboard or mouse operations.

Objectives

- Apply strategies and results from simple story problems involving fractions to more complex problems.

CHECKPOINT

ONLINE 10 min

Students will complete an online Checkpoint. If necessary, read the directions, problems, and answer choices to students and help them with keyboard or mouse operations.

Objectives

- Apply strategies and results from simple story problems involving fractions to more complex problems.

Core Focus
Reasoning with Data and Division

Lesson Overview

LEARN Data and Division	20 minutes	ONLINE
TRY IT Data and Division Reasoning	20 minutes	OFFLINE
CHECKPOINT	20 minutes	OFFLINE

▶ Lesson Objectives

- Graph or write an equation to solve a problem that involves a linear function.
- Estimate or calculate a product or quotient in a whole-number story problem.
- Solve for one variable in a two-variable equation when the value of the other variable is given.

▶ Content Background

Students will apply their math reasoning skills to problems involving multiple representations, such as equations, graphs, and tables. They will analyze data to answer questions for given scenarios. More practice with division of multidigit dividends by two-digit divisors will be incorporated into the problems.

▶ Advance Preparation

Print the Graph for Trucker Data.

Materials to Gather

SUPPLIED

Graph for Trucker Data (printout)

Data and Division Reasoning activity page

Checkpoint (printout)

Checkpoint Answer Key (printout)

ALSO NEEDED:

ruler, dual-scale

ONLINE
20min

LEARN Data and Division

Students will use equations to complete data in a table and graph. They will then answer questions related to the data, which will include the use of multidigit division.

Objectives

- Graph or write an equation to solve a problem that involves a linear function.

- Estimate or calculate a product or quotient in a whole-number story problem.

- Solve for one variable in a two-variable equation when the value of the other variable is given.

TRY IT Data and Division Reasoning

Objectives

Students will practice making, checking, and verifying predictions about quantities of objects. Gather the Graph for Trucker Data printout and ruler. View or print the Reasoning with Data and Division activity page. Students should copy the problems into their Math Notebook and solve them there.

- Graph or write an equation to solve a problem that involves a linear function.

- Estimate or calculate a product or quotient in a whole-number story problem.

- Solve for one variable in a two-variable equation when the value of the other variable is given.

Core Focus
Reasoning with Data and Division

Data and Division Reasoning

Use the information in this scenario to answer all the questions.

A trucker is planning her next trip across several states. She has plenty of time to deliver her haul, so she is looking at data to determine whether to take the back roads, which are more scenic, or the interstate, which is faster. She can average 55 miles per hour on the back roads and 70 miles per hour on the interstate.

1. Use the general equation distance = rate · time to write one equation to represent the data for the back roads and another equation to represent the interstate data. (Use d_b to represent the distance on the back roads and d_i for the distance on the interstate.)

$$d_b = 55t$$
$$d_b = 70t$$

2. Copy the table and enter the missing values. Show your work. **See below.**

Time (h)	Distance for back roads (mi)	Distance for interstate (mi)
5	275	350
10	550	700
15	(a)	1,050
20	1,100	(b)
25	(c)	(d)
30	1,650	2,100

3. Use the same pair of axes to graph at least 3 points for each set of **See below.** data. Draw lines through the points for each graph. (Place the label b at the end of the line for the back roads data and the label i at the end of the line for the interstate data.)

4. The driver receives a notice that the actual distance of the first part of her trip will be 1,925 miles.

(a) How many hours will this trip take on the back roads? Show your work. **35 hours; 1,925 ÷ 55 = 35**

(b) How many hours will this trip take on the interstate? Show your work. **27.5 hours; 1,925 ÷ 70 = 27.5**

TRY IT

Additional Answers

2. (a) 825; $d_b = 55(15)$
   (b) 1,400; $d_i = 70(20)$
   (c) 1,375; $d_b = 55(25)$
   (d) 1,750; $d_i = 70(25)$

3.

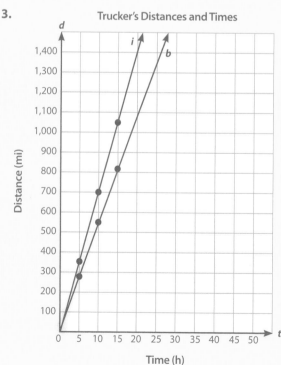

Trucker's Distances and Times

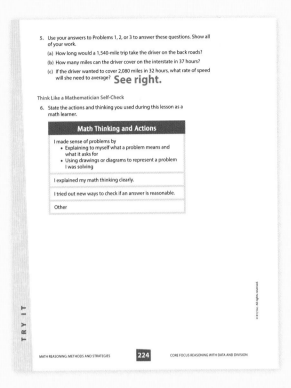

5. Use your answers to Problems 1, 2, or 3 to answer these questions. Show all of your work.

(a) How long would a 1,540-mile trip take the driver on the back roads?

(b) How many miles can the driver cover on the interstate in 37 hours?

(c) If the driver wanted to cover 2,080 miles in 32 hours, what rate of speed will she need to average? **See right.**

Think Like a Mathematician Self-Check

6. State the actions and thinking you used during this lesson as a math learner.

Math Thinking and Actions
I made sense of problems by • Explaining to myself what a problem means and what it asks for • Using drawings or diagrams to represent a problem I was solving
I explained my math thinking clearly.
I tried out new ways to check if an answer is reasonable.
Other

MATH REASONING: METHODS AND STRATEGIES · 224 · CORE FOCUS REASONING WITH DATA AND DIVISION

Additional Answers

5. **(a)** 28 hours; $1{,}540 \div 55 = 28$

(b) 2,590 miles; $70 \cdot 37 = 2{,}590$

(c) 65 miles per hour; $2{,}080 \div 32 = 65$

OFFLINE

CHECKPOINT

20 min

Objectives

The Checkpoint and its answer key are located in the Resources section for this unit in the Online Book Menu of *Math+ Yellow Lesson Guide*. Give students the Checkpoint. Have students complete the Checkpoint on their own. Use the answer key to score the Checkpoint, and then enter the results online.

- Graph or write an equation to solve a problem that involves a linear function.

- Estimate or calculate a product or quotient in a whole-number story problem.

- Solve for one variable in a two-variable equation when the value of the other variable is given.

Unit Review

Lesson Overview		
UNIT REVIEW Look Back	10 minutes	**ONLINE**
UNIT REVIEW Checkpoint Practice	50 minutes	**ONLINE**
↳ **UNIT REVIEW** Prepare for the Checkpoint		

▶ Unit Objectives

- Prioritize and sequence the information in a story problem that involves multiplication or division of decimal numbers.
- Determine when and how to break a multistep whole-number story problem or money problem into simpler parts.
- Use a variety of methods, such as words, numbers, symbols, charts, graphs, tables, diagrams, and models, to explain mathematical reasoning in nonroutine or complex problems.
- Identify and generalize methods for solving problems that are similar to each other.
- Apply strategies and results from simple story problems involving fractions to more complex problems.
- Graph or write an equation to solve a problem that involves a linear function.
- Estimate or calculate a product or quotient in a whole-number story problem.
- Solve for one variable in a two-variable equation when the value of the other variable is given.

Materials to Gather

There are no materials to gather for this lesson.

▶ Advance Preparation

In this lesson, students will have an opportunity to review previous activities in the Math Reasoning: Methods and Strategies unit. Look at the suggested activities in Unit Review: Prepare for the Checkpoint online and gather any needed materials.

ONLINE

10 min

UNIT REVIEW Look Back

Students will review key concepts from the unit to prepare for the Unit Checkpoint.

Objectives

- Review unit objectives.

ONLINE
50min

- Review unit objectives.

Students will complete an online Checkpoint Practice to prepare for the Unit Checkpoint. If necessary, read the directions, problems, and answer choices to students. Have students answer the problems on their own. Review any missed problems with students.

→ UNIT REVIEW Prepare for the Checkpoint

What you do next depends on how students performed in the previous activity, Unit Review: Checkpoint Practice. If students had difficulty with any of the problems, complete the appropriate review activity listed in the table online.

Unit Checkpoint

UNIT CHECKPOINT   60 minutes   **ONLINE**

▶ **Unit Objectives**

- Prioritize and sequence the information in a story problem that involves multiplication or division of decimal numbers.
- Determine when and how to break a multistep whole-number story problem or money problem into simpler parts.
- Use a variety of methods, such as words, numbers, symbols, charts, graphs, tables, diagrams, and models, to explain mathematical reasoning in nonroutine or complex problems.
- Identify and generalize methods for solving problems that are similar to each other.
- Apply strategies and results from simple story problems involving fractions to more complex problems.
- Graph or write an equation to solve a problem that involves a linear function.
- Estimate or calculate a product or quotient in a whole-number story problem.
- Solve for one variable in a two-variable equation when the value of the other variable is given.

Materials to Gather

There are no materials to gather for this lesson.

UNIT CHECKPOINT   ONLINE **60**min   **Objectives**

Students will complete the Unit Checkpoint online. If necessary, read the directions, problems, and answer choices to students and help them with keyboard or mouse operations.

- Assess unit objectives.

Extended Problems: Reasoning

GRADED ASSIGNMENT	60 minutes	OFFLINE

▶ Lesson Objectives

- Determine when and how to break a multistep, whole-number story problem or money problem into simpler parts.
- Use a variety of methods, such as words, numbers, symbols, charts, graphs, tables, diagrams, and models, to explain mathematical reasoning in nonroutine or complex problems.
- Apply strategies and results from simple story problems involving fractions to more complex problems.
- Solve word problems involving addition and subtraction of fractions referring to the same whole, including fractions with unlike denominators.
- Solve real-world problems involving multiplication of fractions and mixed numbers.
- Generate a number or shape pattern that follows a given rule.
- Analyze complex problems using mathematical knowledge and skills.

Materials to Gather

SUPPLIED

Extended Problems: Reasoning (printout)

GRADED ASSIGNMENT

OFFLINE
60 min

Objectives

- Analyze complex problems using mathematical knowledge and skills.

Open the Extended Problems: Reasoning. Read the directions, problems, and answer choices to students, if necessary.

You will grade this assignment.

- Students should complete the assignment on their own.
- Students should submit the completed assignment to you.
- Enter the results online.

Math Reasoning: Solutions

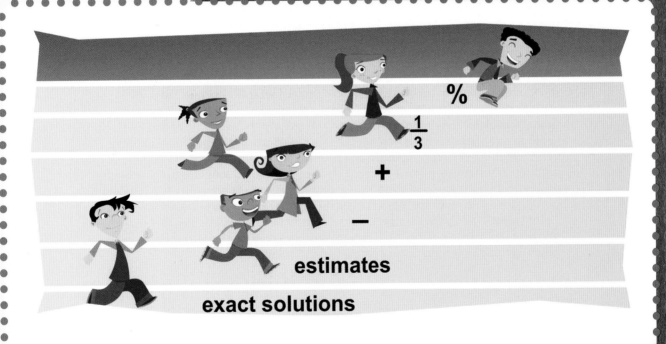

- Express clear and logical solutions to equal-measures problems and rate problems.
- Use estimation in addition or subtraction of fractions to verify whether calculated results are reasonable.
- Convert among different-sized standard measurement units within a given measurement system.
- Solve a story problem involving equal measures.
- Use measurement conversions to solve single- and multistep real-world problems.
- Explain the advantages of exact solutions and approximate solutions to problems involving addition or subtraction of decimal numbers, and give answers to a specified degree of accuracy, such as hundredths.
- Make precise calculations and use the situation presented in a problem involving decimal-number operations to check the validity of the result.
- Evaluate whether a solution for a problem is reasonable.

▶ Big Ideas

Estimation is a useful tool in problem solving.

▶ Unit Introduction

In this unit, students will develop ways to solve story problems by expressing clear and logical solutions to problems that involve equal measures and rate. They will use estimation to verify whether calculated results are reasonable for addition and subtraction of fractions in story problems.

Students will explain the advantages of exact solutions and approximate solutions to story problems involving addition and subtraction of decimal numbers. In these problems, students will make precise calculations as they find solutions to a specified degree of accuracy. They will check the validity of their calculated results. In the process of solving story problems, students will evaluate whether a problem's solution is reasonable.

Throughout this unit, students will continue to use George Pólya's 4-step problem-solving plan to understand the problem, devise and carry out a plan to solve the problem, and then look back and compare the original problem and its solution.

▶ Keywords

approximate solution
degree of accuracy

exact solution
rate

reasonableness

Solve Problems Logically

▶ Lesson Objectives

Express clear and logical solutions to equal-measures problems and rate problems.

▶ Prerequisite Skills

- Solve a story problem involving rate.
- Solve a story problem involving equal measures.
- Express the solution to a story problem clearly and logically.

▶ Content Background

Students will learn to express their solutions to equal-measures story problems clearly and logically. They will write solutions step by step.

The following problem-solving plan, developed by George Pólya, is an effective way to solve a variety of story problems: (1) understand the problem; (2) devise a plan; (3) carry out the plan; and (4) look back. As students work on solving problems, they should follow the 4-step problem-solving plan. In the "carry out the plan" step, they express their solutions to the problem in a clear and logical manner.

Expressing clear and logical solutions to problems is an important part of studying mathematics. This is the "show your work" step used by mathematicians throughout history. The use of clear language and appropriate mathematical notation and terms is critical. Students should support their solutions to a problem with evidence in both words and symbols.

These skills are critical in everyday life. The ability to create and report information to share with others has become a necessary skill in the information age. In fact, many standardized tests now include writing sections in which students are graded on their ability to write and clearly express their understanding.

In an equal-measures story problem, several equal-sized measures, or parts, combine to make a total measurement amount. To solve problems involving equal measures, students can multiply or divide, depending on the situation and information given. When the number of parts and the measure of each part are given, students can multiply to find the total measurement. When the total measurement and the measure of one part are given, they can divide to find the number of parts. When the total measurement and the number of parts are given, they can divide to find the measure of each part.

Materials to Gather

SUPPLIED

Problem-Solving Plan (printout)

Solve Equal-Measures Problems activity page

Print the Problem-Solving Plan.

GET READY Multiply and Divide Equal Measures

ONLINE 10 min

Objectives

Students will solve a problem about the measurement of each equal part in a whole. They also will solve other equal-measures problems.

- Solve a story problem involving rate.
- Solve a story problem involving equal measures.
- Express the solution to a story problem clearly and logically.

LEARN Solve a Guided Equal-Measures Problem

ONLINE 15 min

Objectives

Students will use the 4-step problem-solving plan, as well as clear and logical steps, to find the solution to an equal-measures story problem.

- Express clear and logical solutions to equal-measures problems and rate problems.

LEARN Solve Equal-Measures Problems

OFFLINE 25 min

Objectives

Students will use the 4-step problem-solving plan to solve equal-measures story problems. They will write the steps in a clear and logical order to find the solution. Gather the Problem-Solving Plan. View or print the Solve Equal-Measures Problems activity page.

- Express clear and logical solutions to equal-measures problems and rate problems.

Students should copy the problems from the Activity Book into their Math Notebook as necessary and solve them there.

1. Read the Worked Examples box with students. Give them the Problem-Solving Plan to refer to as they solve the problem.

   Ask: What are you asked to do in this problem? Explain how to calculate the difference in length between one piece of red ribbon and one piece of white ribbon.

2. Have students identify the total amount of red ribbon in the problem, the total amount of white ribbon, and the number of projects in which the ribbon will be used 50 inches; 20 inches; 5 projects

   Remind them that the red ribbon and the white ribbon are cut into equal-sized pieces and shared equally among the 5 projects.

   Ask: Why was division used to find the length of each piece of red ribbon and each piece of white ribbon? The problem is about equal lengths of ribbon that will be used in 5 projects, so the ribbon needed to be divided into equal lengths.

   Ask: Why was subtraction used next? The problem asked for the difference in length between the two different colors of ribbon.

3. Remind students that the "look back" part of the 4-step problem-solving plan gives them an opportunity to check their calculations to make sure they did the math correctly and answered the question in the problem. Have students review the calculations in the "carry out the plan" section. Guide them to use inverse operations to check the math in each calculation.

4. Read Problem 1 with students. Have them ask themselves these questions:

   - **What am I being asked to explain?** how to calculate how many gallons of gas Mr. Keefer's truck uses each year

   - **What information do I have?** Mr. Keefer drives 450 miles a day, 250 days a year. His truck can drive 15 miles on each gallon of gas.

   - **What information do I need?** how many miles Mr. Keefer drives in a year and how fuel efficient his truck is, in terms of miles to the gallon

   - **What number do I divide the number of miles Mr. Keefer drives in a year by to find how much gas he uses in a year?** 15

5. Help students devise a strategy to solve the problem. As they come up with each step of the strategy, have them ask themselves which operation they should use to carry it out. Tell students to write the operation beside each step of their strategy.

6. Have students carry out their plan and do the calculations.

7. Guide students to look back at their work and check their calculations.

8. Have students do Problems 2–4. Remind them to ask themselves questions as they complete each step of the problem-solving plan.

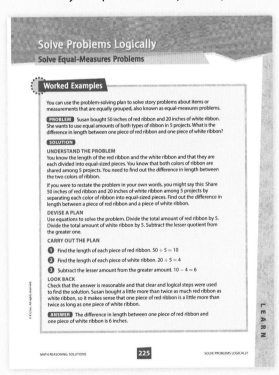

Additional Answers

1. **Step 1:** Multiply. 450 • 250
   Step 2: Divide. 112,500 ÷ 15
   Mr. Keefer's truck uses 7,500 gallons of gas each year.

2. **Step 1:** Multiply. 7 • 3
   Step 2: Multiply. 5 • 3
   Step 3: Subtract the amount of banana chips (lesser product) from the amount of raisins (greater product). 21 − 15
   Tommy's friends ate 6 more ounces of raisins than banana chips.

3. **Step 1:** Divide. 120 ÷ 4
   Step 2: Divide. 212 ÷ 4
   Step 3: Subtract the amount of chicken (lesser quotient) from the amount of turkey (greater quotient). 53 − 30
   One serving of turkey has 23 grams more mass than one serving of chicken.

ONLINE
10 min

TRY IT Work with Equal-Measures Problems

Objectives

Students will complete an online Try It. If necessary, read the directions, problems, and answer choices to students and help them with keyboard or mouse operations.

- Express clear and logical solutions to equal-measures problems and rate problems.

Estimation and Reasonable Answers

Lesson Overview		
GET READY Add and Subtract Fractions	10 minutes	ONLINE
LEARN Use Estimation	15 minutes	ONLINE
LEARN Reasonable Answers	15 minutes	OFFLINE
TRY IT Verify Answers	10 minutes	ONLINE
CHECKPOINT	10 minutes	ONLINE

▶ ## Lesson Objectives

Use estimation in addition or subtraction of fractions to verify whether calculated results are reasonable.

▶ ## Prerequisite Skills

- Use estimation to predict a solution to a story problem and to verify the reasonableness of the calculated result.
- Solve a simple problem involving addition or subtraction of fractions.

▶ ## Content Background

Students will learn to use estimation to verify the reasonableness of answers to addition and subtraction fraction story problems.

The following problem-solving steps were developed by George Pólya and are an effective way to solve a variety of story problems: (1) understand the problem; (2) devise a plan; (3) carry out the plan; and (4) look back. As students work on solving problems, they should follow the 4-step problem-solving plan. In the "carry out the plan" step, students show their solutions to the problem in a clear and logical manner.

Although the context and numbers in story problems vary, good problem solvers know they can use certain strategies over and over to solve similar problems. Estimating the answer to a problem and verifying the reasonableness of the calculated answer to the estimate enhance students' number-sense development. When students learn to use different strategies, they can apply successful strategies to solve more complex problems, instead of treating every problem as a new experience.

Students can estimate and calculate answers to all types of problems. Being able to use the estimate to evaluate the reasonableness of the calculated answer involves students asking themselves questions such as the following: Did I choose the correct operation to solve the problem? How does my calculated answer compare to my estimated answer?

Materials to Gather

SUPPLIED

number lines from Number Line Creator Tool

Reasonable Answers activity page

▶ Advance Preparation

DIRECTIONS FOR USING THE NUMBER LINE CREATOR TOOL

To create number lines from 0 to 5:

1. Set Range:	2. Select Options:	3. Print Number Line:
• Start Number Line at: 0 • End Number Line at: 5	• Tick Marks: ones, halves, fourths • Labels: ones, halves, fourths • Label Format: fractions	• Page Orientation: landscape • Number Lines per Sheet: 4

To create number lines from 2 to 8:

1. Set Range:	2. Select Options:	3. Print Number Line:
• Start Number Line at: 2 • End Number Line at: 8	• Tick Marks: ones, halves, fourths • Labels: ones, halves, fourths • Label Format: fractions	• Page Orientation: landscape • Number Lines per Sheet: 4

GET READY Add and Subtract Fractions

ONLINE 10 min

Students will practice adding and subtracting fractions and mixed numbers with like or unlike denominators.

Objectives

• Use estimation to predict a solution to a story problem and to verify the reasonableness of the calculated result.

• Solve a simple problem involving addition or subtraction of fractions.

LEARN Use Estimation

ONLINE 15 min

Students will use estimation to determine whether the answers to fraction and mixed-number addition and subtraction story problems are reasonable.

Objectives

• Use estimation in addition or subtraction of fractions to verify whether calculated results are reasonable.

LEARN Reasonable Answers

OFFLINE 15 min

Students will use estimation and the 4-step problem-solving plan to verify whether the answer to a story problem is reasonable. They will explain their process in finding out the reasonableness of the answers. Gather the number lines you printed. View or print the Reasonable Answers activity page and read the directions with students.

Students should copy the problems from the Activity Book into their Math Notebook as necessary and solve them there.

1. Read the Worked Example with students. Give them the number line from 2 to 8 showing fourths.

Objectives

• Use estimation in addition or subtraction of fractions to verify whether calculated results are reasonable.

2. Tell students to explain how to use a number line to estimate the sum of $3\frac{7}{10}$ and $3\frac{1}{5}$. Since $3\frac{7}{10}$ is close to but less than the benchmark number $3\frac{3}{4}$, I can locate $3\frac{3}{4}$ on the number line. Then I can count on $3\frac{1}{4}$ units because $3\frac{1}{4}$ is a benchmark number for $3\frac{1}{5}$.

3. Tell students that the Worked Example finds the exact answer. Remind students that they will compare their estimate and exact answer to decide whether the answers are reasonable.

4. Have students read Problem 1. Give them the number line from 0 to 5 showing fourths.

   Ask: What does the problem ask? how many more cups of granola than cups of raisins are in each batch

   Ask: What information is given that isn't necessary for solving the problem? Each batch uses $\frac{5}{6}$ cup of chocolate chips.

5. Have students explain how to use the number line to estimate the answer. Since $4\frac{1}{2}$ is a benchmark number, locate it on the number line. Find that $1\frac{2}{7}$ is close to but less than the benchmark number $1\frac{1}{4}$. Count $1\frac{1}{4}$ units back from $4\frac{1}{2}$ on the number line.

6. Tell students to complete the "look back" step of the problem-solving plan.

   Ask: Is Hector's exact answer reasonable compared with your estimate? Why or why not? Answers will vary. Students may say that they can see on the number line that the estimate is close to the exact answer. They may also change the mixed numbers so the fractions have common denominators and then compare the mixed numbers.

7. Have students finish solving Problem 1. Have them solve the remaining problems. Students may use number lines to help them estimate.

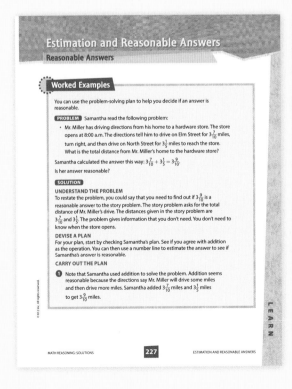

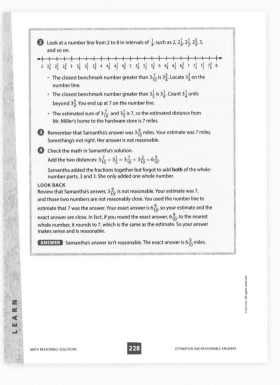

Use estimation to find out if the answer is reasonable. Explain.

1. Hector read this problem:

   Patsy is making trail mix. She needs $4\frac{1}{2}$ cups of granola, $1\frac{2}{7}$ cups of raisins, and $\frac{5}{6}$ cup of chocolate chips for each batch. How many more cups of granola than raisins does she need?

   Hector calculated the answer this way: $4\frac{1}{2} - 1\frac{2}{7} = 3\frac{3}{14}$.

   Is his answer reasonable? **See right.**

2. Anna solved this problem and said the answer was $7\frac{7}{8}$ feet:

   Molly had a piece of lace $4\frac{3}{4}$ feet long. She used $1\frac{1}{8}$ feet for a sewing project and gave her sister $2\frac{1}{4}$ feet to use on a pillow. How much lace did Molly have left?

   Is Anna's answer reasonable? **See right.**

3. Jack solved this problem and said the answer was $1\frac{1}{10}$ feet:

   Trent cut two pieces of wood. One piece of wood was $3\frac{4}{5}$ feet long. He also cut a piece of wood that was $4\frac{7}{10}$ feet long. What was the total length of both pieces of wood?

   Is Jack's answer reasonable? **See right.**

L E A R N

Answers

1. Yes. Estimate the granola at $4\frac{1}{2}$ cups. Estimate the raisins at $1\frac{1}{4}$ cups. Subtract: $4\frac{1}{2} - 1\frac{1}{4} = 3\frac{1}{4}$.

   The estimate, $3\frac{1}{4}$, is close to the exact answer of $3\frac{3}{14}$.

   To further check your answer, calculate that $3\frac{1}{4} = 3\frac{7}{28}$ and that $3\frac{3}{14} = 3\frac{6}{28}$. The estimate is close to the exact answer.

2. No. Estimate that Molly started with about 5 feet of lace, used about 1 foot for her sewing project, and gave her sister about 2 feet. The operations are addition of the lace pieces she used or gave away and subtraction from the amount of lace she started with.

   $5 - (1 + 2) = 2$

   Molly had about 2 feet of lace left.

   Anna's answer was $7\frac{7}{8}$ feet. Your estimate was about 2 feet. Something's not right. Anna's answer is not reasonable. Check the math in Anna's solution.

   Add the amount of lace Molly gave away: $1\frac{1}{8} + 2\frac{1}{4} = 1\frac{1}{8} + 2\frac{2}{8} = 3\frac{3}{8}$.

   Subtract the amount of lace Molly gave away from 5:

   $5 - 3\frac{3}{8} = 4\frac{8}{8} - 3\frac{3}{8} = 1\frac{5}{8}$.

   Anna incorrectly added all three lengths of the lace.

   The exact answer is $1\frac{5}{8}$ feet of lace left. Your estimate and exact answer are close. In fact, if you round the exact answer, $1\frac{5}{8}$, to the nearest whole number, it rounds to 2, which is the same as the estimate. Your answer makes sense and is reasonable.

3. No. Estimate that Trent cut a piece of wood that was about 4 feet long and a piece of wood that was about $4\frac{1}{2}$ feet long. The operation is addition.

   $4 + 4\frac{1}{2} = 8\frac{1}{2}$

   The wood pieces were a total of about $8\frac{1}{2}$ feet long.

   Jack's answer was $1\frac{1}{10}$ feet. Your estimate was about $8\frac{1}{2}$ feet. Something's not right. Jack's answer is not reasonable. Check the math in Jack's solution.

   Add the lengths of the two pieces of wood:

   $3\frac{4}{5} + 4\frac{7}{10} = 3\frac{8}{10} + 4\frac{7}{10} = 7\frac{15}{10} = 8\frac{5}{10} = 8\frac{1}{2}$.

   Jack used subtraction instead of addition.

   The exact answer is $8\frac{1}{2}$ feet of wood pieces. Your estimate and exact answer are the same, so your answer makes sense and is reasonable.

TRY IT Verify Answers

ONLINE 10 min

Objectives

- Use estimation in addition or subtraction of fractions to verify whether calculated results are reasonable.

Students will complete an online Try It. If necessary, read the directions, problems, and answer choices to students and help them with keyboard or mouse operations.

CHECKPOINT

ONLINE 10 min

Objectives

- Use estimation in addition or subtraction of fractions to verify whether calculated results are reasonable.

Students will complete an online Checkpoint. If necessary, read the directions, problems, and answer choices to students and help them with keyboard or mouse operations.

Change Measurement

Lesson Overview

GET READY Measurement Match	10 minutes	ONLINE
LEARN Units of Length	5 minutes	ONLINE
LEARN Units of Capacity	5 minutes	ONLINE
LEARN Units of Time	5 minutes	ONLINE
LEARN Convert Measures	15 minutes	ONLINE
TRY IT Equal Measurements	10 minutes	ONLINE
CHECKPOINT	10 minutes	ONLINE

▶ Lesson Objectives

Convert among different-sized standard measurement units within a given measurement system.

▶ Prerequisite Skills

Write a simple unit conversion, such as inches to feet, as an expression or an equation.

▶ Content Background

Students will learn how to change, or convert, a given measurement to an equivalent measure within the same measurement system. In the English, or customary, system, they may be asked to find the number of inches in 5 feet (60 in.) or the number of gallons in 12 quarts (3 gal). Within the metric system, they may be asked to find the number of centimeters in 3 meters (300 cm) or the number of kilograms in 3,000 grams (3 kg). In this lesson, students will not be asked to convert measurements across the two systems, metric to customary or customary to metric.

All measurement involves a number of a certain unit, such as 14 inches. Units can be nonstandard or standard. A standard unit is one that everyone knows and agrees is a specific size, such as inch, foot, yard, mile, millimeter, centimeter, meter, kilometer, pint, quart, gallon, milliliter, liter, kiloliter, ounce, pound, gram, kilogram, second, minute, hour, and day. We use the terms *greater* or *lesser* when we compare the size of numbers. But units of measurement can be physically measured, so *larger* and *smaller* are appropriate terms to use when comparing the size of different units in measurement.

There are many known measurement equivalents in the English, or customary, measurement system. We will use these unit measurements:

1 foot = 12 inches	1 yard = 3 feet	1 mile = 5,280 feet
1 minute = 60 seconds	1 day = 24 hours	1 year = 365 days
1 year = 52 weeks	1 pint = 2 cups	1 cup = 8 ounces
1 quart = 2 pints	1 gallon = 4 quarts	

There are many known measurement equivalents in the metric measurement system. We will use these unit measurements:

1 centimeter = 10 millimeters   1 decimeter = 10 centimeters

1 meter = 10 decimeters   1 meter = 100 centimeters

1 kilogram = 1,000 grams

It takes more smaller units than larger units to measure the same amount. For example, if it takes 3 feet to measure a distance and there are 12 inches in each foot, then it takes 3 × 12, or 36 inches, to measure the same distance. To convert from feet to inches, we multiply. So to convert from a larger unit to a smaller unit, we multiply. To convert from a smaller unit to a larger unit, we divide.

▶ Common Errors and Misconceptions

Students might incorrectly reason that when a greater number of units is given, they need to divide to convert the units and when a lesser number of units is given, they need to multiply. They also might think they need to divide if the given number of units is a multiple of the conversion unit. For example, in the problem 144 feet = ? inches, students might automatically divide 144 by 12 because 144 is a multiple of 12, rather than realize that they are converting a larger unit to a smaller unit, so they have to multiply.

▶ Advance Preparation

Print the Measurement Conversion Chart.

GET READY   Measurement Match

ONLINE **10**min

Objectives

- Write a simple unit conversion, such as inches to feet, as an expression or an equation.

Students will review standard unit conversions and observe the relative sizes of standard measures related to capacity, length, weight, time, and money.

Gather the Measurement Conversion Chart and encourage students to memorize the standard conversions. Doing so will make their experiences with measurement much easier throughout the study of measurement and in everyday situations.

LEARN   Units of Length

ONLINE **5**min

Objectives

- Convert among different-sized standard measurement units within a given measurement system.

Students will learn about the relationships between units of length.

LEARN Units of Capacity

ONLINE 5 min

Objectives

Students will learn how to convert among liquid measures such as cups, pints, quarts, and gallons.

- Convert among different-sized standard measurement units within a given measurement system.

LEARN Units of Time

ONLINE 5 min

Objectives

Students will learn how to convert units of measurement for time.

- Convert among different-sized standard measurement units within a given measurement system.

LEARN Convert Measures

ONLINE 15 min

Objectives

Students will learn how to change one measurement unit to another.

- Convert among different-sized standard measurement units within a given measurement system.

TRY IT Equal Measurements

ONLINE 10 min

Objectives

Students will complete an online Try It. If necessary, read the directions, problems, and answer choices to students and help them with keyboard or mouse operations.

- Convert among different-sized standard measurement units within a given measurement system.

CHECKPOINT

ONLINE 10 min

Objectives

Students will complete an online Checkpoint. If necessary, read the directions, problems, and answer choices to students and help them with keyboard or mouse operations.

- Convert among different-sized standard measurement units within a given measurement system.

Measurements in Story Problems

Lesson Overview

GET READY Multiplication or Division?	5 minutes	ONLINE
LEARN Story Problems with Measurement	15 minutes	ONLINE
LEARN Nature Story Problems	15 minutes	OFFLINE
TRY IT Using Equal Measures	10 minutes	ONLINE
CHECKPOINT	10 minutes	ONLINE

▶ Lesson Objectives

- Solve a story problem involving equal measures.
- Use measurement conversions to solve single- and multistep real-world problems.

▶ Content Background

Students will learn how to solve story problems involving equal measures.

In an equal-measure story problem, several equal-sized measures, or parts, combine to make a total measurement amount. To solve problems involving equal measures, students can multiply or divide. When they know the number of parts and the measure of each part, they multiply to find the total measurement. For example, each of 3 children drinks 250 milliliters of milk. How many milliliters of milk do they drink altogether? In this problem, the part is the 250 milliliters that each child drinks. Three children drink this amount, so there are 3 of these parts. Students multiply 3 by 250 milliliters to find the total measurement: $3 \times 250 = 750$. The children drink a total of 750 milliliters of milk.

When students know the total measurement and the measure of one part, they divide to find the number of parts. For example, Amy bought 63 inches of ribbon. She cut it into 7-inch pieces. How many pieces of ribbon did she have? In this problem, 63 inches is the total measurement and 7 inches is the measure of one part. To find the number of 7-inch pieces, students divide 63 by 7: $63 \div 7 = 9$. Amy has 9 pieces of ribbon.

When students know the total measurement and the number of parts, they can use division to find the measure of each part. For example, John bought 63 inches of wire. He cut it into 9 equal pieces. How long was each piece? In this problem, the total measurement is 63 inches and the number of equal pieces is 9. Students divide 63 by 9 to find the length of each piece: $63 \div 9 = 7$. Each piece is 7 inches long.

Students will also work with measurement conversions and solve one- and two-step problems using conversions. Make sure students study and learn the measurement conversions for greater ease in solving problems.

Materials to Gather

SUPPLIED

Nature Story Problems activity page

Measurement Conversion Chart (printout)

▶ Common Errors and Misconceptions

Students might incorrectly reason that when a greater number of units is given, they need to divide to convert the units and when a lesser number of units is given, they need to multiply. They also might think they need to divide if the given number of units is a multiple of the conversion unit. For example, in the problem 144 feet = ? inches, students might automatically divide 144 by 12 because 144 is a multiple of 12, rather than realize that they are converting a larger unit to a smaller unit, so they have to multiply.

▶ Advance Preparation

Print the Measurement Conversion Chart.

GET READY Multiplication or Division?	Objectives

Students will decide to either multiply or divide to solve story problems involving equal measures.

- Solve a story problem involving equal measures.

LEARN Story Problems with Measurement	Objectives

Students will multiply and divide to solve problems involving equal measurements.

- Solve a story problem involving equal measures.

LEARN Nature Story Problems	Objectives

Students will solve multiplication and division story problems that involve equal measures. Students will also use measurement conversions to solve problems.

 View or print the Nature Story Problem activity page and gather the Measurement Conversion Chart. Encourage students to memorize the standard conversions, since they will be expected to know these as they complete their later work. Memorizing conversions will make their experiences with measurement much easier throughout the study of measurement and in everyday situations.

1. **Say:** When a problem tells you the total amount and asks you to find the number of parts or the size of each part, you divide.

2. **Say:** When a problem tells you the number of parts and the size of each part and you need to find the total amount, you multiply.

3. Have students read Problem 1 of the Worked Examples aloud.

4. Have students explain how they know they need to multiply. The problem says how much an Asian elephant can drink. Three Asian elephants each drink that same amount. I need to multiply to find the total amount the elephants can drink.

Objectives:
- Solve a story problem involving equal measures.
- Use measurement conversions to solve single- and multistep real-world problems.

5. Ask students to write the number sentence they use to solve the problem. Then have students solve the problem. $3 \times 59 = \underline{\ ?\ }$; $3 \times 59 = 177$

6. Have students write the answer with the measuring unit and explain what the answer means in the problem. 177 gallons; Three elephants can drink 177 gallons of water.

7. Repeat Steps 2–6 for Problem 1. divide; The problem gives the total weight of 5 camels and asks me to find the weight of 1 camel, so I have to divide; $2,500 \div 5 = 500$; 500 kilograms; Each camel weighs 500 kilograms.

8. Guide students to read and solve Problems 2. Encourage students to try to solve the problems without using the Measurement Conversion Chart and then check their work using the chart.

9. Check students' answers as they work. When necessary, help students follow these steps for each problem:

- Write the conversion equation(s) needed to answer the questions.
- Select multiplication or division and explain their choice.
- Write a number sentence and solve it.
- Write the answer and include the measuring unit.
- Use the context of the problem to explain their solution.

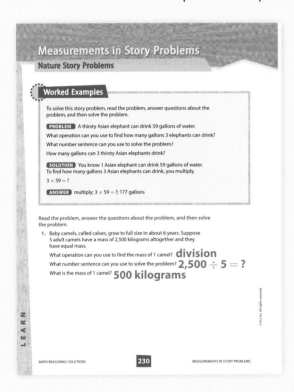

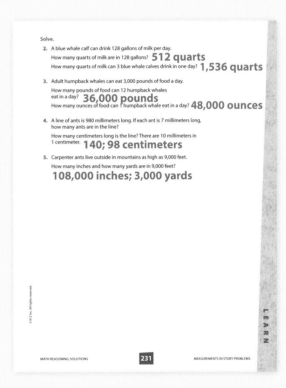

TRY IT Using Equal Measures

ONLINE 10min

Students will complete an online Try It. If necessary, read the directions, problems, and answer choices to students and help them with keyboard or mouse operations.

Objectives

- Solve a story problem involving equal measures.
- Use measurement conversions to solve single- and multistep real-world problems.

CHECKPOINT

ONLINE 10min

Students will complete an online Checkpoint. If necessary, read the directions, problems, and answer choices to students and help them with keyboard or mouse operations.

Objectives

- Solve a story problem involving equal measures.
- Use measurement conversions to solve single- and multistep real-world problems.

Decimal Solutions

Lesson Overview

GET READY Reasonable Answers with Mixed Numbers	10 minutes	ONLINE
LEARN Exact or Approximate Answers	15 minutes	ONLINE
TRY IT Decimal Story Problems	15 minutes	ONLINE
CHECKPOINT	10 minutes	ONLINE

▶ Lesson Objectives

- Explain the advantages of exact solutions and approximate solutions to problems involving addition or subtraction of decimal numbers, and give answers to a specified degree of accuracy, such as hundredths.
- Make precise calculations and use the situation presented in a problem involving decimal-number operations to check the validity of the result.

▶ Prerequisite Skills

- Use estimation to predict a solution to a story problem and to verify the reasonableness of the calculated result.
- Solve a simple problem involving addition or subtraction of fractions.
- Answer a story problem to a specified degree of accuracy, such as hundredths.

▶ Content Background

Students will learn to determine whether an approximate answer or an exact answer is an appropriate solution to a decimal story problem. They will use approximate answers to determine whether exact answers to story problems are valid.

The following problem-solving method was developed by George Pólya and is an effective way to solve a variety of story problems: (1) understand the problem; (2) devise a plan; (3) carry out the plan; and (4) look back. As students work on solving problems, they should follow the 4-step problem-solving plan.

Although the context and numbers in story problems vary, good problem solvers know they can use certain strategies over and over again to solve similar problems. When students are able to use different strategies, they can apply the same strategies to solve more complex problems, instead of treating every problem as a new experience.

Students will learn to evaluate story problems with addition and subtraction of decimal numbers and determine and explain whether an exact answer or an estimate is the appropriate solution. They will learn to answer a story problem to a specified degree of accuracy, such as hundredths.

Materials to Gather

There are no materials to gather for this lesson.

Students should understand that the term *estimate* is a mathematical term that means "about how many" and that different everyday situations require different degrees of precision. In some situations estimation is inappropriate, such as when a pharmacist fills a prescription. Students will learn to base their choice of an appropriate estimation strategy on the context of each story problem. Often an overestimate, or an approximation that is obviously greater than the exact number, is desirable in everyday life. For example, people use an overestimate when they decide how much money they will need to make a purchase or to help them decide how much food they should buy when they are planning a party.

Estimation can make numbers easier to work with when students need to do quick addition, subtraction, multiplication, or division. They can also use estimation to predict solutions to math problems or to predict reasonable solutions to calculations within a problem, such as at each step in long division. They can also compare an estimated value to the final answer to verify that the answer is reasonable.

Sometimes students will be asked for an approximate answer and an exact answer to the same problem. In those cases, they will use estimation as a problem-solving skill and as a way to verify the reasonableness of a calculated answer. They will understand the value of an estimate as part of the problem-solving plan. Students will validate the results of estimated and exact answers by reviewing the original problem and looking back on their plan for solving the problem.

GET READY Reasonable Answers with Mixed Numbers

ONLINE **10**min

Students will estimate and then solve a multistep story problem involving mixed numbers and use the estimate to verify the reasonableness of the answer. Stay with students as they complete the activity and listen to their answer to the last question, which reviews how they know their answer to the story problem is reasonable. Then they can read the given answer.

Objectives

- Use estimation to predict a solution to a story problem and to verify the reasonableness of the calculated result.
- Solve a simple problem involving addition or subtraction of fractions.
- Answer a story problem to a specified degree of accuracy, such as hundredths.

LEARN Exact or Approximate Answers

ONLINE **15**min

Students will decide whether an exact answer or an estimate is appropriate for a situation. They also will work with situations in which either an exact answer or an estimate would be appropriate. They will learn why certain methods are better than others in different situations.

Objectives

- Explain the advantages of exact solutions and approximate solutions to problems involving addition or subtraction of decimal numbers, and give answers to a specified degree of accuracy, such as hundredths.
- Make precise calculations and use the situation presented in a problem involving decimal-number operations to check the validity of the result.

TRY IT Decimal Story Problems

Students will complete an online Try It. If necessary, read the directions, problems, and answer choices to students and help them with keyboard or mouse operations.

- Explain the advantages of exact solutions and approximate solutions to problems involving addition or subtraction of decimal numbers, and give answers to a specified degree of accuracy, such as hundredths.

- Make precise calculations and use the situation presented in a problem involving decimal-number operations to check the validity of the result.

CHECKPOINT

Students will complete an online Checkpoint. If necessary, read the directions, problems, and answer choices to students and help them with keyboard or mouse operations.

- Explain the advantages of exact solutions and approximate solutions to problems involving addition or subtraction of decimal numbers, and give answers to a specified degree of accuracy, such as hundredths.

- Make precise calculations and use the situation presented in a problem involving decimal-number operations to check the validity of the result.

Reasonable Solutions

▶ Lesson Objectives

Evaluate whether a solution for a problem is reasonable.

▶ Prerequisite Skills

Use estimation to predict a solution to a story problem and to verify the reasonableness of the calculated result.

▶ Content Background

Students will learn to evaluate whether a solution to a problem is reasonable.

Although the context and numbers in story problems vary, good problem solvers know they can use certain strategies over and over again to solve similar problems. Estimating the answer to a problem and then verifying the reasonableness of the calculated answer to the estimate enhances students' number-sense development. When students are able to use different strategies, they can apply the same strategies in solving more complex problems, instead of treating every problem as a new experience.

The following problem-solving method was developed by George Pólya and is an effective way to solve a variety of story problems: (1) understand the problem; (2) devise a plan; (3) carry out the plan; and (4) look back. As students work on solving problems, they should follow the 4-step problem-solving plan.

Students can estimate and calculate answers to all types of problems. Being able to use the estimate to evaluate the reasonableness of the calculated answer involves students asking questions such as the following: Did I use the correct operations in my equation? How does my calculated answer compare to my estimated answer? Does my answer make sense with the question in the problem?

▶ Advance Preparation

Print the Reasonable Geometry Solutions.

Materials to Gather

SUPPLIED

Reasonable Geometry Solutions (printout)

ALSO NEEDED

ruler, dual-scale

LEARN Solve a Problem with Alexander

Students will use a problem-solving plan to find the solution to a problem about finding the number of trees that were planted in parks. They will use the strategy of making a table to help them keep track of the multiple steps needed to carry out the plan and find the solution. Students will use estimation throughout the activity to evaluate whether their answers are reasonable.

LEARN Reasonable Geometry Solutions

Students will develop and use a formula to find the angle measures in regular polygons. Gather the Reasonable Geometry Solutions and a ruler.

1. Tell students they will find the measure of angles in regular polygons without using a protractor. Instead, they will draw lines on polygons, observe patterns, and come up with a formula.

2. Remind students that a regular polygon has all sides of equal length and all angles of equal measure. This activity deals only with regular polygons. Tell students that the word *diagonals* in this activity means lines drawn from a vertex to other vertices of a regular polygon.

3. Give students the Reasonable Geometry Solutions printout and ruler. Tell them that they will complete the table as they work through the activity.

4. Tell students to look at the first row, the triangle row. Tell them to note that the "Number of angles" column says 3 and the "Number of triangles formed by diagonals" column says 1.

   Explain the "Number of triangles formed by diagonals" column by asking students to use a ruler to draw a line from any vertex of the triangle (such as the top vertex) to each of the other two vertices. If they use the top vertex, they'll draw lines along the left and right sides of the triangle. Now they have created 1 triangle by drawing diagonals from a vertex. That's why the "Number of triangles formed by diagonals" column has a 1 in it.

   Tell students that this step has helped them begin to develop a pattern for all the regular polygons in the table.

   If needed, help students recall that the sum of the angle measures in a triangle is 180°. Have them complete the "Sum of angle measures in degrees" column for the triangle. 180

   Remind students that this is a regular triangle, where all the angles have equal measure. Have them divide 180 by 3 to complete the "Measure of each angle in degrees" column for the triangle. 60

5. Have students look at the second row, the square row. Tell them to notice given information: 4 angles in a square and 2 triangles formed by diagonals. Have students draw a diagonal from one vertex of the square to the opposite vertex to form 2 triangles. Now they have shown that the 2 in the table is correct.

   Tell them that they don't need to draw diagonals along the sides of the square (or the sides of later polygons in the activity), as they did for the triangle. It is understood that those polygon sides are also the sides of triangles formed by the diagonals they draw.

Objectives

- Evaluate whether a solution for a problem is reasonable.

Objectives

- Evaluate whether a solution for a problem is reasonable.

Tips

Have students explain in their own words how they will use the formula to find the measures of the angles in each of the last four figures.

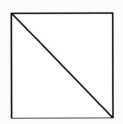

one way to show a square divided into 2 triangles

Have students complete the "Sum of angle measures in degrees" column for the square. Tell them they can use the sum of the angle measures in a triangle, 180°, to help them. Since there are 2 triangles in a square, and the sum of the angle measures in a triangle is 180°, they can multiply 2 by 180. 360

Note that the product, 360, means that the measures of the angles in a square add up to 360°.

Have students divide 360 by 4 to complete the "Measure of each angle in degrees" column for the square. 90

Ask: Is 90° a reasonable answer for the measure of each angle in a square? Yes, it is reasonable because each angle in a square is a right angle. A right angle measures 90°.

6. Have students look at the third row, the pentagon row. Have them start by drawing diagonals from a vertex to the other vertices on the pentagon. Then have them begin filling out the row, always checking to see whether their answers are reasonable.

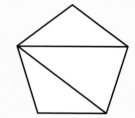

one way to show a pentagon
divided into 3 triangles

Say: You can check to see whether your answers in the table are reasonable by observing patterns and comparing your answers to answers that are already in the table. When you repeat your process for answering questions about each polygon, you can check to see whether the process is helping you find reasonable answers.

Ask: How can you use the number of triangles in a pentagon, 3, and the sum of the angle measures in a triangle, 180°, to find the sum of the angle measures in a pentagon? Multiply 180 by 3.

Ask: How can you use the sum of the angle measures and the number of angles to find the measure of each angle in the pentagon? Divide the total of the angle measures in a pentagon, 540, by 5.

7. Check students' answers for the pentagon:
   - Number of angles: 5
   - Number of triangles formed by diagonals: 3
   - Sum of angle measures in degrees: 540
   - Measure of each angle in degrees: 108

Ask: Think about the steps you've taken to find the sum of the angle measures and the measures of each angle for the triangle and the square. How do you know that you have a reasonable answer to the measure of each angle in a pentagon? The pentagon was divided into 3 triangles. The sum of the angle measures in a triangle is 180°. The sum of the angle measures in 3 triangles is 180 • 3, which equals 540. Because the sum of the angle measures in a pentagon is 540°, 540 ÷ 5 is the measure of each angle in a pentagon. Each angle measures 108°.

8. Have students follow the same process for the hexagon. Check students' answers for the hexagon:
   - Number of angles: 6
   - Number of triangles formed by diagonals: 4
   - Sum of angle measures in degrees: 720
   - Measure of each angle in degrees: 120

9. Tell students that answering the following questions will lead them to derive a formula for finding angle measures of any regular polygon. Tell them that if they use the formula, they won't need to draw diagonals on polygons. Have them refer to the table, with the answers they have found for the triangle, square, pentagon, and hexagon, to answer the following questions.

Ask: Compare the number of triangles to the number of angles in each regular polygon. What do you notice? The number of triangles is 2 fewer than the number of angles.

Ask: Let the variable a represent the number of angles in a regular polygon. What expression describes the number of triangles in a regular polygon? $a - 2$

Have students recall that they multiplied 180 by the number of triangles in the regular polygons to find the sum of the angle measures of the polygons.

Ask: Since the expression $a - 2$ describes the number of triangles in a regular polygon, what expression describes the sum of the angle measures of a regular polygon? $180(a - 2)$

Have students recall that they divided the sum of the angle measures in the regular polygons by the number of angles to get the measure of each angle.

Ask: Think about this: The expression $180(a - 2)$ describes the sum of the angle measures of a regular polygon. The variable a represents the number of angles in a regular polygon. What would happen if you divided the sum of angle measures by the number of angles? I'd get the measure of each angle of the regular polygon.

Ask: What expression describes the measure of each angle in a regular polygon?

$\left(\frac{180(a - 2)}{a} \right)$

10. Continue to explain the formula to students.

Say: Let M represent the measure of each angle of a regular polygon. The formula then becomes the following:

$M = \frac{180(a - 2)}{a}$

Tell students that the formula will work for finding the measure of each angle in any regular polygon.

Have them write the formula at the top of the printout.

11. Have students use the formula to fill in the table for the octagon. They should show their steps to solve the equation in their Math Notebook.

$M = \frac{180(a - 2)}{a} = \frac{180(8 - 2)}{8} = \frac{180(6)}{8} = \frac{1,080}{8} = 135$

Note that the measure of each angle in a regular octagon is 135°.

12. When students finish, have them verify that the formula works by drawing diagonals in the octagon to form triangles. Check students' answers for the octagon:

- Number of angles: 8
- Number of triangles formed by diagonals: 6
- Sum of angle measures in degrees: 1,080
- Measure of each angle in degrees: 135

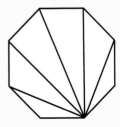

one way to show an octagon divided into 6 triangles

13. Have students write the formula with the values for *a* in the first column to complete the table for a decagon, a 20-gon, a 50-gon, and a 100-gon. Have students use their Math Notebook to find the value of *M* and find the measure of each angle in degrees. Check students' work.

Decagon:
- Equation: $M = \dfrac{180(10 - 2)}{10}$
- Number of angles: 10
- Number of triangles formed by diagonals: 8
- Sum of angle measures in degrees: 1,440
- Measure of each angle in degrees: 144

20-gon:
- Equation: $M = \dfrac{180(20 - 2)}{20}$
- Number of angles: 20
- Number of triangles formed by diagonals: 18
- Sum of angle measures in degrees: 3,240
- Measure of each angle in degrees: 162

50-gon:
- Equation: $M = \dfrac{180(50 - 2)}{50}$
- Number of angles: 50
- Number of triangles formed by diagonals: 48
- Sum of angle measures in degrees: 8,640
- Measure of each angle in degrees: 172.8

100-gon:
- Equation: $M = \dfrac{180(100 - 2)}{100}$
- Number of angles: 100
- Number of triangles formed by diagonals: 98
- Sum of angle measures in degrees: 17,640
- Measure of each angle in degrees: 176.4

14. Ask: As the number of angles increases, the regular polygon starts to look like a circle. What happens to the measure of each angle? The measure of each angle increases.

Tell students that the more angles there are in a regular polygon, the greater each angle is. They can see an example by comparing the square with the octagon to see that each angle of the octagon is a greater size than each angle of the square. They can also compare the angle measurements in the table.

Ask: Is it reasonable to think that the sum of the angle measures increases as the number of angles in the regular polygon increase? Why or why not? Yes, it is reasonable. Since the number of angles in each regular polygon increases, the sum of the angles would also increase.

Ask: Is it reasonable to think that the measure of each angle in a regular polygon would reach 180°? Why or why not? No, it is not reasonable because 180° is a straight angle and cannot form an angle in a polygon.

TRY IT Evaluate Solutions

ONLINE 10 min

Students will complete an online Try It. If necessary, read the directions, problems, and answer choices to students and help them with keyboard or mouse operations.

Objectives

- Evaluate whether a solution for a problem is reasonable.

CHECKPOINT

ONLINE 10 min

Students will complete an online Checkpoint. If necessary, read the directions, problems, and answer choices to students and help them with keyboard or mouse operations.

Objectives

- Evaluate whether a solution for a problem is reasonable.

Core Focus
Measurement Conversions and Problems

Lesson Overview

GET READY Match Measurements	5 minutes	**ONLINE**
LEARN Multiply or Divide to Convert	15 minutes	**ONLINE**
LEARN Conversion Story Problems	15 minutes	**ONLINE**
TRY IT Conversions and Problems	10 minutes	**ONLINE**
CHECKPOINT	15 minutes	**ONLINE**

▶ Lesson Objectives

Use measurement conversions to solve single-step and multistep real-world problems.

▶ Prerequisite Skills

Write a simple unit conversion, such as inches to feet, as an expression or an equation.

▶ Content Background

Students will work with measurement conversions to solve one- and two-step problems. Students must address two key questions in each situation: which conversion equation to use and which operation to use to convert units, multiplication or division. Encourage students to memorize the conversion equations given in the Measurement Conversion Chart to enhance their success with measurement tasks in both math and real-world situations.

▶ Advance Preparation

Print the Measurement Conversion Chart.

Materials to Gather

SUPPLIED

Measurement Conversion Chart (printout)

GET READY Match Measurements

ONLINE
5 min

Objectives

Students will review and memorize common metric measurements for length, capacity, and mass and will practice matching equivalent conversions online. Gather the Measurement Conversion Chart for students to study before they complete the activity.

- Write a simple unit conversion, such as inches to feet, as an expression or an equation.

LEARN Multiply or Divide to Convert

ONLINE 15min

Objectives

- Use measurement conversions to solve single-step and multistep real-world problems.

Students will work through problems involving metric measurement conversions. They will determine which conversion equation to use and whether to use multiplication or division to convert units.

Tips | Encourage students to test their memory of conversion equations as they work through the activity.

LEARN Conversion Story Problems

ONLINE 15min

Objectives

- Use measurement conversions to solve single-step and multistep real-world problems.

Students will work one- and two-step story problems using metric conversions.

Tips | Encourage students to test their memory of conversion equations as they work through the activity.

TRY IT Conversions and Problems

ONLINE 10min

Objectives

- Use measurement conversions to solve single-step and multistep real-world problems.

Students will complete an online Try It. If necessary, read the directions, problems, and answer choices to students and help them with keyboard or mouse operations.

CHECKPOINT

ONLINE 15min

Objectives

- Use measurement conversions to solve single-step and multistep real-world problems.

Students will complete an online Checkpoint. If necessary, read the directions, problems, and answer choices to students and help them with keyboard or mouse operations.

Unit Review

Lesson Overview

UNIT REVIEW Look Back	10 minutes	**ONLINE**
UNIT REVIEW Checkpoint Practice	50 minutes	**ONLINE**
⤳ **UNIT REVIEW** Prepare for the Checkpoint		

▶ Unit Objectives

- Express clear and logical solutions to equal-measures problems and rate problems.

- Use estimation in addition or subtraction of fractions to verify whether calculated results are reasonable.

- Convert among different-sized standard measurement units within a given measurement system.

- Solve a story problem involving equal measures.

- Use measurement conversions to solve single- and multistep real-world problems.

- Explain the advantages of exact solutions and approximate solutions to problems involving addition or subtraction of decimal numbers, and give answers to a specified degree of accuracy, such as hundredths.

- Make precise calculations and use the situation presented in a problem involving decimal-number operations to check the validity of the result.

- Evaluate whether a solution for a problem is reasonable.

▶ Advance Preparation

In this lesson, students will have an opportunity to review previous activities in the Math Reasoning: Solutions unit. Look at the suggested activities in Unit Review: Prepare for the Checkpoint online and gather any needed materials.

Materials to Gather

There are no materials to gather for this lesson.

ONLINE
10 min

UNIT REVIEW Look Back

Students will review key concepts from the unit to prepare for the Unit Checkpoint.

Objectives

- Review unit objectives.

ONLINE
50min

Objectives

- Review unit objectives.

Students will complete an online Checkpoint Practice to prepare for the Unit Checkpoint. If necessary, read the directions, problems, and answer choices to students. Have students answer the problems on their own. Review any missed problems with students.

⇥ UNIT REVIEW Prepare for the Checkpoint

What you do next depends on how students performed in the previous activity, Unit Review: Checkpoint Practice. If students had difficulty with any of the problems, complete the appropriate review activity listed in the table online.

Unit Checkpoint

UNIT CHECKPOINT Online | 60 minutes | **ONLINE**

▶ Unit Objectives

- Express clear and logical solutions to equal-measures problems and rate problems.
- Use estimation in addition or subtraction of fractions to verify whether calculated results are reasonable.
- Convert among different-sized standard measurement units within a given measurement system.
- Solve a story problem involving equal measures.
- Use measurement conversions to solve single- and multistep real-world problems.
- Explain the advantages of exact solutions and approximate solutions to problems involving addition or subtraction of decimal numbers, and give answers to a specified degree of accuracy, such as hundredths.
- Make precise calculations and use the situation presented in a problem involving decimal-number operations to check the validity of the result.
- Evaluate whether a solution for a problem is reasonable.

Materials to Gather

There are no materials to gather for this lesson.

UNIT CHECKPOINT Online

ONLINE 60min

Students will complete the Unit Checkpoint online. If necessary, read the directions, problems, and answer choices to students and help them with keyboard or mouse operations.

Objectives

- Assess unit objectives.

Extended Problems: Reasoning

GRADED ASSIGNMENT   60 minutes   OFFLINE

▶ Lesson Objectives

- Use estimation in addition or subtraction of fractions to verify whether calculated results are reasonable.
- Make precise calculations and use the situation presented in a problem involving decimal-number operations to check the validity of the result.
- Evaluate whether a solution for a problem is reasonable.
- Interpret a fraction as division of the numerator by the denominator $\left(\frac{a}{b} = a \div b\right)$.
- Solve multistep, real-world problems that include conversion of measurement units within a given measurement system.
- Solve multistep word problems using whole numbers.
- Solve measurement word problems involving masses of objects, including problems involving simple fractions or decimals, and problems that require expressing measurements given in a larger unit in terms of a smaller unit.
- Analyze complex problems using mathematical knowledge and skills.

Materials to Gather

SUPPLIED

Extended Problems: Reasoning (printout)

GRADED ASSIGNMENT

OFFLINE 60 min

Objectives

Open the Extended Problems: Reasoning. Read the directions, problems, and answer choices to students, if necessary.

You will grade this assignment.
- Students should complete the assignment on their own.
- Students should submit the completed assignment to you.
- Enter the results online.

- Analyze complex problems using mathematical knowledge and skills.

Data Analysis and Representation

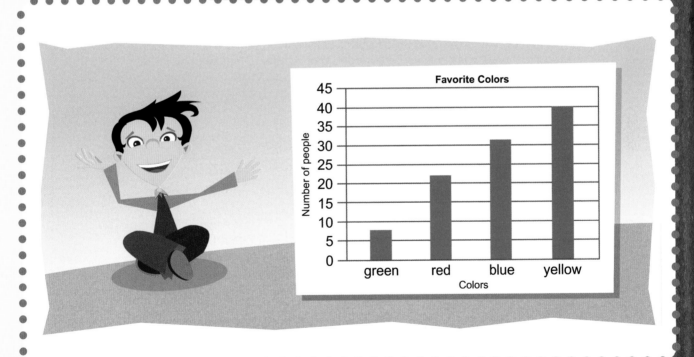

▶ Unit Objectives

- Organize and display single-variable data in a histogram.
- Organize and display single-variable data in a circle graph.
- Create a line plot to display a set of measurements in fractions of a unit.
- Use operations on fractions to solve problems involving information presented in line plots.
- Interpret information displayed in a graph or table.

- Use whole numbers, fractions, and decimals to compare different data sets.
- Explain which types of graphs are appropriate for various data sets.
- Recognize appropriate representations of survey data.
- Evaluate the utility of models, such as graphs and charts, to determine which are most useful and efficient to analyze data and solve problems.

▶ Big Ideas

Graphs and charts are useful ways to represent and compare numerical data.

▶ Unit Introduction

In this unit, students will investigate data representations by organizing and displaying data by using histograms, circle graphs, and line graphs.

The unit continues with students analyzing data by interpreting the information shown in bar graphs, line graphs, circle graphs, Venn diagrams, frequency tables, and histograms. They will use whole numbers, fractions, and decimals to compare different data sets. Their analysis also will include explaining which type of graph is most appropriate to represent a data set.

▶ Keywords

bar graph	histogram	random sample
circle graph	interval	scale
cumulative frequency	label	survey
data	line plot	trend
frequency table	population	

Organize Data to Draw Histograms (A)

Lesson Overview

GET READY Display Coin Tosses on a Tally Chart	5 minutes	OFFLINE
LEARN Frequency Tables and Histograms	15 minutes	ONLINE
LEARN Organize Data in a Frequency Table	20 minutes	OFFLINE
TRY IT Work with Frequency Tables	20 minutes	OFFLINE

▶ **Lesson Objectives**

Organize and display single-variable data in a histogram.

▶ **Prerequisite Skills**

Systematically record numerical data.

▶ **Content Background**

Students will learn that frequency tables organize data for making a histogram. They will create and interpret frequency tables.

A histogram is a special type of bar graph that records the frequency of an occurrence of an event or a group. It is best for students to use a frequency table when preparing to create a histogram. In a frequency table, students list events or groups, tally their frequency, and record each frequency as a number. In a histogram, the horizontal axis shows the events or groups, and the vertical axis shows the frequency. *Frequency* is the number of times an event or group occurs. The bars in a histogram are immediately next to each other with no space between the bars.

▶ **Common Errors and Misconceptions**

- Students might have difficulty interpreting graphs because they have not had enough opportunity to analyze and compare different types of graphs.
- Students might have difficulty determining information on a graph that is implied. For example, students might not be able to determine the value of data points if the points fall between two values shown on the scale. They also might not be able to use a graph to extend the data and make predictions about data points not given on the graph.
- Students might have an idea of how they think data should look when graphed, so they might expect all graphs of those data to reflect their visual image.

▶ **Advance Preparation**

Gather the coin.
  Print two copies of the Large Frequency Table.

Materials to Gather

SUPPLIED

Large Frequency Table (printout)

Organize Data in a Frequency Table activity page

Work with Frequency Tables activity page

ALSO NEEDED

coin with a head and a tail

GET READY Display Coin Tosses on a Tally Chart

Objectives

- Systematically record numerical data.

Students will toss a coin 10 times. They will record the outcomes on a tally chart. Gather the coin.

1. Guide students to create a tally chart in their Math Notebook like the one shown.

Heads or Tails	
Heads	Tails

2. Have students toss the coin and record the outcome by making a tally for heads or tails in their tally chart. They should toss the coin and record the outcome 10 times.

3. After students record the outcomes, have them use their tally chart to answer these questions. Answers will vary.

   - How many times did you toss heads?

   - What fraction represents the number of heads tossed out of the total number of tosses?

   - How many times did you toss tails?

   - What fraction represents the number of tails tossed out of the total number of tosses?

LEARN Frequency Tables and Histograms

Objectives

- Organize and display single-variable data in a histogram.

Students will learn to organize data in a frequency table. They will see how a frequency table is used to create a histogram.

DIRECTIONS FOR USING THE FREQUENCY TABLES AND HISTOGRAMS LEARNING TOOL

1. Click Begin.

2. Click the triangle in the upper right-hand corner to close the histogram.

3. Have students look at the spinner and the "Section" column in the frequency table. Point out that each of the six sections on the spinner matches a row in the frequency table.

   Tell students that the "Tally" column shows a tick mark for each time the spinner lands on that section. Tally marks are used to keep track of the spinner outcomes. The "Total" column shows the frequency from the "Tally" column, but uses numbers instead of tick marks.

4. Have students click Spin to spin the spinner. The result of the spin is recorded on the frequency table with a tally mark and 1 for the total of that outcome.

5. Have students spin the spinner 10 times. They can keep track of the number of spins by using the counter under the spinner. The data from the spins will display on the frequency table.

6. Have students describe the results of 10 spins shown on frequency table.
   Possible answer: After 10 spins, the frequency table showed I landed on A two times, B zero times, C one time, D four times, E two times, and F one time. The outcomes are shown with tally marks and with numbers.

7. Repeat Step 4 until students have spun a total of 30 spins.

8. Click the triangle in the upper right-hand corner to open the histogram.

9. **Have students describe the histogram.** The histogram has six labels at the bottom of the graph for each section on the spinner. The frequency is labeled on the side of the histogram. The result of each spin is recorded on the histogram with a bar. The bar increases by a frequency of 1 to match each spin.

10. Have students compare the data in the frequency table and the histogram.
    Ask: How are the data points from the frequency table shown on the histogram? For each section on the spinner, the frequency table shows the tally and the total number of spins. There are six sections on the spinner, six rows in the frequency table, and six labels on the bottom of the histogram. The frequencies of the spins from the frequency table are shown as the heights of the bars on the histogram.

11. Students may repeat Steps 4–10 and collect data for a new set of spins. Have them click Reset to clear the data.

LEARN Organize Data in a Frequency Table

OFFLINE
20 min

Objectives

- Organize and display single-variable data in a histogram.

Students will create a *frequency* table. They will use it to organize data about the height of the tallest Ferris wheels ever built. Gather the Large Frequency Table printout. View or print the Organize Data in a Frequency Table activity page and read the directions with students.

1. Tell students that *frequency* is the number of times that an event occurs. Read the Worked Examples box with students.

2. Give them the Large Frequency Table printout.
   Say: The frequency table you will complete in Problem 1 will show the frequency of the heights in the data you are given.

   Tell students to read the Tall Ferris Wheels table in Problem 1. Tell them that the heights of the Ferris wheels are the numbers they will use in their frequency table. Explain that the Ferris wheels are located in many different countries, and they will collect data about the heights on the frequency table. They don't need to know how to spell or pronounce the Ferris wheel names.

3. Tell students to write a title at the top of the Large Frequency Table printout. It could be "Tall Ferris Wheels."

4. Guide students to write three headings, one for each column. Have students look at the Worked Example to help them know what each column should be used for. If they have trouble, guide them to understand that the first column on the left needs to have height ranges of meters, from the least to the greatest, so they can mark the frequency of the heights. Tell them they need to organize the ranges of meters in a logical way.

   For column headings, tell them that it makes sense to name the first column "Height range (m)"; the middle column, "Tally"; and the third column, "Frequency."

5. Tell students that in the "Height range (m)" column they need to have height ranges that make sense. Have them look for the least and the greatest heights in the data table. The least height is 64.8 meters. The greatest height is 208 meters.

   Tell them that it makes sense to label the rows under "Height range (m)" by 20-meter ranges, starting with 60–79.

   Tell them to label the rows under "Height range (meters)" as follows: 60–79, 80–99, 100–119, 120–139, 140–159, 160–179, 180–199, and 200–219.

6. Show students how to tally the Ferris wheel heights by putting a tally mark in the 60–79 row in the "Tally" column for each Ferris wheel height in the table from 60 meters to 79 meters. Check that they make a total of 5 tally marks in that row.

   Remind students that as they draw tally marks in this activity they need to draw the fifth tally as a diagonal line through the first 4 tally marks.

7. Have students use the data in the table to complete each row in the "Tally" column.

   Students may choose to start in the second column of the table and work from the top to the bottom of the column, recording a tally mark for each height. If they record data in the frequency table this way, check that they also tally the data from the fourth column.

8. Have students count the tally marks for each row and write the total as a number in that row of the "Frequency" column. They should write a 0 as the frequency for any ranges that have no data.

   Ask: How did you organize and show height data from the table in the frequency table? I made a tally mark for each height from the table. I made the tally in the range each data point belonged in. I counted the tally marks on each row and wrote that number in the frequency column.

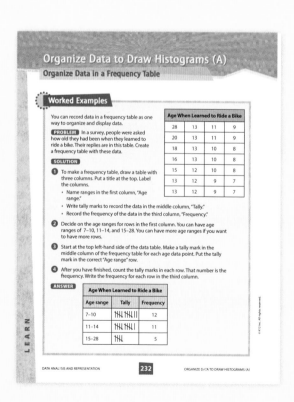

Follow the directions to complete the activity.

1. Create a frequency table for the data. Write a title and column headings.
Put the frequency data in the table. Group the heights so you have one
column with ranges of numbers in a logical sequence, such as 60–79,
80–99, 100–119, and so on. In the second column, use tally marks to
record the number of heights within the ranges. In the third column,
write the frequency number.

See right.

Tall Ferris Wheels

Ferris wheel	Height (m)	Ferris wheel	Height (m)
Beijing Great Wheel	208	Harbin Ferris Wheel	110
Great Berlin Wheel	175	Jinjiang Park Ferris Wheel	108
Singapore Flyer	165	HEP Five	106
Star of Nanchang	160	Grande Roue de Paris	100
London Eye	135	Space Eye	100
Suzhou Ferris Wheel	120	The Great Wheel	94
The Southern Star	120	Aurora Wheel	90
Tianjin Eye	120	Eurowheel	90
Changsha Ferris Wheel	120	Janfusun Fancyworld	88
Zhengzhou Ferris Wheel	120	Mashhad Fun Fair	80
Sky Dream Fukuoka	120	The Ferris Wheel (original Ferris wheel)	80
Diamond and Flowers Ferris Wheel	117	Moscow-850	75
Sky Wheel of Odaiba	115	Polaris Tower	72
Star of Tai Lake	115	Miramar Ferris Wheel	70
Cosmo Clock 21	112.5	Texas Star	65
Tempozan Harbor Village Ferris Wheel	112.5	Riesenrad Vienna	64.8

LEARN

Answers

1.

Tall Ferris Wheels

Height range (m)	Tally	Frequency
60–79	IIII I	5
80–99	IIII I	6
100–119	IIII IIII	10
120–139	IIII II	7
140–159		0
160–179	III	3
180–199		0
200–219	I	1

TRY IT Work with Frequency Tables

Objectives

- Organize and display single-variable data in a histogram.

Students will practice creating and reading frequency tables. Gather the Large
Frequency Table printout. View or print the Work with Frequency Tables activity
page and read the directions with students.

Have students write answers on the Large Frequency Table printout.

Organize Data to Draw Histograms (A)
Work with Frequency Tables

Follow the directions to complete the activity.

1. Create a frequency table for the data.
   - Write a title and column headings.
   - Put the frequency data in the table.
     Group the number of books people read
     so the first column has ranges of numbers
     in a logical sequence. Use 5-book ranges
     starting with 1–5, 6–10, and so on.
   - In the second column, use tally marks
     to record the number of people within
     the ranges.
   - In the third column, write the frequency
     number.

See right.

Book Club

Name	Number of books read in September, October, and November
Betty	12
David	4
Sonia	2
Sophia	15
Steven	7
Paul	9
Bob	20
Marcia	21
Mary	16
Rob	3
Eric	14
Mark	9
Brian	14
Carl	20
Jared	6

TRY IT

Additional Answers

1.

Book Club

Number of books read in September, October, and November	Tally	Frequency
1–5	III	3
6–10	IIII	4
11–15	IIII	4
16–20	III	3
21–25	I	1

Choose the answer.

2. Maurice recorded the number of minutes he did yard work each week for 6 weeks. Which frequency table shows the data?

Week 1: 45 minutes
Week 2: 65 minutes
Week 3: 110 minutes
Week 4: 75 minutes
Week 5: 60 minutes
Week 6: 30 minutes

A.

Yard Work

Time (min)	Tally	Frequency
0–19			1
20–39		0
40–59	||	2
60–79	||	2
80–99		0
100–119			1

B.

Yard Work

Time (min)	Tally	Frequency
0–19			1
20–39			1
40–59	|||	3
60–79			1
80–99		0
100–119		0

C. (circled)

Yard Work

Time (min)	Tally	Frequency
0–19		0
20–39			1
40–59			1
60–79	|||	3
80–99		0
100–119			1

TRY IT

Choose the answer.

3. Lara recorded the number of hours she exercised each month for a year. Which frequency table shows the data?

January: 8 hours   July: 22 hours
February: 7 hours   August: 8 hours
March: 10 hours   September: 10 hours
April: 8 hours   October: 9 hours
May: 14 hours   November: 11 hours
June: 20 hours   December: 6 hours

A.

Exercise

Time (h)	Tally	Frequency
0–4		0
5–9	ＴＨＬ	5
10–14	ＴＨＬ	5
15–19			1
20–24			1

B. (circled)

Exercise

Time (h)	Tally	Frequency
0–4		0
5–9	ＴＨＬＩ	6
10–14	||||	4
15–19		0
20–24	||	2

C.

Exercise

Time (h)	Tally	Frequency
0–4	ＴＨＬＩ	6
5–9		0
10–14	|||	3
15–19		0
20–24	|||	3

TRY IT

4. Deborah recorded the number of servings of fruit that each member of her ballet class ate in a week. Which frequency table shows the data?

Helen: 15
Jane: 9
Gillian: 13
Danielle: 19
Nina: 8
Sally: 17
Vanessa: 18
Claire: 13
Zoe: 12

A. (circled)

Fruit Eaten in a Week

Number	Tally	Frequency
0–5		0
6–10	||	2
11–15	||||	4
16–20	|||	3
21–25		0

B.

Fruit Eaten in a Week

Number	Tally	Frequency
0–5		0
6–10	|||	3
11–15	|||	3
16–20	|||	3
21–25	|||	3

C.

Fruit Eaten in a Week

Number	Tally	Frequency
0–5			1
6–10	||	2
11–15	||||	4
16–20	|||	3
21–25		0

TRY IT

Organize Data to Draw Histograms (B)

Lesson Overview

LEARN Make a Histogram	15 minutes	OFFLINE
LEARN Make a Frequency Table and Histogram	20 minutes	OFFLINE
TRY IT Make and Interpret Histograms	15 minutes	OFFLINE
CHECKPOINT	10 minutes	ONLINE

▶ Lesson Objectives

Organize and display single-variable data in a histogram.

▶ Content Background

Students will continue to learn that frequency tables organize data for making a histogram. They will create and interpret frequency tables.

A histogram is a special type of bar graph that records the frequency of an occurrence of an event or a group. It is best for students to use a frequency table when preparing to create a histogram. In a frequency table, students list events or groups, tally their frequency, and record each frequency as a number. In a histogram, the horizontal axis shows the events or groups, and the vertical axis shows the frequency. *Frequency* is the number of times an event or group occurs. The bars in a histogram have no space between them.

▶ Common Errors and Misconceptions

- Students might have difficulty interpreting graphs because they have not had enough opportunity to analyze and compare different types of graphs.
- Students might have difficulty determining information on a graph that is implied. For example, students might not be able to determine the value of data points if the points fall between two values shown on the scale. They also might not be able to use a graph to extend the data and make predictions about data points not given on the graph.
- Students might have an idea of how they think data should look when graphed, so they might expect all graphs of those data to reflect their visual image.

▶ Advance Preparation

Print three copies of the Draw a Histogram printout.

Materials to Gather

SUPPLIED

Draw a Histogram (printout)

Make a Histogram activity page

Make a Frequency Table and Histogram activity page

Make and Interpret Histograms activity page

ALSO NEEDED

ruler, dual-scale

markers, coloring

LEARN Make a Histogram

Students will use data from a frequency table to make a histogram. Gather one copy of the Draw a Histogram printout, ruler, and markers. View or print the Make a Histogram activity page.

- Organize and display single-variable data in a histogram.

1. Read the Worked Example with students. Show students how each step in the solution was carried out on the histogram.

2. Point out the characteristics of a histogram:
   - The histogram has a title.
   - The horizontal and vertical axes are labeled.
   - The bars are all labeled with ranges. And except for the first bar, which is slightly wider, the bars are the same width.
   - The numbers on the vertical axis correspond to the frequency data.
   - There is no space between the bars.

3. Make sure students understand that the numbers in the "Frequency" column of the frequency table were used to decide the height of the bars on the histogram. For example, for the 10,001–12,000 range, the frequency table shows a frequency of 2. On the graph, the bar above 10,001–12,000 has a height of 2 on the vertical axis.

4. Read the directions for Problems 1–5. Give students the printout, ruler, and markers.

5. Guide students as needed, encouraging them to look at the Worked Example for help. When they get to Problem 3, ask these questions:

   Ask: What is the least frequency? 0

   Ask: What the greatest frequency? 10

   Ask: What range of numbers needs to be on the graph to represent the frequencies? The range needs to be 0–10, but to follow the Worked Example and to make the histogram easier to read, I should include one number beyond 10, so 0–11.

6. For Problem 4, have students use the ruler to help them divide the horizontal axis into 8 evenly spaced intervals. Have them label the intervals from left to right along the horizontal axis.

7. For Problem 5, guide students to draw a bar above the 60–79 range that has a height of 5 on the vertical axis. Have them continue drawing bars for the other ranges: 80–99, 100–119, 120–139, 140–159, 160–179, 180–199, and 200–219. Explain that ranges with a frequency of 0 won't have a bar above the range label. Have students color the bars with markers.

Worked Examples

A histogram is a graph that displays the data from a frequency table. Histograms have bars that represent data. The bars are usually all the same width. The width depends on the range of measurements in the frequency table. The heights of the bars depend on the frequency data.

A histogram has a horizontal axis (the bottom line of the graph) and a vertical axis (the line along the left side of the graph). Each axis is labeled with a name and with numbers that are used for placement of the bars.

World's Longest Roller Coasters

Length range (ft)	Tally	Frequency
2,000–4,000	|||	3
4,001–6,000	||||	4
6,001–8,000	⧄|	6
8,001–10,000	⧄ ||	7
10,001–12,000	||	2

PROBLEM Draw a histogram to display the data in the frequency table.

SOLUTION

1. Write a title at the top of the histogram. The title should describe the data in the frequency table, such as "World's Longest Roller Coasters."

2. Label the horizontal axis and the vertical axis. For the horizontal axis label, write the column name for the range of measurements in the frequency table: "Length range (ft)." For the vertical axis label, write "Frequency."

3. Mark off 5 even sections along the horizontal axis for ranges and write the ranges from the frequency table below the axis. As you mark off the ranges, don't put space between them. The bars on a histogram sit right next to each other.

4. Number the vertical axis. Histograms often show one number greater than the greatest number in the frequency table. When the vertical axis includes one greater number, the scale is easier to read. The frequency table has frequencies from 0 to 7, so number the vertical axis from 0 to 8.

5. Draw a bar for the first range, 2,000–4,000. The frequency is 3, so the bar should stop at the 3 on the vertical axis. Using the data in the frequency table, draw and shade a bar for each range (each row in the frequency table should have one bar in the histogram). Use a ruler to draw the bars.

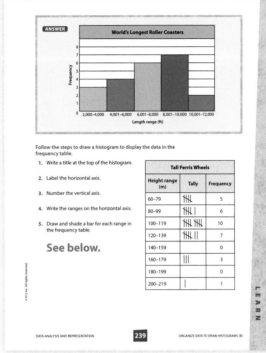

Follow the steps to draw a histogram to display the data in the frequency table.

1. Write a title at the top of the histogram.

2. Label the horizontal axis.

3. Number the vertical axis.

4. Write the ranges on the horizontal axis.

5. Draw and shade a bar for each range in the frequency table.

See below.

Tall Ferris Wheels

Height range (m)	Tally	Frequency
60–79	⧄	5
80–99	⧄		6
100–119	⧄ ⧄	10
120–139	⧄ ||	7
140–159		0
160–179	|||	3
180–199		0
200–219			1

**Answers
1–5.**

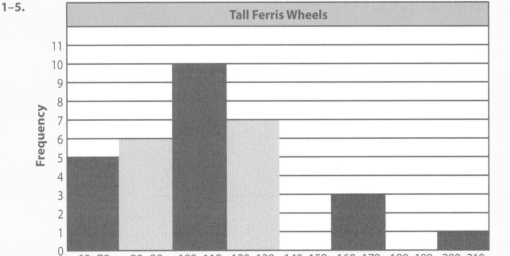

LEARN Make a Frequency Table and Histogram

- Organize and display single-variable data in a histogram.

Students will create a frequency table to organize data. They will use the frequency table to draw a histogram. Gather one copy of the Draw a Histogram printout, ruler, and markers. View or print the Make a Frequency Table and Histogram activity page.

Tips

Guide students to work carefully when creating the frequency table from the data in the table. Have them check the data and their frequency table before they create the histogram.

1. Read the Worked Example with students and make sure they understand the process for creating the frequency table and histogram for the lake temperatures.

2. Read the directions for Problems 1–4. Give students the printout, ruler, and markers.

3. Assist students as needed, encouraging them to look at the Worked Example for help. Guide students to use a range of 1 foot for each distance. Have them write the ranges in the first column of the frequency table. They should start at the top with the shortest distance:

   - 18 ft–18 ft 11 in.
   - 19 ft–19 ft 11 in.
   - 20 ft–20 ft 11 in.
   - 21 ft–21 ft 11 in.

4. After students have completed the "Tally" and "Frequency" columns of the frequency table, explain that they'll use the frequency table to make a histogram.

5. Read the directions for Problems 5–9. Assist students as needed, encouraging them to look at the Worked Example for help. When they get to Problem 7, ask these questions:

   Ask: What is the least frequency? 1

   Ask: What is the greatest frequency? 3

   Ask: What range of numbers needs to be on the graph to represent the frequencies? The range needs to be 0–3, but to make the histogram easier to read, I should include one number beyond 3, so 0–4.

6. If necessary, remind students that the numbering on the vertical axis usually goes one number beyond the greatest frequency to make the scale easier to read. Also explain that the horizontal axis always represents a frequency of 0.

7. For Problem 8, have students use the ruler to help them divide the horizontal axis into 4 evenly spaced intervals. Remind students that there should be no space between the intervals. Have them label the intervals from left to right along the horizontal axis.

8. For Problem 9, guide students to use the data in the frequency table to draw a bar for each range. If students need assistance, start by pointing to the 18 ft–18 ft 11 in. row in the frequency table.

   Ask: What is the frequency for 18 ft–18 ft 11 in.? 3

   Have students create a bar above the 18 ft–18 ft 11 in. range that has a height of 3 on the vertical axis.

   Follow the same process, as needed, to help students draw the remaining bars.

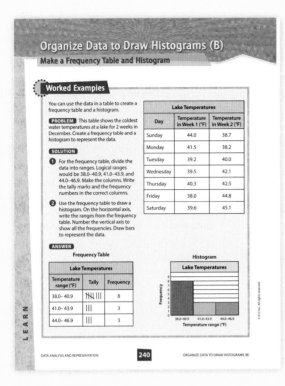

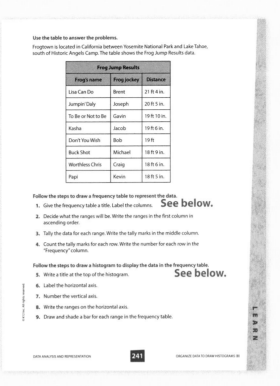

Additional Answers

1–4.   Frequency Table

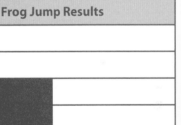

Frog Jump Results		
Distance	Tally	Frequency
18 ft–18 ft 11 in.	|||	3
19 ft–19 ft 11 in.	|||	3
20 ft–20 ft 11 in.			1
21 ft–21 ft 11 in.			1

5–9.   Histogram

Frog Jump Results

(Histogram with vertical axis "Frequency" from 0 to 4, horizontal axis "Distance" with categories: 18 ft–18 ft 11 in., 19 ft–19 ft 11 in., 20 ft–20 ft 11 in., 21 ft–21 ft 11 in.)

TRY IT Make and Interpret Histograms

OFFLINE
15min

Objectives

- Organize and display single-variable data in a histogram.

Students will make a histogram from data in a frequency table. They will also interpret frequency tables to determine which histogram represents the data. Gather one copy of the Draw a Histogram printout, ruler, and markers. View or print the Make and Interpret Histograms activity page and read the directions with students.

Students should copy the problems from the Activity Book into their Math Notebook as necessary and solve them there. They should use the printout for Problems 1–5.

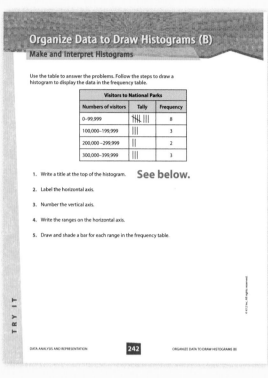

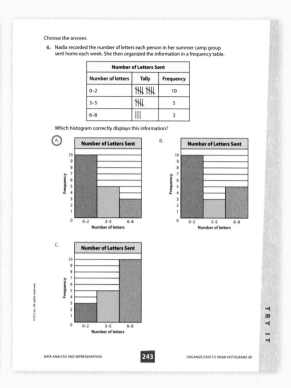

Additional Answers

1–5.

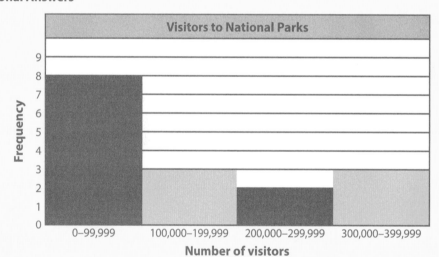

7. Dave recorded the number of runs he scored in each baseball game in one season. He then organized the information in a frequency table.

Runs Scored

Runs	Tally	Frequency
0–3	|||	3
4–7	||	2
8–11	|	1

Which histogram correctly displays this information?

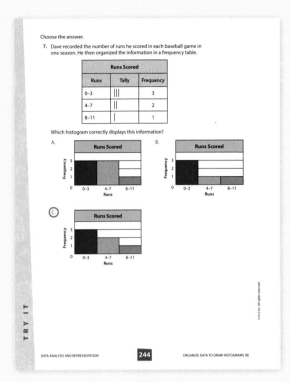

8. Bobbi recorded the number of points she scored in each basketball game she played during the summer. She then organized the information in a frequency table.

Points Scored

Points	Tally	Frequency
0–9	|||	3
10–19	||||	4
20–29	||	2
30–39	|||||	5
40–49	||	2

Which histogram correctly displays this information?

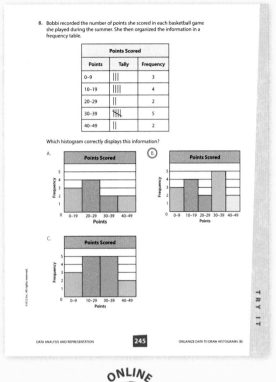

TRY IT

CHECKPOINT

ONLINE 10 min

Objectives

Students will complete an online Checkpoint. If necessary, read the directions, problems, and answer choices to students and help them with keyboard or mouse operations.

- Organize and display single-variable data in a histogram.

Create Circle Graphs

Lesson Overview

GET READY Represent Fractions with Sketches	10 minutes	**OFFLINE**
LEARN Organize Data on a Circle Graph	15 minutes	**OFFLINE**
LEARN Interpret Data and Circle Graphs	15 minutes	**ONLINE**
TRY IT Work with Circle Graphs	10 minutes	**ONLINE**
CHECKPOINT	10 minutes	**ONLINE**

▶ Lesson Objectives

Organize and display single-variable data in a circle graph.

▶ Prerequisite Skills

Represent a fraction with a sketch.

▶ Content Background

Students will learn how to organize and display data in a circle graph.

Circle graphs (sometimes called *pie charts*) are excellent for displaying data when you want to analyze portions of a whole amount, such as a budget or all the categories of books in a library. No other display gives a sense of how the parts of the whole relate to one another like a circle graph does. The data in the sections are generally expressed as actual number values or as fractions or percents of the entire amount.

Students will use the Circle Graphs printout and a ruler to create circle graphs, but they will be asked to only approximate the sizes of the sections.

▶ Advance Preparation

Print two copies of the Circle Graphs.

Materials to Gather

SUPPLIED

Circle Graphs (printout)

Organize Data on a Circle Graph activity page

ALSO NEEDED

compass

ruler, dual-scale

paper, drawing

pencils, coloring

GET READY Represent Fractions with Sketches · OFFLINE 10 min

Objectives

Students will sketch a fraction as part of a whole, part of a set, and as a location on a number line. They will also use a ruler and compass to draw a spinner and its fractional sections. Gather the compass, ruler, drawing paper, and coloring pencils.

- Represent a fraction with a sketch.

1. Tell students to make a sketch to show the fraction $\frac{5}{8}$ as part of a whole.

   Possible answer:

2. Have students explain how they know that their sketch shows $\frac{5}{8}$.

Possible answer: There are 8 parts of the whole, and 5 parts are shaded.

3. Tell students to make a sketch to show $\frac{5}{8}$ as part of a set. Discuss how the sketches look different when they show part of a whole compared to a part of a set.

Possible answer:

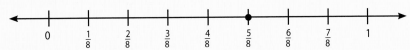

4. Tell students to use their ruler to draw a number line. Have them label the number line from 0 to 1, showing eighths between the whole numbers. Have student label all tick marks with fractions and mark $\frac{5}{8}$ with a dot on a number line.

Answer:

Ask students how many segments the number line between 0 and 1 should be divided into. 8

5. Have students use their compass and ruler to sketch a spinner. The spinner should have the letter A in a section that is $\frac{1}{4}$ of the circle, a B in a section that is $\frac{1}{8}$ of the circle, a C in a section that is $\frac{1}{2}$ of the circle, and a D in a section that is $\frac{1}{8}$ of the circle. To sketch the spinner, have students use the compass to draw a circle, then use the ruler to divide the circle into two halves. Then have them divide one of the halves into two fourths. Have them divide one of the fourths into two eighths. Students should label the sections and may shade them with coloring pencils.

Possible answer:

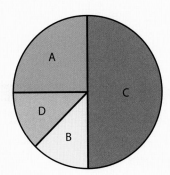

LEARN Organize Data on a Circle Graph

Objectives

- Organize and display single-variable data in a circle graph.

Students will use data to create a circle graph. Gather the Circle Graphs printouts and a ruler. View or print the Organize Data on a Circle Graph activity page and read the directions with students.

1. Tell students that a circle graph is one way to organize data. Tell them that a circle graph can use fractions, decimal numbers, percents, or whole number values. Read the Worked Example with students.

   Say: The Worked Example uses percents, but you will need to use fractions to solve the other problems. You'll need to use your knowledge of fractions and geometry.

2. Give students the printouts. Guide them to make a circle graph to answer Problems 1–5 about the favorite activities. Tell students that they may approximate the sizes of the sections.

   Ask: According to the survey, what activity did the greatest number of students prefer? playing with pets

   Ask: According to the survey, what activities did the fewest number of students prefer? reading and playing outdoors

   Ask: How many students participated in the favorite activities survey, and how do you know? There were 160 students. I added 20, 80, 10, 40, and 10.

3. Explain that if 20 students out of 160 answered "watching movies," the fraction that represents those students out of all the students surveyed would be $\frac{20}{160}$.

   Ask: What can $\frac{20}{160}$ be simplified to? $\frac{1}{8}$

4. Have students keep notes of that fraction and the other fractions for the responses to the survey.

   $\frac{20}{160} = \frac{1}{8}$ (watching movies)

   $\frac{80}{160} = \frac{1}{2}$ (playing with pets)

   $\frac{10}{160} = \frac{1}{16}$ (reading)

   $\frac{40}{160} = \frac{1}{4}$ (playing team sports)

   $\frac{10}{160} = \frac{1}{16}$ (playing outdoors)

5. Have students check their work. Since each fraction of the data represents one part of a whole, students should add the fractions to see if the sum is 1.

   When the fractions are changed to have the common denominator of 16, they should be added like this:

   $\frac{2}{16} + \frac{8}{16} + \frac{1}{16} + \frac{4}{16} + \frac{1}{16} = 1$

6. Have students use the ruler as a straightedge to make sections on a circle on the printout. The sections will approximately represent the five fractions.

   Say: Start by dividing the circle in half. Since $\frac{1}{4}$ is half the size of $\frac{1}{2}$, you can make a section that's half the size of the first section. Divide the remaining $\frac{1}{4}$ of the circle in half so that you have two sections that each show $\frac{1}{8}$. Divide one of those sections in half so that the two sections each show $\frac{1}{16}$.

7. After students make the sections on the circle graph, have them label the sections with the activity and the number of students.

8. Tell students that the last step is to give their circle graph a title.

9. Have students complete the rest of the problems. Guide them to create a table for Problem 11.

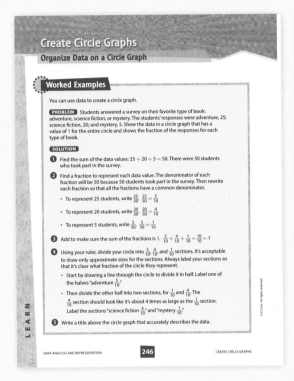

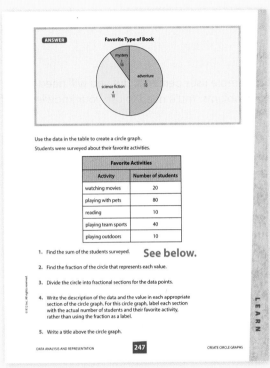

Use the data in the table to create a circle graph.

Students were surveyed about their favorite activities.

Favorite Activities	
Activity	**Number of students**
watching movies	20
playing with pets	80
reading	10
playing team sports	40
playing outdoors	10

1. Find the sum of the students surveyed.   **See below.**

2. Find the fraction of the circle that represents each value.

3. Divide the circle into fractional sections for the data points.

4. Write the description of the data and the value in each appropriate section of the circle graph. For this circle graph, label each section with the actual number of students and their favorite activity, rather than using the fraction as a label.

5. Write a title above the circle graph.

Answers

1–5.

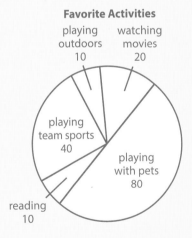

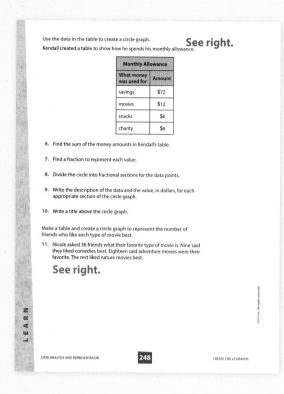

Use the data in the table to create a circle graph. **See right.**
Kendall created a table to show how he spends his monthly allowance.

Monthly Allowance	
What money was used for	Amount
savings	$72
movies	$12
snacks	$6
charity	$6

6. Find the sum of the money amounts in Kendall's table.

7. Find a fraction to represent each value.

8. Divide the circle into fractional sections for the data points.

9. Write the description of the data and the value, in dollars, for each appropriate section of the circle graph.

10. Write a title above the circle graph.

Make a table and create a circle graph to represent the number of friends who like each type of movie best.

11. Nicole asked 36 friends what their favorite type of movie is. Nine said they liked comedies best. Eighteen said adventure movies were their favorite. The rest liked nature movies best.

See right.

Answers 6–10.

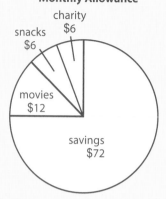

How Kendall Spends His Monthly Allowance

charity $6
snacks $6
movies $12
savings $72

11.

Favorite Movies	
Movie type	Number of friends
comedy	9
adventure	18
nature	9

Favorite Movies

nature 9 | comedy 9
adventure 18

LEARN Interpret Data and Circle Graphs

ONLINE **15** min

Students will choose the circle graph that displays a set of data shown in a table. They will also interpret data in tables and circle graphs to answer questions.

Objectives

- Organize and display single-variable data in a circle graph.

TRY IT Work with Circle Graphs

ONLINE **10** min

Students will complete an online Try It. If necessary, read the directions, problems, and answer choices to students and help them with keyboard or mouse operations.

Objectives

- Organize and display single-variable data in a circle graph.

CHECKPOINT

ONLINE **10** min

Students will complete an online Checkpoint. If necessary, read the directions, problems, and answer choices to students and help them with keyboard or mouse operations.

Objectives

- Organize and display single-variable data in a circle graph.

510 DATA ANALYSIS AND REPRESENTATION

Line Plots (A)

LEARN Create Line Plots with Fractions
60 minutes : OFFLINE

▶ **Lesson Objectives**

Create a line plot to display a set of measurements in fractions of a unit.

Materials to Gather

SUPPLIED

Create Line Plots with Fractions activity
page

OFFLINE
60min

LEARN Create Line Plots with Fractions

Students will learn to create a line plot using an example with whole-number data first; they will then see an example with fractions. View or print the Create Line Plots with Fractions activity page. Students should copy the problems into their Math Notebook and solve them there.

1. Have students read Problem 1 in the Worked Examples. Make sure they understand that the time intervals represent elapsed the time between eruptions, not the times or durations of the eruptions themselves. Also point out that time intervals are rounded to the nearest 5 minutes.

2. **Ask:** How many values are in the data set? 15

3. **Say:** Create the number line as the first step in making a line plot.

4. Have students read Step 1 of the solution and then create a number line in their Math Notebook.

5. **Say:** Let's place the first value in the data set, 65, on the line plot. Place an X above the line at the proper location.

6. Guide students as they place the remaining values on their own number line. Be sure students place a new mark above existing mark(s) for values that repeat. Also emphasize that the Xs should be aligned both vertically and horizontally.

7. Have students create a title to place above the line plot and a label for the numbers below. Emphasize that the label should include the unit of time (minutes).

8. **Say:** A line plot is a type of frequency distribution. Visually you can tell how frequently each data value occurs and where the data values lie.

9. **Ask:** Just by looking at the line plot, what can you say about where the data clusters in this data set? What does that mean? The data in this line plot cluster more to the middle and left. That means that the times between eruptions occur more between 45 and 65 minutes than any other times.

10. Have students read Problem 2 in the Worked Examples and cover up the steps to the solution. They should try the problem on their own, revealing each step as a check of their work.

Objectives

*   Create a line plot to display a set of measurements in fractions of a unit.

Tips

When students complete a line plot, have them count the number of Xs to be sure they have the same number as the number of data values.

11. Emphasize and review, if necessary, the equivalent fractions in this problem.

12. Have students complete Problems 1–5. For Problems 1 and 5, students should title and label the plot appropriately, given the descriptions provided.

13. Make sure students count the number of values for each problem and compare it to the number of marks for each line plot.

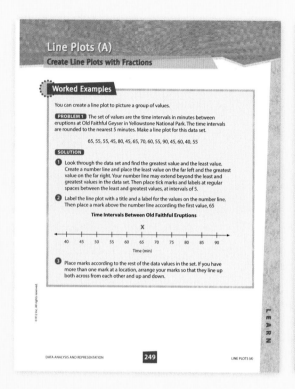

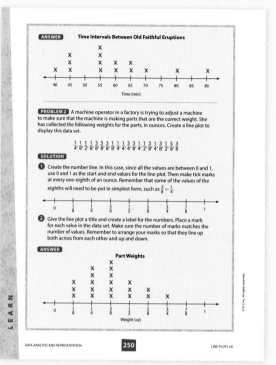

Create a line plot for the data set in your Math Notebook. For data sets that provide information about the data, write a title for the line plot and provide an appropriate label with units for the numbers.

See right.

1. Students ran 100-yard sprints in gym class. Here are their individual times, in seconds:
12, 15, 13, 15, 18, 13, 12, 11, 15, 14, 19, 11, 12, 15, 14

2. $0, \frac{1}{5}, \frac{2}{5}, 1, 0, \frac{3}{5}, 1, \frac{3}{5}, \frac{1}{5}, \frac{2}{5}, \frac{1}{5}, \frac{4}{5}, 0, \frac{3}{5}, \frac{4}{5}$

3. $\frac{1}{6}, \frac{1}{3}, \frac{1}{2}, \frac{1}{6}, \frac{1}{2}, \frac{1}{3}, \frac{2}{3}, \frac{1}{6}, \frac{2}{3}, \frac{1}{6}$

4. $\frac{2}{9}, \frac{1}{3}, \frac{1}{9}, \frac{4}{9}, \frac{2}{9}, \frac{5}{9}, \frac{2}{9}, \frac{5}{9}, \frac{4}{9}, \frac{7}{9}, \frac{8}{9}, \frac{4}{9}, \frac{1}{3}, \frac{2}{9}, \frac{5}{9}, \frac{7}{9}, \frac{5}{9}, \frac{4}{9}, \frac{2}{9}$

5. Insects were captured and measured in a field. The following data show their lengths, in inches:
$\frac{1}{10}, \frac{2}{5}, \frac{3}{10}, \frac{1}{10}, \frac{3}{10}, \frac{1}{2}, \frac{2}{5}, \frac{7}{10}, \frac{1}{10}, \frac{3}{10}, \frac{1}{5}, \frac{2}{5}, \frac{1}{2}, \frac{3}{10}$

LEARN

Answers

1.

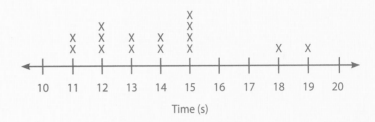

Times for 100-Yard Sprint

Time (s)

2.

3.

4.

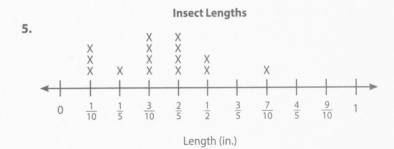

5.

Insect Lengths

Length (in.)

Line Plots (B)

Lesson Overview

LEARN Use Line Plots with Fraction Data	60 minutes	**OFFLINE**

▶ Lesson Objectives

Use operations on fractions to solve problems involving information presented in line plots.

Materials to Gather

SUPPLIED

Use Line Plots with Fraction Data activity page

LEARN Use Line Plots with Fraction Data

OFFLINE 60min

Objectives

- Use operations on fractions to solve problems involving information presented in line plots.

Students will learn how to use data from line plots with fractions to answer questions involving operations with numbers. View or print the Use Line Plots with Fraction Data activity page. Students should copy the problems into their Math Notebook and solve them there.

1. Have students read Problem 1 in the Worked Examples. Be sure they understand that the values represent the weights, in ounces, of parts created by a machine.

   Ask: How many values are in the data set? 18

   Check that students can read values in the set from the line plot.

   Ask: What are the two least values in the data set? $\frac{1}{8}, \frac{1}{8}$

   Ask: Which value or values have the most occurrences? There are 5 values at $\frac{1}{4}$ and 5 values at $\frac{3}{8}$.

2. Have students read Question 1. Emphasize that *difference* indicates subtraction in this question. Before having students read the solution, ask them to perform each step on their own first.

   Ask: What are the least and greatest values in the data set?

   least: $\frac{1}{8}$; greatest: $\frac{3}{4}$

   Ask: How do you find the difference if the denominators are unequal? Make sure the fractions have a least common denominator before subtracting.

   Be sure students understand each step of the computation.

3. Have students read Question 2 and find the sum. You may need to remind them that the denominator stays the same when they add or subtract fractions with a like denominator. Be sure they have converted their answer to simplest form.

4. Have the students read Question 3 and find the sum.

   Ask: How many measurements are at $\frac{3}{8}$? 5

   Make sure students add only the numerators together and not the denominators when finding the sum. Also point out that since there are 5 fractions, all at $\frac{3}{8}$, the total can be found by using multiplication: $5 \cdot \frac{3}{8}$.

5. Have the students read and answer Question 4. Be sure they count the two measurements at $\frac{5}{8}$ and the one at $\frac{3}{4}$ for a total of three.

6. Have students read and answer Question 5. If they haven't noticed already, remind them that the number of measurements at $\frac{5}{8}$ or greater is the same as the answer to Question 4.

7. For Problem 2 in the Worked Examples, check to see that students understand the line plot in terms of the statement of the problem.

   Ask: So what do the Xs represent in this problem? Each X in the line plot represents a beaker with a certain number of liters in it. The number of liters in a beaker is found as a fraction on the number line, below the X. There are 6 beakers, since there are 6 Xs.

8. Before students read Step 1, have them consider ways to solve the problem. They might want to draw the beakers, list the six fractions in order, or try something else. Give them time to think about their strategy.

9. If students struggle to conceptualize what to do, prompt them that they are to compute the average. They will find the total amount and divide it by the number of beakers.

10. Students should complete Problems 1–4 on their own. They should recognize that Problem 4 is similar to Worked Example Problem 2.

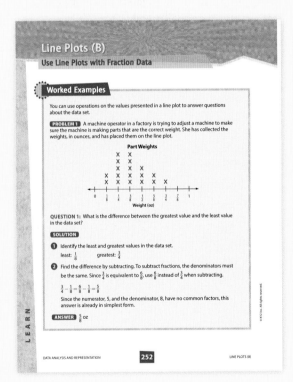

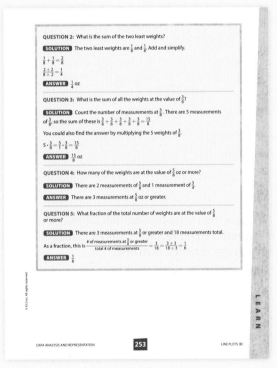

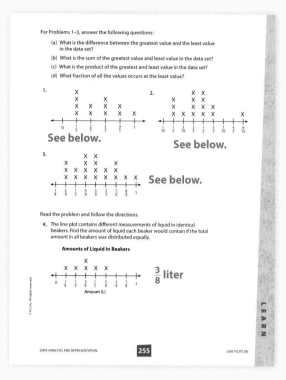

PROBLEM 2 The line plot contains different measurements of liquid, in liters, for identical beakers. Find the amount of liquid each beaker would contain if the total amount in all beakers was distributed equally.

Amounts of Liquid in Beakers

Amount (L)

SOLUTION

1. Since the total amount of liquid is to be distributed equally, calculate the average. Find the total amount of liquid.

$$\frac{1}{6} + \frac{1}{3} + \frac{1}{3} + \frac{2}{3} + \frac{5}{6}$$
$$= \frac{1}{6} + \frac{2}{6} + \frac{2}{6} + \frac{4}{6} + \frac{5}{6}$$
$$= \frac{18}{6}$$
$$= 3$$

The total amount of liquid is 3 liters.

2. Since the total amount of liquid now needs to be distributed equally among the beakers, divide the total amount, 3 liters, by the number of beakers, 6.

$$3 \div 6 = \frac{3}{6} = \frac{1}{2}$$

ANSWER To distribute the total amount of liquid equally, each beaker must contain $\frac{1}{2}$ liter of liquid.

For Problems 1–3, answer the following questions:

(a) What is the difference between the greatest value and the least value in the data set?

(b) What is the sum of the greatest value and least value in the data set?

(c) What is the product of the greatest and least value in the data set?

(d) What fraction of all the values occurs at the least value?

1.

See below.

2.

See below.

3.

See below.

Read the problem and follow the directions.

4. The line plot contains different measurements of liquid in identical beakers. Find the amount of liquid each beaker would contain if the total amount in all beakers was distributed equally.

Amounts of Liquid in Beakers

Amount (L)

$\frac{3}{8}$ liter

Additional Answers

1. (a) $\frac{4}{5}$

   (b) $\frac{6}{5}$

   (c) $\frac{1}{5}$

   (d) $\frac{4}{12} = \frac{1}{3}$

2. (a) $\frac{7}{10}$

   (b) $\frac{11}{10}$

   (c) $\frac{9}{50}$

   (d) $\frac{3}{15} = \frac{1}{5}$

3. (a) $\frac{7}{9}$

   (b) $\frac{11}{9}$

   (c) $\frac{2}{9}$

   (d) $\frac{3}{20}$

Interpret Graphs and Tables

▶ **Lesson Objectives**

Interpret information displayed in a graph or table.

▶ **Prerequisite Skills**

- Organize and display single-variable data in a circle graph.
- Answer questions about one- and two-variable data graphs.

▶ **Content Background**

Students will learn how to interpret graphs and tables. They will also learn how a scale affects a graph.

The primary reason for organizing and representing data in a variety of ways is to be able to interpret the data. Much of our information now comes to us in charts, graphs, and other visual representations. Knowing how to ask and answer questions when encountering data in everyday situations is critical to students' understanding of the world around them. Students need to understand that they can use data in tables and graphs to justify the results of a question or to debate the need for a cause. They should also recognize that they can manipulate data and graphs in ways that misrepresent situations. Knowing what causes such misrepresentations will make students smarter consumers.

▶ **Common Errors and Misconceptions**

- Students might have difficulty interpreting graphs because they have not had enough opportunity to analyze and compare different types of graphs.
- Students might have difficulty determining information on a graph that is implied. For example, students might not be able to determine the value of data points if the points fall between two values shown on the scale. They also might not be able to use a graph to extend the data and make predictions about data points not given on the graph.
- Students might have an idea of how they think data should look when graphed, so they might expect all graphs of those data to reflect their visual image.

Materials to Gather

There are no materials to gather for this lesson.

GET READY Analyze Tally Charts and Pictographs

Students will analyze tally charts and pictographs to answer questions about the data shown.

Objectives

- Answer questions about one- and two-variable data graphs.

LEARN Use Data in Graphs and Tables

Students will interpret data and answer questions about information shown in line graphs, tables, circle graphs, and bar graphs.

Objectives

- Interpret information displayed in a graph or table.

LEARN Understand Different Scales on Graphs

Students will analyze bar graphs to understand how the scales on the graphs affect the data shown.

Objectives

- Interpret information displayed in a graph or table.

TRY IT Work with Graphs and Tables

Students will complete an online Try It. If necessary, read the directions, problems, and answer choices to students and help them with keyboard or mouse operations.

Objectives

- Interpret information displayed in a graph or table.

CHECKPOINT

Students will complete an online Checkpoint. If necessary, read the directions, problems, and answer choices to students and help them with keyboard or mouse operations.

Objectives

- Interpret information displayed in a graph or table.

Fractions, Decimals, and Graphs

Lesson Overview		
GET READY Fraction and Decimal Match	10 minutes	ONLINE
LEARN Graphs with Fractions and Decimals	30 minutes	ONLINE
TRY IT Compare Data	10 minutes	ONLINE
CHECKPOINT	10 minutes	ONLINE

▶ Lesson Objectives

Use whole numbers, fractions, and decimals to compare different data sets.

▶ Prerequisite Skills

Explain that a simple fraction and a decimal amount can represent the same quantity.

▶ Content Background

Students will learn to answer questions about graphs and tables that involve whole numbers, fractions, and decimals.

People organize and represent data in multiple ways through tables and graphs. Within these representations, they use several different types of numbers: the raw data, or the numbers themselves, and also fractional and decimal representations of the data compared to the entire set of data. Students need to be able to move comfortably from one numerical representation to another to be able to accurately interpret and make sense of data.

Materials to Gather

There are no materials to gather for this lesson.

GET READY Fraction and Decimal Match

ONLINE 10 min

Objectives

Students will match the fraction and decimals that have the same value.

- Explain that a simple fraction and a decimal amount can represent the same quantity.

LEARN Graphs with Fractions and Decimals

ONLINE 30 min

Objectives

Students will interpret data in circle graphs, tables, and bar graphs to answer questions about fractions and decimals in data sets.

- Use whole numbers, fractions, and decimals to compare different data sets.

TRY IT Compare Data

ONLINE 10 min

Objectives

Students will complete an online Try It. If necessary, read the directions, problems, and answer choices to students and help them with keyboard or mouse operations.

- Use whole numbers, fractions, and decimals to compare different data sets.

CHECKPOINT

ONLINE 10 min

Objectives

Students will complete an online Checkpoint. If necessary, read the directions, problems, and answer choices to students and help them with keyboard or mouse operations.

- Use whole numbers, fractions, and decimals to compare different data sets.

Choose an Appropriate Graph

Lesson Overview

GET READY Read Data Displays and Select Graphs	10 minutes	ONLINE
LEARN Use the Appropriate Graph	15 minutes	ONLINE
LEARN Compare Graphic Representations	15 minutes	ONLINE
TRY IT Choose an Appropriate Graph for Data	10 minutes	ONLINE
CHECKPOINT	10 minutes	ONLINE

▶ Lesson Objectives

- Explain which types of graphs are appropriate for various data sets.
- Recognize appropriate representations of survey data.

▶ Prerequisite Skills

Interpret information displayed in a graph or table.

▶ Content Background

Students will learn to choose an appropriate graph to match a data set.

Throughout their lives, students may be asked to represent data in a variety of ways, whether in reports for school, documents on the job, or information presented to family and friends. Whether they collect the data themselves or are given data, they should have a good idea of which type of table or graph would be best to communicate what they want to emphasize in the data. This lesson will provide students with some good guidelines to use when deciding how to represent the data they are given.

▶ Common Errors and Misconceptions

- Students might have difficulty interpreting graphs because they have not had enough opportunity to analyze and compare different types of graphs.
- Students might have difficulty determining information on a graph that is implied. For example, students might not be able to determine the value of data points if the points fall between two values shown on the scale. They also might not be able to use a graph to extend the data and make predictions about data points not given on the graph.
- Students might have an idea of how they think data should look when graphed, so they might expect all graphs of those data to reflect their visual image.

Materials to Gather

There are no materials to gather for this lesson.

GET READY Read Data Displays and Select Graphs

ONLINE
10min

Objectives

Students will read graphs to answer questions about the data. Then they will select the type of graph that best represents a given set of data.

- Interpret information displayed in a graph or table.

LEARN Use the Appropriate Graph

ONLINE
15min

Objectives

Students will explore different types of tables and graphs to understand when they are appropriate to represent a data set. They will also match tables and graphs with their descriptions.

- Explain which types of graphs are appropriate for various data sets.

LEARN Compare Graphic Representations

ONLINE
15min

Objectives

Students will read about data sets that describe everyday situations. They will decide which table or graph would be most appropriate to represent the data.

Tips Remind students that more than one type of chart, table, or graph may be appropriate to represent a data set. Have them think about this example: What types of tables or graphs could you use to represent data about the heights of different trees in a park? Explain.

- Explain which types of graphs are appropriate for various data sets.
- Recognize appropriate representations of survey data.

TRY IT Choose an Appropriate Graph for Data

ONLINE
10min

Objectives

Students will complete an online Try It. If necessary, read the directions, problems, and answer choices to students and help them with keyboard or mouse operations.

- Explain which types of graphs are appropriate for various data sets.

CHECKPOINT

ONLINE
10min

Objectives

Students will complete an online Checkpoint. If necessary, read the directions, problems, and answer choices to students and help them with keyboard or mouse operations.

- Explain which types of graphs are appropriate for various data sets.

Core Focus
Data Representations

▶ Lesson Objectives

- Recognize appropriate representations of survey data.
- Evaluate the utility of models, such as graphs and charts, to determine which are most useful and efficient to analyze data and solve problems.

▶ Content Background

In this lesson, students will learn how to choose the most appropriate graph to display a given set of data.

Certain types of graphs represent certain types of data better than others. For example, a line plot organizes data into clusters, so a line plot is a good graph to use for finding outliers, mean, median, or mode. The bars in bar graphs and double bar graphs make these graphs good representations for comparing countable, or noncontinuous, data. A line graph uses a line segment to show continuous data over time. Line graphs are useful for seeing trends in data or changes in the data over time.

Whenever you ask students questions about a graph, make sure they have a copy of the graph to refer to and that the graph includes all the essential elements, such as the labels on its axes, a scale, and a title. Some types of graphs, such as double bar graphs and double line graphs, also need a legend. It is important to present a graph along with the data from which it was generated.

When students make a single bar graph, make sure that the bars do not touch each other—there should be at least a slight space between them. When students make a double bar graph, only the two bars in each paired set of bars should touch. There must be space between each pair of bars. If all the bars are touching, it is not a bar graph but a histogram.

Altering the scale affects the appearance of a graph. For example, using a scale with a range that is much greater than the range of the data can minimize the differences in the data. Including additional intervals can maximize the differences in the data. These types of alterations can result in graphs that are misleading.

Here is an example. All the graphs shown on the following page represent the same data from the table. Graph A represents the data accurately. Graph B uses a large scale to minimize the changes in the data. Graph C uses additional intervals to maximize the changes in the data. Graph B and Graph C could be considered misleading.

Materials to Gather

SUPPLIED

The Best Data Display activity page

Data Display Selection activity page

	1st Quarter	2nd Quarter	3rd Quarter	4th Quarter
Store 1	23	27	50	22
Store 2	30	28	34	31

Graph A

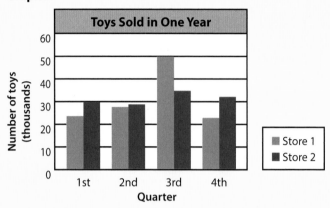

Graph B

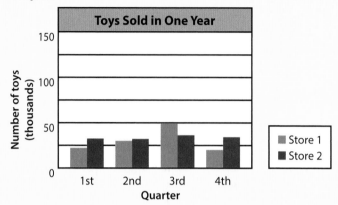

Graph C

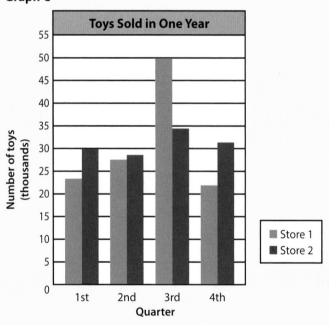

▶ Common Errors and Misconceptions

- Students might have difficulty interpreting graphs because they have not had enough opportunity to analyze and compare different types of graphs.

- Students might have difficulty determining information on a graph that is implied. For example, students might not be able to determine the value of data points if the points fall between two values shown on the scale. They also might not be able to use a graph to extend the data and make predictions about data points not given on the graph.

- Students might have an idea of how they think the data should look when graphed, so they might expect all graphs of those data to reflect their visual image.

LEARN Select the Best Graph

ONLINE
15min

Objectives

Students will learn how to select a graph that best represents a given set of data. They will learn that a graph should show the needed information without being misleading.

- Recognize appropriate representations of survey data.
- Evaluate the utility of models, such as graphs and charts, to determine which are most useful and efficient to analyze data and solve problems.

LEARN The Best Data Display

OFFLINE
15min

Objectives

Students will learn how to correctly label all parts of a data display. They will also learn how to explain whether a graph is a good choice to display a given set of data. View or print The Best Data Display activity page.

- Recognize appropriate representations of survey data.
- Evaluate the utility of models, such as graphs and charts, to determine which are most useful and efficient to analyze data and solve problems.

1. Read the problem in the Worked Example with students. Have them try to answer the problem before reading the solution and answer. Then read the solution and answer together. Discuss whether students' answers were correct, keeping in mind that there are many possible correct answers.

2. Read the directions with students. Have them complete Problem 1. Students should copy the problems from the Activity Book into their Math Notebook as necessary and solve them there.

3. Read Problem 2 together. Explain that all three data displays show the data. Tell students that one display might be more appropriate than another depending on what information they want to show.

   Ask: If you wanted to know which month had the most sunny days, which data display should you use? bar graph

   Ask: If you wanted to know how many months had 20 or more sunny days, which data display should you use? Explain. line plot or bar graph; accept reasonable explanations

4. Discuss whether there would be an appropriate situation to use the line graph using Problem 2 as an example. Ask students to think about whether the data are continuous over time.

   To assist students in answering, point to the line segment between two of the data points. Ask students to explain what data the line segment represents. Help students realize that the data about sunny days are countable and **not** continuous, so the line graph may not the best way to display the data. Point out that although the line segments that connect the points give the appearance that there are data between the points, there really are no meaningful data between the points. For example, there is no "month" between the point for January and the point for February and, therefore, no data about the number of sunny days.

5. Have students complete the remaining problems on their own.

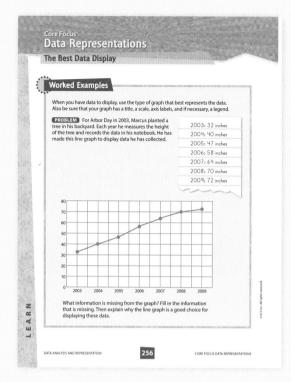

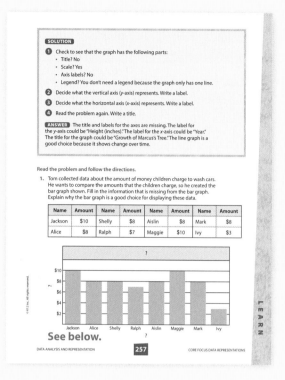

Additional Answers

1. Accept all reasonable answers. **Sample answers:**

- Title: What Other Children Charge to Wash Cars

- Horizontal axis label: Name of child

- Vertical axis label: Amount charged ($)

- Explanation: The bar graph is a good choice because each bar can represent the amount that each child charges. The data are countable.

Read the problem and follow the directions.

2. Gregory collected data about the number of sunny days each month for a year.

Month	Number of days
January	17
February	16
March	17
April	18
May	20
June	25
July	27
August	26
September	23
October	20
November	18
December	16

On the next page are three ways to display the data. Which data display do you think best shows the data? Explain your answer.

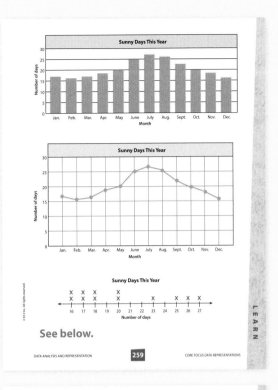

See below.

Choose the answer.

3. Louise collected the following data about the favorite colors of some boys and girls.

Color	Number of boys	Number of girls	Color	Number of boys	Number of girls
orange	50	49	green	27	13
purple	34	21	red	3	19

Which data display best represents the data?

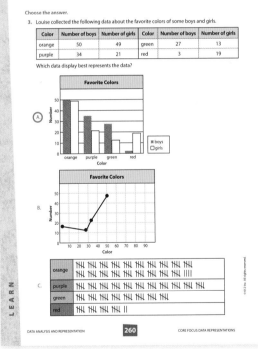

4. Halle collected the following data about the number of miles she ran each day.

Day	Number of miles	Day	Number of miles	Day	Number of miles	Day	Number of miles
Day 1	4	Day 3	4	Day 5	3	Day 7	5
Day 2	6	Day 4	2	Day 6	4		

Which data display best shows the number of miles that occurs most often?

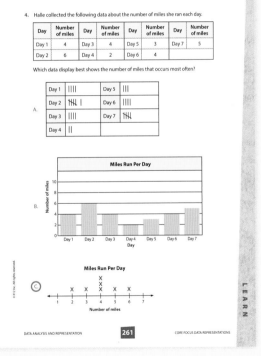

Additional Answers

2. Either the line plot or bar graph is correct. **Sample explanation for line plot:** The line plot shows how many months cluster around each number of days. **Sample explanation for bar graph:** The data are countable, so the bar graph makes the number of days data easy to compare. The line graph is not correct because the data do not represent a change in the total amount of sunny days over time.

TRY IT Data Display Selection

Objectives

Students will practice selecting the best data display for given sets of data. View or print the Data Display Selection activity page and read the directions with students. They should copy the problems from the Activity Book into their Math Notebook as necessary and solve them there.

- Recognize appropriate representations of survey data.
- Evaluate the utility of models, such as graphs and charts, to determine which are most useful and efficient to analyze data and solve problems.

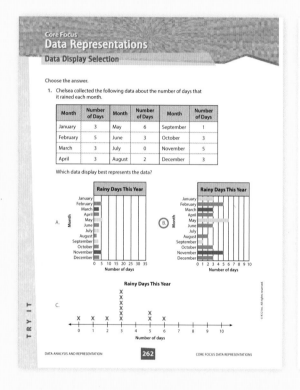

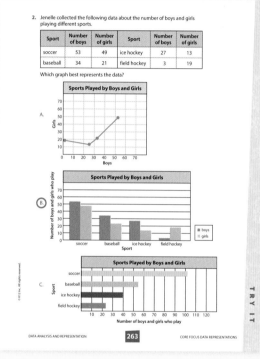

Choose the answer.

3. Tom collected the following data about the amount other children were charging to wash cars.

Name	Amount	Name	Amount	Name	Amount	Name	Amount
Jackson	$10	Shelly	$8	Aislin	$8	Mark	$8
Alice	$8	Ralph	$7	Maggie	$10	Ivy	$3

Which data display is used to show the amount that occurs most often?

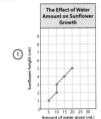

What Other Children Charge to Wash Cars

A

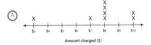

Amount charged ($)

B.

Jackson	卌 卌	Aislin	卌 |||
Alice	卌 |||	Maggie	卌 卌
Shelly	卌 |||	Mark	卌 |||
Ralph	卌 ||	Ivy	|||

---

4. Kent wanted to know if he would do better on tests if he spent more time studying his notes. Kent collected the following data.

Subject	Time	Score	Subject	Time	Score	Subject	Time	Score
math	30 min	10	math	10 min	5	reading	15 min	7
spelling	15 min	6	math	20 min	7	spelling	15 min	5
math	25 min	8	spelling	25 min	9			

Which data display will best show this information?

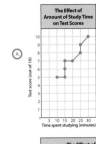

A

B.

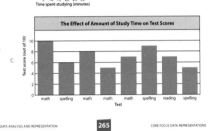

C.

Choose the answer.

5. Gina wanted to know if her sunflowers would grow taller if she gave them more water. Gina collected the following data.

Water	Growth	Water	Growth
10 mL	2 cm	15 mL	4 cm
5 mL	1 cm	10 mL	3 cm
20 mL	5 cm		

Which data display will best show this information?

A.

10 mL of water	||
5 mL of water		
20 mL of water	卌
15 mL of water	||||
10 mL of water	|||

B.

The Effect of Water Amount on Sunflower Growth

C.

The Effect of Water Amount on Sunflower Growth

Think Like a Mathematician Self-Check

6. State the actions and thinking you used during this lesson as a math learner.

Math Thinking and Actions
I made sense of problems by • Explaining to myself what a problem means and what it asks for • Using drawings or diagrams to represent a problem I was solving
I explained my math thinking clearly.
I tried out new ways to check if an answer is reasonable.
Other

Objectives

- Recognize appropriate representations of survey data.

- Evaluate the utility of models, such as graphs and charts, to determine which are most useful and efficient to analyze data and solve problems.

Students will complete an online Checkpoint. If necessary, read the directions, problems, and answer choices to students and help them with keyboard or mouse operations.

Unit Review

Lesson Overview		
UNIT REVIEW Look Back	10 minutes	**ONLINE**
UNIT REVIEW Checkpoint Practice	50 minutes	**ONLINE**
⮞ **UNIT REVIEW** Prepare for the Checkpoint		

▶ Unit Objectives

- Organize and display single-variable data in a histogram.
- Organize and display single-variable data in a circle graph.
- Create a line plot to display a set of measurements in fractions of a unit.
- Use operations on fractions to solve problems involving information presented in line plots.
- Interpret information displayed in a graph or table.
- Use whole numbers, fractions, and decimals to compare different data sets.
- Explain which types of graphs are appropriate for various data sets.
- Recognize appropriate representations of survey data.
- Evaluate the utility of models, such as graphs and charts, to determine which are most useful and efficient to analyze data and solve problems.

Materials to Gather

There are no materials to gather for this lesson.

▶ Advance Preparation

In this lesson, students will have an opportunity to review previous activities in the Data Analysis and Representation unit. Look at the suggested activities in Unit Review: Prepare for the Checkpoint online and gather any needed materials.

UNIT REVIEW Look Back

ONLINE 10 min

Objectives

Students will review key concepts from the unit to prepare for the Unit Checkpoint.

- Review unit objectives.

UNIT REVIEW Checkpoint Practice

ONLINE 50 min

Objectives

Students will complete an online Checkpoint Practice to prepare for the Unit Checkpoint. If necessary, read the directions, problems, and answer choices to students. Have students answer the problems on their own. Review any missed problems with students.

- Review unit objectives.

⮞ UNIT REVIEW Prepare for the Checkpoint

What you do next depends on how students performed in the previous activity, Unit Review: Checkpoint Practice. If students had difficulty with any of the problems, complete the appropriate review activity listed in the table online.

Unit Checkpoint

Lesson Overview

UNIT CHECKPOINT Online	60 minutes	**ONLINE**

Unit Objectives

- Organize and display single-variable data in a histogram.
- Organize and display single-variable data in a circle graph.
- Create a line plot to display a set of measurements in fractions of a unit.
- Use operations on fractions to solve problems involving information presented in line plots.
- Interpret information displayed in a graph or table.
- Use whole numbers, fractions, and decimals to compare different data sets.
- Explain which types of graphs are appropriate for various data sets.
- Recognize appropriate representations of survey data.
- Evaluate the utility of models, such as graphs and charts, to determine which are most useful and efficient to analyze data and solve problems.

Materials to Gather

There are no materials to gather for this lesson.

UNIT CHECKPOINT Online

ONLINE 60min

Students will complete the Unit Checkpoint online. If necessary, read the directions, problems, and answer choices to students and help them with keyboard or mouse operations.

Objectives

- Assess unit objectives.

Extended Problems: Real-World Application

▶ Lesson Objectives

- Interpret information displayed in a graph or table.
- Identify the ordered pairs resulting from corresponding terms from two patterns, and graph the ordered pairs on a coordinate plane.
- Solve real-world problems involving division of a unit fraction by a nonzero whole number or division of a whole number by a unit fraction.
- Graph points in the first quadrant of the coordinate plane, and interpret coordinate values of points in the context of the situation.
- Draw a scaled picture graph to represent a data set with several categories.
- Solve two-step "how many more" and "how many less" problems using information presented in scaled bar graphs.
- Apply mathematical knowledge and skills to evaluate and analyze real-world situations.

Materials to Gather

SUPPLIED

Extended Problems: Real-World Application (printout)

OFFLINE
60 min

GRADED ASSIGNMENT

Objectives

- Apply mathematical knowledge and skills to evaluate and analyze real-world situations.

Open the Extended Problems: Real-World Application. Read the directions, problems, and answer choices to students, if necessary.

You will grade this assignment.

- Students should complete the assignment on their own.
- Students should submit the completed assignment to you.
- Enter the results online.

Semester Review

Lesson Overview		
SEMESTER REVIEW Look Back	30 minutes	**ONLINE**
SEMESTER REVIEW Checkpoint Practice	30 minutes	**ONLINE**
⬎ **SEMESTER REVIEW** Prepare for the Checkpoint		

▶ Semester Objectives

- Use the order of operations to simplify expressions with mixed operations.
- Interpret a numerical expression without evaluating the expression.
- Simplify expressions with grouping symbols.
- Find a mathematical expression that corresponds to a given word phrase.
- Evaluate numerical expressions using order of operations (expressions include with parentheses and powers, whole numbers only).
- Identify or use an expression or an equation to answer questions about a problem.
- Use a letter to represent an unknown value in an expression or an equation.
- Evaluate a simple algebraic expression in one variable by using substitution.
- Graph or write an equation to solve a problem that involves a linear function.
- Use the situation presented in a problem to describe the meaning of each coordinate of an ordered pair displayed on a graph.
- Given a rule such as "Add 3," generate and graph ordered pairs on a coordinate plane.
- Graph to compare the corresponding terms of two patterns.
- Estimate or determine the number of cubes required to fill a solid figure.
- Determine the perimeter of a plane figure and use appropriate units.
- Construct a cube or a rectangular box from a two-dimensional pattern and determine the surface area.
- Use squares to approximate the area of an irregular shape.
- Explain and determine the volume of a solid figure and use appropriate units.
- Differentiate among appropriate units to measure perimeter, area, and volume.
- Use the fact that volume is additive to solve problems.
- Use a variety of methods, such as words, numbers, symbols, charts, graphs, tables, diagrams, and models, to explain mathematical reasoning in nonroutine or complex problems.
- Prioritize and sequence the information in a story problem that involves multiplication or division of decimal numbers.
- Determine when and how to break a multistep whole-number story problem or money problem into simpler parts.
- Apply strategies and results from simple story problems involving fractions to more complex problems.

Materials to Gather

There are no materials to gather for this lesson.

- Identify and generalize methods for solving problems that are similar to each other.
- Solve for one variable in a two-variable equation when the value of the other variable is given.
- Estimate or calculate a product or quotient in a whole-number story problem.
- Solve a story problem involving equal measures.
- Use estimation in addition or subtraction of fractions to verify whether calculated results are reasonable.
- Explain the advantages of exact solutions and approximate solutions to problems involving addition or subtraction of decimal numbers, and give answers to a specified degree of accuracy, such as hundredths.
- Make precise calculations and use the situation presented in a problem involving decimal-number operations to check the validity of the result.
- Evaluate whether a solution for a problem is reasonable.
- Evaluate the utility of models, such as graphs and charts, to determine which are most useful and efficient to analyze data and solve problems.
- Recognize appropriate representations of survey data.
- Create a line plot to display a set of measurements in fractions of a unit.
- Organize and display single-variable data in a histogram.
- Organize and display single-variable data in a circle graph.
- Interpret information displayed in a graph or table.
- Explain which types of graphs are appropriate for various data sets.
- Use whole numbers, fractions, and decimals to compare different data sets.

▶ Advance Preparation

In this lesson, students will have an opportunity to review previous activities from the semester. Look at the suggested activities in Semester Review: Prepare for the Checkpoint online and be prepared to gather any needed materials.

SEMESTER REVIEW Look Back

ONLINE
30min

Objectives

- Review semester objectives.

As students prepare to complete the semester, they should refresh their knowledge of the math they have learned thus far. You may notice that some of the objectives in the Semester Review are not necessarily included in the Semester Checkpoint. Some of these concepts are particularly important to review in order to be successful with the upcoming topics students will encounter, and others contribute to a greater understanding of the concepts that are being assessed. Therefore, a complete review of the objectives in this lesson is recommended.

To review, students will play a Super Genius game. If students answer a problem incorrectly, the correct answer will display. Be sure to help students understand why the answer is correct before students move on to the next problem. If they miss several problems, have students play the game again.

Students will also use the geoboard to review some important geometric concepts. Students should choose the Challenge Mode, Level 3, and work at least five problems. If they have time, students should continue the challenge.

ONLINE
30min

- Review semester objectives.

Students will complete an online Checkpoint Practice to prepare for the Semester Checkpoint. If necessary, read the directions, problems, and answer choices to students. Have students answer the problems on their own. Review any missed problems with students.

➡ **SEMESTER REVIEW** Prepare for the Checkpoint

What you do next depends on how students performed in the previous activity, Semester Review: Checkpoint Practice. If students had difficulty with any of the problems, complete the appropriate review activity listed in the table online.

Because there are many concepts to review, consider using the Your Choice day to continue preparing for the Semester Checkpoint.

Semester Checkpoint 1

SEMESTER CHECKPOINT   60 minutes | ONLINE

▶ Semester Objectives

- Use the order of operations to simplify expressions with mixed operations.
- Interpret a numerical expression without evaluating the expression.
- Simplify expressions with grouping symbols.
- Find a mathematical expression that corresponds to a given word phrase.
- Evaluate numerical expressions using order of operations (expressions include with parentheses and powers, whole numbers only).
- Identify or use an expression or an equation to answer questions about a problem.
- Use a letter to represent an unknown value in an expression or an equation.
- Evaluate a simple algebraic expression in one variable by using substitution.
- Graph or write an equation to solve a problem that involves a linear function.
- Use the situation presented in a problem to describe the meaning of each coordinate of an ordered pair displayed on a graph.
- Given a rule such as "Add 3," generate and graph ordered pairs on a coordinate plane.
- Graph to compare the corresponding terms of two patterns.
- Estimate or determine the number of cubes required to fill a solid figure.
- Determine the perimeter of a plane figure and use appropriate units.
- Construct a cube or a rectangular box from a two-dimensional pattern and determine the surface area.
- Use squares to approximate the area of an irregular shape.
- Explain and determine the volume of a solid figure and use appropriate units.
- Differentiate among appropriate units to measure perimeter, area, and volume.
- Use the fact that volume is additive to solve problems.
- Use a variety of methods, such as words, numbers, symbols, charts, graphs, tables, diagrams, and models, to explain mathematical reasoning in nonroutine or complex problems.
- Prioritize and sequence the information in a story problem that involves multiplication or division of decimal numbers.
- Determine when and how to break a multistep whole-number story problem or money problem into simpler parts.
- Apply strategies and results from simple story problems involving fractions to more complex problems.
- Identify and generalize methods for solving problems that are similar to each other.
- Solve for one variable in a two-variable equation when the value of the other variable is given.

Materials to Gather

There are no materials to gather for this lesson.

- Estimate or calculate a product or quotient in a whole-number story problem.
- Solve a story problem involving equal measures.
- Use estimation in addition or subtraction of fractions to verify whether calculated results are reasonable.
- Explain the advantages of exact solutions and approximate solutions to problems involving addition or subtraction of decimal numbers, and give answers to a specified degree of accuracy, such as hundredths.
- Make precise calculations and use the situation presented in a problem involving decimal-number operations to check the validity of the result.
- Evaluate whether a solution for a problem is reasonable.
- Evaluate the utility of models, such as graphs and charts, to determine which are most useful and efficient to analyze data and solve problems.
- Recognize appropriate representations of survey data.
- Create a line plot to display a set of measurements in fractions of a unit.
- Organize and display single-variable data in a histogram.
- Organize and display single-variable data in a circle graph.
- Interpret information displayed in a graph or table.
- Explain which types of graphs are appropriate for various data sets.
- Use whole numbers, fractions, and decimals to compare different data sets.

SEMESTER CHECKPOINT

ONLINE
60min

Objectives

Students will complete this part of the Semester Checkpoint online. If necessary, read the directions, problems, and answer choices to students and help them with keyboard or mouse operations.

- Assess semester objectives.

Semester Checkpoint 2

SEMESTER CHECKPOINT   60 minutes ┆ **OFFLINE**

▶ Semester Objectives

- Find a mathematical expression that corresponds to a given word phrase.
- Given a rule such as "Add 3," generate and graph ordered pairs on a coordinate plane.
- Graph to compare the corresponding terms of two patterns.
- Use the fact that volume is additive to solve problems.

Materials to Gather

Semester Checkpoint 2 (printout)
Semester Checkpoint 2 Answer Key
  (printout)

OFFLINE 60 min

SEMESTER CHECKPOINT

Objectives

- Assess semester objectives.

This part of the Semester Checkpoint and its answer key are located in the Resources section for this unit in the Online Book Menu of *Math+ Yellow Lesson Guide*. Give students the Semester Checkpoint 2. Have students complete the Semester Checkpoint 2 on their own. Use the answer key to score the Semester Checkpoint 2, and then enter the results online.

Glossary

acute angle — an angle that measures greater than 0° and less than 90°

acute triangle — a triangle with three acute angles

addend — one of the two or more numbers that are added to find a sum

algorithm — a step-by-step way to solve a problem

angle — a figure formed by two rays that share the same endpoint; The rays are called the sides of the angle.

approximate solution — an estimate for the answer to a problem

area — the amount of space on a flat surface, most often measured in square units

area model — a model for multiplication that shows the product of two factors as the total number of squares on a rectangular grid; One factor is the number of rows, and the other factor is the number of columns.

array — a pattern of objects or numbers placed in a rectangular formation of rows and columns

attributes — characteristics of an object, such as number of sides or types of angles

axis (plural: axes) — a number line that appears in a graph, such as the x-axis or y-axis in a coordinate plane

bar graph — a graph that uses bars to show how much of a given category is in the data

base — the number repeatedly multiplied when the number has an exponent

base of a figure — the bottom side or face of a geometric figure

boundary number — the upper or lower limit used to round a number to a given place value

circle graph — a circular chart that shows divisions according to how data results are distributed

clustering — finding addends that are nearly alike in order to use a product to estimate their sum

common factor — a factor that is shared by two or more whole numbers

commutative property — a rule that says no matter what order you use to add two numbers (or multiply two numbers), the answer will not change

compass — a tool used to draw circles and to measure in constructions

congruent — exactly the same size and same shape, even though orientation can vary

conjecture — an idea that might be true on the basis of observations but is not yet proven to be true

coordinate — a location on the coordinate plane, designated by an x-value and a y-value

coordinate plane — a plane on which points can be located that has an x-axis and a y-axis perpendicular to each other

cubed — the result of the operation where a number has been multiplied by itself two times, such as 5 cubed = 5^3 = 5 × 5 × 5 = 125; When the volume of a cube is found, the dimensions are cubed, and the volume is expressed in units cubed.

cubic unit — a cube that is 1 unit on each side; a measure of volume

cumulative frequency — the sum of all the frequencies of given data

data — numerical information that has been gathered

decimal number — a number written with a decimal point; sometimes called a decimal fraction

decimal place-value chart — a chart with a separate column for each place value in a decimal number

decompose — to break into parts

degree — a unit used to measure angles

degree of accuracy — the place value that is to be used to report an answer, such as tens or hundredths

denominator — the number in a fraction that is below the fraction bar

difference — the answer to a subtraction problem

distributive property — a rule that says that multiplying a number by a sum gives the same answer as multiplying the number by each addend of the sum and then adding the products

dividend — the number to be divided; The dividend divided by the divisor equals the quotient.

divide out a common factor — to simplify an expression by dividing a numerator and denominator by a factor they share

division — an operation to share equally or group an amount into equal parts

divisor — the number that divides the dividend; The dividend divided by the divisor equals the quotient.

edge — a line segment or curve where two surfaces of a solid figure meet

enlargement — an increase in a product due to multiplication by a positive factor greater than 1

equal measures — a type of multiplication or division problem that uses the same measurement, such as centimeters, over and over

equation — a number sentence; two expressions that are shown as equal to one another

equiangular triangle — a triangle with three 60° angles

equilateral triangle — a triangle that has all sides equal in length

equivalent decimals — decimal numbers whose values are the same, such as 0.2 and 0.20

estimate (n.) — a very good guess or rough calculation of an answer, when the exact answer is not necessary

estimate (v.) — to make a very good guess or rough calculation of an answer when the exact answer is not necessary

evaluate — to find the value of an expression

exact solution — a precise solution that is not an estimate or an approximation

expanded form — a way to write a number that shows the place value of each of its digits; for example, $543 = 5 \times 100 + 4 \times 10 + 3 \times 1$

exponent — the number of times a base number is multiplied by itself

expression — one or more numbers and symbols that show a certain value, such as $2 + 3$, or $3 \times ?$, or $10 - 4 + 1$

factor — one of two or more numbers that are multiplied

formula — a standard equation that is used to compute values, such as area, perimeter, or volume

fraction — a number that shows part of a set, a point on a number line, a part of a whole, a quotient, or a ratio

frequency table — a table that shows the number of times pieces of data occur

friendly numbers — numbers such as 5 and 10, or multiples of 5 and 10, that are easier to add, subtract, multiply, and divide

function table — a table that lists input values and output values for a function rule

gallon (gal) — the English, or customary, unit for measuring capacity that equals 128 fl oz or 4 qt

graph — a pictorial way to display data

greatest common factor (GCF) — the greatest whole number that is a factor of two or more given whole numbers

grouping symbols — symbols—such as parentheses ( ) and braces [ ]—used to enclose an expression

height — how tall an object is from the top straight down to its base

histogram — a graph with adjoining bars; used to show the frequency of data or data groups

hundredths — the place value immediately to the right of the tenths place; 10 thousandths = 1 hundredth and 10 hundredths = 1 tenth

improper fraction — a fraction whose numerator is greater than or equal to its denominator

input — a number that will be used in a function rule to determine the value of the output

integers — the whole numbers and their opposites

interior angle — any angle inside a polygon

intersecting lines — lines that cross at one point

interval — the distance between two points, as between two numbers on a number line

inverse operations — opposite operations that undo each other; Subtraction and addition are inverse operations; division and multiplication are inverse operations.

irregular shape — a polygon that does not have all sides and angles equal in measure, or any figure that does not have any specific form

isosceles triangle — a triangle that has at least 2 sides equal in length; An equilateral triangle is a special type of isosceles triangle.

justify conclusions — to give a clear explanation for the steps and solution to a problem

label — one of the informative indicators at various places on data displays such as tables and graphs

least common denominator (LCD) — the least common multiple of two or more denominators

least common multiple (LCM) — the least number, other than 0, that is a multiple of two or more given whole numbers; used for the least common denominator

like denominators — denominators that are exactly the same in two or more fractions

line — a straight path of points that goes on forever in both directions

linear function — a function that when graphed forms a straight line

linear unit — a unit that has one dimension: length

line plot — a number line that shows all the pieces of data with a mark or marks above each piece of data to show how many times that piece of data occurred

minuend — a number from which another number is subtracted

mixed number — a whole number and a proper fraction that show a single amount

multiple — the product of a given number and any whole number

multiplication — an operation that is a shortcut for adding the same number over and over a certain number of times

multiplication fact family — a set of four related multiplication and division facts that use the same set of three numbers

net — a two-dimensional pattern to fold into a three-dimensional figure

number line — a line consisting of points equally spaced, each of which corresponds to a unique number

numerator — the number in a fraction that is above the fraction bar

obtuse angle — an angle that measures greater than $90°$ and less than $180°$

obtuse triangle — a triangle with one angle greater than $90°$

ordered pair — a pair of numbers that names the location of a point

order of operations — a set of rules that tells the correct order to use to solve a problem that has more than one operation

origin — the coordinate $(0, 0)$ on a coordinate plane

outlier — a piece of data that has a value much less than or much greater than the rest of the data

output — the result of applying a function rule to the value of an input

parallel lines — lines in the same flat surface that never intersect

parallelogram — a quadrilateral with two pairs of parallel sides

partial product — the product of each place value when a multidigit factor is multiplied by a single-digit or multidigit factor; The sum of the partial products is the final product for the problem.

perimeter — the distance around the edge of a shape

perpendicular lines — lines that intersect and form angles that measure 90°

pictorial model — a graphical representation consisting of a picture or drawing

pint (pt) — the English, or customary, unit for measuring capacity that equals 6 fl oz or 2 c

place value — the value of a digit depending on its position, or place, in a number

point on a coordinate plane — a dot that marks a coordinate; a location on a coordinate plane, designated by an x-value and a y-value

population — a group on which data results are collected

power — a product in which all the factors are the same; For example, 16 is the fourth power of 2, because $2 \cdot 2 \cdot 2 \cdot 2 = 16$.

power of 10 — any number that can be written as 10 to the nth power, where n is an integer

product — the answer to a multiplication problem

proper fraction — a fraction in which the numerator is less than the denominator

protractor — a tool to measure the degrees in an angle

quadrants — the four regions that are created by the x-axis and the y-axis in a coordinate plane

quadrilateral — a polygon with 4 sides

quantity — an amount shown as a number

quart (qt) — the English, or customary, unit for measuring capacity that equals 32 fl oz or 2 pt

quotient — the answer to a division problem; The dividend divided by the divisor equals the quotient.

random sample — a group that is chosen by chance from a larger group or population

rate — a fraction comparison of two numbers with different units

ray — a straight path of points that has an endpoint at one end and goes on forever out from that endpoint

reasonableness — the sense that an answer is correct, given the facts

reasoning — the series of thoughts and steps used to understand a problem, to create a plan to solve a problem, to reach a solution, and to accurately explain results

reciprocal — two numbers whose product is 1

rectangle — a parallelogram with four 90°angles; A square is a special type of rectangle.

regrouping — the renaming of a number from one place value or representation to another, such as 1 ten and 3 ones = 13 ones or $2\frac{3}{4} = 1\frac{7}{4}$

remainder — the amount left over after dividing

representation — a way of displaying information, such as a model, a number, a graph, or an equation

rhombus (plural: rhombuses) — a parallelogram that has all sides equal in length; A square is a special type of rhombus.

right angle — an angle that measures exactly 90°

right prism — a prism whose lateral edges are perpendicular to the bases

right triangle — a triangle with a right angle

round (v.) — to change a number to the nearest place value asked in a problem; For example, rounding 532 to the nearest ten would be 530.

ruler — a tool to measure length, typically marked in centimeters or inches.

scale — the ratio of measurement lengths to the values they represent, such as a one-mark-to-one-value scale on a graph or a one-mark-to-five-value scale

scalene triangle — a triangle that has no sides equal in length

scaling effect — enlargement or shrinking of a factor due to multiplication by a positive factor greater than or less than 1

sequence information — to put information in a particular order

shrinking — a decrease in a product due to multiplication by a positive factor less than 1

simplest form of a fraction — a fraction in which the numerator and the denominator have no common factor other than 1 or −1; also called a fraction in lowest terms

solution — the answer to a problem

solve — to determine the answer to a problem

square — a parallelogram that has all sides equal in length and four 90° angles

squared — the result of the operation where a number has been multiplied by itself, such as 5 squared = $5^2 = 5 \times 5 = 25$; When the area of a square is found, the dimensions are squared, and the area is expressed in units squared.

square unit — a square with sides of a particular side length, such as a square meter, used to measure area

straight angle — an angle that measures exactly 180°; A straight angle is a line.

strategy — a technique used to solve a problem, such as working backward or drawing a diagram

substitution — the replacement of an equivalent value for another

sum — the answer to an addition problem

sum of angle measures — the total of the angle measures of the angles of a polygon

surface area — the combined area of all the surfaces of a solid figure

survey — a strategy for collecting data by asking questions of a group of people

tenths — the place value immediately to the right of the ones place after the decimal; 10 hundredths = 1 tenth and 10 tenths = 1

term — a part of an expression that can be a number, a variable, or a product of numbers and variables

thousandths — the place value immediately to the right of the hundredths place after the decimal; 10 thousandths = 1 hundredth

trapezoid — a quadrilateral with exactly one pair of parallel sides

trend — a consistent pattern in data

triangle — a polygon with 3 sides

two-dimensional pattern — a net or pattern that can be folded to form a three-dimensional figure

unit — an object or amount used to measure, such as paper clips as a nonstandard unit for length or kilograms as a standard unit for mass

unit fraction — a fraction with a numerator of 1, such as $\frac{1}{3}$ or $\frac{1}{7}$

unlike denominators — denominators that are different in two or more fractions

variable — a letter or symbol that represents a quantity

vertex (plural: vertices) — the common endpoint of the two rays or segments that form an angle less than 180°; The vertex of a 180° angle is any point along the line.

volume — the amount of space taken up by a three-dimensional object; measured in cubic units

whole numbers — zero and the counting numbers (0, 1, 2, 3, 4, 5, 6, and so on)

x-axis — the horizontal axis on a coordinate plane, perpendicular to the y-axis

x-coordinate — the first value in an ordered pair, such as 5 in the ordered pair (5, 6)

yard (yd) — the English, or customary, unit for measuring length that equals 36 in. or 3 ft

y-axis — the vertical axis on a coordinate plane, perpendicular to the x-axis

y-coordinate — the second value in an ordered pair, such as 6 in the ordered pair (5, 6)